INTRODUCTION TO

MODERN ALGEBRA AND MATRIX THEORY

BY

O. SCHREIER

AND

E. SPERNER

TRANSLATED BY

MARTIN DAVIS

AND

MELVIN HAUSNER

SECOND EDITION

CHELSEA PUBLISHING COMPANY

NEW YORK, N. Y.

LIBRARY OF CONGRESS CATALOGUE CARD NUMBER 59-6890

PRINTED IN THE UNITED STATES OF AMERICA

EDITOR'S PREFACE

Schreier and Sperner's justly famous *Einführung in die Algebra und Analytische Geometrie* was originally published in two volumes. Both of these volumes (with the omission of the final part of Volume I, on projective geometry) are here presented in a one-volume English translation, under the title *Introduction to Modern Algebra and Matrix Theory.*

It may be noted that Chapter V of the present translation (Volume II, Chapter II of the original) incorporates the material of the authors' book *Lectures on Matrices* (*Vorlesungen über Matrizen*).

F. S. A. G.

FROM THE PREFACE TO *PROJECTIVE GEOMETRY*

With the present publication of *Projective Geometry,* the project of translating the famous German-language textbook *Einführung in die Analytische Geometrie und Algebra,* by Otto Schreier and Emanuel Sperner, originally published in two volumes, is now complete. As is well known, the purpose of that textbook was to offer a course in Algebra and Analytic Geometry which, when supplemented with a course on the Calculus, would give the student all he needs for a profitable continuation of his studies in modern mathematics. The Preface to the German Edition (see below) gives a more detailed description of the two volumes.

The only change that has been made has been to divide the two volumes somewhat differently in order that they might be usable independently. The first volume and the early part of the second volume were combined into a single book under the title *Introduction to Modern Algebra and Matrix Theory.* The balance, consisting of the major portion of the second volume is published herewith as *Projective Geometry of n Dimensions.* The titles of the two books indicate their respective contents.

F. S. A. G.

TRANSLATOR'S PREFACE

We wish to thank Dr. F. Steinhardt for his very valuable help in the preparation of the present translation. Thanks are due, also, to Miss Zelma Ann McCormick.

MARTIN DAVIS
MELVIN HAUSNER

FROM THE PREFACE TO VOLUME I OF THE GERMAN EDITION

Otto Schreier had planned, a few years ago, to have his lectures on Analytic Geometry and Algebra published in book form. Death overtook him in Hamburg on June 2, 1929, before he had really begun to carry out his plan. The task of doing this fell on me, his pupil. I had at my disposal some sets of lecture notes taken at Schreier's courses, as well as a detailed (if not quite complete) syllabus of his course drawn up at one time by Otto Schreier himself. Since then, I have also given the course myself, in Hamburg, gaining experience in the process.

In writing the book I have followed Schreier's presentation as closely as possible, so that the textbook might retain the characteristics impressed on the subject matter in Otto Schreier's treatment. In particular, as regards choice and arrangement of material, I have followed Schreier's outline faithfully, except for a few changes of minor importance.

This textbook is motivated by the idea of offering the student, in two basic courses on Calculus and Analytic Geometry, all that he needs for a profitable continuation of his studies adapted to modern requirements. It is evident that this implies a stronger emphasis than has been customary on algebra, in line with the recent developments in that subject.

The prerequisites for reading this book are few indeed. For the early parts, a knowledge of the real number system—such as is acquired in the first few lectures of almost any calculus course—is sufficient. The later chapters make use of some few theorems on continuity of real functions and on sequences of real numbers. These also will be familiar to the student from the calculus. In some sections which give intuitive interpretations of the subject matter, use is made of some well-known theorems of elementary geometry, whose derivation on an axiomatic basis would of course be beyond the scope of this text.

What the book contains may be seen in outline by a glance at the table of contents. The student is urged not to neglect the exercises at the end of each section; among them will be found many an important addition to the material presented in the text.

To Messrs. E. Artin and W. Blaschke in Hamburg I wish to extend my most cordial thanks for their manifold help. I also wish to express my gratitude for reading the proofs, to Miss A. Voss (Hamburg) and to Messrs. R. Brauer (Koenigsberg), G. Feigl (Berlin), K. Henke (Hamburg), and E. Schubarth (Basel).

EMANUEL SPERNER

FROM THE PREFACE TO VOLUME II OF THE GERMAN EDITION

The second volume of *Einführung in die Analytische Geometrie und Algebra* . . . is divided into three chapters, the first two of which [Chapters IV and V of the present translation] deal with algebraic topics, while the last, and longest, [to be published as a separate volume.—*Ed.*] is an analytic treatment of (n-dimensional) projective geometry.

The authors' earlier monograph, *Vorlesungen über Matrizen* (*Hamburger Einzelschriften*, Vol. 12) has been incorporated into [Chapter V of] the present book, with a few re-arrangements and omissions in order to achieve a more organic whole.

• • •

To Mr. W. Blaschke (Hamburg) I owe a debt of gratitude for his continuous interest and help. I also wish to thank Messrs. O. Haupt (Erlangen) and K. Henke (Hamburg) for many valuable hints and suggestions. In preparing the manuscript, my wife has given me untiring assistance. For reading the proofs I am indebted to Mr. H. Bueckner (Koenigsberg), in addition to those named above.

Koenigsberg, October 1935.

EMANUEL SPERNER

TABLE OF CONTENTS

EDITOR'S PREFACE iii
TRANSLATORS' PREFACE iii
AUTHORS' PREFACE v

CHAPTER I

AFFINE SPACE; LINEAR EQUATIONS

§ 1. n-dimensional Affine Space 1
§ 2. Vectors 6
§ 3. The Concept of Linear Dependence 16
§ 4. Vector Spaces in R_n 19
§ 5. Linear Spaces 27
§ 6. Linear Equations 34
Homogeneous Linear Equations 36
Non-homogeneous Linear Equations 40
Geometric Applications 44

CHAPTER II

EUCLIDEAN SPACE; THEORY OF DETERMINANTS

§ 7. Euclidean Length 50
Appendix to § 7: Calculating with the Summation Sign 60
§ 8. Volumes and Determinants 63
Fundamental Properties of Determinants 69
Existence and Uniqueness of Determinants 74
Volumes 83
§ 9. The Principal Theorems of Determinant Theory 87
The Complete Development of a Determinant 87
The Determinant as a Function of its Column Vectors 89
The Multiplication Theorem 96
The Development of a Determinant by Rows or Columns 98
Determinants and Linear Equations 100
Laplace's Expansion Theorem 105
§ 10. Transformation of Coordinates 117
General Linear Coordinate Systems 117
Cartesian Coordinate Systems 126
Continuous Deformation of a Linear Coordinate System 131
§ 11. Construction of Normal Orthogonal Systems and Applications 140
§ 12. Rigid Motions 153
Rigid Motions in R_2 162
Rigid Motions in R_3 168
§ 13. Affine Transformations 180

CHAPTER III

FIELD THEORY; THE FUNDAMENTAL THEOREM OF ALGEBRA

§ 14. The Concept of a Field 187
§ 15. Polynomials over a Field 204
§ 16. The Field of Complex Numbers 218
§ 17. The Fundamental Theorem of Algebra 230

CHAPTER IV

ELEMENTS OF GROUP THEORY

§ 18. The Concept of a Group 245
§ 19. Subgroups; Examples 251
§ 20. The Basis Theorem for Abelian Groups 260

CHAPTER V

LINEAR TRANSFORMATIONS AND MATRICES

§ 21. The Algebra of Linear Transformations 273
§ 22. Calculation with Matrices 283
Linear Transformations Under a Change of Coordinate System 293
The Determinant of a Linear Transformations 296
Linear Dependence of Matrices 297
Calculation With Matric Polynomials 298
The Transpose of a Matrix 301
§ 23. The Minimal Polynomial; Invariant Subspaces 303
The Minimal Polynomial 303
Invariant Subspaces 305
The Nullspace of a Linear Transformation $f(\sigma)$ 306
Decomposition of L into Invariant Subspaces 310
Geometric Interpretation 315
§ 24. The Diagonal Form and its Applications 320
Unitary Transformations 327
Orthogonal Transformations 334
Hermitian and Symmetric Matrices (Principal Axis Transformations) 340
§ 25. The Elementary Divisors of a Polynomial Matrix 344
§ 26. The Normal Form 355
Consequences 363
Linear Transformation with Prescribed Elementary Divisors . 365
The Jordan Normal Form 367
INDEX 373

CHAPTER I

AFFINE SPACE; LINEAR EQUATIONS

§ 1. *n*-dimensional Affine Space

There is an intimate connection between the properties of lines, planes, and space and those of certain numerical structures. It is this relation which provides the foundation for analytic geometry. Our first task will be to establish it.

1. The straight line or one-dimensional space. Let us fix two distinct points O and E on the line g (Fig. 1). We call the point O the *origin* and the point E the *unit point*. We employ the segment OE as

Fig. 1

a unit for measuring lengths on the line g. The point O divides the line into two rays. The ray on which E lies is called the *positive* ray; the other is called the *negative* ray. We now assign a real number to every point of g, called the *abscissa* (*coordinate*) of that point; namely, to a point P on the positive ray we assign, as its abscissa, the number which measures the length of the segment OP (i.e. the ratio of the length of OP to that of OE). To a point Q on the negative ray we assign, as its abscissa, the negative of the number measuring the length of OQ. We note that O is assigned the abscissa 0, and E is assigned the abscissa 1. It is intuitively clear that by means of this assignment every real number appears as an abscissa and in fact precisely once.[1] Thus a point and its abscissa determine each other uniquely. *Every point of the line determines one and only one real number, and every real number determines one and only one point of the line.* We also express this by saying that there is a *one-to-one* correspondence between the points of a line and the totality of all

[1] As we have already remarked in the preface, we assume a knowledge of the real numbers and their simplest laws (rules of calculation). A rigorous exposition of the real number system may be found in modern texts on the calculus.

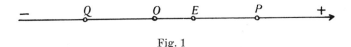

real numbers. If this correspondence is set up by the method described above, we shall say that a *coordinate system* has been introduced on the line. Observe that the coordinate system is completely determined by the choice of origin and unit point.

2. The plane or two-dimensional space. Let us take two intersecting lines in the plane, the x_1-*axis* and the x_2-*axis* (Fig. 2). Let O be their point of intersection. We choose a fixed point E_1 (different from O) on the x_1-axis and similarly a point E_2 on the x_2-axis. We may then introduce a coordinate system on the x_1-axis with O as origin and E_1 as unit point, and a coordinate system on the x_2-axis with O as origin and E_2 as unit point.[2]

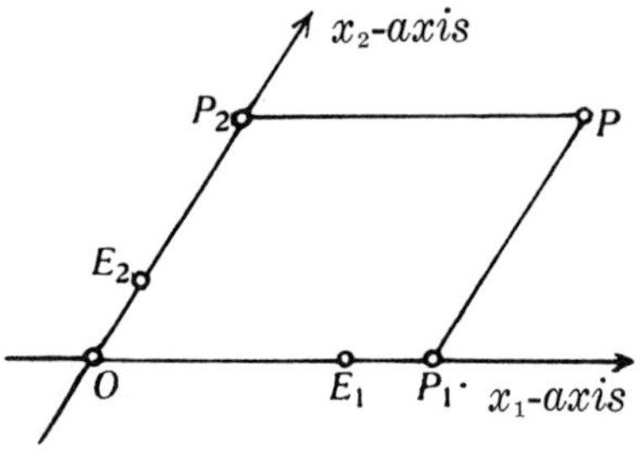

Fig. 2

We shall now assign to every point P of the plane a pair of real numbers which we call the *coordinates* of that point. We draw the two lines through P which are parallel respectively to the two axes. Let the one intersect the x_1-axis in the point P_1, and the other intersect the x_2-axis in the point P_2. Let x_1 be the abscissa of the point P_1 in the coordinate system we have introduced on the x_1-axis, and similarly let x_2 be the abscissa of the point P_2 in the coordinate system we have introduced on the x_2-axis. We then assign the numbers x_1, x_2 to the point P as its coordinates. x_1 is called its *first* coordinate and x_2 its *second*.[3] For every pair x_1, x_2 of real numbers, there will be one and only one point having x_1 as its first, and x_2 as its second, coordinate. For, let P_1 be that point on the x_1-axis which has x_1 as its abscissa on this axis, and let P_2 be that point on the x_2-axis which has x_2 as its abscissa on the x_2-axis. The line through P_1 parallel to the x_2-axis and the line through P_2 parallel to the x_1-axis will meet at a point P. P will then have x_1 and x_2 as its first and second coordinates respectively, and is obviously the only such point.

We denote the point whose coordinates are x_1, x_2 by the symbol (x_1, x_2). The position of the numbers x_1 and x_2 in this symbol is essen-

---

[2] We wish to call attention to the fact that the segments OE_1 and OE_2 need by no means have the same length.

[3] The first coordinate will also be called the *abscissa*, the second the *ordinate*.

tial; for the first number appearing is the first coordinate and the other number is the second.[4]

Thus a point and its coordinate determine each other uniquely. *There is a one-to-one correspondence between the points of the plane and the ordered pairs of real numbers.* If this correspondence is set up as described above we shall say that a **(linear) coordinate system** has been introduced in the plane. Such a coordinate system is completely determined by the choice of the *coordinate axes* (i.e. the x_1-axis and the x_2-axis) and the *unit points* on them. The point O is called the *origin* of the coordinate system.

3. Three-dimensional space. Through a point O of space, we pass three lines, the x_1-axis, x_2-axis, and x_3-axis, which do not all lie in one plane (Fig. 3). Determine a point E_i on the x_i-axis ($i = 1, 2, 3$). We

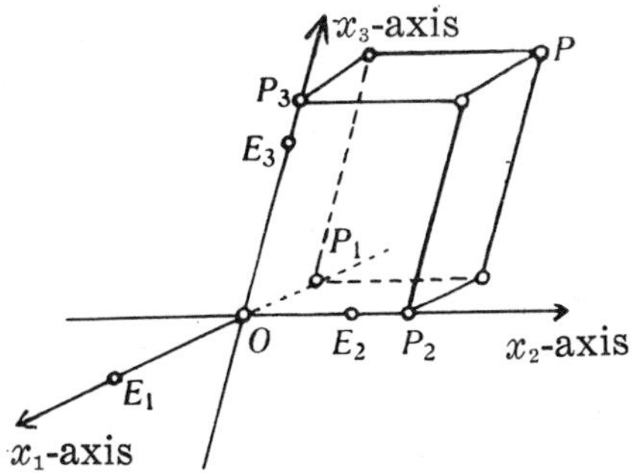

Fig. 3

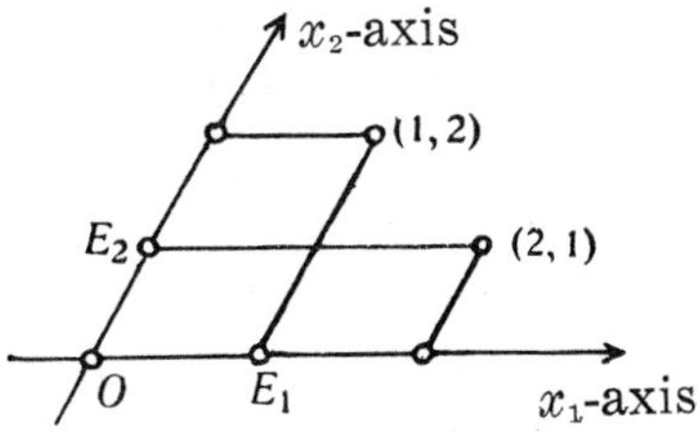

Fig. 4

introduce the coordinate system on the x_i-axis ($i = 1, 2, 3$) which has O as origin and E_i as unit point.

We can pass a plane through any two of these coordinate axes. These planes are called the *coordinate planes.* The plane through the x_1-axis and the x_2-axis is called the *x_1, x_2-plane*; similarly for the *x_2, x_3-plane* and the *x_1, x_3-plane.*

We shall now assign to each point P of space an ordered triple of real numbers, which we shall call its *coordinates.* First we pass through P a plane e_1 parallel to the x_2, x_3-plane, a plane e_2 parallel to the x_1, x_3-plane, a plane e_3 parallel to the x_1, x_2-plane. The x_1-axis and the plane e_1 intersect in a point P_1, the x_2-axis and e_2 in P_2, and the x_3-axis and e_3 in

[4] The point (1, 2), say, is thus different from the point (2, 1) (cf. Fig. 4).

P_3. Let x_1 be the abscissa of the point P_1 in the coordinate system we have introduced on the x_1-axis; similarly let x_2 be the abscissa of P_2 on the x_2-axis, x_3 that of P_3 on the x_3-axis. We then assign the numbers x_1, x_2, x_3 to the point P as it coordinates. x_1 is called its *first* coordinate, x_2 its *second*, and x_3 its *third*. For every triple x_1, x_2, x_3 of real numbers there will be one and only one point of space having x_1 as its first coordinate, x_2 as its second coordinate, and x_3 as its third coordinate. For, let P_1 be the point on the x_1-axis having x_1 as its abscissa on this axis, P_2 the point on the x_2-axis having x_2 as its abscissa on the x_2-axis and P_3 the point on the x_3-axis having x_3 as its abscissa on the x_3-axis. Pass through P_1 the plane e_1 parallel to the x_2, x_3-plane, through P_2 the plane e_2 parallel to the x_1, x_3-plane, and through P_3 the plane e_3 parallel to the x_1, x_2-plane. Let P be the point of intersection of the three planes e_1, e_2, and e_3. Then P has x_1 as its first, x_2 as its second, and x_3 as its third, coordinate, and it is the only such point. The point with coordinates x_1, x_2, x_3 is denoted by the symbol (x_1, x_2, x_3). Here again the position of the numbers x_1, x_2, x_3 in this symbol is essential; the numbers, reading from left to right, are the first, second, and third, coordinates.

Once again a point and its coordinates determine each other uniquely. *There is a one-to-one correspondence between the points of space and the ordered triples of real numbers.* If this correspondence is set up as above, we will say that a (linear) *coordinate system* has been introduced in space. Such a coordinate system is completely determined by the choice of the *origin O*, the *coordinate axes* and the *unit points* on those axes.

4. *n*-dimensional space. We have defined definite one-to-one correspondences between the points of a line and the totality of real numbers, similarly between the points of the plane and the ordered pairs of real numbers, and also between the points of space and the ordered triples of real numbers. By means of these correspondences, geometric concepts and theorems on the line, in the plane, and in space are converted into algebraic concepts and theorems concerning the corresponding numerical structures. Conversely, considerations involving these numerical structures may be converted into considerations involving the corresponding geometric configurations. Now the basic principle of analytic geometry is to investigate, instead of line, plane, and space themselves, the corresponding numerical structures, and only afterwards to carry over the algebraic results obtained to the geometric configurations, i.e. to give the algebraic results a *geometric interpretation.*[5]

By means of the one-to-one correspondence, a numerical structure and its corresponding geometric configuration are, so to speak, mapped on one another; each gives an accurate picture of the other. For this reason, the totality of real numbers is itself called a one-dimensional space and the individual numbers are called points of that space; similarly the totality of ordered pairs of real numbers is called a two-dimensional space and the ordered pairs themselves are called its points; the total of ordered triples of real numbers is called a three-dimensional space and the ordered triples themselves are called its points. This terminology, which will be extended further, has the advantage of itself conveying the geometric interpretation.

The ideas discussed may be generalized considerably. In fact, we make the following definitions:

An ordered n-tuple of real numbers, i.e. a system $(x_1, x_2, \ldots, x_n)$ of n real numbers in a definite order, is called a *point* (n a positive integer). The numbers $x_1, x_2, \ldots, x_n$ are called the *coordinates* of the point; in particular, x_1 is called its first, x_2 its second, ..., x_n its n-th coordinate. Two points $P = (x_1, x_2, \ldots, x_n)$ and $Q = (y_1, y_2, \ldots, y_n)$ are said to be the *same* (or to *coincide*) if and only if $x_1 = y_1$ $x_2 = y_2$, $\ldots, x_n = y_n$. The totality of all n-tuples of real numbers is called **n-dimensional affine space.**

n-dimensional affine space is denoted by $\boldsymbol{R_n}$. The spaces R_1, R_2, and R_3 can be given an intuitive geometrical interpretation, as explained above. For $n \geqq 4$, however, an immediate intuitive interpretation of R_n is no longer possible.

[5] To be sure we often use our intuition as a heuristic device. But the concepts and proofs are always of an algebraic nature.

§ 2. Vectors

An important and convenient device for the study of R_n is the concept of vector, which we shall introduce in what follows. We first proceed intuitively.

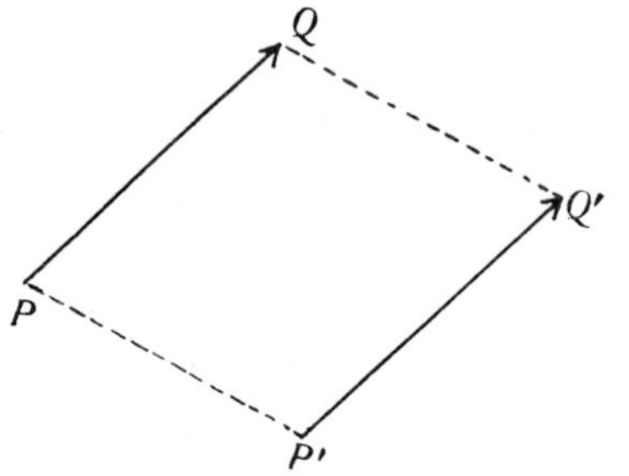

Fig. 5

A segment PQ in ordinary, "physical" space (Fig. 5) is determined by its endpoints P and Q. If we designate one of the two points P, Q as the initial point, and the other as the terminal point, of the segment, we say that the segment is *directed*. We may *direct* a segment (or give it a *sense*) in one of two ways. Let P, say, be the initial point and Q the terminal point (indicated in the figure by an arrow going from P to Q), and let us denote the segment, as thus directed, by $\overrightarrow{PQ}$. For short, we call the directed segment $\overrightarrow{PQ}$ a *vector*. We say that the vector $\overrightarrow{PQ}$ goes from P to Q or that it carries P into Q. We define two vectors to be *equal* if and only if they are parallel, have the same length, and have the same sense. Thus two vectors may be equal even if they have different positions in space. A vector has a definite orientation and length, but no definite position. A vector may be arbitrarily displaced parallel to itself, or, what amounts to the same thing, its initial point may be chosen arbitrarily. Observe however, that by our definition of equality, the vectors $\overrightarrow{PQ}$ and $\overrightarrow{QP}$ are unequal.

We now introduce a coordinate system in space. Let P then have the coordinates x_1, x_2, x_3 and Q the coordinates y_1, y_2, y_3. The directed segment $\overrightarrow{PQ}$ is determined by the coordinates x_1, x_2, x_3 of its initial point P and the differences $a_1 = y_1 - x_1$, $a_2 = y_2 - x_2$ $a_3 = y_3 - x_3$. For, this information determines the coordinates of the endpoint Q, *viz.* as $y_1 = x_1 + a_1, y_2 = x_2 + a_2, y_3 = x_3 + a_3$. If we now displace the directed segment $\overrightarrow{PQ}$ parallel to itself, say onto $\overrightarrow{P'Q'}$ (Fig. 5), then the coordinates of the point P will of course be changed. However, the change in the i-th coordinate x_i $(i = 1, 2, 3)$ of the point P is exactly the same as the change in the i-th coordinate y_i of Q. Thus, the differences $y_i - x_i$ of the coordinates remain unchanged. We call the numbers $y_i - x_i$ the "*components*" of the vector $\overrightarrow{PQ}$. *Equal vectors have equal components.* The converse statement also is clearly true; for if two vectors have equal components, we need only choose the same initial point for both in order to make them coincide. Hence, *a vector is uniquely determined by its components.* This fact enables us to use the following notation[1]:

$$\overrightarrow{PQ} = \{a_1, a_2, a_3\}.$$

We denote vectors by small German letters, e.g. $\mathfrak{a} = \{a_1, a_2, a_3\}$. If $\overrightarrow{PQ} = \mathfrak{a}$, we may say that *the vector* $\mathfrak{a}$ *carries the point P into the point Q*, or that Q is obtained from P by *applying* the vector $\mathfrak{a}$ at P. Note that the vector $\overrightarrow{PQ}$ has the components $y_1 - x_1$, $y_2 - x_2$, $y_3 - x_3$, whereas the vector $\overrightarrow{QP}$ has the components $x_1 - y_1$, $x_2 - y_2$, $x_3 - y_3$. Thus:

$$\overrightarrow{QP} = \{-a_1, -a_2, -a_3\}.$$

Now let P be an arbitrary point in space, with coordinates x_1, x_2, x_3 (Fig. 6). The vector $\overrightarrow{OP}$ which carries the origin O to the point P has

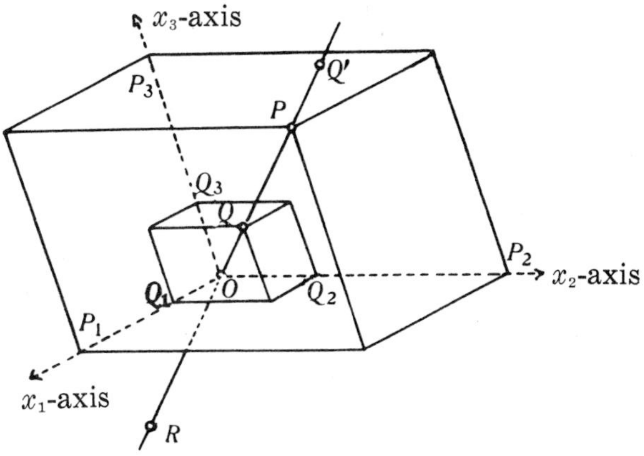

Fig. 6

the components $x_1 - 0 = x_1$, $x_2 - 0 = x_2$, $x_3 - 0 = x_3$, so that

$$\overrightarrow{OP} = \{x_1, x_2, x_3\}.$$

---

[1] This is a notation, not a new definition of a vector. The vector with components a_1, a_2, a_3 is denoted by $\{a_1, a_2, a_3\}$ (braces).

Next choose a point Q on the segment OP, Q having coordinates y_1, y_2, y_3. As in § 1, pass three planes through P parallel to the coordinate planes. Let the intersection of these planes with the coordinate axes be P_1, P_2, P_3. Likewise, let Q_1, Q_2, Q_3 be the points correspondingly determined by Q. Then by well-known theorems on similar triangles, we have:

$$\overline{OQ} : \overline{OP} = \overline{OQ_1} : \overline{OP_1} = \overline{OQ_2} : \overline{OP_2} = \overline{OQ_3} : \overline{OP_3}.$$ [2]

Since the point $Q_i\,(i = 1, 2, 3)$ lies on the same side of O on the x_i-axis as does P_i, it follows that y_i has the same sign as x_i, so that

$$y_1 : x_1 = y_2 : x_2 = y_3 : x_3$$

or

$$y_1 = \lambda x_1, \qquad y_2 = \lambda x_2, \qquad y_3 = \lambda x_3,$$

where λ is some positive number between 0 and 1.

Thus we have for the vector $\overrightarrow{OQ}$:

$$\overrightarrow{OQ} = \{\lambda x_1, \lambda x_2, \lambda x_3\}.$$

In the same way, if Q' is on the extension of the line OP through P, we have

$$\overrightarrow{OQ'} = \{\lambda' x_1, \lambda' x_2, \lambda' x_3\},$$

where λ' is now a number > 1.

Now consider the vector $\overrightarrow{PO}$. Its components are $-x_1, -x_2, -x_3$. We apply the vector $\overrightarrow{PO} = \{-x_1, -x_2, -x_3\}$ to O as initial point, so that its end point falls on a point R. Then R has the coordinates $-x_1, -x_2, -x_3$. $\overrightarrow{OR}$ and $\overrightarrow{PO}$ are parallel since considered as vectors they have the same components and are thus equal. The point R thus lies on the extension of the segment PO through O. Applying these results to the vector $\overrightarrow{OR}$, we obtain: If S is a point on the extension of PO through O then the vector $\overrightarrow{OS}$ satisfies

$$\overrightarrow{OS} = \{-\lambda x_1, -\lambda x_2, -\lambda x_3\},$$

where $O \leqq \lambda \leqq 1$ if S lies on the segment OR, while $\lambda > 1$ if S lies on the extension of OR through R.

The vector $\{\lambda x_1, \lambda x_2, \lambda x_3\}$ is called the *product* of $\{x_1, x_2, x_3\}$ by λ, and, setting $\{x_1, x_2, x_3\} = \mathfrak{x}$, we write

[2] $\overline{PQ}$ means the length of the segment PQ.

$$\{\lambda x_1, \lambda x_2, \lambda x_3\} = \lambda \mathfrak{x}.$$

For $\lambda = 0$, we obtain

$$\lambda \cdot \mathfrak{x} = \{0, 0, 0\}.$$

The expression $\{0, 0, 0\}$ is thus also considered a vector and is called the *null vector*.

By means of these conventions, we may summarize our results in a simple way as follows:

If x_1, x_2, x_3 are the coordinates of a point P and $\mathfrak{x} = \{x_1, x_2, x_3\}$, then the line through the origin O and the point P consists of the end points of all vectors $\lambda\mathfrak{x}$ for λ real whose initial points are at O. The segment OP in particular consists of the end points of all vectors $\lambda\mathfrak{x}$ for which $0 \leqq \lambda \leqq 1$.

Further, let A be an arbitrary point of space (Fig. 7). Let B be the point into which A is carried by the vector $\mathfrak{x} = \{x_1, x_2, x_3\}$, i.e. $\overrightarrow{AB} = \mathfrak{x}$.

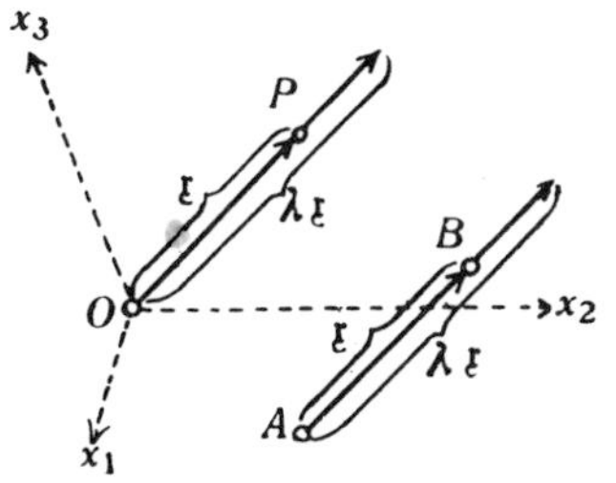

Fig. 7

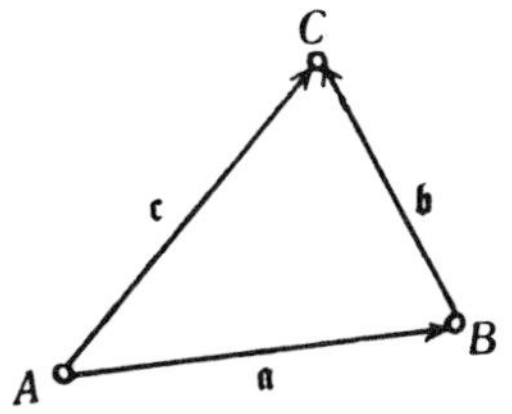

Fig. 8

$\overrightarrow{AB}$ is parallel to $\overrightarrow{OP}$. Observing that every vector $\lambda\mathfrak{x}$ starting at A is parallel to the vector $\lambda\mathfrak{x}$ starting at O, we immediately obtain the following:

The line through the points A and B consists of all the points into which A is carried by the vectors $\lambda \cdot \overrightarrow{AB}$ with real λ. In particular, for $0 \leqq \lambda \leqq 1$ we obtain all the points of the segment AB.

We now proceed to define *addition* of vectors. Let there be given two vectors $\mathfrak{a} = \{a_1, a_2, a_3\}$, $\mathfrak{b} = \{b_1, b_2, b_3\}$. Given an arbitrary point A, it is carried by the vector $\mathfrak{a}$ into a point B which is carried, in turn, into a point C by the vector $\mathfrak{b}$ (Fig. 8). Thus $\overrightarrow{AB} = \mathfrak{a}$, $\overrightarrow{BC} = \mathfrak{b}$. We denote the vector $\overrightarrow{AC}$ by $\mathfrak{c}$; let its components be c_1, c_2, c_3. The components of the vector $\mathfrak{c}$ can be determined very simply from the components of the vectors $\mathfrak{a}$ and $\mathfrak{b}$. Let A have, say, the coordinates x_1, x_2, x_3, B the coordinates y_1, y_2, y_3, and C the coordinates z_1, z_2, z_3.

Then for $i = 1, 2, 3$, the formulas

$$a_i = y_i - x_i, \qquad b_i = z_i - y_i, \qquad c_i = z_i - x_i$$

hold, and thus, since $z_i - x_i = (z_i - y_i) + (y_i - x_i)$, we have

$$c_i = b_i + a_i.$$

Because of this relation, we call the vector $\mathfrak{c}$ the *sum* of the vectors $\mathfrak{a}$ and $\mathfrak{b}$ and we write

$$\mathfrak{c} = \mathfrak{a} + \mathfrak{b}$$

or

$$\{a_1 + b_1,\ a_2 + b_2,\ a_3 + b_3\} = \{a_1,\ a_2,\ a_3\} + \{b_1,\ b_2,\ b_3\}.$$

Thus: *To add vectors, we add their corresponding components.* We now wish to make an application of this. We consider the line determined by two points A and B of space (Fig. 9). An arbitrary point C

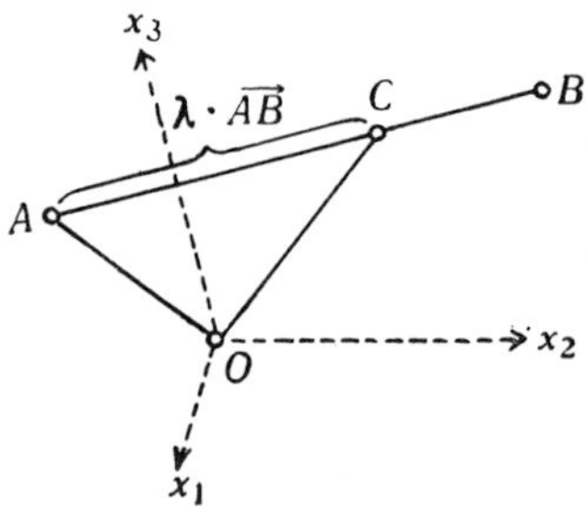

Fig. 9

of this line is obtained from A by applying the vector $\lambda \cdot \overrightarrow{AB}$ at A, where λ is a real number uniquely determined by C. We have

$$\begin{aligned} \overrightarrow{OC} &= \overrightarrow{OA} + \overrightarrow{AC} \\ &= \overrightarrow{OA} + \lambda \cdot \overrightarrow{AB}. \end{aligned}$$

Now suppose that A has the coordinates x_1, x_2, x_3, B the coordinates y_1, y_2, y_3, and C the coordinates z_1, z_2, z_3. We then have

$$\overrightarrow{OC} = \{z_1,\ z_2,\ z_3\}, \qquad \overrightarrow{OA} = \{x_1,\ x_2,\ x_3\},$$
$$\overrightarrow{AB} = \{y_1 - x_1,\ y_2 - x_2,\ y_3 - x_3\}.$$

It follows that

$$\begin{aligned} \{z_1,\ z_2,\ z_3\} &= \{x_1,\ x_2,\ x_3\} + \{\lambda (y_1 - x_1),\ \lambda (y_2 - x_2),\ \lambda (y_3 - x_3)\} \\ &= \{x_1 + \lambda (y_1 - x_1),\ x_2 + \lambda (y_2 - x_2),\ x_3 + \lambda (y_3 - x_3)\}. \end{aligned}$$

But two vectors are equal only if their components are equal. Thus it follows that

$$z_1 = x_1 + \lambda(y_1 - x_1),$$
$$z_2 = x_2 + \lambda(y_2 - x_2),$$
$$z_3 = x_3 + \lambda(y_3 - x_3).$$

C was an arbitrary point of the line through A and B. Hence the left-hand sides of these equations give us the coordinates of all the points on this line if we let the parameter λ run through all the real numbers. If we restrict λ by the condition $0 \leqq \lambda \leqq 1$, we obtain only the points of the segment AB. The above system of three equations is called the *parametric representation* of the line.

Up to now in this section we have restricted ourselves to considering ordinary, "physical" space. We shall now carry over the formulation of our concepts to n-dimensional space. We first define line and line segment in R_n in analogy with the results just obtained.

Let $P = (x_1, x_2, \cdots, x_n)$, $Q = (y_1, y_2, \cdots, y_n)$ be two points in R_n. The **straight line** through P, Q is the totality of all points $(z_1, z_2, \ldots, z_n)$ whose coordinates are given by the equations

$$z_i = x_i + \lambda(y_i - x_i), \qquad i = 1, 2, \cdots, n,$$

where the parameter λ takes on all real values. The **segment** PQ is defined as the totality of all points on the line through P, Q for which $0 \leqq \lambda \leqq 1$ in the above equations.

The points P, Q of the segment PQ are called the endpoints of the segment. A segment PQ is *directed* if we call one of the points P, Q the initial point, and the other, the terminal point. If P is the initial point, the directed segment is denoted by $\overrightarrow{PQ}$; if Q is the initial point then it is denoted by $\overrightarrow{QP}$. A directed segment is called a **vector.** The n differences $y_1 - x_1$, $y_2 - x_2$, $\ldots$, $y_n - x_n$ of the coordinates are called the *components* of the vector $\overrightarrow{PQ}$. The differences $x_1 - y_1$, $x_2 - y_2$, $\ldots$, $x_n - y_n$ are, accordingly, the components of the vector $\overrightarrow{QP}$. Two vectors are called *equal* if and only if their respective components are equal. A vector is thus uniquely determined by its components. The vector whose components are $a_1, a_2, \cdots, a_n$ is therefore denoted by

$$\{a_1, a_2, \cdots, a_n\}.$$

The expression $\{0, 0, \ldots, 0\}$, which has not been given a meaning by the above definitions, will also be called a vector, *viz.* the *null vector*.

The initial point P of a vector $\mathfrak{a} = \{a_1, a_2, \cdots, a_n\}$ can be chosen arbitrarily. But, once P is chosen, the endpoint Q is uniquely determined. If $x_1, x_2, \cdots, x_n$ are the coordinates of P, then the coordinates $y_1, y_2, \cdots, y_n$ of Q are given by the equations

$$y_i = x_i + a_i, \qquad i = 1, 2, \cdots, n.$$

For then, the i-th component of the vector $\overrightarrow{PQ}$ is indeed $y_i - x_i = a_i$.

The *sum* of the vectors $\overrightarrow{PQ}$ and $\overrightarrow{QR}$ is again defined to be the vector $\overrightarrow{PR}$, so that

$$\overrightarrow{PQ} + \overrightarrow{QR} = \overrightarrow{PR}.$$

If $a_1, a_2, \cdots, a_n$ are the components of the vector $\overrightarrow{PQ}$, $b_1, b_2, \cdots, b_n$ the components of the vector $\overrightarrow{QR}$, then the components of the vector PR are $a_1 + b_1, a_2 + b_2, \cdots, a_n + b_n$, as one can verify just as in the previous case. Thus:

$$\{a_1, a_2, \cdots, a_n\} + \{b_1, b_2, \cdots, b_n\} = \{a_1 + b_1, a_2 + b_2, \cdots, a_n + b_n\}.$$

We shall now deduce a few rules concerning addition of vectors. It will be seen that the rules of addition of vectors resemble the rules of addition of numbers in many respects.

The vector $\{a_1 + b_1, a_2 + b_2, \cdots, a_n + b_n\}$ is equal to the vector $\{b_1 + a_1, b_2 + a_2, \cdots, b_n + a_n\}$. It then follows that the order of the summands $\mathfrak{a} = \{a_1, a_2, \cdots, a_n\}$, $\mathfrak{b} = \{b_1, b_2, \cdots, b_n\}$ is immaterial. In symbols:

$$\mathfrak{a} + \mathfrak{b} = \mathfrak{b} + \mathfrak{a}.$$

This is the so-called *commutative law* of addition.

If we add $\mathfrak{c} = \{c_1, c_2, \cdots, c_n\}$, to the sum $\mathfrak{a} + \mathfrak{b}$ we obtain the vector

$$\{a_1 + b_1 + c_1, a_2 + b_2 + c_2, \cdots, a_n + b_n + c_n\}.$$

We obtain the same result if we add $\mathfrak{a}$ to the sum $\mathfrak{b} + \mathfrak{c}$. Thus

$$(\mathfrak{a} + \mathfrak{b}) + \mathfrak{c} = \mathfrak{a} + (\mathfrak{b} + \mathfrak{c}).$$

This rule is called the *associative law* of addition. As a consequence, we may denote the sum of the three vectors $\mathfrak{a}, \mathfrak{b}, \mathfrak{c}$ simply by $\mathfrak{a} + \mathfrak{b} + \mathfrak{c}$ without using parentheses, since the sum is independent of the particular method of parenthesizing.

In the same way, we see that the sum of arbitrarily many vectors is independent of the particular method of carrying out the addition. The sum of the k vectors[3]

$$\begin{aligned} \mathfrak{a}_1 &= \{a_1^{(1)}, a_2^{(1)}, \cdots, a_n^{(1)}\}, \\ \mathfrak{a}_2 &= \{a_1^{(2)}, a_2^{(2)}, \cdots, a_n^{(2)}\}, \\ &\cdots\cdots\cdots\cdots \\ \mathfrak{a}_k &= \{a_1^{(k)}, a_2^{(k)}, \cdots, a_n^{(k)}\} \end{aligned}$$

is, independently of both the order of the summands and the order in which the various individual summations are carried out, equal to

$$\sum_{i=1}^{k} \mathfrak{a}_i = \left\{\sum_{i=1}^{k} a_1^{(i)}, \sum_{i=1}^{k} a_2^{(i)}, \cdots, \sum_{i=1}^{k} a_n^{(i)}\right\}.$$ [4]

Finally we define the product of a vector and a number to be that vector which is obtained from the given vector by multiplying each of its components by the given number; that is,

$$\lambda\{a_1, a_2, \cdots, a_n\} = \{a_1, a_2, \cdots, a_n\}\lambda = \{\lambda a_1, \lambda a_2, \cdots, \lambda a_n\}.$$

If we multiply the vector $\mathfrak{a}$ by the two numbers λ and μ successively, then the associative law holds:

$$\mu(\lambda\cdot\mathfrak{a}) = (\mu\cdot\lambda)\mathfrak{a}.$$

For, both sides of this equation are equal to

$$\{\mu\cdot\lambda\cdot a_1, \mu\cdot\lambda\cdot a_2, \cdots, \mu\cdot\lambda\cdot a_n\}.$$

Thus the parenthesization is also unnecessary for products of this sort, and we write

$$\mu\cdot\lambda\cdot\mathfrak{a} = \mu\cdot(\lambda\mathfrak{a}) = (\mu\cdot\lambda)\mathfrak{a}.$$

---

[3] The superscripts (i) appearing in $a_1^{(i)}, a_2^{(i)}, \cdots, a_n^{(i)}$ refer to the particular vector $\mathfrak{a}_i$ of which they are components, and must not be confused with exponents.

[4] The sign $\sum_{i=1}^{k}$ is, as usual, the summation sign and denotes a summation over all indices $i=1$ to k. In the present case we have

$$\begin{aligned} \sum_{i=1}^{k} \mathfrak{a}_i &= \mathfrak{a}_1 + \mathfrak{a}_2 + \cdots + \mathfrak{a}_k, \\ \sum_{i=1}^{k} a_1^{(i)} &= a_1^{(1)} + a_1^{(2)} + \cdots + a_1^{(k)}, \text{ etc.} \end{aligned}$$

If $\mathfrak{a} = \{a_1, a_2, \cdots, a_n\}$, $\mathfrak{b} = \{b_1, b_2, \cdots, b_n\}$ are two arbitrary vectors, we have

$$\lambda(\mathfrak{a}+\mathfrak{b}) = \{\lambda a_1 + \lambda b_1, \lambda a_2 + \lambda b_2, \cdots, \lambda a_n + \lambda b_n\} = \lambda \mathfrak{a} + \lambda \mathfrak{b}.$$

If μ is also a real number, we have

$$(\lambda+\mu)\mathfrak{a} = \{\lambda a_1 + \mu a_1, \lambda a_2 + \mu a_2, \cdots, \lambda a_n + \mu a_n\} = \lambda \mathfrak{a} + \mu \mathfrak{a}.$$

Rules of this sort, which permit us to "multiply out," are called *distributive laws.*

If $\mathfrak{a} = \{a_1, a_2, \cdots, a_n\}$, then, for short, we denote the vector $(-1)\cdot\mathfrak{a} = \{-a_1, -a_2, \cdots, -a_n\}$ by $-\mathfrak{a}$. If $\mathfrak{b} = \{b_1, b_2, \cdots, b_n\}$ is a second vector, then we write $\mathfrak{b}-\mathfrak{a}$ as an abbreviation for

$$\mathfrak{b}+(-\mathfrak{a}).$$

We immediately obtain

$$\mathfrak{b}-\mathfrak{a} = \{b_1 - a_1, b_2 - a_2, \cdots, b_n - a_n\}$$

and

$$\mathfrak{a}-\mathfrak{a} = \{0, 0, \cdots, 0\}.$$

The symbol on the right denotes the null vector, which we also represent by the symbol 0 where there is no fear of confusion with the number 0. We have for every vector $\mathfrak{a}$:

$$\mathfrak{a}+0 = \mathfrak{a}.$$

The equation

$$\mathfrak{a}+\mathfrak{x} = \mathfrak{b}$$

can now be solved for $\mathfrak{x}$, namely by adding the vector $-\mathfrak{a}$ to both sides:

$$\mathfrak{x} = \mathfrak{b}-\mathfrak{a}.$$

When is $\lambda\cdot\mathfrak{a} = \{\lambda a_1, \lambda a_2, \cdots, \lambda a_n\} = 0$? This is certainly the case if $\lambda = 0$. If, however, $\lambda \neq 0$, then the vanishing of the products λa_i $(i = 1, 2, \ldots, n)$ implies that each a_i $(i = 1, 2, \ldots, n)$ vanishes. $\mathfrak{a}$ is thus the null vector. *If* $\lambda\mathfrak{a} = 0$ *then at least one of the factors* λ *and* $\mathfrak{a}$ *must vanish.*

For the sake of later applications we shall define the so-called scalar product of two vectors. If $\mathfrak{a} = \{a_1, a_2, \cdots, a_n\}$ and $\mathfrak{b} = \{b_1, b_2, \cdots, b_n\}$, then the *scalar product* $\mathfrak{a}\cdot\mathfrak{b}$ of the vectors $\mathfrak{a}$ and $\mathfrak{b}$ is defined by the formula

$$\mathfrak{a}\cdot\mathfrak{b} = a_1\cdot b_1 + a_2\cdot b_2 + \cdots + a_n\cdot b_n.$$

We shall not discuss the geometric interpretation of $\mathfrak{a} \cdot \mathfrak{b}$ (or, as we sometimes write, $\mathfrak{a}\mathfrak{b}$) at this point, but we shall, for the time being, use the symbol $\mathfrak{a} \cdot \mathfrak{b}$ merely as an abbreviation for the right-hand side of the above equation. Let us, however, explicitly call attention to the fact that the scalar product is, by its definition, not a vector, but a number. If $\mathfrak{a} = \mathfrak{b}$, we write $\mathfrak{a}^2$ for $\mathfrak{a} \cdot \mathfrak{a}$

We proceed to deduce some important rules of calculation for the scalar product. First, the commutative law holds, i.e.,

$$\mathfrak{a} \cdot \mathfrak{b} = \mathfrak{b} \cdot \mathfrak{a},$$

since $\sum_{i=1}^{n} a_i b_i = \sum_{i=1}^{n} b_i a_i$.

Next, if λ is any real number, then the following associative laws hold:

$$\lambda(\mathfrak{a} \cdot \mathfrak{b}) = (\lambda \mathfrak{a}) \cdot \mathfrak{b} = \mathfrak{a} \cdot (\lambda \mathfrak{b}).$$

For, each of these three expressions is equal to $\sum_{i=1}^{n} \lambda a_i b_i$.[5]

Finally, the distributive law

$$\mathfrak{a} \cdot (\mathfrak{b} + \mathfrak{c}) = \mathfrak{a} \cdot \mathfrak{b} + \mathfrak{a} \cdot \mathfrak{c},$$

where $\mathfrak{a}$, $\mathfrak{b}$, $\mathfrak{c}$ are any three vectors, is satisfied. For, the left-hand side of the equation is $= \sum_{i=1}^{n} a_i (b_i + c_i)$, and the right-hand side is

$$= \sum_{i=1}^{n} a_i b_i + \sum_{i=1}^{n} a_i c_i = \sum_{i=1}^{n} (a_i b_i + a_i c_i) = \sum_{i=1}^{n} a_i (b_i + c_i).$$ [6]

It may happen that the scalar product $\mathfrak{a} \cdot \mathfrak{b}$ of two vectors vanishes without either of the vectors $\mathfrak{a}$ and $\mathfrak{b}$ vanishing. For example, let $\mathfrak{a} = \{2, 1\}$, $\mathfrak{b} = \{1, -2\}$. Then $\mathfrak{a} \cdot \mathfrak{b} = 2 \cdot 1 - 1 \cdot 2 = 0$. Two vectors $\mathfrak{a}$ and $\mathfrak{b}$ whose scalar product $\mathfrak{a} \cdot \mathfrak{b} = 0$ are called *orthogonal* to each other. The significance of this terminology will become clear later (§ 7).

---

[5] However the expressions $(\mathfrak{a} \cdot \mathfrak{b}) \cdot \mathfrak{c}$ and $\mathfrak{a} \cdot (\mathfrak{b} \cdot \mathfrak{c})$ are *not* in general equal, where $\mathfrak{a}$ $\mathfrak{b}$ and $\mathfrak{c}$ are vectors. For, $(\mathfrak{a} \cdot \mathfrak{b}) \cdot \mathfrak{c}$ means the product of the *vector* $\mathfrak{c}$ by the *number* $(\mathfrak{a} \cdot \mathfrak{b})$ and $\mathfrak{a} \cdot (\mathfrak{b} \cdot \mathfrak{c})$ means the product of the vector $\mathfrak{a}$ by the number $(\mathfrak{b} \cdot \mathfrak{c})$.

[6] If we add $\sum_{i=1}^{n} A_i$ and $\sum_{i=1}^{n} B_i$, we have

$$\begin{aligned} \sum_{i=1}^{n} A_i + \sum_{i=1}^{n} B_i &= A_1 + A_2 + \cdots + A_n + B_1 + B_2 + \cdots + B_n \\ &= (A_1 + B_1) + (A_2 + B_2) + \cdots + (A_n + B_n) \\ &= \sum_{i=1}^{n} (A_i + B_i). \end{aligned}$$

Exercises

1. Given the segment PQ in R_n

$$P = (x_1, x_2, \cdots, x_n),\ Q = (y_1, y_2, \cdots, y_n)$$

and two points R and S on the segment, show that the segment RS is a part of the segment PQ, i.e. that every point of RS is also a point of PQ.

2. Let $P = (x_1, x_2, \cdots, x_n)$, $Q = (y_1, y_2, \cdots, y_n)$ be two distinct points in R_n. Let S and T be any two distinct points on the line through P and Q. Show that the line through S and T is the same as the line through P and Q (i.e. that any point on one line also lies on the other).

3. Show that the totality of points in the plane whose coordinates with respect to a given coordinate system are given by

$$z_1 = x_1 + \lambda (y_1 - x_1), \qquad z_2 = x_2 + \lambda (y_2 - x_2)$$

with arbitrary real λ, corresponds to the intuitive concept of the line through the points $P = (x_1, x_2)$, $Q = (y_1, y_2)$. Do the concepts of segment and vector in R_2 likewise agree with the corresponding intuitive notions?

4. Add the vectors

a) $3\{1, -7, 5\} - 2\{0, 2, -2\} + \{-2, 26, -18\}$,

b) $\{2, 1, -1, 3\} + 2\{1, -1, -2, -1\} - \{-4, 1, 5, -1\}$,

c) $4\{1, 2\} + 3\{7, 1\} - \{20, 1\} - 5\{1, 2\}$,

d) $-\{2, 3, -1, 0, 0\} + 2\{3, -1, 4, 1, -1\} + \{-5, 7, -6, 2, 7\}$.

5. Solve for $\mathfrak{x}$ in each of the following equations:

a) $2\{-1, 5, 1, 1\} - 4\mathfrak{x} = \{2, 14, -2, -2\}$,

b) $\{3, 7, 1\} + 2\mathfrak{x} = \{6, 10, 4\} - \mathfrak{x}$,

c) $\mathfrak{a} + 3\mathfrak{b} + \mathfrak{x} = 4(\mathfrak{x} - \mathfrak{a}) + 5\mathfrak{a} + \lambda(\mathfrak{x} - \mathfrak{b})$.

6. We call the vector in R_n whose i-th component is 1 and all of whose other components vanish, the *i-th unit vector* of R_n, and denote it by $\mathfrak{e}_i$. Thus

$$\mathfrak{e}_1 = \{1, 0, 0, \cdots, 0\},\quad \mathfrak{e}_2 = \{0, 1, 0, \cdots, 0\},\ \cdots,\ \mathfrak{e}_n = \{0, 0, \cdots, 0, 1\}.$$

Show that for any vector $\mathfrak{a}$ of R_n, we have

$$\mathfrak{a} = (\mathfrak{a} \cdot \mathfrak{e}_1)\,\mathfrak{e}_1 + (\mathfrak{a} \cdot \mathfrak{e}_2)\,\mathfrak{e}_2 + \cdots + (\mathfrak{a} \cdot \mathfrak{e}_n)\,\mathfrak{e}_n.$$

§ 3. The Concept of Linear Dependence

In making further applications of vectors, we shall require the concept of linear dependence. We make the following definition:

We call p vectors $\mathfrak{a}_1, \mathfrak{a}_2, \cdots, \mathfrak{a}_p$ **linearly dependent** if there are p numbers $\lambda_1, \lambda_2, \ldots, \lambda_p$, not all 0, such that

$$\lambda_1 \mathfrak{a}_1 + \lambda_2 \mathfrak{a}_2 + \cdots + \lambda_p \mathfrak{a}_p = 0.$$

Of course, the zero on the right denotes the null vector.

If no such p numbers exist, then the p vectors $\mathfrak{a}_1, \mathfrak{a}_2, \cdots, \mathfrak{a}_p$ are called **linearly independent.**

If p vectors $\mathfrak{a}_1, \mathfrak{a}_2, \cdots, \mathfrak{a}_p$ are linearly independent, then the equation $\lambda_1 \mathfrak{a}_1 + \lambda_2 \mathfrak{a}_2 + \cdots + \lambda_p \mathfrak{a}_p = 0$ can hold only if $\lambda_1 = \lambda_2 = \cdots = \lambda_p = 0$. Conversely, by the definition of linear dependence, it is clear that if the equation $\lambda_1 \mathfrak{a}_1 + \lambda_2 \mathfrak{a}_2 + \cdots + \lambda_p \mathfrak{a}_p = 0$ holds only if every λ_i $(i = 1, 2, \ldots, p)$ vanishes, then the vectors $\mathfrak{a}_1, \mathfrak{a}_2, \cdots, \mathfrak{a}_p$ are linearly independent.

Examples: The three vectors $\{1, 3, 1\}$, $\{-1, 1, 3\}$, $\{-5, -7, 3\}$ of R_3 are linearly dependent. For, we have

$$3\{1, 3, 1\} - 2\{-1, 1, 3\} + \{-5, -7, 3\} = 0.$$

The four vectors $\{1, 5\}$, $\{9, 10\}$, $\{1, 1\}$, and $\{-2, -1\}$ of R_2 are also linearly dependent. For,

$$\{1, 5\} - \{9, 10\} + 2\{1, 1\} - 3\{-2, -1\} = 0.$$

On the other hand, the two vectors $\{1, 0\}$, $\{0, 1\}$ are linearly independent. For, if we had $\lambda_1\{1, 0\} + \lambda_2\{0, 1\} = 0$, it would follow upon carrying out the indicated addition that $\{\lambda_1, \lambda_2\} = 0$, and so $\lambda_1 = 0$, $\lambda_2 = 0$. In the same way, we see that the n vectors

$$\mathfrak{e}_1 = \{1, 0, 0, \cdots, 0\},\ \mathfrak{e}_2 = \{0, 1, 0, \cdots, 0\}, \cdots, \mathfrak{e}_n = \{0, 0, \cdots, 0, 1\},$$

i.e. the n *unit vectors* of R_n (cf. exercise 6, § 2), are linearly independent. For, if

$$\lambda_1 \mathfrak{e}_1 + \lambda_2 \mathfrak{e}_2 + \cdots + \lambda_n \mathfrak{e}_n = 0$$

then $\{\lambda_1, \lambda_2, \cdots, \lambda_n\} = 0$, and thus $\lambda_1 = \lambda_2 = \cdots = \lambda_n = 0$.

A single vector $\mathfrak{a} \neq 0$ of R_n is certainly linearly independent. For from $\lambda \mathfrak{a} = 0$ it follows that $\lambda = 0$. If, however, $\mathfrak{a} = 0$, then $\lambda \mathfrak{a} = 0$, for all λ, so that $\mathfrak{a}$ is linearly dependent.

Since the summands in the equation $\lambda_1 \mathfrak{a}_1 + \lambda_2 \mathfrak{a}_2 + \cdots + \lambda_p \mathfrak{a}_p = 0$ may be permuted in any way, the concept of linear dependence is independent of the order of the vectors $\mathfrak{a}_1, \mathfrak{a}_2, \cdots, \mathfrak{a}_p$.

We now easily prove the following theorems:

THEOREM 1. *If a subset of the p vectors $\mathfrak{a}_1, \mathfrak{a}_2, \cdots, \mathfrak{a}_p$ is linearly dependent, then the set of p vectors itself is linearly dependent.*

For suppose, say, the first r vectors $\mathfrak{a}_1, \mathfrak{a}_2, \cdots, \mathfrak{a}_r$ $(r < p)$ are linearly dependent.[1] Then there are r numbers $\lambda_1, \lambda_2, \cdots, \lambda_r$, not all zero,

[1] We may assume this of the first r, for otherwise we would only have to change the order of the vectors $\mathfrak{a}_1, \mathfrak{a}_2, \cdots, \mathfrak{a}_p$.

such that

$$\lambda_1 \mathfrak{a}_1 + \lambda_2 \mathfrak{a}_2 + \cdots + \lambda_r \mathfrak{a}_r = 0.$$

Setting $\lambda_{r+1} = \lambda_{r+2} = \cdots = \lambda_p = 0$, we have

$$\lambda_1 \mathfrak{a}_1 + \lambda_2 \mathfrak{a}_2 + \cdots + \lambda_r \mathfrak{a}_r + \lambda_{r+1} \mathfrak{a}_{r+1} + \cdots + \lambda_p \mathfrak{a}_p = 0$$

where the numbers $\lambda_1, \lambda_2, \cdots, \lambda_p$ are not all zero. Thus the p vectors $\mathfrak{a}_1, \mathfrak{a}_2, \cdots, \mathfrak{a}_p$ are linearly dependent.

THEOREM 2. *If p vectors $\mathfrak{a}_1, \mathfrak{a}_2, \cdots, \mathfrak{a}_p$ are linearly independent, then so is every subset of these p vectors.*

For otherwise, by Theorem 1, the p vectors would be linearly dependent.

If a vector $\mathfrak{b}$ can be represented in the form

$$\mathfrak{b} = \lambda_1 \mathfrak{a}_1 + \lambda_2 \mathfrak{a}_2 + \cdots + \lambda_p \mathfrak{a}_p,$$

then we shall say that the vector $\mathfrak{b}$ is a *linear combination* of the vectors $\mathfrak{a}_1, \mathfrak{a}_2, \cdots, \mathfrak{a}_p$. We now have the following:

THEOREM 3. *If the p vectors $\mathfrak{a}_1, \mathfrak{a}_2, \cdots, \mathfrak{a}_p$ are linearly dependent and if $p > 1$, then at least one of these vectors is a linear combination of the others.*

For, there are numbers λ_i which do not all vanish for which the equation

$$\lambda_1 \mathfrak{a}_1 + \lambda_2 \mathfrak{a}_2 + \cdots + \lambda_p \mathfrak{a}_p = 0,$$

holds. Let, say, $\lambda_p \neq 0$. Then it follows that

$$\mathfrak{a}_p = -\frac{\lambda_1}{\lambda_p} \mathfrak{a}_1 - \frac{\lambda_2}{\lambda_p} \mathfrak{a}_2 - \cdots - \frac{\lambda_{p-1}}{\lambda_p} \mathfrak{a}_{p-1},$$

i.e. $\mathfrak{a}_p$ is a linear combination of the vectors $\mathfrak{a}_1, \mathfrak{a}_2, \cdots, \mathfrak{a}_{p-1}$.

THEOREM 4. *If one of the vectors $\mathfrak{a}_1, \mathfrak{a}_2, \cdots, \mathfrak{a}_p$ is a linear combination of the others, then vectors $\mathfrak{a}_1, \mathfrak{a}_2, \cdots, \mathfrak{a}_p$ are linearly dependent.*

For suppose that, say,

$$\mathfrak{a}_1 = \lambda_2 \mathfrak{a}_2 + \lambda_3 \mathfrak{a}_3 + \cdots + \lambda_p \mathfrak{a}_p.$$

It then follows that

$$\mathfrak{a}_1 - \lambda_2 \mathfrak{a}_2 - \lambda_3 \mathfrak{a}_3 - \cdots - \lambda_p \mathfrak{a}_p = 0.$$

This relation proves the linear dependence of the vectors $\mathfrak{a}_1, \mathfrak{a}_2, \cdots, \mathfrak{a}_p$ since the coefficient of $\mathfrak{a}_1$ is 1, and so $\neq 0$.

Theorem 5. *If the vectors* $\mathfrak{a}_1, \mathfrak{a}_2, \cdots, \mathfrak{a}_p$ *are linearly independent, and the vectors* $\mathfrak{a}_1, \mathfrak{a}_2, \cdots, \mathfrak{a}_p, \mathfrak{b}$ *are linearly dependent, then* $\mathfrak{b}$ *is a linear combination of* $\mathfrak{a}_1, \mathfrak{a}_2, \cdots, \mathfrak{a}_p$.

For, we have an equation of the form

$$\lambda_1 \mathfrak{a}_1 + \lambda_2 \mathfrak{a}_2 + \cdots + \lambda_p \mathfrak{a}_p + \lambda_{p+1} \mathfrak{b} = 0,$$

where not all λ_i vanish. Now if $\lambda_{p+1} = 0$, then the last term in this equation would drop out and we would have a linear equation in the vectors $\mathfrak{a}_1, \mathfrak{a}_2, \cdots, \mathfrak{a}_p$ not all of whose coefficients vanish. But this is impossible because of the linear independence of the vectors $\mathfrak{a}_1, \mathfrak{a}_2, \cdots, \mathfrak{a}_p$. Thus $\lambda_{p+1} \neq 0$, and we may solve for $\mathfrak{b}$ to obtain

$$\mathfrak{b} = -\frac{\lambda_1}{\lambda_{p+1}} \mathfrak{a}_1 - \frac{\lambda_2}{\lambda_{p+1}} \mathfrak{a}_2 - \cdots - \frac{\lambda_p}{\lambda_{p+1}} \mathfrak{a}_p.$$

which proves our contention. Theorem 5 immediately yields

Theorem 6. *If the vectors* $\mathfrak{a}_1, \mathfrak{a}_2, \cdots, \mathfrak{a}_p$ *are linearly independent, and if* $\mathfrak{b}$ *is not a linear combination of* $\mathfrak{a}_1, \mathfrak{a}_2, \cdots, \mathfrak{a}_p$, *then the vectors* $\mathfrak{a}_1, \mathfrak{a}_2, \cdots, \mathfrak{a}_p, \mathfrak{b}$ *are linearly independent.*

Exercises

1. Prove the linear dependence of the vectors: a) $\{1,3\}, \{2,6\}$, b) $\{2,-1,-2\}, \{6,-3,-6\}$, c) $\{5,2\}, \{10,4\}, \{-15,-6\}$.

Prove the linear independence of the vectors: a) $\{1,3\}, \{2,5\}$, b) $\{2,-1,-2\}, \{6,-3,1\}$, c) $\{5,2\}, \{10,0\}$.

2. Theorem 4 of this section is sometimes useful in establishing linear dependence. In this manner, show that the vectors

a) $\{1, 5\}, \{1, 3\}, \{-1, -7\}$.
b) $\{2, -1, 7, 3\}, \{1, 4, 11, -2\}, \{3, -6, 3, 8\}$,
c) $\{3, 1, 1\}, \{2, 5, -1\}, \{1, -4, -1\}, \{1, 1, 1\}$,

are linearly dependent. Show also that any two of the vectors in a) and any three of the vectors in c) are linearly independent.

3. The p *vectors* $\mathfrak{a}_1, \mathfrak{a}_2, \cdots, \mathfrak{a}_p$ are linearly dependent a) if one of these vectors is the null vector, or b) if two of the vectors are equal.

4. Prove that two vectors are linearly dependent if and only if when taken with the same initial point, they lie along the same line. Or, if two linearly independent vectors are taken with the same initial point, then their endpoints and their common initial point do not lie on a straight line.

§ 4. Vector Spaces in R_n

Let L be a *non-empty*[1] set of vectors of R_n, with the properties:

1. If $\mathfrak{a}$ is a vector of the set L, then $\lambda \cdot \mathfrak{a}$ belongs to L for *every* real λ.

[1] I.e. the set is to contain at least one element (vector).

2. If $\mathfrak{a}$ and $\mathfrak{b}$ are two (not necessarily distinct) vectors of the set L, then the vector $\mathfrak{a} + \mathfrak{b}$ also belongs to L.

Such a set of vectors, satisfying conditions 1. and 2., is called a **vector space** in R_n (or subspace of R_n).

If $\mathfrak{a}_1, \mathfrak{a}_2, \cdots, \mathfrak{a}_p$ are vectors of L, then it follows from condition 2. that $\mathfrak{a}_1 + \mathfrak{a}_2$ belongs to L, and also that the sum of the vectors $(\mathfrak{a}_1 + \mathfrak{a}_2)$ and $\mathfrak{a}_3$, i.e. $\mathfrak{a}_1 + \mathfrak{a}_2 + \mathfrak{a}_3$, belongs to L. It further follows that the sum of the vectors $(\mathfrak{a}_1 + \mathfrak{a}_2 + \mathfrak{a}_3)$ and $\mathfrak{a}_4$, i.e. $\mathfrak{a}_1 + \mathfrak{a}_2 + \mathfrak{a}_3 + \mathfrak{a}_4$, belongs to L, etc. In this way it follows that $\mathfrak{a}_1 + \mathfrak{a}_2 + \cdots + \mathfrak{a}_p$ is a vector of L. It further follows that every linear combination $\lambda_1 \mathfrak{a}_1 + \lambda_2 \mathfrak{a}_2 + \cdots + \lambda_p \mathfrak{a}_p$ is in L; for by 1., $\lambda_i \mathfrak{a}_i$ is in L for $i = 1, 2, \ldots, p$, and so the sum of all the vectors $\lambda_i \mathfrak{a}_i$ $(i = 1, 2, \ldots, p)$, i.e. the linear combination in question, is in L.

A vector space always contains the null vector. For, it contains at least one vector $\mathfrak{a}$ and hence also the vector $0 \cdot \mathfrak{a} = \mathfrak{0}$.

As an example of a vector space, in R_n, we consider the set L of all linear combinations of p fixed vectors $\mathfrak{a}_1, \mathfrak{a}_2, \cdots, \mathfrak{a}_p$, i.e. the totality of all vectors $\lambda_1 \mathfrak{a}_1 + \lambda_2 \mathfrak{a}_2 + \cdots + \lambda_p \mathfrak{a}_p$ with real coefficients λ_i. Let, say, $\lambda_1 \mathfrak{a}_1 + \lambda_2 \mathfrak{a}_2 + \cdots + \lambda_p \mathfrak{a}_p$ be a definite vector of L. Then the vector

$$\lambda \cdot (\lambda_1 \mathfrak{a}_1 + \lambda_2 \mathfrak{a}_2 + \cdots + \lambda_p \mathfrak{a}_p) = (\lambda \cdot \lambda_1) \mathfrak{a}_1 + (\lambda \cdot \lambda_2) \mathfrak{a}_2 + \cdots + (\lambda \cdot \lambda_p) \mathfrak{a}_p$$

is also a linear combination of $\mathfrak{a}_1, \mathfrak{a}_2, \cdots, \mathfrak{a}_p$ and so belongs to L. If $\mu_1 \mathfrak{a}_1 + \mu_2 \mathfrak{a}_2 + \cdots + \mu_p \mathfrak{a}_p$ is a second vector of L, then it follows similarly that the vector

$$(\lambda_1 \mathfrak{a}_1 + \lambda_2 \mathfrak{a}_2 + \cdots + \lambda_p \mathfrak{a}_p) + (\mu_1 \mathfrak{a}_1 + \mu_2 \mathfrak{a}_2 + \cdots + \mu_p \mathfrak{a}_p)$$
$$= (\lambda_1 + \mu_1) \mathfrak{a}_1 + (\lambda_2 + \mu_2) \mathfrak{a}_2 + \cdots + (\lambda_p + \mu_p) \mathfrak{a}_p$$

is a vector of L. Thus L is a vector space. We say that this space is the space *spanned* by the vectors $\mathfrak{a}_1, \mathfrak{a}_2, \cdots, \mathfrak{a}_p$.

The geometric interpretation of vector spaces will be given in § 5.

We now prove the fundamental **replacement theorem** of Steinitz. We state it as follows:

THEOREM 1. *Let* $\mathfrak{a}_1, \mathfrak{a}_2, \cdots, \mathfrak{a}_p$ *be any* p *vectors, and let* L *be the vector space spanned by them. Let* $\mathfrak{b}_1, \mathfrak{b}_2, \cdots, \mathfrak{b}_q$ *be* q *linearly independent vectors of* L. *Then we may replace a certain set of* q *vectors from among the vectors* $\mathfrak{a}_1, \mathfrak{a}_2, \cdots, \mathfrak{a}_p$ *by the vectors* $\mathfrak{b}_1, \mathfrak{b}_2, \cdots, \mathfrak{b}_q$, *so that the remaining vectors of* $\mathfrak{a}_1, \mathfrak{a}_2, \cdots, \mathfrak{a}_p$ *together with the vectors* $\mathfrak{b}_1, \mathfrak{b}_2, \cdots, \mathfrak{b}_q$ *span the (entire) vector space* L.

It should be noted that we are not given that $p \geqq q$, but that this follows from the theorem.

The proof proceeds by *mathematical induction.*

We first observe that the theorem is trivial for $q = 0$, i.e. if no vectors $\mathfrak{b}_i$ are given.

Now take $q > 0$ and assume the result to be already proved for $q - 1$ vectors $\mathfrak{b}_i$, where $q - 1$ is therefore $\geqq 0$. We wish to show that this assumption implies that the theorem holds for the q vectors $\mathfrak{b}_1, \mathfrak{b}_2, \cdots, \mathfrak{b}_q$. Since these q vectors are linearly independent, so are the $q - 1$ vectors $\mathfrak{b}_1, \mathfrak{b}_2, \cdots, \mathfrak{b}_{q-1}$. By induction hypothesis we therefore have that $q - 1$ of the vectors $\mathfrak{a}_1, \mathfrak{a}_2, \cdots, \mathfrak{a}_p$ may be replaced by $\mathfrak{b}_1, \mathfrak{b}_2, \cdots, \mathfrak{b}_{q-1}$. We imagine the vectors $\mathfrak{a}_i$ $(i = 1, 2, \ldots, p)$ numbered so that $\mathfrak{a}_1, \mathfrak{a}_2, \cdots, \mathfrak{a}_{q-1}$ are the vectors which may be replaced by $\mathfrak{b}_1, \mathfrak{b}_2, \cdots, \mathfrak{b}_{q-1}$. Since we have assumed the theorem correct for $q - 1$ vectors $\mathfrak{b}_i$, the vectors $\mathfrak{b}_1, \mathfrak{b}_2, \cdots, \mathfrak{b}_{q-1}, \mathfrak{a}_q, \mathfrak{a}_{q+1}, \cdots, \mathfrak{a}_p$ span the vector space L. But the vector $\mathfrak{b}_q$ also belongs to L, and so must be of the form

$$\mathfrak{b}_q = \sum_{i=1}^{q-1} \lambda_i \mathfrak{b}_i + \sum_{i=q}^{p} \lambda_i \mathfrak{a}_i$$

where $\lambda_1, \lambda_2, \cdots, \lambda_p$ are certain real numbers. The numbers from λ_q on, i.e. the numbers $\lambda_q, \lambda_{q+1}, \cdots, \lambda_p$, cannot all vanish,[2] for otherwise $\mathfrak{b}_q$ would be a linear combination of the vectors $\mathfrak{b}_1, \mathfrak{b}_2, \cdots, \mathfrak{b}_{q-1}$, and so the vectors $\mathfrak{b}_1, \mathfrak{b}_2, \cdots, \mathfrak{b}_q$ would be linearly dependent by Theorem 4 of the last section contrary to our hypothesis. Thus let, say, $\lambda_q \neq 0$. (This may be accomplished, if need be, by suitably reordering the vectors $\mathfrak{a}_q, \mathfrak{a}_{q+1}, \cdots, \mathfrak{a}_p$.) We can then solve for $\mathfrak{a}_q$ and obtain[3]

$$\begin{aligned}\mathfrak{a}_q &= \frac{1}{\lambda_q} \mathfrak{b}_q - \frac{1}{\lambda_q} \sum_{i=1}^{q-1} \lambda_i \mathfrak{b}_i - \frac{1}{\lambda_q} \sum_{i=q+1}^{p} \lambda_i \mathfrak{a}_i \\ &= \frac{1}{\lambda_q} \mathfrak{b}_q - \sum_{i=1}^{q-1} \frac{\lambda_i}{\lambda_q} \mathfrak{b}_i - \sum_{i=q+1}^{p} \frac{\lambda_i}{\lambda_q} \mathfrak{a}_i .\end{aligned}$$

We now consider some arbitrary vector $\mathfrak{c}$ of L. It may be represented as a linear combination of the vectors $\mathfrak{b}_1, \mathfrak{b}_2, \cdots, \mathfrak{b}_{q-1}, \mathfrak{a}_q, \mathfrak{a}_{q+1}, \cdots, \mathfrak{a}_p$ say,

$$\mathfrak{c} = \sum_{i=1}^{q-1} \mu_i \mathfrak{b}_i + \sum_{i=q}^{p} \mu_i \mathfrak{a}_i .$$

---

[2] In particular the sum $\sum_{i=q}^{p} \lambda_i \mathfrak{a}_i$ in the last equation must actually contain summands.

[3] By the Distributive Law, we may multiply a sum of vectors by a number by multiplying each vector in the sum by that number. Thus,

$$\frac{1}{\lambda_q} \sum_{i=1}^{q-1} \lambda_i \mathfrak{b}_i = \sum_{i=1}^{q-1} \frac{\lambda_i}{\lambda_q} \mathfrak{b}_i, \qquad \frac{1}{\lambda_q} \sum_{i=q+1}^{p} \lambda_i \mathfrak{a}_i = \sum_{i=q+1}^{p} \frac{\lambda_i}{\lambda_q} \mathfrak{a}_i.$$

with certain real numbers $\mu_1, \mu_2, \cdots, \mu_p$. If we substitute on the right the expression we have just obtained for $\mathfrak{a}_q$, we obtain

$$\begin{aligned} \mathfrak{c} &= \sum_{i=1}^{q-1} \mu_i \mathfrak{b}_i + \sum_{i=q+1}^{p} \mu_i \mathfrak{a}_i + \mu_q \left(\frac{1}{\lambda_q} \mathfrak{b}_q - \sum_{i=1}^{q-1} \frac{\lambda_i}{\lambda_q} \mathfrak{b}_i - \sum_{i=q+1}^{p} \frac{\lambda_i}{\lambda_q} \mathfrak{a}_i \right) \\ &= \sum_{i=1}^{q-1} \left(\mu_i - \frac{\mu_q \lambda_i}{\lambda_q} \right) \mathfrak{b}_i + \frac{\mu_q}{\lambda_q} \mathfrak{b}_q + \sum_{i=q+1}^{p} \left(\mu_i - \frac{\mu_q \lambda_i}{\lambda_q} \right) \mathfrak{a}_i . \end{aligned}$$

But this means that $\mathfrak{c}$ is a linear combination of the vectors $\mathfrak{b}_1, \mathfrak{b}_2, \cdots, \mathfrak{b}_q, \mathfrak{a}_{q+1}, \cdots, \mathfrak{a}_p$. Since $\mathfrak{c}$ was an arbitrary vector of L, L is spanned also by the vectors $\mathfrak{b}_1, \mathfrak{b}_2, \cdots, \mathfrak{b}_q, \mathfrak{a}_{q+1}, \mathfrak{a}_{q+2}, \cdots, \mathfrak{a}_p$, as was to be proved.

The theorem was true if the number q of vectors $\mathfrak{b}_i$ $(i = 1, 2, \ldots, q)$ was 0; it then follows by the above process for $q = 1$ if only there is a linearly independent vector to be found in L,[4] and so for $q = 2$ if there are two linearly independent vectors in L, and so on. It thus holds in general, i.e. for every $q = 0, 1, 2, \ldots,$ provided there are q linearly independent vectors in L.

We now wish to draw some easy consequences from our theorem. First, as observed above, under the hypotheses of the replacement theorem the number q of vectors $\mathfrak{b}_i$ is at most as large as the number p of vectors $\mathfrak{a}_i$. For otherwise there would not be q vectors $\mathfrak{a}_i$ to be replaced by $\mathfrak{b}_1, \mathfrak{b}_2, \cdots, \mathfrak{b}_q$. And conversely, it follows that, if $\mathfrak{b}_1, \mathfrak{b}_2, \cdots, \mathfrak{b}_q$ are any vectors of L, with $q > p$, then the vectors $\mathfrak{b}_1, \mathfrak{b}_2, \cdots, \mathfrak{b}_q$ are necessarily linearly dependent, for otherwise, by what has just been said, we should have $q \leqq p$. Observing that L consists by hypothesis of all linear combinations of the vectors $\mathfrak{a}_1, \mathfrak{a}_2, \cdots, \mathfrak{a}_p$, we have

THEOREM 2. *Any set of more than p linear combinations of p given vectors is always linearly dependent.*

Let $\mathfrak{e}_i$ once again denote the i-th unit vector of R_n (cf. § 2, exercise 6). Every vector of R_n is a linear combination of the unit vectors $\mathfrak{e}_1, \mathfrak{e}_2, \cdots, \mathfrak{e}_n$. For, we may verify immediately by calculation that for any vector $\mathfrak{a} = \{a_1, a_2, \cdots, a_n\}$ of R_n,

$$\mathfrak{a} = a_1 \mathfrak{e}_1 + a_2 \mathfrak{e}_2 + \cdots + a_n \mathfrak{e}_n .$$

The totality of vectors of R_n is thus a vector space spanned by the vectors $\mathfrak{e}_1, \mathfrak{e}_2, \cdots, \mathfrak{e}_n$. By Theorem 2, it follows that any set of more

[4] It is recommended that the beginner carry out the above inductive step from $q-1$ to q in particular for $q-1=0$, $q=1$.

than n vectors of R_n is linearly dependent. However, the vectors $\mathfrak{e}_1, \mathfrak{e}_2, \cdots, \mathfrak{e}_n$ are linearly independent (cf. § 3). It follows that there are n linearly independent vectors in R_n, but that there can be no set of more than n linearly independent vectors in R_n. In other words,

THEOREM 3. *The maximal number of linearly independent vectors in R_n is n.*

Now let L be any vector space in R_n. By Theorem 3, the maximal number of linearly independent vectors of L is certainly $\leqq n$. Let p be this maximal number in the sense that there exist p linearly independent vectors of L, while any set of more than p vectors of L is always linearly dependent. We call p the **dimension** of L. Thus,

$$0 \leqq p \leqq n.$$

$p = 0$ means that there are no linearly independent vectors in L, so that L consists of the null vector alone.[5] We now assume that $p > 0$. Let $\mathfrak{a}_1, \mathfrak{a}_2, \cdots, \mathfrak{a}_p$ be any p linearly independent vectors of L. Then, if $\mathfrak{b}$ is any vector of L, the vectors $\mathfrak{a}_1, \mathfrak{a}_2, \cdots, \mathfrak{a}_p, \mathfrak{b}$ are certainly linearly dependent, for these are more than p vectors of L. By Theorem 5 of § 3, it follows that $\mathfrak{b}$ is a linear combination of the vectors $\mathfrak{a}_1, \mathfrak{a}_2, \cdots, \mathfrak{a}_p$. On the other hand, every linear combination of $\mathfrak{a}_1, \mathfrak{a}_2, \cdots, \mathfrak{a}_p$ is in L. Thus, the vector space L is precisely the totality of linear combinations of $\mathfrak{a}_1, \mathfrak{a}_2, \cdots, \mathfrak{a}_p$. We accordingly call any system of p linearly independent vectors of L, such as $\mathfrak{a}_1, \mathfrak{a}_2, \cdots, \mathfrak{a}_p$, a **basis** of L. We now prove

THEOREM 4. *Every vector of* L *can be represented in exactly one way as a linear combination of the basis vectors* $\mathfrak{a}_1, \mathfrak{a}_2, \cdots, \mathfrak{a}_p$.

For otherwise, if

$$\mathfrak{b} = \lambda_1 \mathfrak{a}_1 + \lambda_2 \mathfrak{a}_2 + \cdots + \lambda_p \mathfrak{a}_p = \mu_1 \mathfrak{a}_1 + \mu_2 \mathfrak{a}_2 + \cdots + \mu_p \mathfrak{a}_p$$

were two different representations of a vector $\mathfrak{b}$ of L, it would follow that

$$(\lambda_1 - \mu_1)\mathfrak{a}_1 + (\lambda_2 - \mu_2)\mathfrak{a}_2 + \cdots + (\lambda_p - \mu_p)\mathfrak{a}_p = 0.$$

If the representations were different, not all of the differences $\lambda_i - \mu_i$ $(i = 1, 2, \ldots, p)$ would vanish, so that the vectors $\mathfrak{a}_1, \mathfrak{a}_2, \cdots, \mathfrak{a}_p$ would be linearly dependent, which is not the case.

[5] The null-vector does indeed form a vector space. For, $\lambda \cdot 0 = 0$, $0 + 0 = 0$.

If L is spanned by q vectors $\mathfrak{a}_1, \mathfrak{a}_2, \cdots, \mathfrak{a}_q$, which need not be linearly independent, then its dimension is easily determined by the following theorem:

THEOREM 5. *The dimension of the vector space spanned by the vectors* $\mathfrak{a}_1, \mathfrak{a}_2, \cdots, \mathfrak{a}_q$ *is equal to the maximal number of linearly independent vectors among* $\mathfrak{a}_1, \mathfrak{a}_2, \cdots, \mathfrak{a}_q$.[6]

Let p be this maximal number. Then among the q vectors $\mathfrak{a}_i$, there are p linearly independent vectors, which we may assume are $\mathfrak{a}_1, \mathfrak{a}_2, \cdots, \mathfrak{a}_p$. By the definition of p, any $p + 1$ of the vectors $\mathfrak{a}_i$ are linearly dependent, hence, in particular, so are the vectors

$$\mathfrak{a}_1, \mathfrak{a}_2, \cdots, \mathfrak{a}_p, \mathfrak{a}_{p+k}$$

for $1 \leqq k \leqq q - p$. By Theorem 5 of § 3, $\mathfrak{a}_{p+k}$ is then a linear combination of $\mathfrak{a}_1, \mathfrak{a}_2, \cdots, \mathfrak{a}_p$, say,

$$\mathfrak{a}_{p+k} = \lambda_1^{(k)} \mathfrak{a}_1 + \lambda_2^{(k)} \mathfrak{a}_2 + \cdots + \lambda_p^{(k)} \mathfrak{a}_p, \qquad k = 1, 2, \cdots, q - p.$$

Furthermore, every vector $\mathfrak{b}$ of L is a linear combination of the vectors $\mathfrak{a}_1, \mathfrak{a}_2, \cdots, \mathfrak{a}_q$:

$$\mathfrak{b} = \mu_1 \mathfrak{a}_1 + \mu_2 \mathfrak{a}_2 + \cdots + \mu_q \mathfrak{a}_q.$$

Replacing $\mathfrak{a}_{p+1}, \mathfrak{a}_{p+2}, \cdots, \mathfrak{a}_q$ in this equation by the values just obtained, we have, by an easy calculation,

$$\mathfrak{b} = \left(\mu_1 + \sum_{k=1}^{q-p} \mu_{p+k} \lambda_1^{(k)}\right) \mathfrak{a}_1 + \left(\mu_2 + \sum_{k=1}^{q-p} \mu_{p+k} \lambda_2^{(k)}\right) \mathfrak{a}_2 + \cdots + \left(\mu_p + \sum_{k=1}^{q-p} \mu_{p+k} \lambda_p^{(k)}\right) \mathfrak{a}_p.$$

Thus every vector $\mathfrak{b}$ of L is a linear combination of the p vectors $\mathfrak{a}_1, \mathfrak{a}_2, \cdots, \mathfrak{a}_p$. Since, conversely, every linear combination of these p vectors also belongs to L, L consists of all linear combinations of $\mathfrak{a}_1, \mathfrak{a}_2, \cdots, \mathfrak{a}_p$. By Theorem 2 of this section, it now follows that any set of more than p vectors of L is always linearly dependent. Since, on the other hand, there certainly do exist p linearly independent vectors of L, e.g. $\mathfrak{a}_1, \mathfrak{a}_2, \cdots, \mathfrak{a}_p$, we see that p is the dimension of L and that $\mathfrak{a}_1, \mathfrak{a}_2, \cdots, \mathfrak{a}_p$ form a basis of L. Theorem 5 is thus proved.

Now, let there be given another vector space L*, contained in L, and thus consisting entirely of vectors of L. L* is called a *proper* subspace

[6] Observe the difference between the definition of dimension and the statement of Theorem 5. The dimension of a vector space is defined as the maximal number of linearly independent vectors for the entire vector space. But Theorem 5 states that the dimension is equal to the maximal number of linearly independent vectors among the finite set $\mathfrak{a}_1, \mathfrak{a}_2, \cdots, \mathfrak{a}_n$, of vectors spanning the space.

of L if it does not contain all the vectors of L, and an *improper* subspace otherwise.

If L* has the same dimension as L, and thus has dimension p, then L* is identical with L. For, if $\mathfrak{a}_1, \mathfrak{a}_2, \cdots, \mathfrak{a}_p$ is a basis of L*, then it is also a basis of L, since any p linearly independent vectors of L form a basis of L. Thus L and L* both consist of all the linear combinations of $\mathfrak{a}_1, \mathfrak{a}_2, \cdots, \mathfrak{a}_p$, and so are identical. It follows that *the dimension of every proper subspace of* L *is less than that of* L. On the other hand, every subspace of L whose dimension is less than that of L, is certainly a proper subspace of L.

Now let $\mathfrak{b}_1, \mathfrak{b}_2, \cdots, \mathfrak{b}_k$ be any linearly independent vectors of the space L of dimension p. Let $\mathfrak{a}_1, \mathfrak{a}_2, \cdots, \mathfrak{a}_p$ be any basis of L. By the Steinitz replacement theorem, we may replace k of the vectors $\mathfrak{a}_i$, say $\mathfrak{a}_1, \mathfrak{a}_2, \cdots, \mathfrak{a}_k$, by $\mathfrak{b}_1, \mathfrak{b}_2, \cdots, \mathfrak{b}_k$, so that the system

$$\mathfrak{b}_1, \mathfrak{b}_2, \cdots, \mathfrak{b}_k, \mathfrak{a}_{k+1}, \cdots, \mathfrak{a}_p$$

also spans all of L. Since p is the dimension of L, the p vectors $\mathfrak{b}_1, \mathfrak{b}_2. \cdots, \mathfrak{b}_k, \quad \mathfrak{a}_{k+1}, \cdots, \mathfrak{a}_p$ are linearly independent by Theorem 5, and are thus a basis of L. We have just proved

THEOREM 6. *Any k $(k \leqq p)$ linearly independent vectors*

$$\mathfrak{b}_1, \mathfrak{b}_2, \cdots, \mathfrak{b}_k$$

of L *can be extended to form a basis of* L *by suitably adjoining to them $p - k$ other vectors* $\mathfrak{a}_{k+1}, \mathfrak{a}_{k+2}, \cdots, \mathfrak{a}_p$.

Let L′ and L″ be any two vector spaces in R_n. By the *intersection* D of L′ and L″ we mean the set of all those vectors belonging to both L′ and L″. D is non-empty, for it certainly contains the null vector, which is in both L′ and L″. Furthermore, if $\mathfrak{a}$ belongs to D, i.e. to both L′ and L″, so does $\lambda\mathfrak{a}$, and if $\mathfrak{a}$ and $\mathfrak{b}$ are any vectors of D, i.e. of both L′ and L″, so is the vector $\mathfrak{a} + \mathfrak{b}$. This shows that D is a vector space.

We now form the totality S of all vectors of the form $\mathfrak{a}' + \mathfrak{a}''$, where $\mathfrak{a}'$ belongs to L′ and $\mathfrak{a}''$ to L″. S is called the *sum* of L′ and L″, and is also a vector space. For, S is certainly non-empty, and contains for every of its elements $\mathfrak{a}' + \mathfrak{a}''$ ($\mathfrak{a}'$ in L′, $\mathfrak{a}''$ in L″) the vector

$$\lambda(\mathfrak{a}' + \mathfrak{a}'') = \lambda\mathfrak{a}' + \lambda\mathfrak{a}'',$$

since $\lambda\mathfrak{a}'$ is in L′ and $\lambda\mathfrak{a}''$ is in L″; and finally if $\mathfrak{a}' + \mathfrak{a}''$, $\mathfrak{b}' + \mathfrak{b}''$ ($\mathfrak{a}', \mathfrak{b}'$ in L′, $\mathfrak{a}'', \mathfrak{b}''$ in L″) are two vectors of S, then so is

$$(\mathfrak{a}' + \mathfrak{a}'') + (\mathfrak{b}' + \mathfrak{b}'') = (\mathfrak{a}' + \mathfrak{b}') + (\mathfrak{a}'' + \mathfrak{b}''),$$

since $\mathfrak{a}' + \mathfrak{b}'$ is in L′ and $\mathfrak{a}'' + \mathfrak{b}''$ is in L″. We now prove

THEOREM 7. *If the dimensions of the vector spaces* L′, L″, D, *and* S *are respectively* p', p'', d, *and* s, *then* $p' + p'' = d + s$.

To prove this, let $\mathfrak{a}_1, \mathfrak{a}_2, \cdots, \mathfrak{a}_d$ be a basis of D. Using Theorem 6, we adjoin, on the one hand, the q vectors $\mathfrak{b}_1, \mathfrak{b}_2, \cdots, \mathfrak{b}_q$ to this set to form a basis of L′, where $q = p' - d$, and on the other hand the r vectors $\mathfrak{c}_1, \mathfrak{c}_2, \cdots, \mathfrak{c}_r$ to form a basis of L″ where $r = p'' - d$. Each vector of S is a linear combination of the vectors $\mathfrak{a}_i, \mathfrak{b}_i, \mathfrak{c}_i$, for it is of the form $\mathfrak{a}' + \mathfrak{a}''$, where

$$\mathfrak{a}' = \sum_{i=1}^{d} \lambda_i \mathfrak{a}_i + \sum_{i=1}^{q} \mu_i \mathfrak{b}_i,$$

$$\mathfrak{a}'' = \sum_{i=1}^{d} \varrho_i \mathfrak{a}_i + \sum_{i=1}^{r} \sigma_i \mathfrak{c}_i.$$

(The coefficients $\lambda_i, \mu_i, \varrho_i, \sigma_i$ are certain real numbers.)

But, we can also show that the totality of all the vectors $\mathfrak{a}_i, \mathfrak{b}_i, \mathfrak{c}_i$ is linearly independent. For, from an equation of the form

$$\sum_{i=1}^{d} \alpha_i \mathfrak{a}_i + \sum_{i=1}^{q} \beta_i \mathfrak{b}_i + \sum_{i=1}^{r} \gamma_i \mathfrak{c}_i = 0$$

it follows that

$$\sum_{i=1}^{r} \gamma_i \mathfrak{c}_i = -\sum_{i=1}^{d} \alpha_i \mathfrak{a}_i - \sum_{i=1}^{q} \beta_i \mathfrak{b}_i.$$

The vector $\sum_{i=1}^{r} \gamma_i \mathfrak{c}_i$ on the left is, on the one hand, a linear combination of $\mathfrak{c}_1, \mathfrak{c}_2, \cdots, \mathfrak{c}_r$, and on the other hand is a linear combination of $\mathfrak{a}_1, \mathfrak{a}_2, \cdots, \mathfrak{a}_d, \mathfrak{b}_1, \mathfrak{b}_2, \cdots, \mathfrak{b}_q$, by virtue of its equality to the right-hand side so that it belongs to L″ as well as to L′, and so to D. Thus, it is a linear combination of $\mathfrak{a}_1, \mathfrak{a}_2, \cdots, \mathfrak{a}_d$ alone, say

$$\sum_{i=1}^{r} \gamma_i \mathfrak{c}_i = \sum_{i=1}^{d} \delta_i \mathfrak{a}_i.$$

From the last two equations we have

$$\sum_{i=1}^{d} \delta_i \mathfrak{a}_i = -\sum_{i=1}^{d} \alpha_i \mathfrak{a}_i - \sum_{i=1}^{q} \beta_i \mathfrak{b}_i$$

or

$$\sum_{i=1}^{d} (\alpha_i + \delta_i) \mathfrak{a}_i + \sum_{i=1}^{q} \beta_i \mathfrak{b}_i = 0.$$

However, the vectors $\mathfrak{a}_1, \mathfrak{a}_2, \cdots, \mathfrak{a}_d, \mathfrak{b}_1, \mathfrak{b}_2, \cdots, \mathfrak{b}_q$, as a basis of

L′, are linearly independent. Thus, all the coefficients in the last equation vanish, and in particular,

$$\beta_1 = \beta_2 = \cdots = \beta_q = 0.$$

Hence all that is left of the equation

$$\sum_{i=1}^{d} \alpha_i \mathfrak{a}_i + \sum_{i=1}^{q} \beta_i \mathfrak{b}_i + \sum_{i=1}^{r} \gamma_i \mathfrak{c}_i = 0$$

is

$$\sum_{i=1}^{d} \alpha_i \mathfrak{a}_i + \sum_{i=1}^{r} \gamma_i \mathfrak{c}_i = 0.$$

However, the coefficients in this equation must all vanish, since the vectors $\mathfrak{a}_i$, $\mathfrak{c}_i$ combined form a basis of L″ and so are linearly independent. Thus all of the coefficients α_i, β_i, γ_i, necessarily vanish, so that the totality of all the vectors $\mathfrak{a}_i$, $\mathfrak{b}_i$, $\mathfrak{c}_i$ is linearly independent.

Since on the other hand, as we have already seen above, every vector of S is a linear combination of $\mathfrak{a}_i$, $\mathfrak{b}_i$, $\mathfrak{c}_i$, these vectors form a basis of S. The dimension s of the vector space S is thus

$$s = d + q + r = d + (p' - d) + (p'' - d) = p' + p'' - d.$$

Thus, we obtain

$$p' + p'' = d + s.$$

Exercises

1. Determine whether each of the following sets of vectors forms a vector space:
   i. the set of all vectors of R_n whose first component is an integer;
   ii. the set of all vectors of R_n whose first component $= 0$;
   iii. the set of all vectors of R_n $(n \geqq 2)$ at least one of whose first two components is 0;
   iv. the set of all vectors of R_n $(n \geqq 2)$ whose first two components x_1, x_2 satisfy the equation $3x_1 + 4x_2 = 0$;
   v. the set of all vectors of R_n $(n \geqq 2)$ whose first two components x_1, x_2 satisfy the equation $7x_1 - x_2 = 1$.
2. In R_4, let the vector space L_1 be spanned by the four vectors

$$\{3, -1, 1, 2\}, \ \{4, -1, -2, 3\}, \ \{10, -3, 0, 7\}, \ \{-1, 1, -7, 0\},$$

and let the space L_2 be spanned by the two vectors $\{2, -4, -3, 7\}$, $\{5, 2, 2, -1\}$. Determine the dimensions of L_1 and L_2, and of their intersection and their sum.

§ 5. Linear Spaces

The line through two points $P = (x_1, x_2, \cdots, x_n)$, $Q = (y_1, y_2, \cdots, y_n)$ of R_n was defined in § 2 as the totality of points $(z_1, z_2, \cdots, z_n)$ whose coordinates are given by the equations

$$z_i = x_i + \lambda(y_i - x_i), \qquad i = 1, 2, \cdots, n,$$

where λ runs through all real values. This may be formulated more simply by means of vectors. Set

$$\mathfrak{a} = \overrightarrow{PQ} = \{y_1 - x_1, \; y_2 - x_2, \; \cdots, \; y_n - x_n\}.$$

By § 2, the vector

$$\lambda \mathfrak{a} = \{\lambda(y_1 - x_1), \lambda(y_2 - x_2), \cdots, \lambda(y_n - x_n)\}$$

carries the point P into the point whose coordinates are

$$x_i + \lambda(y_i - x_i), \; i = 1, 2, \ldots, n,$$

i.e. into the general point $(z_1, z_2, \cdots, z_n)$ of our line. We thus have for R_n the following result which has already been verified for R_3:

The line through the distinct points P and Q is the totality of points into which P is carried by the vectors $\lambda \cdot \mathfrak{a} = \lambda \cdot \overrightarrow{PQ}$ for arbitrary real λ.

Now, the totality of vectors $\lambda\mathfrak{a}$ with real λ is a vector space L (namely the space spanned by $\mathfrak{a}$). The vector $\mathfrak{a}$ is a basis of L, and the dimension of L is 1. Our line through P and Q thus consists of all points to which P is carried by some vector of the one-dimensional vector space L.

By analogy with this result we now give the following definition:

A **linear space *of dimension p*** is the totality of points of R_n $(p \leqq n)$ into which a fixed point P is carried by the vectors of a p-dimensional vector space L of R_n.

We shall also say simply that the p-dimensional linear space is obtained from P by *applying* the vectors of L.

The meaning of this definition will be made clearer by an example.

Let L be a two-dimensional vector space in R_3, or in ordinary physical space. Let $\mathfrak{a}$, $\mathfrak{b}$ be a basis of L. To begin with, let some fixed point P of the space be taken as the initial point of the vectors $\mathfrak{a}$ and $\mathfrak{b}$ (Fig. 10).

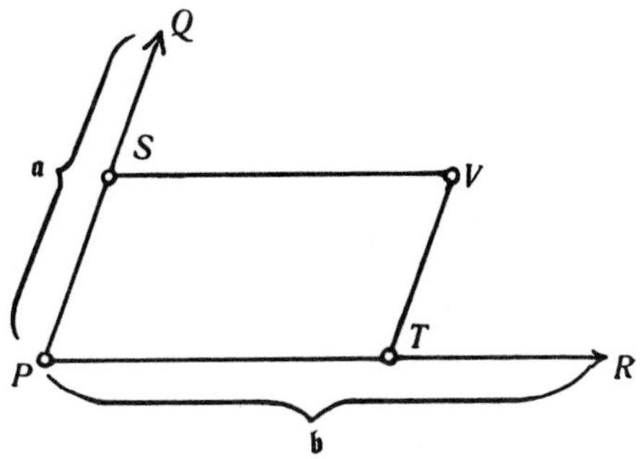

Fig. 10

Let their terminal points be Q and R respectively. Since $\mathfrak{a}$, $\mathfrak{b}$, as a basis of L, are linearly independent, the points P, Q, R determine a plane e in space. We now assert that the two-dimensional linear space which is obtained from P by applying the vectors of L, is the plane e in ordinary space. For, the point S into which P is carried by a vector $\lambda\mathfrak{a}$ is on the line through P and Q, and so in the plane e. Similarly, the point T into which P is carried by a vector $\mu\mathfrak{b}$ is on the line through P and R, and hence is also in e. An arbitrary vector of L is of the form $\lambda\mathfrak{a} + \mu\mathfrak{b}$. Let P be carried by the vector $\lambda\mathfrak{a} + \mu\mathfrak{b}$ into the point V. By the definition of addition of vectors we may also obtain V as follows: First, the point P is carried by the vector $\lambda\mathfrak{a}$ into S, and then from the point S by the vector $\mu\mathfrak{b}$ into V. Or, first the vector $\mu\mathfrak{b}$ carries P into T, and then T is carried to V by the vector $\lambda\mathfrak{a}$. Now, $SV \parallel PT$ and $PS \parallel TV$. Thus V is necessarily in e. Moreover it is clear that any point of e can be obtained in this way. Our assertion is thus proved.

A zero-dimensional vector space (in which there is no linearly independent vector) consists of the null vector alone. A point P is carried by this vector into the point P. Thus a linear space of dimension 0 is a point. A linear space of dimension 1 is a line, as we have seen above. A linear space of dimension 2 is called a *plane*, and a linear space of dimension $n - 1$ in R_n is called a *hyperplane*. (A hyperplane in R_2 is thus a line, a hyperplane in R_3 is a plane.)

All points of a linear space are equivalent to one another. This means that if a linear space L is obtained by applying the vectors of the vector space L, then it also obtained from any other one of its

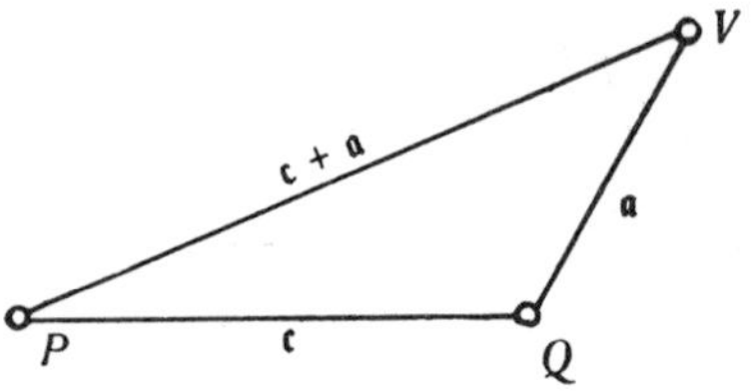

Fig. 11

points in the same manner. For, let Q be another point of L (Fig. 11). Then the vector $\mathfrak{c} = \overrightarrow{PQ}$ certainly belongs to L. If we carry Q into V by an arbitrary vector $\mathfrak{a}$ of L, then $\overrightarrow{PV} = \overrightarrow{PQ} + \overrightarrow{QV} = \mathfrak{c} + \mathfrak{a}$ is also a vector of L, so that V is a point of the linear space. On the other hand, we obtain all the points of L in this way. For if V is an arbitrary point of L, then $\overrightarrow{QV} = \overrightarrow{QP} + \overrightarrow{PV} = -\mathfrak{c} + \overrightarrow{PV}$, so that $\overrightarrow{QV}$ is a vector of L, since $-\mathfrak{c}$ and $\overrightarrow{PV}$ are.

All the vectors of R_n form a vector space of dimension n, as we have seen in § 4. R_n is obtained from the origin $O = (0, 0, \ldots, 0)$ by applying the vectors of this vector space. For, any point $P = (x_1, x_2, \cdots, x_n)$ of R_n is the point into which O is carried by the vector

$$\{x_1, x_2, \cdots, x_n\}.$$

Thus affine R_n is itself a linear space of n dimensions.

We now choose a fixed point P_0 of the linear space L. Let us further assume, in what follows, that the dimension p of L is > 0. Furthermore, let $\mathfrak{a}_1, \mathfrak{a}_2, \cdots, \mathfrak{a}_p$ be a basis of the vector space L which generates L. If P is then an arbitrary point of L, then the vector P_0P, as a vector of L, has a representation of the form

$$\overrightarrow{P_0 P} = y_1 \mathfrak{a}_1 + y_2 \mathfrak{a}_2 + \cdots + y_p \mathfrak{a}_p,$$

where the y_i $(i = 1, 2, \ldots, p)$ are real numbers. This representation is unique. The p numbers $y_1, y_2, \ldots, y_p$ are thus uniquely determined in that order by the point P, and moreover, P is uniquely determined by the numbers $y_1, y_2, \ldots, y_p$ in this way. Hence, with each point P of L is associated a p-tuple $y_1, y_2, \ldots, y_p$ of real numbers in a one-to-one manner. We have thus introduced a coordinate system in the p-dimensional linear space L. We call it a **(linear) coordinate system.** The numbers y_i $(i = 1, 2, \ldots, p)$ are called the *coordinates* of the point P. The point P_0 is called the *origin of the coordinate system.* A coordinate system in L is determined by the choice of an origin P_0 in L and a basis $\mathfrak{a}_1, \mathfrak{a}_2, \cdots, \mathfrak{a}_p$ of L.

Now suppose there is given $p+1$ points $P_k = (x_1^{(k)}, x_2^{(k)}, \cdots, x_n^{(k)})$, $k = 0, 1, \ldots, p$ which do *not* lie in any linear space of dimension $< p$. Let us consider the p vectors $\mathfrak{a}_k = \overrightarrow{P_0 P_k}$, $k = 1, 2, \ldots, p$. We shall show that they are linearly independent. For, if they were linearly dependent, then the vector space spanned by them would have dimension $< p$. By applying the vectors of this vector space to P_0, we obtain a linear space which on the one hand has dimension $< p$, and on the other contains the points $P_0, P_1, \ldots, P_p$, which contradicts our assumption.

The vectors $\mathfrak{a}_k$ $(k = 1, 2, \ldots, p)$ are therefore linearly independent. Thus, the vector space L spanned by them has dimension p. By applying the vectors of L to P_0, we obtain a p-dimensional linear space L. L certainly contains all of the points P_k. Moreover, we contend that L is the only linear space of dimension p which contains the points $P_0, P_1, \ldots, P_p$. For, let us assume that L' is another such linear space. Then L' is obtained from any one of its points, and in particular from P_0, by applying all the vectors of a certain p-dimensional vector space L′. The p vectors $\mathfrak{a}_k = \overrightarrow{P_0 P_k}$ $(k = 1, 2, \ldots, p)$ necessarily belong to L′. Since they linearly independent, these vectors form a basis of L′, proving that L and L′ are identical. Thus L and L' also coincide. *Any $p+1$ points which do not all lie in the same linear space of dimension less than p thus determine one and only one p-dimensional linear space which contains them.* This result contains, as special cases, the propositions that two distinct points uniquely determine a line, and that three non-collinear points uniquely determine a plane.

Let $P = (x_1, x_2, \cdots, x_n)$ be an arbitrary point of the linear space L (which is determined by the points $P_0, P_1, \ldots, P_p$). The vector P_0P, as a vector of L, is then of the form

$$\overrightarrow{P_0 P} = \lambda_1 \mathfrak{a}_1 + \lambda_2 \mathfrak{a}_2 + \cdots + \lambda_p \mathfrak{a}_p .$$

But

$$\overrightarrow{P_0 P} = \{x_1 - x_1^{(0)}, x_2 - x_2^{(0)}, \cdots, x_n - x_n^{(0)}\}$$

and

$$\mathfrak{a}_k = \{x_1^{(k)} - x_1^{(0)}, x_2^{(k)} - x_2^{(0)}, \cdots, x_n^{(k)} - x_n^{(0)}\}, \qquad k = 1, 2, \cdots, p.$$

It thus follows that

$$\{x_1 - x_1^{(0)}, x_2 - x_2^{(0)}, \cdots, x_n - x_n^{(0)}\}$$
$$= \sum_{k=1}^{p} \lambda_k \{x_1^{(k)} - x_1^{(0)}, x_2^{(k)} - x_2^{(0)}, \cdots, x_n^{(k)} - x_n^{(0)}\}$$
$$= \sum_{k=1}^{p} \{\lambda_k (x_1^{(k)} - x_1^{(0)}), \lambda_k (x_2^{(k)} - x_2^{(0)}), \cdots, \lambda_k (x_n^{(k)} - x_n^{(0)})\}$$
$$= \left\{\sum_{k=1}^{p} \lambda_k (x_1^{(k)} - x_1^{(0)}), \sum_{k=1}^{p} \lambda_k (x_2^{(k)} - x_2^{(0)}), \cdots, \sum_{k=1}^{p} \lambda_k (x_n^{(k)} - x_n^{(0)})\right\}.$$

However, since two vectors are equal only if their components are equal, we have

$$x_i - x_i^{(0)} = \sum_{k=1}^{p} \lambda_k (x_i^{(k)} - x_i^{(0)}), \qquad i = 1, 2, \cdots, n,$$

or

$$x_i = \sum_{k=1}^{p} \lambda_k x_i^{(k)} + x_i^{(0)} \left(1 - \sum_{k=1}^{p} \lambda_k\right).$$

Furthermore, if we now set

$$\lambda_0 = 1 - \sum_{k=1}^{p} \lambda_k, \text{ i.e. } \sum_{k=0}^{p} \lambda_k = 1,$$

we finally have

$$x_i = \sum_{k=0}^{p} \lambda_k x_i^{(k)}, \qquad i = 1, 2, \cdots, n.$$

Thus the coordinates of an arbitrary point of L may be represented in this form. The numbers $\lambda_1, \lambda_2, \cdots, \lambda_p$ are uniquely determined by $\overrightarrow{P_0 P} = \sum_{i=1}^{p} \lambda_i \mathfrak{a}_i$ and consequently, so is λ_0. Conversely, if we begin with $p+1$ numbers λ_k ($k = 0, 1, 2, \ldots, p$), satisfying the condition $\sum_{k=0}^{p} \lambda_k = 1$, then the point whose coordinates are $x_i = \sum_{k=0}^{p} \lambda_k x_i^{(k)}$ ($i = 1, 2, \ldots, n$) is a point of L. For, the point P of L for which $\overrightarrow{P_0 P} = \sum_{i=1}^{p} \lambda_i \mathfrak{a}_i$ holds, has these coordinates by what has just been proved. We thus have the following result:

All points $P = (x_1, x_2, \ldots, x_n)$ of L are obtained, and each only once, by letting the numbers λ_k ($k = 0, 1, 2, \ldots, p$) in the equations

$$x_i = \sum_{k=0}^{p} \lambda_k x_i^{(k)}, \qquad i = 1, 2, \cdots, n,$$

take on all (real) values, subject to the sole condition

$$\sum_{k=0}^{p} \lambda_k = 1.$$

Now, let L and L' be two linear spaces in R_n, and let L and L' be the associated vector spaces generating them. Let D be the intersection of L and L'. We define the *intersection* D of L and L' as the totality of those points which belong to L as well as to L'. D may be empty, i.e. L and L' may have no points in common. Otherwise, let P_0 be a fixed point and P be an arbitrary point of D. The vector $\overrightarrow{P_0P}$ then belongs to L and L', and so to D. Conversely, if a vector $\mathfrak{a}$ of D carries P_0 into a point P, we see that P is in L and L', and hence in D. D is thus a linear space, and is indeed that space which is generated by applying the vectors of D to P_0. Thus, the dimension of D is just the dimension of D.

We say that the linear spaces L and L' are **parallel** to each other if one of the two vector spaces L and L' is contained in the other. In this case, if, say, L is contained in L', $\mathrm{D} = \mathrm{L}$. Then, if the intersection of L and L' is non-empty, D is obtained from any of its points by applying the vectors of L, i.e., we have $D = L$. Hence, *two parallel linear spaces either have no points in common, or else one is contained in the other.*

Exercises

1. Three vectors of R_3 are linearly dependent if and only if they are parallel to some plane.

2. If P and Q are two points of a linear space L, then the entire line through P and Q belongs to L. Conversely, if a set L of points of R_n has this property, then L is a linear space.

3. Show that the definition of coordinate system given on p. 30 agrees, for $n = 3$, with the definition for ordinary physical space given in § 1.

4. Show that the definition of parallelism in R_2 and R_3 agrees with the intuitive notion of parallelism in the plane and space.

5. Let L be a linear space in R_n whose dimension is $< n$. Let P be a point outside of L.

i. Consider all lines which join the fixed point P to an arbitrary point of L. Let M be the set of all points on these lines. Is M a linear space?

ii. Let λ be a fixed real number, and let the point set N be defined as follows: A point S belongs to N if and only if there is a point Q in L satisfying $\overrightarrow{PS} = \lambda \cdot \overrightarrow{PQ}$. Is N a linear space?

6. Let g_1 and g_2 be two distinct lines in R_n. Consider all lines going through an arbitrary point of g_1 and an arbitrary point of g_2. Let M be the set of all points on all of these lines. Determine whether M is a linear space, *i*) in case the lines g_1 and g_2 intersect, *ii*) in case they are parallel, *iii*) in case they are skew.

7. Let L_1 and L_2 be two linear spaces which are not parallel. How can one determine a linear space of the smallest possible dimension which contains L_1 and is parallel to L_2? Is there more than one such space of smallest possible dimension? When is this dimension $< n$?

8. Let L_1 and L_2 be two arbitrary linear spaces in R_n. When does there exist a linear space L whose dimension is $< n$, and which contains both L_1 and L_2?

§ 6. Linear Equations

Linear spaces may be represented by linear equations. In order to obtain this representation, we must first derive some important algebraic results on systems of linear equations.

Let a *system of m linear*[1] *equations in n unknowns* $x_1, x_2, \ldots, x_n$ be given in the following form:

$$
\begin{aligned}
a_{11}\, x_1 + a_{12}\, x_2 + \cdots + a_{1n}\, x_n &= b_1, \\
a_{21}\, x_1 + a_{22}\, x_2 + \cdots + a_{2n}\, x_n &= b_2, \\
\cdot\ \cdot\ \cdot\ \cdot\ \cdot\ \cdot\ \cdot\ \cdot\ &\cdot\ \cdot\ \cdot \\
a_{i1}\, x_1 + a_{i2}\, x_2 + \cdots + a_{in}\, x_n &= b_i, \\
\cdot\ \cdot\ \cdot\ \cdot\ \cdot\ \cdot\ \cdot\ \cdot\ &\cdot\ \cdot\ \cdot \\
a_{m1} x_1 + a_{m2} x_2 + \cdots + a_{mn} x_n &= b_m.
\end{aligned} \tag{1}
$$

Let the real[2] numbers a_{ik}, b_i occurring here as coefficients be given. Here, a_{ik} $(1 \leqq i \leqq m,\ 1 \leqq k \leqq n)$ is the coefficient of x_k in the i-th equation; the *first* subscript of a_{ik} thus gives the equation, the *second*, the unknown, to which a_{ik} belongs. b_i $(1 \leqq i \leqq m)$ is the so-called *constant term of the i-th* equation.

Under what conditions is such a system of equations solvable for the x_i? That is, when are there numbers $x_1, x_2, \ldots, x_n$, which simultaneously satisfy all of the above m equations? To resolve this question, we begin by considering the system of coefficients a_{ik} on the left-hand sides of our equations. We arrange these coefficients according to their positions in these equations in the rectangular array

$$
\begin{pmatrix}
a_{11} & a_{12} & a_{13} & \cdots & a_{1n} \\
a_{21} & a_{22} & a_{23} & \cdots & a_{2n} \\
\cdot & \cdot & \cdot & \cdot & \cdot \\
a_{i1} & a_{i2} & a_{i3} & \cdots & a_{in} \\
\cdot & \cdot & \cdot & \cdot & \cdot \\
a_{m1} & a_{m2} & a_{m3} & \cdots & a_{mn}
\end{pmatrix}. \tag{2}
$$

---

[1] An equation of the form $a_1 x_1 + a_2 x_2 + \cdots + a_n x_n = b$ is called *linear* or *of the first degree* in the quantities x_i.

[2] As before, the discussions of this and of the following sections will be restricted to real numbers. We shall later (§ 14) investigate the question: For which more general domains do the results continue to hold?

Such a rectangular array of numbers (elements) is called a **matrix** and will usually, as above, be enclosed in parentheses. We shall speak of the (horizontal) *rows* and the (vertical) *columns* of such a matrix. The elements occurring in a matrix are called its entries, so that a_{ik} is thus the entry of the i-th row and the k-th column of the matrix. The first subscript i of a_{ik} is therefore also called the row index and the second k, the column index. The arrangement of the entries in a matrix is essential, and may not be changed at will.

We now associate a vector with each column of the matrix (2); specifically, we associate with the k-th column the vector

$$\mathfrak{a}_k = \{a_{1k}, a_{2k}, \cdots, a_{mk}\}, \qquad k = 1, 2, \cdots, n,$$

whose components are the entries of the k-th column in the same order. These *column vectors* $\mathfrak{a}_k$ are m-dimensional vectors. We also form the vector

$$\mathfrak{b} = \{b_1, b_2, \cdots, b_m\},$$

whose components are the constant terms of the system (1) in the order of their occurrence. The i-th equation of the system (1) has as coefficients precisely the i-th components of the vectors $\mathfrak{a}_1, \mathfrak{a}_2, \cdots, \mathfrak{a}_n, \mathfrak{b}$, so that the validity of equations (1) is equivalent to the validity of the single vector equation

$$\mathfrak{a}_1 \cdot x_1 + \mathfrak{a}_2 \cdot x_2 + \cdots + \mathfrak{a}_n \cdot x_n = \mathfrak{b}. \tag{3}$$

This follows immediately from the rules of vector algebra (§ 2). Now, when do there exist numbers $x_1, x_2, \ldots, x_n$ satisfying this equation?

Consider the vector space L spanned by the vectors $\mathfrak{a}_1, \mathfrak{a}_2, \cdots, \mathfrak{a}_n$ in R_m. If equation (3) is solvable for the x_i, then $\mathfrak{b}$ is a linear combination of $\mathfrak{a}_1, \mathfrak{a}_2, \cdots, \mathfrak{a}_n$ and so belongs to L. Conversely, if $\mathfrak{b}$ belongs to L, then equation (3) is solvable.

Furthermore, let L* be the vector space spanned by the vectors $\mathfrak{a}_1, \mathfrak{a}_2, \cdots, \mathfrak{a}_n, \mathfrak{b}$. A vector $\mathfrak{c}$ of L* is then of the form

$$\mathfrak{c} = \lambda_1 \mathfrak{a}_1 + \lambda_2 \mathfrak{a}_2 + \cdots + \lambda_n \mathfrak{a}_n + \lambda \mathfrak{b}. \tag{4}$$

If $\mathfrak{b}$ belongs to L, then equation (3) is satisfied by certain numbers $x_1, x_2, \ldots, x_n$, and by substituting in (4) the value of $\mathfrak{b}$ given by (3), we obtain

$$\mathfrak{c} = (\lambda_1 + \lambda x_1)\, \mathfrak{a}_1 + (\lambda_2 + \lambda x_2)\, \mathfrak{a}_2 + \cdots + (\lambda_n + \lambda x_n)\, \mathfrak{a}_n.$$

Thus in this case, every vector $\mathfrak{c}$ of L* is a linear combination of $\mathfrak{a}_1, \mathfrak{a}_2, \cdots, \mathfrak{a}_n$ and so is in L. Conversely, since every vector of L is also in L*, in this case, L and L* are identical. Now, by Theorem 5 of § 4, the dimension of L is exactly the maximal number of linearly independent vectors among the vectors $\mathfrak{a}_1, \mathfrak{a}_2, \cdots, \mathfrak{a}_n$, and the dimension of L* is, similarly, equal to the maximal number of linearly independent vectors among $\mathfrak{a}_1, \mathfrak{a}_2, \cdots, \mathfrak{a}_n, \mathfrak{b}$. If L and L* are to be identical, then these maximal numbers must be the same. Conversely, if these numbers are the same, then L, being a subspace of L*, has the same dimension as L*, and is thus identical with L*. Thus the following result is proved:

THEOREM 1. *The equations* (1) *are solvable for the* x_i *if and only if the maximal number of linearly independent vectors among* $\mathfrak{a}_1, \mathfrak{a}_2, \cdots, \mathfrak{a}_n$ *is the same as the maximal number of linearly independent vectors among* $\mathfrak{a}_1, \mathfrak{a}_2, \cdots, \mathfrak{a}_n, \mathfrak{b}$.

The vectors $\mathfrak{a}_1, \mathfrak{a}_2, \cdots, \mathfrak{a}_n$ are the column vectors of the matrix (2). We call the maximal number of linearly independent column vectors of a matrix the **rank** of the matrix. Now, let us consider also the following matrix:

$$\begin{pmatrix} a_{11} & a_{12} & \cdots & a_{1n} & b_1 \\ a_{21} & a_{22} & \cdots & a_{2n} & b_2 \\ \cdot & \cdot & \cdot & \cdot & \cdot \\ a_{m1} & a_{m2} & \cdots & a_{mn} & b_m \end{pmatrix}. \tag{5}$$

This is obtained from (2) by annexing a last column, in which the constant terms of equations (1) occur, and occur in the same order. The matrix (2) is called the *coefficient* matrix, while (5) is called the *augmented* matrix of the system of equations (1). The column vectors of the augmented matrix of the system are $\mathfrak{a}_1, \mathfrak{a}_2, \cdots, \mathfrak{a}_n, \mathfrak{b}$, and so its rank is the maximal number of linearly independent vectors among them. Using this terminology we may express Theorem 1 in the following form:

THEOREM 2. *The equations* (1) *are solvable for the* x_i *if and only if the rank of the coefficient matrix of the system* (1) *is equal to the rank of the augmented matrix.*

In § 9 we shall be introduced to simple methods for determining the rank of a matrix. Theorem 2 will thus yield a convenient method for determining the solvability of a system of equations.

Homogeneous Linear Equations

We now wish to obtain information concerning all the solutions of the system (1), under the assumption that it is solvable. We first investigate the special case in which the constant terms $b_1, b_2, \ldots, b_m$ in the equations (1) all vanish. We are thus interested in all the solutions of the equations

$$
(6) \quad \begin{aligned}
a_{11} x_1 + a_{12} x_2 + \cdots + a_{1n} x_n &= 0, \\
a_{21} x_1 + a_{22} x_2 + \cdots + a_{2n} x_n &= 0, \\
\cdots\cdots\cdots\cdots\cdots &\cdots \\
a_{m1} x_1 + a_{m2} x_2 + \cdots + a_{mn} x_n &= 0.
\end{aligned}
$$

Such a system of equations is called ***homogeneous** in the x_i*. The coefficient matrix of the system (6), which in this case is simply called the matrix of the system (6) (because the augmented matrix differs from it only by a column which consists entirely of zeros) again is of the form (2). The column vectors of this will again be denoted by $\mathfrak{a}_1, \mathfrak{a}_2, \cdots, \mathfrak{a}_n$. As above, we see at once that the equations of the system (6) hold simultaneously if and only if the vector equation

$$
(7) \quad \mathfrak{a}_1 \cdot x_1 + \mathfrak{a}_2 \cdot x_2 + \cdots + \mathfrak{a}_n \cdot x_n = 0
$$

holds. Every solution $x_1, x_2, \ldots, x_n$ of the system (6) also satisfies equation (7), and conversely.

Any set of n numbers $x_1, x_2, \ldots, x_n$ which satisfy the system (6) (or equivalently the equation (7)) are now taken to be the components of an n-dimensional vector $\mathfrak{x} = \{x_1, x_2, \cdots, x_n\}$. We call such a vector a *vector solution* of the system (6). We assert that

The totality of vector solutions of the system of equations (6) *forms a vector space.*

First we note that the system (6) always has at least one solution, namely the trivial solution, $x_1 = x_2 = \ldots = x_n = 0$. Furthermore, if $\mathfrak{x} = \{x_1, x_2, \cdots, x_n\}$ is an arbitrary vector solution, then

$$
\lambda \mathfrak{x} = \{\lambda x_1, \lambda x_2, \cdots, \lambda x_n\}
$$

is also a vector solution, since the validity of the equation

$$
(\lambda x_1) \mathfrak{a}_1 + (\lambda x_2) \mathfrak{a}_2 + \cdots + (\lambda x_n) \mathfrak{a}_n = 0
$$

follows from that of (7) upon multiplication by λ. Moreover, if $\mathfrak{y} = \{y_1, y_2, \cdots, y_n\}$ is another vector solution, then

$$
\mathfrak{a}_1 y_1 + \mathfrak{a}_2 y_2 + \cdots + \mathfrak{a}_n y_n = 0.
$$

Adding this to (7), we obtain

$$
\mathfrak{a}_1 (x_1 + y_1) + \mathfrak{a}_2 (x_2 + y_2) + \cdots + \mathfrak{a}_n (x_n + y_n) = 0,
$$

so that the vector $\mathfrak{x}+\mathfrak{y} = \{x_1+y_1, x_2+y_2, \cdots, x_n+y_n\}$ is also a vector solution of (6). Thus our assertion is completely proved.

Let the rank of the matrix of the system (6) be r. Then there are r linearly independent column vectors. By a suitable interchange of the columns of our matrix, we may arrange that these shall be the first r column vectors. The transformed matrix will have the same rank as the original matrix, for the maximal number of linearly independent column vectors is clearly seen to be independent of the arrangement of the columns. Interchanging the columns merely involves a renumbering of the unknowns x_i in the equations (6). We may assume that we had, in the first place, suitably numbered the unknowns in this way, so that the first r column vectors $\mathfrak{a}_1, \mathfrak{a}_2, \cdots, \mathfrak{a}_r$ of our matrix are linearly independent. Since any $r+1$ column vectors are linearly dependent, by definition of rank, the vectors

$$\mathfrak{a}_1, \mathfrak{a}_2, \cdots, \mathfrak{a}_r, \mathfrak{a}_k,$$

where k is one of the numbers $r+1, r+2, \ldots, n$, are linearly dependent.[3] By Theorem 5 of § 3, $\mathfrak{a}_k$ is thus a linear combination of $\mathfrak{a}_1, \mathfrak{a}_2, \cdots, \mathfrak{a}_r$, and so we have

$$\mathfrak{a}_k = z_1^{(k)}\mathfrak{a}_1 + z_2^{(k)}\mathfrak{a}_2 + \cdots + z_r^{(k)}\mathfrak{a}_r, \qquad k = r+1, r+2, \cdots, n.$$

Setting $z_i^{(k)} = -y_i^{(k)}$, we have

$$y_1^{(k)}\mathfrak{a}_1 + y_2^{(k)}\mathfrak{a}_2 + \cdots + y_r^{(k)}\mathfrak{a}_r + \mathfrak{a}_k = 0, \qquad k = r+1, r+2, \cdots, n.$$

Each of these $n-r$ equations has the form (7), and these equations yield, for $k = r+1, \ldots, n$, the vector solutions

$$\begin{aligned}
\mathfrak{y}_1 &= \{y_1^{(r+1)}, y_2^{(r+1)}, \cdots, y_r^{(r+1)}, 1, 0, 0, \cdots, 0\},\\
\mathfrak{y}_2 &= \{y_1^{(r+2)}, y_2^{(r+2)}, \cdots, y_r^{(r+2)}, 0, 1, 0, \cdots, 0\},\\
&\cdots\cdots\cdots\cdots\cdots\cdots\cdots\cdots\\
\mathfrak{y}_{n-r} &= \{y_1^{(n)}, \ y_2^{(n)}, \ \cdots, y_r^{(n)}, \ 0, 0, \cdots, 0, 1\}
\end{aligned}$$

of the system (6). These $n-r$ vectors are linearly independent. For, if an equation of the form

$$\lambda_1\mathfrak{y}_1 + \lambda_2\mathfrak{y}_2 + \cdots + \lambda_{n-r}\mathfrak{y}_{n-r} = 0$$

holds, then this equation remains correct upon replacement of each of the vectors $\mathfrak{y}_1, \mathfrak{y}_2, \cdots, \mathfrak{y}_{n-r}$ by its i-th component ($i = 1, 2, \ldots, n$). If, in particular, they are replaced by their $(r+1)$-st, $(r+2)$-nd,

[3] Of course this also holds for $k = 1, 2, \ldots, r$, but we will not need this fact.

$\ldots$, n-th components, we obtain the equations

$$\lambda_1 = 0,\ \lambda_2 = 0,\ \cdots,\ \lambda_{n-r} = 0$$

respectively. But this implies that the vectors $\mathfrak{y}_1, \mathfrak{y}_2, \cdots, \mathfrak{y}_{n-r}$ are linearly independent.

Thus if $\mathfrak{z} = \{z_1, z_2, \cdots, z_n\}$ is any vector solution of the system (6), then we have

$$z_1 \mathfrak{a}_1 + z_2 \mathfrak{a}_2 + \cdots + z_n \mathfrak{a}_n = 0.$$

We now form the vectors

$$\begin{array}{lll} z_{r+1}\,\mathfrak{y}_1 &= \{z_{r+1}\, y_1^{(r+1)},\ z_{r+1}\, y_2^{(r+1)},\ \cdots,\ z_{r+1}\, y_r^{(r+1)},\ z_{r+1},\ 0,\ \cdots,\ 0\}, \\ z_{r+2}\,\mathfrak{y}_2 &= \{z_{r+2}\, y_1^{(r+2)},\ z_{r+2}\, y_2^{(r+2)},\ \cdots,\ z_{r+2}\, y_r^{(r+2)},\ 0,\ z_{r+2},\ \cdots,\ 0\}, \\ \cdots & \cdots \\ z_n\,\mathfrak{y}_{n-r} &= \{z_n\, y_1^{(n)},\ z_n\, y_2^{(n)},\ \cdots,\ z_n\, y_r^{(n)},\ 0,\ 0,\ \cdots,\ z_n\}. \end{array}$$

We add these vectors and subtract their sum from $\mathfrak{z}$, thus forming the vector $\mathfrak{z} - \sum_{i=1}^{n-r} z_{r+i}\, \mathfrak{y}_i$. It is easily seen, upon noting the form of the last $n - r$ components of the vectors $z_{r+i}\, \mathfrak{y}_i$ that the last $n - r$ components of the vector $\mathfrak{z} - \sum_{i=1}^{n-r} z_{r+i}\, \mathfrak{y}_i$. vanish. Thus,

(8) $\mathfrak{z} - z_{r+1}\,\mathfrak{y}_1 - z_{r+2}\,\mathfrak{y}_2 - \cdots - z_n\,\mathfrak{y}_{n-r} = \{\bar{z}_1, \bar{z}_2, \cdots, \bar{z}_r, 0, 0, \cdots, 0\}$,

where the $\bar{z}_i$ $(i = 1, 2, \ldots, r)$ are certain real numbers. Now, however, the vector $\mathfrak{z} - \sum_{i=1}^{n-r} z_{r+i}\, \mathfrak{y}_i$, as a linear combination of vector solutions of (6), is itself a vector solution, since the vector solutions of (6) form a vector space. Thus,

$$\bar{z}_1 \mathfrak{a}_1 + \bar{z}_2 \mathfrak{a}_2 + \cdots + \bar{z}_r \mathfrak{a}_r = 0.$$

Since the vectors $\mathfrak{a}_1, \mathfrak{a}_2, \cdots, \mathfrak{a}_r$ are linearly independent, it follows that $\bar{z}_1 = \bar{z}_2 = \cdots = \bar{z}_r = 0$. It then follows from (8) that

$$\mathfrak{z} = z_{r+1}\,\mathfrak{y}_1 + z_{r+2}\,\mathfrak{y}_2 + \cdots + z_n\,\mathfrak{y}_{n-r}.$$

Thus each vector solution $\mathfrak{z}$ of (6) is a linear combination of the vectors $\mathfrak{y}_1, \mathfrak{y}_2, \cdots, \mathfrak{y}_{n-r}$. *These vectors, since they are linearly independent, form a basis of the vector space of all vector solutions, so that the dimension of this space is $n - r$.* We thus have the following theorem:

THEOREM 3. *If the (coefficient) matrix of the system of equations*

(6) has rank r, then the set of vector solutions of this system is an $(n-r)$-dimensional vector space.

The rank of the matrix (2) is certainly $\leqq n$. Now, if it equals n, then the space of vector solutions of equations (6) is, by Theorem 3, of dimension 0, and so consists of the null vector alone. Equations (6) then have only the trivial solution $x_1 = x_2 = \ldots = x_n = 0$. If however the rank of the matrix is $< n$, then the dimension of the space of vector solutions is > 0. Thus, in this case, equations (6) have a non-trivial solution $x_1, x_2, \ldots, x_n$, in which not all x_i vanish. Thus we have

THEOREM 4. *The system of equations* (6) *has a non-trivial solution, i.e. a solution $x_1, x_2, \ldots, x_n$ such that not all x_i vanish, if and only if the rank of the matrix of* (6) *is less than n.*

The column vectors of the matrix (2) are m-dimensional vectors where m is the number of equations in (6). But by § 5, the maximal number of linearly independent vectors of R_m is m. Thus the matrix (2) has at most m linearly independent column vectors, and so its rank is always $\leqq m$. If the number m of equations in (6) is less than n, then these equations will always have, by Theorem 4, a non-trivial solution. Thus, we have

THEOREM 5. *If the number of equations in the system of homogeneous equations* (6) *is less than the number of unknowns, then the system must have non-trivial solutions.*

Non-homogeneous Linear Equations

We now return to our study of the system (1) of non-homogeneous equations. However, we shall consider the system (6) of homogeneous equations which arises from (1) upon setting $b_1 = b_2 = \ldots = b_m = 0$, along with the system (1) itself. Let us assume that the system (1) has solutions, and let $\mathfrak{x} = \{x_1, x_2, \cdots, x_n\}$ be a vector solution of (1). Then, by (3),

$$\mathfrak{a}_1 x_1 + \mathfrak{a}_2 x_2 + \cdots + \mathfrak{a}_n x_n = \mathfrak{b}, \tag{8}$$

where $\mathfrak{a}_i$ is again the i-th column vector of the matrix (2), and where $\mathfrak{b} = \{b_1, b_2, \cdots, b_m\}$. Now let $\mathfrak{y} = \{y_1, y_2, \cdots, y_n\}$ be an arbitrary solution of the homogeneous system (6), so that by (7), we have

$$y_1 \mathfrak{a}_1 + y_2 \mathfrak{a}_2 + \cdots + y_n \mathfrak{a}_n = 0.$$

Adding the last two equations, we obtain

$$(x_1 + y_1)\,\mathfrak{a}_1 + (x_2 + y_2)\,\mathfrak{a}_2 + \cdots + (x_n + y_n)\,\mathfrak{a}_n = \mathfrak{b}.$$

But this states that the vector $\mathfrak{x} + \mathfrak{y}$ is a vector solution of the system (1). Conversely, any solution of (1) is representable as the sum of some *fixed* vector solution $\mathfrak{x}$ of (1) and a suitable solution $\mathfrak{y}$ of the system (6). For, if $\mathfrak{z} = \{z_1, z_2, \cdots, z_n\}$ is an arbitrary vector solution of (1), we have

$$z_1\,\mathfrak{a}_1 + z_2\,\mathfrak{a}_2 + \cdots + z_n\,\mathfrak{a}_n = \mathfrak{b}.$$

Subtracting equation (8) from this equation, we obtain

$$(z_1 - x_1)\,\mathfrak{a}_1 + (z_2 - x_2)\,\mathfrak{a}_2 + \cdots + (z_n - x_n)\,\mathfrak{a}_n = 0.$$

But this states that the vector $(\mathfrak{z} - \mathfrak{x}) = \mathfrak{y}$ is a vector solution of the system (6). Thus, we have

$$\mathfrak{z} = \mathfrak{x} + \mathfrak{y},$$

which was to be proved. We formulate this result as follows:

THEOREM 6. *All the solutions $\mathfrak{z}$ of the non-homogeneous system of equations* (1) *are of the form $\mathfrak{z} = \mathfrak{x} + \mathfrak{y}$, where $\mathfrak{x}$ is a fixed solution of the non-homogeneous system* (1) *and $\mathfrak{y}$ runs through all solutions of the corresponding homogeneous system* (6).

Finally, we shall shed some further light on the concept of rank of a matrix. First we show that *the rank of a matrix is unchanged by the interchange of rows or of columns.* We have already seen this for columns; for if we interchange two columns, the totality of column vectors remains unchanged, and hence so does the maximal number of linearly independent vectors among them. Now, any matrix of the form (2) can be considered as a matrix of a homogeneous system of the form (6). If the dimension of the vector space of all vector solutions of this system is p, then the rank of the matrix is, by Theorem 3, equal to $n - p$ where n is the number of columns of our matrix. Any interchange of rows in our matrix merely induces a similar interchange of the equations of the corresponding system of the form (6). The totality of vector solutions of the altered system is certainly the same as that of the original system. Thus, the dimension p of the space of all vector solutions remains unchanged, and hence so does the rank of the matrix, which, as we have seen, is equal to $n - p$.

We now associate a vector with each row of the matrix (2); that is, we associate with the i-th row, the vector

$$\bar{\mathfrak{a}}_i = \{a_{i1}, a_{i2}, \cdots, a_{in}\}, \qquad i = 1, 2, \cdots, m,$$

the components of which are then the entries of the i-th row in their order of appearance. These *row vectors* are vectors of n-dimensional space. Let s be the maximal number of linearly independent row vectors. Let the rank of the matrix (i.e. the maximal number of linearly independent column vectors) be denoted by r, as above. We will show first that we always have $r \leqq s$.

By suitable interchanges of the rows of the matrix, we can arrive at a new matrix whose first s row vectors are linearly independent. By what has just been proved, the rank of the new matrix is also r. Moreover, the maximal number of linearly independent row vectors is unchanged, since only their order was altered. In order to avoid a new notation, we assume that the matrix (2) had its first s row vectors linearly independent to start with. This entails no loss in generality, by what has just been said.

Once again, we consider the system of equations (6) corresponding to the matrix (2), whose coefficients thus are the entries of the given matrix. The i-th equation of the system (6) is, by the definition of scalar product of two vectors (cf. § 2), equivalent to the vector equation

$$(9) \qquad \bar{\mathfrak{a}}_i\, \mathfrak{x} = 0, \qquad i = 1, 2, \cdots, m,$$

where we have set $\mathfrak{x} = \{x_1, x_2, \cdots, x_n\}$. This is again merely an abbreviated notation. Every vector solution of the system (6) (or of (9)) is in particular a vector solution of the first s equations of (6) (or of the first s equations of (9)). But the converse also holds, namely: *Every system of n numbers $x_1, x_2, \ldots, x_n$ satisfying the first s equations of* (6) (*or of* (9)), *satisfies all of the equations of* (6) (*or of* (9)). In order to see this, we must prove that if $\mathfrak{x}$ satisfies the equations

$$\bar{\mathfrak{a}}_i\, \mathfrak{x} = 0$$

for $i = 1, 2, \ldots, s$, then it also satisfies these equations for $i = s + 1$, $s + 2, \ldots, m$. Now the vectors $\bar{\mathfrak{a}}_1, \bar{\mathfrak{a}}_2, \cdots, \bar{\mathfrak{a}}_s$ are linearly independent, while by the definition of s, any $s + 1$ row vectors are linearly dependent, e.g. the vectors $\bar{\mathfrak{a}}_1, \bar{\mathfrak{a}}_2, \cdots, \bar{\mathfrak{a}}_s, \bar{\mathfrak{a}}_k$ for $1 \leqq k \leqq m$. By Theorem 5 of § 3, it follows that for each k, $1 \leqq k \leqq m$, a relation of the form

$$\bar{\mathfrak{a}}_k = \lambda_1^{(k)}\, \bar{\mathfrak{a}}_1 + \lambda_2^{(k)}\, \bar{\mathfrak{a}}_2 + \cdots + \lambda_s^{(k)}\, \bar{\mathfrak{a}}_s,$$

holds. If we form the scalar product of both sides of this equation with the vector $\mathfrak{x}$ and apply the distributive law on the right, we obtain

$$\bar{\mathfrak{a}}_k \cdot \mathfrak{x} = \lambda_1^{(k)}(\bar{\mathfrak{a}}_1 \cdot \mathfrak{x}) + \lambda_2^{(k)}(\bar{\mathfrak{a}}_2 \cdot \mathfrak{x}) + \cdots + \lambda_s^{(k)}(\bar{\mathfrak{a}}_s \cdot \mathfrak{x}).$$

Since $\bar{\mathfrak{a}}_i \mathfrak{x} = 0$ for $i = 1, 2, \ldots, s$, the right-hand side of this last equation becomes the null vector, so that

$$\bar{\mathfrak{a}}_k \cdot \mathfrak{x} = 0, \qquad k = 1, 2, \cdots, m,$$

and in particular for $k = s + 1, s + 2, \ldots, m$, as was to be proved.

The vector space of all solutions of the first s equations of (6) *is thus identical with the space of solutions of the entire system* (6). Its dimension is thus $n - r$ since r was used to denote the rank of the matrix (2). It thus follows that the rank of the matrix of the first s equations, i.e. of the matrix which consists only of the first s rows of (2) is equal to $n - (n - r) = r$. But the column vectors of this matrix are vectors with s components. Thus the maximal number r of linearly independent column vectors of this matrix is $\leqq s$ since, by Theorem 3 of § 4, any $s + 1$ vectors of s-dimensional space are linearly dependent. Recalling the definition of the numbers r and s, we may state our result as follows:

The maximal number of linearly independent column vectors of a matrix is at most as large as the maximal number of linearly independent row vectors.

We now consider along with (2) the matrix

$$\begin{pmatrix} a_{11} & a_{21} & a_{31} & \cdots & a_{m1} \\ a_{12} & a_{22} & a_{32} & \cdots & a_{m2} \\ \cdot & \cdot & \cdot & \cdot & \cdot \\ a_{1n} & a_{2n} & a_{3n} & \cdots & a_{mn} \end{pmatrix},$$

which is called the *transpose* of the matrix (2). Thus, this transposed matrix has the rows of (2) as columns and the columns of (2) as rows. The maximal number of linearly independent column vectors of this matrix is s, and the maximal number of its linearly independent row vectors is r. Applying the result proved above to the matrix (2) and also to its transpose, we obtain the two inequalities $r \leqq s$ and $s \leqq r$. But these inequalities can hold simultaneously only if $s = r$. Thus we we have proved

THEOREM 7. *The maximal number of linearly independent column vectors of a matrix is equal to the maximal number of linearly independent row vectors of that matrix.*

Thus the rank of a matrix is also equal to the maximal number of linearly independent row vectors.

Geometric Applications

We are now in a position to prove the following converse of Theorem 3:

THEOREM 8. *With any given vector space* L *of* R_n, *we can always associate a system of homogeneous linear equations in n unknowns such that all vectors of* L, *and no others, are vector solutions of this system.*

By Theorem 3, the rank of this system must be $n - p$, where p is the dimension of L. Thus, by Theorem 7 there must be at least $n - p$ equations in our system. We shall see that this number actually suffices. We first determine a basis, $\mathfrak{a}_1, \mathfrak{a}_2, \cdots, \mathfrak{a}_p$ of L where we set, say, $\mathfrak{a}_i = \{a_{i1}, a_{i2}, \cdots, a_{in}\}$. If in addition we set

$$\mathfrak{x} = \{x_1, x_2, \cdots, x_n\},$$

then the equations

$$\mathfrak{a}_i \mathfrak{x} = 0, \qquad i = 1, 2, \cdots, p, \tag{10}$$

form a system of homogeneous linear equations in the unknowns $x_1, x_2, \ldots, x_n$, whose matrix is

$$\begin{pmatrix} a_{11} & a_{12} & \cdots & a_{1n} \\ a_{21} & a_{22} & \cdots & a_{2n} \\ \cdot & \cdot & \cdot & \cdot \\ a_{p1} & a_{p2} & \cdots & a_{pn} \end{pmatrix}$$

This matrix has rank p, since the p row vectors $\mathfrak{a}_1, \mathfrak{a}_2, \cdots, \mathfrak{a}_p$, being a basis of L, are linearly independent. Any vector solution $\mathfrak{x}$ of the equations (10) is orthogonal[4] to any vector $\lambda_1 \mathfrak{a}_1 + \lambda_2 \mathfrak{a}_2 + \cdots + \lambda_p \mathfrak{a}_p$

[4] Two vectors $\mathfrak{a}$ and $\mathfrak{b}$ are called orthogonal to each other if their scalar product $\mathfrak{a} \cdot \mathfrak{b} = 0$ (§ 2). Here we are using the terms "orthogonal" and "scalar product" merely as abbreviations. We have defined them in a purely algebraic manner and they are not to be taken as having any other meaning. To be sure there is a geometric interpretation behind all this. But the geometric meaning of these terms first becomes clear in R_n with *euclidean* length. This will be discussed in § 7.

of L. For, by (10), we have

$$\mathfrak{x} \cdot (\lambda_1 \mathfrak{a}_1 + \lambda_2 \mathfrak{a}_2 + \cdots + \lambda_p \mathfrak{a}_p) = \lambda_1 (\mathfrak{x} \mathfrak{a}_1) + \lambda_2 (\mathfrak{x} \mathfrak{a}_2) + \cdots + \lambda_p (\mathfrak{x} \mathfrak{a}_p) = 0.$$

Conversely, any vector $\mathfrak{x}$ which is orthogonal to all the vectors of L is a vector solution of the system (10). For in particular, $\mathfrak{x}$ will then be orthogonal to the vectors $\mathfrak{a}_1, \mathfrak{a}_2, \cdots, \mathfrak{a}_p$, i.e.

$$\mathfrak{x} \mathfrak{a}_i = 0, \quad i = 1, 2, \cdots, p.$$

We shall call a vector orthogonal to the vector space L if it is orthogonal to every vector of L; and we now have the following result:

The totality of vectors which are orthogonal to L *is a vector space* L′ *of dimension* $n - p$. *It consists precisely of all vector solutions of the equations* (10).

We now seek those vectors which are orthogonal to the vector space L′ just obtained. We choose a basis $\mathfrak{b}_1, \mathfrak{b}_2, \cdots, \mathfrak{b}_{n-p}$ of L′. The $\mathfrak{b}_i$, as vectors of L′, are orthogonal to L, and thus in particular to $\mathfrak{a}_1, \mathfrak{a}_2, \cdots, \mathfrak{a}_p$. Thus, for $i = 1, 2, \ldots, p$, we have

$$\mathfrak{b}_1 \mathfrak{a}_i = 0, \quad \mathfrak{b}_2 \mathfrak{a}_i = 0, \quad \cdots, \quad \mathfrak{b}_{n-p} \mathfrak{a}_i = 0.$$

Now we see that just as for L, the totality of all vectors orthogonal to L′ consists of all the vector solutions of the equations

$$(11) \qquad \mathfrak{b}_1 \mathfrak{x} = 0, \quad \mathfrak{b}_2 \mathfrak{x} = 0, \quad \cdots, \quad \mathfrak{b}_{n-p} \mathfrak{x} = 0.$$

Thus the vectors $\mathfrak{a}_1, \mathfrak{a}_2, \cdots, \mathfrak{a}_p$ are orthogonal to L′. But the vectors which are orthogonal to L′ form a vector space L″ of dimension $n - (n - p) = p$. Since the p vectors $\mathfrak{a}_1, \mathfrak{a}_2, \cdots, \mathfrak{a}_p$ are in L″ and are linearly independent, they form a basis of L″. But this means that L″ is identical with L. Thus the vectors of L are precisely the vector solutions of the equations (11), i.e. of a certain system of $n - p$ linear homogeneous equations. This proves Theorem 8.

Once again, we return to Theorem 6. This theorem has another important geometrical interpretation. In connection with Theorem 6, we spoke of a vector solution $\mathfrak{x} = \{x_1, x_2, \cdots, x_n\}$. However, we shall now consider the n numbers $x_1, x_2, \ldots, x_n$ which satisfy the system (1), as the coordinates of a point $P = (x_1, x_2, \ldots, x_n)$ of R_n. We then call such a point P a *point solution* of (1). We shall then derive some easy consequences of Theorem 6. We first prove

A. *Let* $P = (x_1, x_2, \ldots, x_n)$ *be a point solution of the system* (1), *and let* $\mathfrak{y} = \{ y_1, y_2, \ldots, y_n \}$ *be a vector solution of the corresponding homogeneous system* (6). *If the vector* $\mathfrak{y}$ *carries P into Q, then Q is also a point solution of* (1).

For, if $O = (0, 0, \ldots, 0)$ is the origin in R_n, then

$$\overrightarrow{OP} = \{x_1, x_2, \cdots, x_n\}$$

is a vector solution of the system (1). By Theorem 6, the vector

$$\{x_1, x_2, \cdots, x_n\} + \mathfrak{y} = \{x_1 + y_1, x_2 + y_2, \cdots, x_n + y_n\}$$

is then also a vector solution of (1). On the other hand, we have

$$\overrightarrow{OQ} = \overrightarrow{OP} + \overrightarrow{PQ} = \{x_1, x_2, \cdots, x_n\} + \mathfrak{y} = \{x_1 + y_1, x_2 + y_2, \cdots, x_n + y_n\}$$

The n numbers $x_1 + y_1, x_2 + y_2, \cdots, x_n + y_n$ which satisfy the equations (1), are thus the coordinates of Q, and so Q is a point solution of (1).

It also follows from Theorem 6 (cf. also the proof of Theorem 6) that $\mathfrak{z} - \mathfrak{x}$ is a vector solution of the homogeneous system (6) if $\mathfrak{z}$ and $\mathfrak{x}$ are vector solutions of (1). If

$$\mathfrak{x} = \{x_1, x_2, \cdots, x_n\}, \ \mathfrak{z} = \{z_1, z_2, \cdots, z_n\},$$

then the points $P = (x_1, x_2, \ldots, x_n)$ and $Q = (z_1, z_2, \ldots, z_n)$ are point solutions of (1). Then,

$$\overrightarrow{PQ} = \{z_1 - x_1, z_2 - x_2, \cdots, z_n - x_n\} = \mathfrak{z} - \mathfrak{x}.$$

We have thus proved

B. *If P and Q are two point solutions of* (1), *then* $\overrightarrow{PQ}$ *is a vector solution of the corresponding homogeneous system* (6).

We can now prove

THEOREM 9. *The point solutions of a solvable system of equations of the type* (1) *form a linear space. This space has dimension* $n - r$, *where* r *is the rank of the coefficient matrix of the system.*[5] *Conversely, every linear space may be represented as the totality of all point solutions of some suitable system of linear equations.*

Again we consider, along with (1), the corresponding homogeneous system (6). Let L be the vector space of all vector solutions of (6). Let $P = (x_1, x_2, \ldots, x_n)$ be a definite point solution of (1). By theorems A and B, which were just proved, all point solutions of the

[5] Since the system of equations is assumed solvable, r is also the rank of the augmented matrix.

equations (1), and only these, are obtained by applying all the vectors of L to the point P. However, by this process we obtain from P a linear space whose dimension is that of L, i.e. $n - r$.

Conversely, let there be given a linear space L. L is obtained from any one of its points, say from $P = (\xi_1, \xi_2, \cdots, \xi_n)$, by applying the vectors of a certain vector space L (§ 5). By Theorem 8, there is a system of linear homogeneous equations whose vector solutions are precisely the vectors of L, say

$$
\begin{aligned}
a_{11} x_1 + a_{12} x_2 + \cdots + a_{1n} x_n &= 0, \\
a_{21} x_1 + a_{22} x_2 + \cdots + a_{2n} x_n &= 0, \\
\cdots\cdots & \cdots \\
a_{m1} x_1 + a_{m2} x_2 + \cdots + a_{mn} x_n &= 0.
\end{aligned} \tag{12}
$$

If in these equations we replace the variables x_i by the coordinates ξ_i of the point P, then these equations will of course not, in general, be satisfied. Let the numbers b_i be defined by

$$
\begin{aligned}
a_{11} \xi_1 + a_{12} \xi_2 + \cdots + a_{1n} \xi_n &= b_1, \\
a_{21} \xi_1 + a_{22} \xi_2 + \cdots + a_{2n} \xi_n &= b_2, \\
\cdots\cdots & \cdots \\
a_{m1} \xi_1 + a_{m2} \xi_2 + \cdots + a_{mn} \xi_n &= b_m.
\end{aligned}
$$

We now employ these constants b_i to form the following equations:

$$
\begin{aligned}
a_{11} x_1 + a_{12} x_2 + \cdots + a_{1n} x_n &= b_1, \\
a_{21} x_1 + a_{22} x_2 + \cdots + a_{2n} x_n &= b_2, \\
\cdots\cdots & \cdots \\
a_{m1} x_1 + a_{m2} x_2 + \cdots + a_{mn} x_n &= b_m.
\end{aligned} \tag{13}
$$

By what has just been proved, the point solutions of (13) are obtained from any fixed point solution of (13), say P, by applying all vector solutions of (12), i.e. all vectors of the space L. Thus the point solutions of (13) are indeed the points of the linear space L, and Theorem 9 is proved.

We note that the system (12), and thus the system (13), consists of exactly $n - p$ equations, where p is the dimension of L or of L.

The point solutions of a single linear equation not all of whose coefficients vanish always form a hyperplane, by Theorem 9. And conversely, by the last remark, every hyperplane can be represented by a single linear equation ("represented" in the sense of Theorem 9).

In particular, a linear equation represents:

a line — in the plane,
a plane — in three-dimensional space.

Exercises

1. Are the following systems of equations solvable?

a)
$$\begin{aligned} 2x_1 + 4x_2 &= 1, \\ 3x_1 + 6x_2 &= 10; \end{aligned}$$

b)
$$\begin{aligned} x_1 + x_2 + x_3 &= 0, \\ x_1 + 2x_2 - x_3 &= 5; \end{aligned}$$

c)
$$\begin{aligned} x_1 + x_3 &= 1, \\ x_1 - x_2 &= 0, \\ x_2 + x_3 &= 0. \end{aligned}$$

2. Prove that if the two equations

$$\begin{aligned} a_1 x_1 + a_2 x_2 + \cdots + a_n x_n &= b, \\ c_1 x_1 + c_2 x_2 + \cdots + c_n x_n &= d \end{aligned}$$

represent the same hyperplane of R_n, then the corresponding coefficients are proportional, i.e. there is a non-zero number λ such that

$$a_1 = \lambda c_1,\ a_2 = \lambda c_2,\ \ldots,\ a_n = \lambda c_n,\ b = \lambda d.$$

Conversely, if this condition is fulfilled, then both of these equations represent the same hyperplane.

3. Two hyperplanes

$$\begin{aligned} a_1 x_1 + a_2 x_2 + \cdots + a_n x_n &= b, \\ c_1 x_1 + c_2 x_2 + \cdots + c_n x_n &= d, \end{aligned}$$

of R are parallel if and only if the left-hand sides of the equations are proportional, i.e. if there is a non-zero number λ such that

$$a_1 = \lambda c_1,\ a_2 = \lambda c_2,\ \ldots,\ a_n = \lambda c_n.$$

4. Using the algorithm employed in the proof of Theorem 3, determine a basis of the vector space of all vector solutions of the systems

a)
$$\begin{aligned} x_1 + x_2 - x_3 &= 0, \\ x_1 + 2x_3 &= 0, \\ 2x_1 + x_2 + x_3 &= 0; \end{aligned}$$

b)
$$\begin{aligned} x_1 + 3x_3 - 2x_4 + x_5 &= 0, \\ x_2 - x_3 - x_4 + 5x_5 &= 0. \end{aligned}$$

5. Methods were given in the proofs of Theorems 8 and 9 which enable one to represent a given linear space by a system of equations. Determine in this way

a) the equation of the line in R_2 passing through the points $(0, 1)$ and $(2, 3)$,

b) the equation of the plane in R_3 through the points $(0, 0, 0)$, $(1, 1, 1)$, $(0, 0, 1)$,

c) the system of equations of the line in R_3 passing through the points $(-1, -1, -1)$ and $(0, 3, 0)$.

6. Let two systems of linear equations in n-variables be given. Each represents a linear space in R_n. The intersection of these two spaces is also a linear space. How do we obtain a system of equations which represents the intersection? Show that two planes (i.e. linear spaces of dimension 2) of R_4 can intersect

a) in no point,
b) in one point,
c) in a line,
d) in a plane, i.e. they can be identical.

How can one determine which of these cases holds, given the two systems of equations?

Analogously: When do two lines of R_3 intersect?

7. Consider the hyperplane

$$a_1 x_1 + a_2 x_2 + \cdots + a_n x_n - b = 0$$

of R_n. When the coordinates of a point $P = (y_1, y_2, \ldots, y_n)$ not on the hyperplane are substituted for the variables x_i, the left-hand side of the equation, i.e.

$$a_1 y_1 + a_2 y_2 + \cdots + a_n y_n - b,$$

is not equal to 0. We now divide the points of R_n not on the hyperplane into two classes as follows: If $P = (y_1, y_2, \ldots, y_n)$ is such a point, we put it in the first or second class according to whether the value $a_1 y_1 + a_2 y_2 + \cdots + a_n y_n - b$ is > 0 or < 0. Show that any two points of the same class can be joined by a polygonal path which does not intersect the hyperplane. Also if any point of one class is joined by a polygonal path to any point of the other class, then this path intersects the hyperplane in at least one point. In this sense, we say that *the hyperplane separates the two classes*. We also say that the two classes are on different *sides* of the hyperplane.

CHAPTER II

EUCLIDEAN SPACE; THEORY OF DETERMINANTS

§ 7. Euclidean Length

In this section, our fundamental geometric concepts will be extended significantly. We have previously not been in a position to discuss measurements in our abstractly defined n-dimensional space. As yet, we do not know what is to be understood by the distance between two points, by the angle between two lines or vectors, by areas, or by volumes in R_n. On the other hand, we certainly want the geometry of R_n to contain the ordinary geometry of the line, the plane, and space, as special cases. In order to accomplish this, we must extend to R_n the definitions of as many intuitive geometric concepts as possible. How then are we to arrive at a reasonable definition of the distance between two points of R_n, or what comes to the same thing, of the length of a segment in R_n? From our standpoint, we must of course require that our definition of length coincide with the intuitive notion of the length of a segment in the special cases R_1, R_2, and R_3, with the usual geometric interpretation of these spaces (cf. § 1).

Let us first consider how we may calculate the distance between two points of ordinary space if the coordinates of the points are given in a coordinate system. We begin with one-dimensional space, i.e. with the line. Let a coordinate system be introduced on the line as in § 1. We take the distance between the origin and the unit point as our unit of length. By the definition of the abscissa of a point on the line (cf. § 1) we have at once that the point P whose abscissa is x has the distance $|x|$ from the origin.[1] If now, we are given two points P and Q whose abscissas are x and y respectively, let us determine the distance from P to Q, i.e. the length of the segment PQ and denote this length by $\overline{PQ}$. If x and y are both positive (Fig. 12a), then no matter whether

[1] By $|x|$ we shall mean, as usual, the absolute value of the real number x, i.e. $|x| = x$ if $x \geqq 0$, and $|x| = -x$ if $x < 0$.

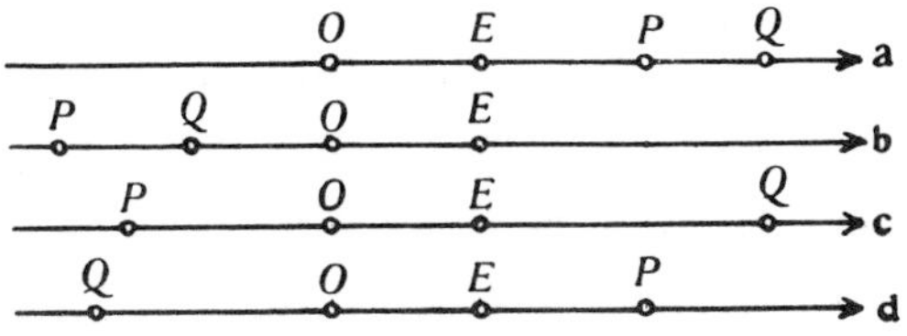

Fig. 12

$x > y$, $x = y$, or $x < y$, we have:

$$\overline{PQ} = |\,\overline{OQ} - \overline{OP}\,| = |\,y - x\,|.$$

If x and y are both negative (Fig. 12b), then we have:

$$\overline{PQ} = |\,\overline{OP} - \overline{OQ}\,| = |\,(-x) - (-y)\,| = |\,y - x\,|.$$

If however $x < 0$, $y > 0$, then (Fig. 12c):

$$\overline{PQ} = \overline{OP} + \overline{OQ} = (-x) + y = |\,y - x\,|.$$

If, finally, $x > 0$, $y < 0$, then (Fig. 12d):

$$\overline{PQ} = \overline{OP} + \overline{OQ} = x + (-y) = |\,y - x\,|.$$

In each case, therefore, the distance between P and Q is $|\,y - x\,|$.

We next consider the distance between two points in the plane. In order to obtain a convenient expression for this distance, we do not consider an arbitrary coordinate system, but rather a rectangular one, a so-called *Cartesian* coordinate system. We demand, in fact, that the x_1-axis and the x_2-axis be perpendicular to one another (Fig. 13). We moreover demand that the unit points E_1 and E_2 on the x_1-axis and the x_2-axis respectively be equidistant from the origin. We take the common distance $\overline{OE_1} = \overline{OE_2}$ as our unit of measurement in the plane. Let us then be given two points $P = (x_1, x_2)$ and $Q = (y_1, y_2)$. We construct PP_1 and PP_2 (Fig. 13) through P, perpendicular to the x_1-axis and the x_2-axis respectively. Similarly QQ_1 and QQ_2 are line segments through Q perpendicular to the x_1-axis and the x_2-axis respectively. Let R be the intersection of PP_1 and QQ_2. The triangle PRQ has a right angle at R. Thus, we have for the distance $\overline{PQ}$:

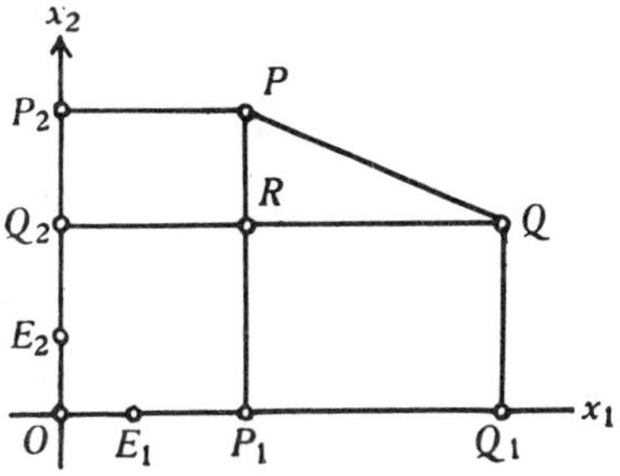

Fig. 13

$$\overline{PQ} = +\sqrt{\overline{RQ}^2 + \overline{PR}^2} = +\sqrt{\overline{P_1Q_1}^2 + \overline{P_2Q_2}^2}.$$

But we already know how to evaluate the distances $\overline{P_1Q_1}$ and $\overline{P_2Q_2}$. In fact by the above considerations concerning distances on the line,

$$\overline{P_1Q_1} = |y_1 - x_1|, \qquad \overline{P_2Q_2} = |y_2 - x_2|.$$

If we further observe that for a and b real, we have $(|b - a|)^2 = (b - a)^2$, we obtain

$$\overline{PQ} = +\sqrt{(y_1 - x_1)^2 + (y_2 - x_2)^2}.$$

We next introduce a Cartesian coordinate system in three dimensional ordinary space, i.e. a coordinate system such that the three coordinate axes are mutually perpendicular (Fig. 14) and such that

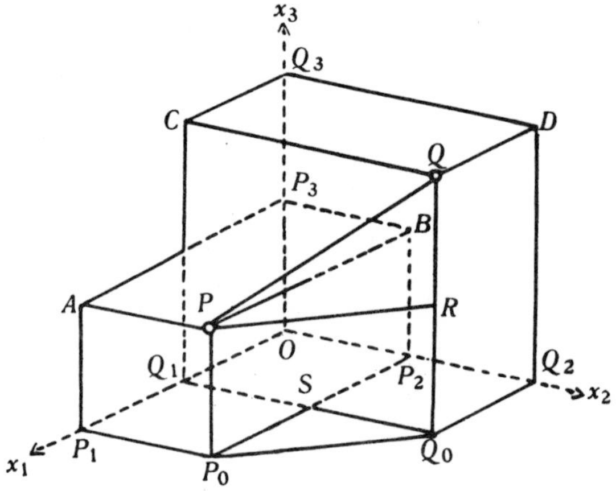

Fig. 14

the unit points E_1, E_2, and E_3, on the x_1-axis, the x_2-axis, and the x_3-axis respectively, are equidistant from the origin O. We take $\overline{OE_1}$ $(= \overline{OE_2} = \overline{OE_3})$ as our unit of measurement in space. Once again, let there be given two points $P = (x_1, x_2, x_3)$ and $Q = (y_1, y_2, y_3)$. We now pass three planes through P parallel to the three coordinate planes, and three more through Q also parallel to the coordinate planes. Thus two rectangular parallelepipeds $O, P_1, P_0, P_2, P_3, A, P, B$ and $O, Q_1, Q_0, Q_2, Q_3, C, Q, D$ are formed. Let the plane through P which was constructed parallel to the x_1, x_2-plane cut the edge QQ_0 of the second rectangular parallelepiped in R; let S be the intersection of the edges P_2P_0 and Q_0Q_1. Then we have

$$\overline{P_0S} = \overline{P_1Q_1} = |y_1 - x_1|,$$
$$\overline{SQ_0} = \overline{P_2Q_2} = |y_2 - x_2|,$$
$$\overline{RQ} = \overline{P_3Q_3} = |y_3 - x_3|.$$

[2] The symbol $+\sqrt{}$ shall mean the absolute value of the square root.

Furthermore $P_0 S \perp Q_0 S,\ PR \perp QR$ so that:

$$\overline{P_0 Q_0} = {}_{+}\sqrt{\overline{P_0 S}^2 + \overline{S Q_0}^2} = {}_{+}\sqrt{(y_1 - x_1)^2 + (y_2 - x_2)^2},$$

$$\overline{PQ} = {}_{+}\sqrt{\overline{PR}^2 + \overline{RQ}^2} = {}_{+}\sqrt{\overline{P_0 Q_0}^2 + (y_3 - x_3)^2}$$

$$= {}_{+}\sqrt{(y_1 - x_1)^2 + (y_2 - x_2)^2 + (y_3 - x_3)^2}\,.$$

By analogy with these results for line, plane, and space, we now make the following definition:

By the **distance** $\overline{PQ}$ between the points $P = (x_1, x_2, \ldots, x_n)$ and $Q = (y_1, y_2, \ldots, y_n)$ of R_n, we shall mean the number

$$\overline{PQ} = {}_{+}\sqrt{(y_1 - x_1)^2 + (y_2 - x_2)^2 + \cdots + (y_n - x_n)^2}$$

With this definition of distance introduced in it, R_n is called a **euclidean space.**

If we interpet R_1, R_2, and R_3 in intuitive geometric terms; by employing, as in § 1, a one-to-one correspondence between their elements and the points on the line, in the plane, and in space, respectively, but this time using a Cartesian coordinate system for the plane and for space, then, by the above, our definition of distance agrees with the natural concept of distance.[3] This so-called *euclidean determination of length* in R_n will be further justified by far-reaching analogies with the intuitive notion of distance.

First of all, the distance between two points $P = (x_1, x_2, \ldots, x_n)$ and $Q = (y_1, y_2, \ldots, y_n)$ in euclidean R_n is, by definition, always a non-negative number:

$$\overline{PQ} \geqq 0.$$

When is $\overline{PQ} = 0$? By the definition of distance, we shall have in this case:

$$(y_1 - x_1)^2 + (y_2 - x_2)^2 + \cdots + (y_n - x_n)^2 = 0.$$

Since each of the terms on the left is a square, and so is non-negative, the sum can vanish only if each term is $= 0$. Thus, we must have

---

[3] The distance between the points $P = (x)$ and $Q = (y)$ of R_1 is

$${}_{+}\sqrt{(y - x)^2} = |y - x|,$$

and is therefore the same as on the line.

$$(y_1-x_1)^2=0,\ (y_2-x_2)^2=0,\ \cdots,\ (y_n-x_n)^2=0,$$

i.e.

$$y_1=x_1,\ y_2=x_2,\ \cdots,\ y_n=x_n.$$

Thus the two points coincide. It is clear from the definition of distance that conversely, if $P=Q$, then $\overline{PQ}=0$. We thus have the following result, which completely agrees with intuition:

THEOREM 1. *The distance between two points of euclidean R_n is 0 if and only if the two points coincide.*

Before we derive further properties of length, we introduce several useful notations. We may, namely, also speak of the length of a vector in euclidean R_n. A vector is, in fact, nothing but a directed line segment. But by the length of a segment we of course mean the distance between its endpoints. If the point $P=(x_1, x_2, \ldots, x_n)$ is carried to $Q=(y_1, y_2, \ldots, y_n)$ by the vector $\mathfrak{a}=\{a_1, a_2, \cdots, a_n\}$, then

$$\overline{PQ}={}_+\sqrt{\sum_{i=1}^{n}(y_i-x_i)^2}={}_+\sqrt{\sum_{i=1}^{n}a_i^2}.$$

Accordingly, define the **length of the vector** $\mathfrak{a}$, which we denote by $|\mathfrak{a}|$, by the formula:

$$|\mathfrak{a}|={}_+\sqrt{\sum_{i=1}^{n}a_i^2}={}_+\sqrt{\mathfrak{a}^2}. \tag{1}$$

By Theorem 1, $|\mathfrak{a}|=0$ only if the endpoints of $\mathfrak{a}$ coincide, i.e. if $\mathfrak{a}$ is the null vector. In any other case, $|\mathfrak{a}|>0$. We also call the length $|\mathfrak{a}|$ "*the absolute value of the vector* $\mathfrak{a}$."

Let there now be given two vectors $\mathfrak{a}$, $\mathfrak{b}$ each of absolute value 1, i.e. $|\mathfrak{a}|=|\mathfrak{b}|=1$. By (1), $\mathfrak{a}^2=\mathfrak{b}^2=1$. We consider the vector $\mathfrak{a}-\mathfrak{b}$. The square of its absolute value is, by (1), equal to $(\mathfrak{a}-\mathfrak{b})^2$ and on the other hand is $\geqq 0$. By the distributive law, we further have

$$(\mathfrak{a}-\mathfrak{b})^2=\mathfrak{a}^2-2\mathfrak{a}\mathfrak{b}+\mathfrak{b}^2,$$

so that

$$\mathfrak{a}^2+\mathfrak{b}^2-2\mathfrak{a}\mathfrak{b}\geqq 0. \tag{2}$$

Since $\mathfrak{a}^2=\mathfrak{b}^2=1$ this yields

$$\mathfrak{a}\cdot\mathfrak{b}\leqq 1. \tag{3}$$

Hence *the scalar product of two vectors of length* 1 *is always* $\leqq 1$.

Now equality holds in (2), and hence also in (3), if and only if

$$(\mathfrak{a}-\mathfrak{b})^2=0.$$

That is, if $\mathfrak{a} - \mathfrak{b} = 0$, i.e. $\mathfrak{a} = \mathfrak{b}$.

Let $\mathfrak{u}$ and $\mathfrak{v}$ be two vectors $\neq 0$. Then $|\mathfrak{u}| \neq 0$, $|\mathfrak{v}| \neq 0$. We may therefore multiply $\mathfrak{u}$ by $\frac{1}{|\mathfrak{u}|}$ and $\mathfrak{v}$ by $\frac{1}{|\mathfrak{v}|}$ The resulting vectors $\frac{\mathfrak{u}}{|\mathfrak{u}|}$ and $\frac{\mathfrak{v}}{|\mathfrak{v}|}$ have length 1. For, $|\mathfrak{a}|^2 = \mathfrak{a}^2$ for any vector $\mathfrak{a}$, by (1). Thus

$$\left|\frac{\mathfrak{u}}{|\mathfrak{u}|}\right|^2 = \frac{\mathfrak{u}}{|\mathfrak{u}|} \cdot \frac{\mathfrak{u}}{|\mathfrak{u}|} = \frac{\mathfrak{u}^2}{|\mathfrak{u}|^2} = 1.$$

Similarly for $\frac{\mathfrak{v}}{|\mathfrak{v}|}$. Thus by (3),

$$\frac{\mathfrak{u}}{|\mathfrak{u}|} \cdot \frac{\mathfrak{v}}{|\mathfrak{v}|} \leqq 1, \tag{4}$$

or

$$\mathfrak{u} \cdot \mathfrak{v} \leqq |\mathfrak{u}| \cdot |\mathfrak{v}|. \tag{5}$$

We easily see that (5) continues to hold if one or both of the vectors $\mathfrak{u}$, $\mathfrak{v}$ are 0, and that in fact in such a case equality holds. Thus (5) holds for any two vectors $\mathfrak{u}$ and $\mathfrak{v}$ whatsoever. If equality holds in (5) for non-vanishing vectors $\mathfrak{u}$ and $\mathfrak{v}$, then it also does in (4). Thus by the remark made in connection with (3), $\frac{\mathfrak{u}}{|\mathfrak{u}|} = \frac{\mathfrak{v}}{|\mathfrak{v}|}$.

Since (5) holds for arbitrary $\mathfrak{u}, \mathfrak{v}$, it continues to hold if $\mathfrak{u}$ is replaced by $-\mathfrak{u}$. But, $|-\mathfrak{u}| = |\mathfrak{u}|$, so that $-\mathfrak{u} \cdot \mathfrak{v} = |\mathfrak{u}| \cdot |\mathfrak{v}|$. Combining this and (5), we have

$$|\mathfrak{u} \cdot \mathfrak{v}| \leqq |\mathfrak{u}| \cdot |\mathfrak{v}|, \tag{6}$$

since the absolute value $|\mathfrak{u} \cdot \mathfrak{v}|$ of the real number $\mathfrak{u} \cdot \mathfrak{v}$ is equal to one of the two numbers $\mathfrak{u} \cdot \mathfrak{v}$, $-\mathfrak{u} \cdot \mathfrak{v}$.

Since both sides of (6) are $\geqq 0$, we may square (6). Now, $|\mathfrak{u} \cdot \mathfrak{v}|^2 = (\mathfrak{u} \cdot \mathfrak{v})^2$, and, by (1), $|\mathfrak{u}|^2 = \mathfrak{u}^2$, $|\mathfrak{v}|^2 = \mathfrak{v}^2$. Thus:

$$(\mathfrak{u} \cdot \mathfrak{v})^2 \leqq \mathfrak{u}^2\mathfrak{v}^2. \tag{7}$$

This relation is the so-called CAUCHY-SCHWARZ INEQUALITY. In what follows, we shall usually employ not (7), but its equivalents (5) and (6).

We shall now derive an extremely important property of euclidean length.

THEOREM 2. *For any three points P, Q, R of euclidean R_n we have*

$$\overline{PQ} + \overline{QR} \geqq \overline{PR}.$$

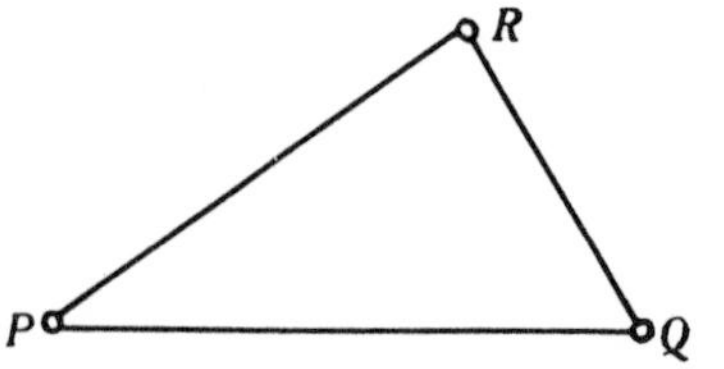

Fig. 15

This is the so-called *triangle inequality* (Fig. 15). It expresses the intuitive fact that the straight line is the shortest path between two points.

To prove this, let $\overrightarrow{PQ} = \mathfrak{u}$, $\overrightarrow{QR} = \mathfrak{v}$, so that $\overrightarrow{PR} = \mathfrak{u} + \mathfrak{v}$. By definition of the length of a vector, Theorem 2 takes on the form

$$(8) \qquad |\,\mathfrak{u}\,| + |\,\mathfrak{v}\,| \geqq |\,\mathfrak{u} + \mathfrak{v}\,|.$$

We square (8). By (1), we obtain on the right-hand side $|\,\mathfrak{u} + \mathfrak{v}\,|^2 = (\mathfrak{u} + \mathfrak{v})^2 = \mathfrak{u}^2 + 2\,\mathfrak{u}\mathfrak{v} + \mathfrak{v}^2$. Thus, we obtain

$$(9) \qquad |\mathfrak{u}|^2 + 2|\mathfrak{u}|\cdot|\mathfrak{v}| + |\mathfrak{v}|^2 \geqq \mathfrak{u}^2 + 2\,\mathfrak{u}\mathfrak{v} + \mathfrak{v}^2.$$

If we observe that $|\,\mathfrak{u}\,|^2 = \mathfrak{u}^2$ and $|\,\mathfrak{v}\,|^2 = \mathfrak{v}^2$, (9) follows directly from inequality (5). But now the reasoning which led from (8) to (9) is reversible, so that (9) also implies (8).[4] This completes the proof of Theorem 2.

When does equality hold in Theorem 2? That is, when does

$$\overline{PQ} + \overline{QR} = \overline{PR}$$

hold? In ordinary space, we know that this holds if and only if Q lies on the segment PR. Now, this same result also holds in euclidean R_n. The segment PR in R_n is defined (§ 2) as the totality of all points $Q = (y_1, y_2, \ldots, y_n)$ for which

$$y_i = x_i + \lambda(z_i - x_i), \qquad 0 \leqq \lambda \leqq 1, \qquad i = 1, 2, \cdots, n,$$

where $P = (x_1, x_2, \cdots, x_n)$, $R = (z_1, z_2, \cdots, z_n)$. Now:

$$\overline{PQ} + \overline{QR} = {}_{+}\sqrt{\sum_{i=1}^{n}(y_i - x_i)^2} + {}_{+}\sqrt{\sum_{i=1}^{n}(z_i - y_i)^2}.$$

If we substitute $z_i - y_i = (z_i - x_i) - (y_i - x_i)$ in this equation, and note that $y_i - x_i = \lambda(z_i - x_i)$, then, by an easy calculation, we have

[4] If a, b are two non-negative real numbers, then $a^2 \geqq b^2$ holds if and only if $a \geqq b$. I.e. (9) above implies (8).

$$+\sqrt{\sum_{i=1}^{n}(y_i-x_i)^2} = |\lambda| \cdot +\sqrt{\sum_{i=1}^{n}(z_i-x_i)^2},$$

$$+\sqrt{\sum_{i=1}^{n}(z_i-y_i)^2} = |1-\lambda| \cdot +\sqrt{\sum_{i=1}^{n}(z_i-x_i)^2}.$$ [5]

But we had $0 \leqq \lambda \leqq 1$ so that

$$\lambda = |\lambda|,\ 0 \leqq 1-\lambda = |1-\lambda|.$$

Therefore:

$$\overline{PQ}+\overline{QR} = \lambda \cdot +\sqrt{\sum_{i=1}^{n}(z_i-x_i)^2} + (1-\lambda) \cdot +\sqrt{\sum_{i=1}^{n}(z_i-x_i)^2}$$

$$= +\sqrt{\sum_{i=1}^{n}(z_i-x_i)^2} = \overline{PR}.$$

The points of the segment do indeed satisfy the intuitively expected condition $\overline{PQ}+\overline{QR}=\overline{PR}$.

But they are, moreover, the only points of this sort. For, if this equation is true for some point Q, then equality must hold in (8) and (9), if once again we set $\overrightarrow{PQ}=\mathfrak{u}$, $\overrightarrow{QR}=\mathfrak{v}$. If $\mathfrak{u}=0$ or $\mathfrak{v}=0$, then Q coincides with P or R respectively, and so certainly lies on the segment PR. We may thus assume $\mathfrak{u} \neq 0$, $\mathfrak{v} \neq 0$ in what follows. Since equality now holds in (9), $\mathfrak{u} \cdot \mathfrak{v} = |\mathfrak{u}| \cdot |\mathfrak{v}|$. As we have already seen in connection with relation (5), this yields $\frac{\mathfrak{u}}{|\mathfrak{u}|} = \frac{\mathfrak{v}}{|\mathfrak{v}|}$. If we set $\frac{|\mathfrak{u}|}{|\mathfrak{v}|} = \mu$, we obtain

$$\mathfrak{u} = \mu \cdot \mathfrak{v},$$

where $\mu > 0$. Since $y_k - x_k$ and $z_k - y_k$ are the components of $\mathfrak{u}$ and respectively, we have for $k = 1, 2, \ldots, n$ that

$$y_k - x_k = \mu \cdot (z_k - y_k).$$

---

[5] We must always take the absolute value of the square root. Thus

$$+\sqrt{\lambda^2 \sum_{i=1}^{n}(z_i-x_i)^2} = +\sqrt{\lambda^2}\ +\sqrt{\sum_{i=1}^{n}(z_i-x_i)^2} = |\lambda|\ +\sqrt{\sum_{i=1}^{n}(z_i-x_i)^2}$$

and

$$+\sqrt{(1-\lambda)^2 \sum_{i=1}^{n}(z_i-x_i)^2} = |1-\lambda|\ +\sqrt{\sum_{i=1}^{n}(z_i-x_i)^2}.$$

Concerning calculations with the summation sign, cf. the appendix at the end of this section.

If we solve this equation for y_k, we obtain:

$$y_k = \frac{x_k + \mu \cdot z_k}{\mu + 1} = x_k + \frac{\mu}{\mu + 1}(z_k - x_k).$$

Since $\mu > 0$, we have $0 < \frac{\mu}{\mu+1} < 1$, and setting $\lambda = \frac{\mu}{\mu+1}$, we obtain for $k = 1, 2, \ldots, n$ that

$$y_k = x_k + \lambda(z_k - x_k), \qquad 0 < \lambda < 1.$$

But this says precisely that the point $Q = (y_1, y_2, \ldots, y_n)$ lies on the segment PR. Thus we have shown that, for euclidean R_n:

THEOREM 3. *The relation*

$$\overline{PQ} + \overline{QR} = \overline{PR}$$

subsists between the three points P, Q, R if and only if Q lies on the segment PR.

We shall now define angle in R_n. In ordinary space, the scalar product of two vectors has an important geometric interpretation if a Cartesian coordinate system is used. Let $\mathfrak{a} = \{a_1, a_2, a_3\}$ and $\mathfrak{b} = \{b_1, b_2, b_3\}$ be two non-vanishing vectors of R_3 or of ordinary space. If we take both of these vectors with the same initial point P, and with terminal points Q and R respectively, then we call $\sphericalangle RPQ$ the angle between the vectors $\mathfrak{a}$ and $\mathfrak{b}$ (Fig. 16). This angle is clearly independent of our choice of P. We shall denote this angle simply by $(\mathfrak{a}, \mathfrak{b})$. The law of cosines of trigonometry then states that

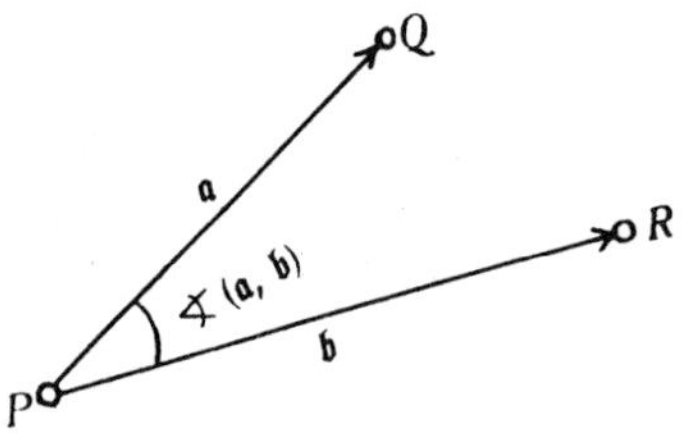

Fig. 16

$$\overline{RQ}^2 = \overline{PR}^2 + \overline{PQ}^2 - 2\,\overline{PR} \cdot \overline{PQ} \cdot \cos(\mathfrak{a}, \mathfrak{b}).$$

Now

$$\overrightarrow{PR} + \overrightarrow{RQ} = \overrightarrow{PQ}, \qquad \overrightarrow{RQ} = \overrightarrow{PQ} - \overrightarrow{PR} = \mathfrak{a} - \mathfrak{b},$$

so that

$$\overline{RQ} = |\mathfrak{a} - \mathfrak{b}|.$$

If we further observe that $\overline{PR} = |\mathfrak{b}|$ and $\overline{PQ} = |\mathfrak{a}|$, then we have by the law of cosines, that

$$|\mathfrak{a}-\mathfrak{b}|^2 = |\mathfrak{a}|^2+|\mathfrak{b}|^2-2|\mathfrak{a}|\cdot|\mathfrak{b}|\cdot\cos(\mathfrak{a},\mathfrak{b}).$$

Now by (1), we have

$$|\mathfrak{a}-\mathfrak{b}|^2 = (\mathfrak{a}-\mathfrak{b})^2 = \mathfrak{a}^2-2\mathfrak{a}\mathfrak{b}+\mathfrak{b}^2 = |\mathfrak{a}|^2+|\mathfrak{b}|^2-2\mathfrak{a}\mathfrak{b}.$$

Hence

$$\mathfrak{a}\cdot\mathfrak{b} = |\mathfrak{a}|\cdot|\mathfrak{b}|\cdot\cos(\mathfrak{a},\mathfrak{b}),$$

$$\cos(\mathfrak{a},\mathfrak{b}) = \frac{\mathfrak{a}\cdot\mathfrak{b}}{|\mathfrak{a}|\cdot|\mathfrak{b}|}.$$

The scalar product of two vectors is equal to the product of the absolute values of the two vectors by the cosine of their included angle.

This result now indicates how the **angle between two vectors** $\mathfrak{a}$ and $\mathfrak{b}$ in euclidean R_n is to be defined if $\mathfrak{a}$ and $\mathfrak{b}$ are both $\neq 0$. We simply define the cosine of the angle $(\mathfrak{a},\mathfrak{b})$, in analogy with the formula just obtained for three-dimensional space, by the equation

$$\cos(\mathfrak{a},\mathfrak{b}) = \frac{\mathfrak{a}\cdot\mathfrak{b}}{|\mathfrak{a}|\cdot|\mathfrak{b}|}. \tag{10}$$

If we further require that $0 \leqq (\mathfrak{a},\mathfrak{b}) \leqq \pi$, then the angle $(\mathfrak{a},\mathfrak{b})$ is uniquely determined by (10).

We must, however, still show that the right-hand side of (10) is always $\leqq 1$ in absolute value, since otherwise the definition would be meaningless. But this follows directly from the Cauchy-Schwarz inequality. In the form (6), this now gives [6]

$$|\mathfrak{a}\cdot\mathfrak{b}| \leqq |\mathfrak{a}|\cdot|\mathfrak{b}|$$

i.e.,

$$\left|\frac{\mathfrak{a}\cdot\mathfrak{b}}{|\mathfrak{a}|\cdot|\mathfrak{b}|}\right| \leqq 1,$$

which was to be proved.

When are two non-vanishing vectors $\mathfrak{a}$ and $\mathfrak{b}$ perpendicular to each other? They are perpendicular if and only if

$$\cos(\mathfrak{a},\mathfrak{b}) = \frac{\mathfrak{a}\cdot\mathfrak{b}}{|\mathfrak{a}|\cdot|\mathfrak{b}|} = 0$$

i.e. since $\mathfrak{a} \neq 0$, $\mathfrak{b} \neq 0$, if and only if

$$\mathfrak{a}\cdot\mathfrak{b} = 0.$$

Two non-vanishing vectors are perpendicular to each other if and

[6] $|\mathfrak{a}\cdot\mathfrak{b}|$ is the absolute value of the *number* $\mathfrak{a}\cdot\mathfrak{b}$ This is not to be confused with the length $|\mathfrak{a}|$ of a *vector* $\mathfrak{a}$

only if their scalar product vanishes. Thus the previously introduced terminology "orthogonal vectors" is justified.

For example, any pair of unit vectors $\mathfrak{e}_i$, $\mathfrak{e}_k$, $i \neq k$, are orthogonal, since $\mathfrak{e}_i \cdot \mathfrak{e}_k = 0$. We may also put this as follows: In euclidean R_n, the unit vectors are pairwise perpendicular.

Exercises

1. Prove that three points P, Q, R in euclidean R_n are collinear if and only if one of the following three equations holds:

$$\overline{PQ} + \overline{QR} = \overline{PR}, \quad \overline{PR} + \overline{RQ} = \overline{PQ}, \quad \overline{QP} + \overline{PR} = \overline{QR}.$$

Does this agree with one's geometric intuition?

2. M is called the *midpoint of the segment* PQ if

$$\overline{PM} = \overline{QM}.$$

What are the coordinates of M if $P = (x_1, x_2, \ldots, x_n)$, $Q = (y_1, y_2, \ldots, y_n)$?

3. Let there be given two distinct points $P = (x_1, x_2, \ldots, x_n)$, $Q = (y_1, y_2, \ldots, y_n)$. The locus of points equidistant from P and Q is a hyperplane e. If R and S are two arbitrary points of e, then PQ and RS are orthogonal to each other.

4. Let $\mathfrak{e}_1, \mathfrak{e}_2, \cdots, \mathfrak{e}_n$ be the unit vectors of euclidean R_n and $\mathfrak{a}$, $\mathfrak{b}$ arbitrary vectors. Prove that

$$\cos(\mathfrak{a}, \mathfrak{b}) = \sum_{i=1}^{n} \cos(\mathfrak{a}, \mathfrak{e}_i) \cos(\mathfrak{b}, \mathfrak{e}_i).$$

Appendix to § 7

Calculating with the Summation Sign

Since we shall have to use the summation sign a good deal in what follows, we shall now set down the most important rules for operating with this symbol. These rules hold equally well whether the summands are numbers or vectors, or for that matter, any quantities which obey the same laws of addition as do numbers and vectors. The correctness of these rules is easily seen by simply writing out the sums.

1. A sum is independent of the particular index of summation employed. Thus:

$$\sum_{i=1}^{n} a_i = \sum_{k=1}^{n} a_k = \sum_{h=1}^{n} a_h = a_1 + a_2 + \cdots + a_n.$$

2. The distributive law

$$\sum_{i=1}^{n} c\,a_i = c \sum_{i=1}^{n} a_i$$

holds. Stated in words: A factor which is under the summation sign but which does not involve the index of summation, can be written in front of the summation sign.

3. We have immediately from the commutative and associative laws—a sum is independent of the order and the bracketing of the summands—that

$$\sum_{i=1}^{n} a_i + \sum_{i=1}^{n} b_i = \sum_{i=1}^{n} (a_i + b_i),$$

or more generally

$$\sum_{i=1}^{n} a_i + \sum_{i=1}^{n} b_i + \cdots + \sum_{i=1}^{n} g_i = \sum_{i=1}^{n} (a_i + b_i + \cdots + g_i).$$

4. If two summations are performed in succession, a *double sum* results. The expression

$$\sum_{i=1}^{n} \left(\sum_{k=1}^{m} a_{ik} \right)$$

means the following: First, for each fixed $i = 1, 2, \ldots, n$, the sum $a_{i1} + a_{i2} + \cdots + a_{im}$ is to be formed, and then the sums $\sum_{k=1}^{m} a_{ik}$, $i = 1, 2, \ldots, n$, thus obtained, are themselves to be added. However, we have

$$\sum_{i=1}^{n} \left(\sum_{k=1}^{m} a_{ik} \right) = \sum_{k=1}^{m} \left(\sum_{i=1}^{n} a_{ik} \right),$$

i.e. the two summation signs in a double sum may be interchanged. Hence, we may omit the parentheses entirely, and set

$$\sum_{i=1}^{n} \sum_{k=1}^{m} a_{ik} = \sum_{i=1}^{n} \left(\sum_{k=1}^{m} a_{ik} \right) = \sum_{k=1}^{m} \left(\sum_{i=1}^{n} a_{ik} \right).$$

Corresponding results hold for 3-fold, 4-fold, ..., r-fold sums. In an r-fold sum we must sum over r indices. If we denote the indices by $i_1, i_2, \ldots, i_r$, then such a summation is written, say, as

$$\sum_{i_1=1}^{n_1} \sum_{i_2=1}^{n_2} \cdots \sum_{i_r=1}^{n_r} a_{i_1, i_2, \ldots, i_r}.$$

5. We often employ a single summation sign in indicating multiple summations. For example, the symbol

$$\sum_{i,k=1}^{n} a_{ik},$$

indicates that the two indices i and k are to run through the values

$1, 2, \ldots, n$ independently of one another. We may also express this by saying that the summation is taken over all ordered pairs i, k which can be formed with the integers $1, 2, \ldots, n$. The sum has n^2 summands. An r-fold sum of this sort is

$$\sum_{\nu_1, \nu_2, \ldots, \nu_r = 1}^{n} a_{\nu_1, \nu_2, \cdots, \nu_r}.$$

Thus, here we are to sum over all ordered r-tuples $(\nu_1, \nu_2, \cdots, \nu_r)$ where $1 \leqq \nu_i \leqq n$. This sum has n^r summands.

6. It may happen that the summation in a double sum is to be taken, not over all ordered pairs i, k, of indices but rather only over certain of these. In this case, the condition which informs us which of the pairs are to be summed over, are written underneath the summation sign. For example, the symbol

$$\sum_{\substack{i, k = 1 \\ i < k}}^{n} A_i^{(k)},$$

represents a summation over only those pairs i, k for which $i < k$, i.e. for which the lower index of $A_i^{(k)}$ is less than the upper one. For $n = 3$, for example, we have

$$\sum_{\substack{i, k = 1 \\ i < k}}^{3} A_i^{(k)} = A_1^{(2)} + A_1^{(3)} + A_2^{(3)}.$$

Another sum of this sort is the following:

$$\sum_{\substack{i, k = 1 \\ i \geqq k}}^{3} A_i^{(k)} = A_1^{(1)} + A_2^{(1)} + A_3^{(1)} + A_2^{(2)} + A_3^{(2)} + A_3^{(3)}.$$

7. Finally, we consider the *product rule*

$$\left(\sum_{i=1}^{n} a_i\right)\left(\sum_{i=1}^{m} b_i\right) = \sum_{i=1}^{n} \sum_{k=1}^{m} a_i b_k,$$

or more generally

$$\left(\sum_{i=1}^{n_1} a_i^{(1)}\right)\left(\sum_{i=1}^{n_2} a_i^{(2)}\right) \cdots \left(\sum_{i=1}^{n_r} a_i^{(r)}\right) = \sum_{i_1=1}^{n_1} \sum_{i_2=1}^{n_2} \cdots \sum_{i_r=1}^{n_r} a_{i_1}^{(1)} \cdot a_{i_2}^{(2)} \cdots a_{i_r}^{(r)}.$$

We verify these by actually writing out the sums. Note that while two distinct indices, and r distinct indices, respectively, must be written on the right, this is not necessary on the left. We note the special cases

$$\left(\sum_{i=1}^{n} a_i\right)^2 = \sum_{i,k=1}^{n} a_i a_k; \qquad \left(\sum_{i=1}^{n} a_i\right)^r = \sum_{i_1, i_2, \cdots, i_r = 1}^{n} a_{i_1} \cdot a_{i_2} \cdots a_{i_r}.$$

§ 8. Volumes and Determinants

We continue with our introduction of metric concepts into n-dimensional geometry. Our next task will be the definition of volume.

The evaluation of the area of a parallelogram is fundamental for the calculation of areas in the plane. A correspondingly fundamental role is played by the evaluation of the area of a parallelepiped in three-dimensional space. Thus we shall next introduce in R_n a notion which corresponds to the parallelogram in the plane and the parallelepiped in three-dimensional space. How can a parallelogram be described analytically? Let us consider the parallelogram A, B, C, D in the plane (Fig. 17). Let P be a point which is either in the interior of, or on the boundary of, the parallelogram. Let us draw lines through P parallel to the sides of the parallelogram. Let one of these intersect AB in E, the other, AD in F. Then

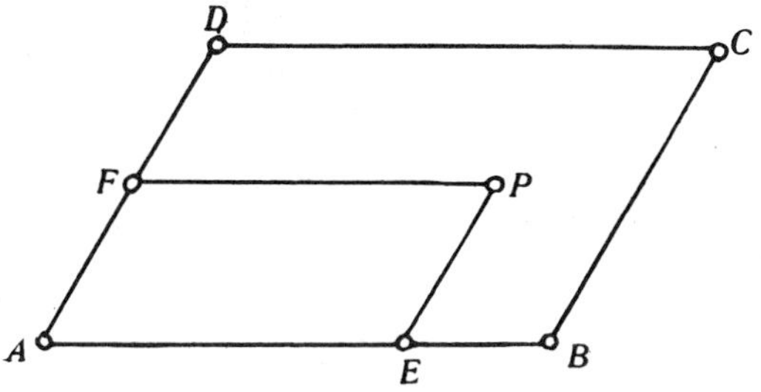

Fig. 17

$$\overrightarrow{AP} = \overrightarrow{AE} + \overrightarrow{EP} = \overrightarrow{AE} + \overrightarrow{AF}.$$

Now, however, by § 2, $\overrightarrow{AE} = \lambda_1 \overrightarrow{AB}$, where $0 \leqq \lambda_1 \leqq 1$, and similarly $\overrightarrow{AF} = \lambda_2 \overrightarrow{AD}$, where $0 \leqq \lambda_2 \leqq 1$. Thus

$$\overrightarrow{AP} = \lambda_1 \overrightarrow{AB} + \lambda_2 \overrightarrow{AD}, \qquad 0 \leqq \lambda_i \leqq 1.$$

Conversely, it is also clear that if a vector $\lambda_1 \overrightarrow{AB} + \lambda_2 \overrightarrow{AD}$ carries the point A to the point P, then the point P thus obtained belongs to the parallelogram if $0 \leqq \lambda_i \leqq 1$ for $i = 1, 2$. We may also express this result, using somewhat different notation (in that we write $\mathfrak{a}_1$ for $\overrightarrow{AB}$ and $\mathfrak{a}_2$ for $\overrightarrow{AD}$), as follows:

If $\mathfrak{a}_1, \mathfrak{a}_2$ are two linearly independent vectors in R_2, then the totality of all points into which some fixed point is carried by all vectors of *the form* $\lambda_1 \mathfrak{a}_1 + \lambda_2 \mathfrak{a}_2$ *where* $0 \leqq \lambda_1 \leqq 1$, $0 \leqq \lambda_2 \leqq 1$, *forms a parallelogram.*

Here we must assume that the *edge vectors* $\mathfrak{a}_1$, $\mathfrak{a}_2$ are linearly independent, since otherwise the end-points of the vectors $\mathfrak{a}_1$, $\mathfrak{a}_2$ and therefore, also, those of all vectors $\lambda_1 \mathfrak{a}_1 + \lambda_2 \mathfrak{a}_2$ lie on the same straight line if all the vectors have some fixed point as their common initial point, and thus these end-points would not form a parallelogram.

In three-dimensional space we may proceed quite analogously. Consider the parallelepiped A, B, C, D, E, F, G, H in Fig. 18, and a point

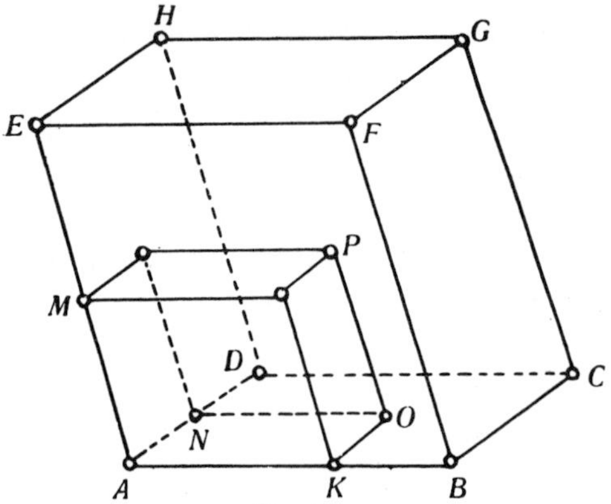

Fig. 18

P in it. Then we have, as is clear from the figure,

$$\overrightarrow{AP} = \overrightarrow{AK} + \overrightarrow{KO} + \overrightarrow{OP} = \overrightarrow{AK} + \overrightarrow{AN} + \overrightarrow{AM} = \lambda_1 \overrightarrow{AB} + \lambda_2 \overrightarrow{AD} + \lambda_3 \overrightarrow{AE},$$

where $0 \leqq \lambda_i \leqq 1$ for $i = 1, 2, 3$. Thus we have:

If $\mathfrak{a}_1 \mathfrak{a}_2, \mathfrak{a}_3$ *are three linearly independent vectors in* R_3, *then the totality of all points into which some fixed point is carried by all vectors of the form* $\lambda_1 \mathfrak{a}_1 + \lambda_2 \mathfrak{a}_2 + \lambda_3 \mathfrak{a}_3$ *where* $0 \leqq \lambda_i \leqq 1$ $(i = 1, 2, 3)$ *forms a parallelepiped.*

The linear independence of the edge vectors $\mathfrak{a}_1$, $\mathfrak{a}_2$ is again necessary, since otherwise the end-points of these vectors and hence of any vector of the form $\lambda_1 \mathfrak{a}_1 + \lambda_2 \mathfrak{a}_2 + \lambda_3 \mathfrak{a}_3$, all would lie in a linear space of dimension $\leqq 2$ if all the vectors have a common initial point, and so could not form a parallelepiped.

We now define the *n-dimensional* **parallelotope** as a generalization of the two dimensional parallelogram and the three dimensional parallelepiped.

The totality of all points into which some fixed point of R_n is carried by any vector of the form $\lambda_1 \mathfrak{a}_1 + \lambda_2 \mathfrak{a}_2 + \cdots + \lambda_n \mathfrak{a}_n$ where $0 \leqq \lambda_i \leqq 1$

$(i = 1, 2, \ldots, n)$ is called an *n-dimensional parallelotope*. Here, $\mathfrak{a}_1, \mathfrak{a}_2, \ldots, \mathfrak{a}_n$ are any n definite linearly independent vectors of R_n, which will be called the *edge vectors* of the parallelotope.

Now that we have defined parallelotope, which provides an analogue of parallelogram and parallelepiped for R_n, the question of a suitable definition of the volume of a parallelotope arises. We shall not proceed as in the case of distance, in § 7. There, we first obtained an algebraic expression for the length of a segment in ordinary space and then, by a natural generalization of this algebraic expression, we obtained a definition of distance between two points of R_n. Then we were able to, so to speak, justify this definition by verifying that it satisfied analogues in R_n of essential intuitive properties of length. However, in defining the volume of an n-dimensional parallelotope it is useful to adopt precisely the opposite course. Namely, we shall first seek the essential properties of area and volume in two and three dimensions respectively, and then we shall attempt to define the volume of an n-dimensional parallelotope in such a way that it has these properties. It will then turn out that such a definition of volume is possible in only one way. We shall in fact obtain an algebraic expression for this volume, which will reduce to ordinary volume for the case of one-, two-, and three-dimensional space. We now proceed to carry out this program.

We first demand that the volume be independent of certain changes of position of the parallelotope in space. For, we observe that both the area of a parallelogram in the plane, and the volume of a parallelepiped in space, remain unchanged if the parallelogram and the parallelepided respectively are subjected to translation. This (in the plane) amounts to nothing but the following: The area of the parallelogram with edge-vectors $\mathfrak{a}_1$, $\mathfrak{a}_2$, consisting of all points into which the point A is carried by any of the vectors $\lambda_1 \mathfrak{a}_1 + \lambda_2 \mathfrak{a}_2$ where $0 \leqq \lambda_i \leqq 1$, is independent of the particular choice of the point A. If we take any other point B as initial point for all vectors of the form $\lambda_1 \mathfrak{a}_1 + \lambda_2 \mathfrak{a}_2$ $(0 \leqq \lambda_i \leqq 1)$, then the end-points form a parallelogram of the same area. The area of a parallelogram is thus a function of its edge vectors alone. Parallelograms which have the same edge vectors have the same area. Similarly, two parallelepipeds in space have the same volume if they have the same edge vectors. We demand that the same hold of the volume of a parallelotope in R_n, i.e. that it be completely determined by the n edge vectors of the parallelotope. Accordingly, we will denote the volume of a parallelotope with edge vectors $\mathfrak{a}_1, \mathfrak{a}_2, \cdots, \mathfrak{a}_n$ by

$$V(\mathfrak{a}_1, \mathfrak{a}_2, \cdots, \mathfrak{a}_n).$$

To be able to perform measurements of any sort, we must first set up some suitable unit of measurement. Thus, we must first set up a *unit volume*, i.e., decide on some portion of space to which we assign the volume 1. We accordingly define a parallelotope in R_n which has the n unit vectors $\mathfrak{e}_1, \mathfrak{e}_2, \cdots, \mathfrak{e}_n$ as its edge vectors, to have volume 1, i.e. we require that

$$V(\mathfrak{e}_1, \mathfrak{e}_2, \cdots, \mathfrak{e}_n) = 1.$$

What meaning has this condition in the space R_n in which euclidean length has been introduced? In euclidean space, the unit vectors are of length 1, as we can check without difficulty, and are perpendicular to each other (§ 7). A parallelotope in R_n whose edge vectors are of equal length and mutually perpendicular is called an *n-dimensional cube.* In euclidean R_2 such a parallelotope is in fact nothing but a square, and in R_3, a cube. Our condition then states that certain n-dimensional cubes whose edge vectors are of length 1, have volume 1. If we interpret euclidean R_2 and R_3 geometrically, by setting up a Cartesian coordinate system,[1] (as in § 7) then this condition agrees with the usual definition of ordinary area and volume, respectively.

Areas and volumes are given by non-negative numbers, and we require the same of the volume of an n-dimensional parallelotope:

$$V(\mathfrak{a}_1, \mathfrak{a}_2, \cdots, \mathfrak{a}_n) \geqq 0.$$

Furthermore, we know from elementary geometry that parallelograms with equal bases and altitudes have the same area, and that, similarly, parallelepipeds with bases of equal area and equal altitudes have the same volume. For this reason parallelograms A, B, C, D and A, B, E, C in Fig. 19 have the same area, and parallelepipeds A, B, C, D, E, F, G, H and A, B, C, D, F, K, L, G have the same volume. Let $\mathfrak{a}_1, \mathfrak{a}_2$ be the edge vectors of parallelogram A, B, C, D. Then, since $\overrightarrow{AC} = \overrightarrow{AB} + \overrightarrow{BC}$, the parallelogram A, B, E, C has the edge vectors $\mathfrak{a}_1$ and $\mathfrak{a}_1 + \mathfrak{a}_2$. Thus two parallelograms with edge vectors $\mathfrak{a}_1$, $\mathfrak{a}_2$ and $\mathfrak{a}_1 + \mathfrak{a}_2$, $\mathfrak{a}_2$ respectively have the same area. Of course, a parallelogram with edge vectors $\mathfrak{a}_1, \mathfrak{a}_1 + \mathfrak{a}_2$ also has the same area. This is

[1] As we have already remarked, the coordinate axes in such a coordinate system are perpendicular to each other, and the unit points on the axes are at distance 1 from the origin.

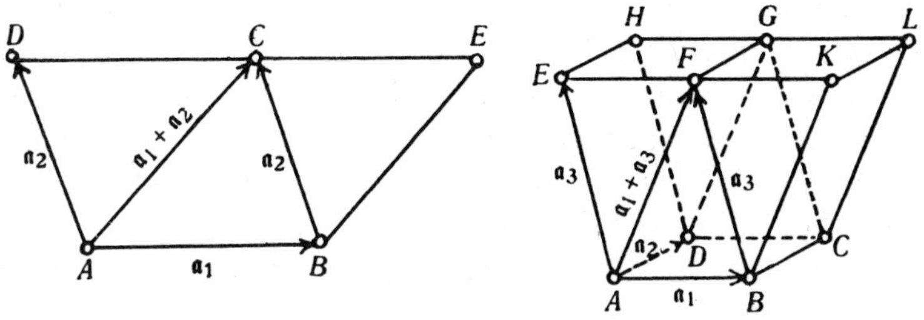

Fig. 19.

clear simply on the basis of considerations of symmetry, since neither one of the edge vectors $\mathfrak{a}_1$ and $\mathfrak{a}_2$ of the parallelogram A, B, C, D is particularly distinguished from the other. Similarly, if the parallelepiped A, B, C, D, E, F, G, H has the edge vectors $\mathfrak{a}_1, \mathfrak{a}_2, \mathfrak{a}_3$ then (Fig. 19) the parallelepiped A, B, C, D, F, K, L, G has the edge vectors $\mathfrak{a}_1, \mathfrak{a}_2, \mathfrak{a}_1 + \mathfrak{a}_3$. Thus if we are given a parallelepiped with edge vectors $\mathfrak{a}_1, \mathfrak{a}_2, \mathfrak{a}_3$, and if we form a new one from it by replacing the edge vector $\mathfrak{a}_3$ by $\mathfrak{a}_1 + \mathfrak{a}_3$, then the two parallelepipeds have the same volume. Of course we could equally well have replaced the edge vector $\mathfrak{a}_3$ by $\mathfrak{a}_2 + \mathfrak{a}_3$; or we could have replaced $\mathfrak{a}_1$ by $\mathfrak{a}_1 + \mathfrak{a}_2$ or $\mathfrak{a}_1 + \mathfrak{a}_3$, or $\mathfrak{a}_2$ by $\mathfrak{a}_1 + \mathfrak{a}_2$ or $\mathfrak{a}_2 + \mathfrak{a}_3$. By analogy with this, we require that the volume of an n-dimensional parallelotope with edge vectors $\mathfrak{a}_1, \mathfrak{a}_2, \cdots, \mathfrak{a}_n$ be equal to the volume of the parallelotope obtained by replacement of an $\mathfrak{a}_i$, $1 \leqq i \leqq n$, by a vector of the form $\mathfrak{a}_i + \mathfrak{a}_k$ where $i \neq k$, $1 \leqq k \leqq n$. Expressing this in a formula, we require that

$$V(\mathfrak{a}_1, \mathfrak{a}_2, \cdots, \mathfrak{a}_i, \cdots, \mathfrak{a}_n) = V(\mathfrak{a}_1, \mathfrak{a}_2, \cdots, \mathfrak{a}_i + \mathfrak{a}_k, \cdots, \mathfrak{a}_n).$$

We shall need to consider one last property of ordinary area and volume. Consider the two parallelograms A, B, C, D and A, B, E, F in Fig. 20. Let A, B, C, D have the edge vectors $\mathfrak{a}_1, \mathfrak{a}_2$. Then A, B, E, F has the edge vectors $\mathfrak{a}_1, \lambda\mathfrak{a}_2$ where λ is some real number. We know that the areas of the two parallelograms are to each other as the length of the side $\overline{AD}$ is to the length of the side $\overline{AF}$. However, we have

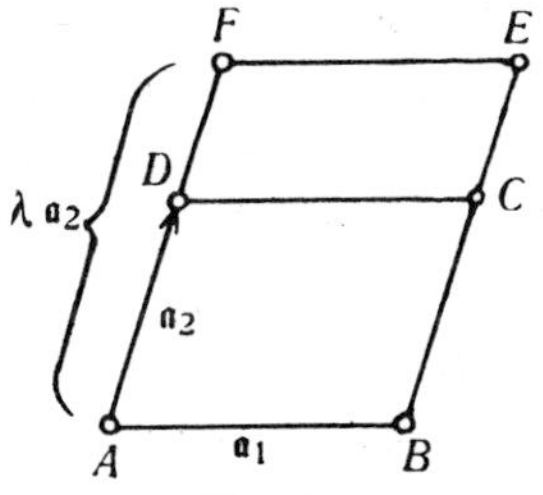

Fig. 20

$$\frac{\overline{AF}}{\overline{AD}} = \frac{+\sqrt{(\lambda\mathfrak{a}_2)^2}}{+\sqrt{\mathfrak{a}_2^2}} = +\sqrt{\frac{\lambda^2\mathfrak{a}_2^2}{\mathfrak{a}_2^2}} = |\lambda|.$$

Thus, the area of A, B, E, F is that of A, B, C, D multiplied by $|\lambda|$. We may also express this result as follows: If, in a parallelogram with edge vectors $\mathfrak{a}_1$, $\mathfrak{a}_2$, $\mathfrak{a}_2$ is replaced by $\lambda\mathfrak{a}_2$, then the area is multiplied by $|\lambda|$. Of course, the same holds for $\mathfrak{a}_1$. In exactly the same way, we prove: If one of the edge vectors of a parallelepiped is multiplied by λ, then the volume is multiplied by $|\lambda|$.

We require the same of the volume of an n-dimensional parallelotope. Namely, we require that

$$V(\mathfrak{a}_1, \mathfrak{a}_2, \cdots, \lambda\mathfrak{a}_i, \cdots, \mathfrak{a}_n) = |\lambda| \cdot V(\mathfrak{a}_1, \mathfrak{a}_2, \cdots, \mathfrak{a}_i, \cdots, \mathfrak{a}_n).$$

What does our problem look like at this stage? We wish to define the volume of an n-dimensional parallelotope in such a way that the properties we have listed are satisfied. That is, we are seeking a function $V(\mathfrak{a}_1, \mathfrak{a}_2, \cdots, \mathfrak{a}_n)$ which assigns to any set of n vectors $\mathfrak{a}_1, \mathfrak{a}_2, \cdots, \mathfrak{a}_n$ of R_n a uniquely determined real functional value

$$V(\mathfrak{a}_1, \mathfrak{a}_2, \cdots, \mathfrak{a}_n)$$

and which has the following properties:

1. $V(\mathfrak{a}_1, \mathfrak{a}_2, \cdots, \mathfrak{a}_n) \geqq 0$;
2. $V(\mathfrak{a}_1, \mathfrak{a}_2, \cdots, \mathfrak{a}_n)$ is to remain unchanged if a $\mathfrak{a}_i$ is replaced by $\mathfrak{a}_i + \mathfrak{a}_k$ $(i \neq k)$;
3. $V(\mathfrak{a}_1, \mathfrak{a}_2, \cdots, \mathfrak{a}_n)$ is to go over into $|\lambda| \cdot V(\mathfrak{a}_1, \mathfrak{a}_2, \cdots, \mathfrak{a}_n)$ if some $\mathfrak{a}_i$ is replaced by $\lambda\mathfrak{a}_i$;
4. $V(\mathfrak{e}_1, \mathfrak{e}_2, \cdots, \mathfrak{e}_n) = 1$.

We here remove the restriction imposed as part of the definition of parallelotope to the effect that the vectors $\mathfrak{a}_1, \mathfrak{a}_2, \cdots, \mathfrak{a}_n$ are linearly independent. That is, we permit any ordered n-tuple $\mathfrak{a}_1, \mathfrak{a}_2, \cdots, \mathfrak{a}_n$ of vectors of R_n as arguments of the function $V(\mathfrak{a}_1, \mathfrak{a}_2, \cdots, \mathfrak{a}_n)$.

Now, it is by no means clear to begin with that there exists such a function V. But we shall show that this is indeed the case, and that moreover there is only one such function. To this end, we first introduce another function, which will turn out to be intimately related to the function V, and which is moreover of great importance in algebra. This new function, which we shall denote by $D(\mathfrak{a}_1, \mathfrak{a}_2, \cdots, \mathfrak{a}_n)$, will satisfy properties somewhat different from 1. — 4. above. Namely, we shall not require that it satisfy 1., and in place of 3., we shall require that if $\mathfrak{a}_i$ be replaced by $\lambda\mathfrak{a}_i$, D be multiplied, not by $|\lambda|$, but by λ itself. Thus, *i)* $D(\mathfrak{a}_1, \mathfrak{a}_2, \cdots, \mathfrak{a}_n)$ *is to remain unchanged if some* $\mathfrak{a}_i$ *is replaced by* $\mathfrak{a}_i + \mathfrak{a}_k$ $(i \neq k)$;

ii) $D(\mathfrak{a}_1, \mathfrak{a}_2, \cdots, \mathfrak{a}_n)$ *is to go over into* $\lambda \cdot D(\mathfrak{a}_1, \mathfrak{a}_2, \cdots, \mathfrak{a}_n)$ *if* $\mathfrak{a}_i$ *is replaced by* $\lambda\mathfrak{a}_i$;

iii) $D(\mathfrak{e}_1, \mathfrak{e}_2, \cdots, \mathfrak{e}_n) = 1$.

A function which satisfies these three properties[2] will be called a **determinant.** It may be considered either a function of n vectors, or, since each of these vectors has n components, a function of n^2 numbers. If the components of the vector $\mathfrak{a}_i$ $(1 \leqq i \leqq n)$ are $a_{i1}, a_{i2}, \cdots, a_{in}$, then we write:

$$D(\mathfrak{a}_1, \mathfrak{a}_2, \cdots, \mathfrak{a}_n) = \begin{vmatrix} a_{11} & a_{12} & \cdots & a_{1n} \\ a_{21} & a_{22} & \cdots & a_{2n} \\ \cdot & \cdot & \cdot & \cdot \\ a_{n1} & a_{n2} & \cdots & a_{nn} \end{vmatrix}.$$

We accordingly call the function $D(\mathfrak{a}_1, \mathfrak{a}_2, \cdots, \mathfrak{a}_n)$ an *n-by-n determinant.*

Fundamental Properties of Determinants

Before we investigate the existence of such a function, we shall derive several easy consequences of properties *i)*, *ii)*, *iii)*. We assert:

THEOREM 1. $D(\mathfrak{a}_1, \mathfrak{a}_2, \cdots, \mathfrak{a}_n)$ *remains unchanged if* $\mathfrak{a}_i$ *is replaced by* $\mathfrak{a}_i + \lambda\mathfrak{a}_k$ *where* $k \neq i$ *and* λ *is any real number.*

For, if $\lambda = 0$, the theorem is trivial. But if $\lambda \neq 0$, then by *ii)*, replacing the vector $\mathfrak{a}_k$ in $D(\mathfrak{a}_1, \mathfrak{a}_2, \cdots, \mathfrak{a}_n)$ by $\lambda\mathfrak{a}_k$,

$$D(\mathfrak{a}_1, \mathfrak{a}_2, \cdots, \lambda\mathfrak{a}_k, \cdots, \mathfrak{a}_n) = \lambda \cdot D(\mathfrak{a}_1, \mathfrak{a}_2, \cdots, \mathfrak{a}_k, \cdots, \mathfrak{a}_n).$$

Furthermore, replacing $\mathfrak{a}_i$ by $\mathfrak{a}_i + \lambda\mathfrak{a}_k$ on the left, we have by *i)* that

$$\begin{aligned} D(\mathfrak{a}_1, \cdots, \mathfrak{a}_i + \lambda\mathfrak{a}_k, \cdots, \lambda\mathfrak{a}_k, \cdots, \mathfrak{a}_n) &= D(\mathfrak{a}_1, \cdots, \mathfrak{a}_i, \cdots, \lambda\mathfrak{a}_k, \cdots, \mathfrak{a}_n) \\ &= \lambda \cdot D(\mathfrak{a}_1, \cdots, \mathfrak{a}_i, \cdots, \mathfrak{a}_k, \cdots, \mathfrak{a}_n). \end{aligned}$$

If we now replace $\lambda\mathfrak{a}_k$ by $\frac{1}{\lambda} \cdot (\lambda \cdot \mathfrak{a}_k) = \mathfrak{a}_k$ on the left, then by *ii)*,

---

[2] Those who prefer to give names to the three characteristic properties of determinants may, for example, call *i)* the invariance property, *ii)* the homogeneity property, and *iii)* the normalization.

$$\begin{aligned} D(\mathfrak{a}_1, \cdots, \mathfrak{a}_i + \lambda\,\mathfrak{a}_k, \cdots, \mathfrak{a}_k, \cdots, \mathfrak{a}_n) &= \frac{1}{\lambda}\cdot D(\mathfrak{a}_1, \cdots, \mathfrak{a}_i + \lambda\,\mathfrak{a}_k, \cdots, \lambda\,\mathfrak{a}_k, \cdots, \mathfrak{a}_n) \\ &= \frac{1}{\lambda}\cdot(\lambda\cdot D(\mathfrak{a}_1, \cdots, \mathfrak{a}_i, \cdots, \mathfrak{a}_k, \cdots, \mathfrak{a}_n)) \\ &= D(\mathfrak{a}_1, \mathfrak{a}_2, \cdots, \mathfrak{a}_n), \end{aligned}$$

which was to be proved.

The value of the determinant $D(\mathfrak{a}_1, \mathfrak{a}_2, \cdots, \mathfrak{a}_n)$ remains unchanged if $\mathfrak{a}_i$ is replaced by $\mathfrak{a}_i + \lambda\,\mathfrak{a}_k$, $i \neq k$. Then the value of

$$D(\mathfrak{a}_1, \mathfrak{a}_2, \cdots, \mathfrak{a}_i + \lambda\,\mathfrak{a}_k, \cdots, \mathfrak{a}_n) = D(\mathfrak{a}_1, \mathfrak{a}_2, \cdots, \mathfrak{a}_n)$$

itself remains unchanged if $\mathfrak{a}_i + \lambda\,\mathfrak{a}_k$ is replaced on the left by $\mathfrak{a}_i + \lambda\,\mathfrak{a}_k + \mu\,\mathfrak{a}_j$, where $j \neq i, k$. Continuing thus, we see that the value of a determinant remains unaltered upon the addition to some fixed $\mathfrak{a}_i$ of arbitrary multiples of the remaining vectors. However, this yields:

THEOREM 2. *The value of* $D(\mathfrak{a}_1, \mathfrak{a}_2, \cdots, \mathfrak{a}_n)$ *remains unchanged if one adds to an* $\mathfrak{a}_i$ *a linear combination of the remaining vectors* $\mathfrak{a}_k$ $(k \neq i)$, *that is if* $\mathfrak{a}_i$ *is replaced by* $\mathfrak{a}_i + \sum_{\substack{k=1 \\ k \neq i}}^{n} \lambda_k\,\mathfrak{a}_k$.

If one of the vectors $\mathfrak{a}_i$ is equal to 0, then it remains unchanged if it is multiplied by 0; thus in this case, replacing $\mathfrak{a}_i$ by $0 \cdot \mathfrak{a}_i$ does not alter the value of the determinant. However, by *ii*), this replacement changes the value of the determinant to $0\ D(\mathfrak{a}_1, \mathfrak{a}_2, \cdots, \mathfrak{a}_n) = 0$. Therefore, we must have that $D(\mathfrak{a}_1, \mathfrak{a}_2, \cdots, \mathfrak{a}_n) = 0$. This gives:

THEOREM 3. *If one of the vectors* $\mathfrak{a}_i$ *is the null vector, then*

$$D(\mathfrak{a}_1, \mathfrak{a}_2, \cdots, \mathfrak{a}_n) = 0.$$

If now one of the vectors $\mathfrak{a}_i$ is a linear combination of the remaining vectors, say:

$$\mathfrak{a}_i = \sum_{\substack{k=1 \\ k \neq i}}^{n} \lambda_k\,\mathfrak{a}_k,$$

then $\mathfrak{a}_i$ may be replaced by $\mathfrak{a}_i - \sum_{\substack{k=1 \\ k \neq i}}^{n} \lambda_k\,\mathfrak{a}_k$, i.e. by the null vector, without changing the value of the determinant as was proved above. On the other hand, the determinant now has one of its argument vectors vanishing, and so must be zero. Recalling Theorem 3 of § 3, we have:

THEOREM 4. *If the vectors* $\mathfrak{a}_1, \mathfrak{a}_2, \cdots, \mathfrak{a}_n$ *are linearly dependent, then* $D(\mathfrak{a}_1, \mathfrak{a}_2, \cdots, \mathfrak{a}_n) = 0$.

If in particular (for $n \geqq 2$) two of the vectors $\mathfrak{a}_i$ are equal to one another, then the vectors $\mathfrak{a}_1, \mathfrak{a}_2, \cdots, \mathfrak{a}_n$ are linearly dependent, so that

$$D(\mathfrak{a}_1, \mathfrak{a}_2, \cdots, \mathfrak{a}_n) = 0.$$

We wish to remark on a point which will be of use later. We may prove for any function $V(\mathfrak{a}_1, \mathfrak{a}_2, \cdots, \mathfrak{a}_n)$ which satisfies conditions 2. and 3. above, that $V(\mathfrak{a}_1, \mathfrak{a}_2, \cdots, \mathfrak{a}_n) = 0$ whenever $\mathfrak{a}_1, \mathfrak{a}_2, \cdots, \mathfrak{a}_n$ are linearly dependent. The proof, which is almost word for word identical to that just given for $D(\mathfrak{a}_1, \mathfrak{a}_2, \cdots, \mathfrak{a}_n)$, is left to the reader.

As yet we do not know whether the value of the determinant $D(\mathfrak{a}_1, \mathfrak{a}_2, \cdots, \mathfrak{a}_n)$ is dependent on the order of the vectors $\mathfrak{a}_i$. We shall see that, as a matter of fact, this is the case. Namely, we prove

THEOREM 5. *If we interchange two of the vectors* $\mathfrak{a}_1, \mathfrak{a}_2, \cdots, \mathfrak{a}_n$ *leaving the remaining ones unchanged, the sign of the determinant is changed.*

Let $\mathfrak{a}_i$ and $\mathfrak{a}_k$ be the two vectors which are to be interchanged. We shall arrive at this interchange by a sequence of successive substitutions, where we know just how each of these substitutions changes the value of the determinant. Each of these substitutions will, moreover, involve only the vectors $\mathfrak{a}_i$ and $\mathfrak{a}_k$, the other vectors remaining unchanged. We need therefore indicate only what is to be done with these two vectors. First, we replace $\mathfrak{a}_i$ by $\mathfrak{a}_i + \mathfrak{a}_k$, which leaves the value of the determinant unchanged, by *i*). At this point, we have

in the *i*-th position, the vector $\mathfrak{a}_i + \mathfrak{a}_k$,
in the *k*-th position, the vector $\mathfrak{a}_k$.

By Theorem 1, the value of the determinant still remains unchanged if we next replace $\mathfrak{a}_k$ by $\mathfrak{a}_k - (\mathfrak{a}_i + \mathfrak{a}_k)$, i.e. by $-\mathfrak{a}_i$. At this point we have

in the *i*-th position, the vector $\mathfrak{a}_i + \mathfrak{a}_k$,
in the *k*-th position, the vector $-\mathfrak{a}_i$.

Again by *i*), the value of the determinant is not changed if we now replace $\mathfrak{a}_i + \mathfrak{a}_k$ by $\mathfrak{a}_i + \mathfrak{a}_k + (-\mathfrak{a}_i)$, i.e., by $\mathfrak{a}_k$. At this point we have

in the *i*-th position, the vector $\mathfrak{a}_k$,
in the *k*-th position, the vector $-\mathfrak{a}_i$.

Finally, if we replace $-\mathfrak{a}_i$ by $-(-\mathfrak{a}_i) = \mathfrak{a}_i$ in the *k*-th position, then by *ii*) the sign of the determinant is changed. But, at this point we have

in the *i*-th position, the vector $\mathfrak{a}_k$,
in the *k*-th position, the vector $\mathfrak{a}_i$,

while the vectors in the other positions have remained unchanged. These substitutions have resulted in a change of sign of the determinant, and this proves the theorem.

We shall now prove a very important result, known as the *addition theorem* for determinants. If, namely, we replace the vector $\mathfrak{a}_1$ by a sum, say $\mathfrak{a}_1 = \mathfrak{b} + \mathfrak{c}$, we have

THEOREM 6. $D(\mathfrak{b} + \mathfrak{c}, \mathfrak{a}_2, \mathfrak{a}_3, \cdots, \mathfrak{a}_n)$
$$= D(\mathfrak{b}, \mathfrak{a}_2, \mathfrak{a}_3, \cdots, \mathfrak{a}_n) + D(\mathfrak{c}, \mathfrak{a}_2, \mathfrak{a}_3, \cdots, \mathfrak{a}_n).$$

For if the vectors $\mathfrak{a}_2, \mathfrak{a}_3, \cdots, \mathfrak{a}_n$ are linearly dependent, then by Theorem 1 of § 3, so are the vectors $\mathfrak{b} + \mathfrak{c}, \mathfrak{a}_2, \mathfrak{a}_3, \cdots, \mathfrak{a}_n$ and $\mathfrak{b}, \mathfrak{a}_2, \mathfrak{a}_3, \cdots, \mathfrak{a}_n$ and $\mathfrak{c}, \mathfrak{a}_2, \mathfrak{a}_3, \cdots, \mathfrak{a}_n$. Thus each of the three determinants in our equation vanishes so that the equation indeed holds. If, however, $\mathfrak{a}_2, \mathfrak{a}_3, \cdots, \mathfrak{a}_n$ are linearly independent, then these $n - 1$ vectors may be extended to form a basis of R_n by adjoining to them some additional vector $\mathfrak{a}'$. Thus, we have, say,

$$\mathfrak{b} = \lambda_1 \mathfrak{a}' + \lambda_2 \mathfrak{a}_2 + \lambda_3 \mathfrak{a}_3 + \cdots + \lambda_n \mathfrak{a}_n,$$
$$\mathfrak{c} = \mu_1 \mathfrak{a}' + \mu_2 \mathfrak{a}_2 + \mu_3 \mathfrak{a}_3 + \cdots + \mu_n \mathfrak{a}_n.$$

If in $D(\mathfrak{b}, \mathfrak{a}_2, \mathfrak{a}_3, \cdots, \mathfrak{a}_n)$ we replace the vector $\mathfrak{b}$ by $\mathfrak{b} - \sum_{i=2}^{n} \lambda_i \mathfrak{a}_i$, i.e. by $\lambda_1 \mathfrak{a}'$, then by Theorem 2, the determinant remains unchanged. The same holds if in $D(\mathfrak{c}, \mathfrak{a}_2, \mathfrak{a}_3, \cdots, \mathfrak{a}_n)$ we replace the vector $\mathfrak{c}$ by $\mathfrak{c} - \sum_{i=2}^{n} \mu_i \mathfrak{a}_i = \mu_1 \mathfrak{a}'$, and if in $D(\mathfrak{b} + \mathfrak{c}, \mathfrak{a}_2, \mathfrak{a}_3, \cdots, \mathfrak{a}_n)$ we replace the vector $\mathfrak{b} + \mathfrak{c}$ by $\mathfrak{b} + \mathfrak{c} - \sum_{i=2}^{n} (\lambda_i + \mu_i) \mathfrak{a}_i = (\lambda_1 + \mu_1) \mathfrak{a}'$. Thus, by *ii*), we have

$$D(\mathfrak{b}, \mathfrak{a}_2, \mathfrak{a}_3, \cdots, \mathfrak{a}_n) = \lambda_1 \cdot D(\mathfrak{a}', \mathfrak{a}_2, \mathfrak{a}_3, \cdots, \mathfrak{a}_n),$$
$$D(\mathfrak{c}, \mathfrak{a}_2, \mathfrak{a}_3, \cdots, \mathfrak{a}_n) = \mu_1 \cdot D(\mathfrak{a}', \mathfrak{a}_2, \mathfrak{a}_3, \cdots, \mathfrak{a}_n),$$
$$D(\mathfrak{b} + \mathfrak{c}, \mathfrak{a}_2, \mathfrak{a}_3, \cdots, \mathfrak{a}_n) = (\lambda_1 + \mu_1) \cdot D(\mathfrak{a}', \mathfrak{a}_2, \mathfrak{a}_3, \cdots, \mathfrak{a}_n).$$

Addition of the first two of these equations yields

$$D(\mathfrak{b}, \mathfrak{a}_2, \mathfrak{a}_3, \cdots, \mathfrak{a}_n) + D(\mathfrak{c}, \mathfrak{a}_2, \mathfrak{a}_3, \cdots, \mathfrak{a}_n) = (\lambda_1 + \mu_1) \cdot D(\mathfrak{a}', \mathfrak{a}_2, \mathfrak{a}_3, \cdots, \mathfrak{a}_n).$$

Comparison of the last two equations immediately gives us our result.

It is clear from the proof that the theorem is also correct if we replace, not $\mathfrak{a}_1$, but $\mathfrak{a}_i$ by the sum of two vectors. Furthermore, if

$$\mathfrak{a}_1 = \mathfrak{b}_1 + \mathfrak{b}_2 + \cdots + \mathfrak{b}_r,$$

then by what has been proved, we obtain

$$D\left(\sum_{i=1}^{r} \mathfrak{b}_i, \mathfrak{a}_2, \mathfrak{a}_3, \cdots, \mathfrak{a}_n\right)$$
$$= D(\mathfrak{b}_1, \mathfrak{a}_2, \mathfrak{a}_3, \cdots, \mathfrak{a}_n) + D\left(\sum_{i=2}^{r} \mathfrak{b}_i, \mathfrak{a}_2, \mathfrak{a}_3, \cdots, \mathfrak{a}_n\right)$$
$$= D(\mathfrak{b}_1, \mathfrak{a}_2, \mathfrak{a}_3, \cdots, \mathfrak{a}_n) + D(\mathfrak{b}_2, \mathfrak{a}_2, \mathfrak{a}_3, \cdots, \mathfrak{a}_n) + D\left(\sum_{i=3}^{r} \mathfrak{b}_i, \mathfrak{a}_2, \mathfrak{a}_3, \cdots, \mathfrak{a}_n\right)$$
$$\cdots\cdots\cdots\cdots$$
$$= \sum_{i=1}^{r} D(\mathfrak{b}_i, \mathfrak{a}_2, \cdots, \mathfrak{a}_n).$$

We may thus shift the summation sign to in front of the determinant. Again, the same also holds for each of the vectors $\mathfrak{a}_2, \mathfrak{a}_3, \cdots, \mathfrak{a}_n$. If we now set[3]

$$\mathfrak{a}_i = \mathfrak{b}_i^1 + \mathfrak{b}_i^2 + \cdots + \mathfrak{b}_i^r \ (i = 1, 2, \cdots, n)$$

and successively shift the summation signs in the expression

$$D\left(\sum_{k=1}^{r} \mathfrak{b}_1^k, \sum_{k=1}^{r} \mathfrak{b}_2^k, \sum_{k=1}^{r} \mathfrak{b}_3^k, \cdots, \sum_{k=1}^{r} \mathfrak{b}_n^k\right)$$

to in front of the determinant, we have

$$D(\mathfrak{a}_1, \mathfrak{a}_2, \cdots, \mathfrak{a}_n) = D\left(\sum_{\nu_1=1}^{r} \mathfrak{b}_1^{\nu_1}, \sum_{\nu_2=1}^{r} \mathfrak{b}_2^{\nu_2}, \sum_{\nu_3=1}^{r} \mathfrak{b}_3^{\nu_3}, \cdots, \sum_{\nu_n=1}^{r} \mathfrak{b}_n^{\nu_n}\right)$$
$$= \sum_{\nu_1=1}^{r} D\left(\mathfrak{b}_1^{\nu_1}, \sum_{\nu_2=1}^{r} \mathfrak{b}_2^{\nu_2}, \sum_{\nu_3=1}^{r} \mathfrak{b}_3^{\nu_3}, \cdots, \sum_{\nu_n=1}^{r} \mathfrak{b}_n^{\nu_n}\right)$$
$$= \sum_{\nu_1=1}^{r}\left[\sum_{\nu_2=1}^{r} D\left(\mathfrak{b}_1^{\nu_1}, \mathfrak{b}_2^{\nu_2}, \sum_{\nu_3=1}^{r} \mathfrak{b}_3^{\nu_3}, \cdots, \sum_{\nu_n=1}^{r} \mathfrak{b}_n^{\nu_n}\right)\right]$$
$$\cdots\cdots\cdots\cdots$$
$$= \sum_{\nu_1=1}^{r}\sum_{\nu_2=1}^{r}\sum_{\nu_3=1}^{r}\cdots\sum_{\nu_n=1}^{r} D(\mathfrak{b}_1^{\nu_1}, \mathfrak{b}_2^{\nu_2}, \mathfrak{b}_3^{\nu_3}, \cdots, \mathfrak{b}_n^{\nu_n}).$$

We thus have

THEOREM 7. *If* $\mathfrak{a}_i = \sum_{k=1}^{r} \mathfrak{b}_i^k \ (i = 1, 2, \cdots, n)$, *then*

$$D(\mathfrak{a}_1, \mathfrak{a}_2, \cdots, \mathfrak{a}_n) = \sum_{\nu_1, \nu_2, \cdots, \nu_n = 1}^{r} D(\mathfrak{b}_1^{\nu_1}, \mathfrak{b}_2^{\nu_2}, \mathfrak{b}_3^{\nu_3}, \cdots, \mathfrak{b}_n^{\nu_n}).$$

---

[3] The numbers $1, 2, \ldots, r$ in $\mathfrak{b}_i^1, \mathfrak{b}_i^2, \cdots, \mathfrak{b}_i^r$ are of course superscripts and not exponents. In this and in the next section, we shall systematically omit parentheses around superscripts, since there is no danger of confusion with exponents.

Existence and Uniqueness of Determinants

Theorems 1 through 7, which have just been proved, hold for any function $D(\mathfrak{a}_1, \mathfrak{a}_2, \cdots, \mathfrak{a}_n)$ which satisfies the three properties *i*), *ii*), *iii*). As yet, however, we do not even know whether there exists such a function. We now proceed to prove that this is indeed the case, and in the process we also show that there is only one such function.

The function $D(\mathfrak{a}_1, \mathfrak{a}_2, \cdots, \mathfrak{a}_n)$ which we are seeking is to be a function of n vectors of R_n. It is to be so defined that to every ordered n-tuple $\mathfrak{a}_1, \mathfrak{a}_2, \cdots, \mathfrak{a}_n$ of vectors of R_n, a uniquely determined real number, namely $D(\mathfrak{a}_1, \mathfrak{a}_2, \cdots, \mathfrak{a}_n)$, is to be assigned as the corresponding functional value. Our proof proceeds by induction on n. We first consider the case $n = 1$. In this case, the determinant is to be a function of a single vector $\mathfrak{a}_1$ or $\mathfrak{a}$ of R_1. There is only one component in $\mathfrak{a}$; we set $\mathfrak{a} = \{ a \}$. By *iii*), we must have for the unit vector $\mathfrak{e} = \{ 1 \}$, that

$$D(\mathfrak{e}) = 1.$$

Now, $\mathfrak{a} = \{a\} = a \cdot \{1\} = a \cdot \mathfrak{e}$, and so by *ii*),

$$D(\mathfrak{a}) = D(a \cdot \mathfrak{e}) = a \cdot D(\mathfrak{e}) = a.$$

We have thus proved: If there is any function $D(\mathfrak{a})$ for $n = 1$, then this is necessarily the function $D(\mathfrak{a}) = a$, so that there is certainly at most one such function.[4] This function $D(\mathfrak{a}) = a$ does, however, satisfy the three conditions *i*), *ii*), *iii*), so that there actually is a function $D(\mathfrak{a})$ for $n = 1$. For, property *i*) holds vacuously for $n = 1$, since there are no two vectors $\mathfrak{a}_i$, $\mathfrak{a}_k$ with $i \neq k$.[5] We further have for the function $a = D(\mathfrak{a})$ that

$$D(\lambda \mathfrak{a}) = D(\lambda \{a\}) = D(\{\lambda \cdot a\}) = \lambda \cdot a = \lambda \cdot D(\mathfrak{a}).$$

so that property *ii*) is satisfied. Finally, property *iii*) is obviously satisfied.

We now employ the principle of mathematical induction, and we thus assume that for dimension $n - 1$ the existence and uniqueness

---

[4] It should be noted that we have deduced this result from properties *ii*) and *iii*) alone.

[5] Although *i*) is vacuous for $n = 1$, we shall have to employ the existence and uniqueness of the function $D(\mathfrak{a}) = a$ for $n = 1$ as an induction hypothesis. The inductive procedure to be given will however make it clear that in proceeding from $n = 1$ to $n = 2$, condition *i*) for $n = 1$ will not be used, so that the result for $n = 2$ holds independently.

of the function $D(\mathfrak{a}_1, \mathfrak{a}_2, \cdots, \mathfrak{a}_{n-1})$ has been proved, and proceed to prove the existence and uniqueness of the function

$$D(\mathfrak{a}_1, \mathfrak{a}_2, \cdots, \mathfrak{a}_n)$$

for dimension n. We may assume $n \geqq 2$. We first prove uniqueness.

Let $\mathfrak{a}_i = \{a_{i1}, a_{i2}, \cdots, a_{in}\}$ for $i = 1, 2, \ldots, n$. Let us set

$$\begin{aligned} \mathfrak{b}_i^1 &= \{a_{i1}, a_{i2}, \cdots, a_{i,n-1}, 0\} \\ \mathfrak{b}_i^2 &= \{0, 0, \cdots, 0, a_{in}\} \end{aligned}$$

so that

$$\mathfrak{a}_i = \mathfrak{b}_i^1 + \mathfrak{b}_i^2,$$

and then by Theorem 7, we have for any function $D(\mathfrak{a}_1, \mathfrak{a}_2, \cdots, \mathfrak{a}_n)$ which satisfies properties *i*), *ii*), *iii*), above, that

$$D(\mathfrak{a}_1, \mathfrak{a}_2, \cdots, \mathfrak{a}_n) = \sum_{\nu_1, \nu_2, \cdots, \nu_n = 1}^{2} D(\mathfrak{b}_1^{\nu_1}, \mathfrak{b}_2^{\nu_2}, \cdots, \mathfrak{b}_n^{\nu_n}).$$

Since the last components of the vectors $\mathfrak{b}_1^1, \mathfrak{b}_2^1, \cdots, \mathfrak{b}_n^1$ are 0, they may be considered as vectors of R_{n-1}. However, in R_{n-1}, the maximal number of linearly independent vectors is $n - 1$, so that the n vectors $\mathfrak{b}_1^1, \mathfrak{b}_2^1, \cdots, \mathfrak{b}_n^1$ must be linearly dependent.[6] Further, since the first $n - 1$ components of each of the vectors $\mathfrak{b}_1^2, \mathfrak{b}_2^2, \cdots, \mathfrak{b}_n^2$ vanish, they may be considered as vectors of R_1. Since in R_1 any pair of vectors are linearly dependent, the same is true of any pair of the vectors $\mathfrak{b}_1^2, \mathfrak{b}_2^2, \cdots, \mathfrak{b}_n^2$.[7] By Theorem 4 of this section, the term $D(\mathfrak{b}_1^1, \mathfrak{b}_2^1, \cdots, \mathfrak{b}_n^1)$ of the sum on the right of the equation displayed immediately above, vanishes. For the same reason, and by Theorem 1 of § 3, each summand $D(\mathfrak{b}_1^{\nu_1}, \mathfrak{b}_2^{\nu_2}, \cdots \mathfrak{b}_n^{\nu_n})$ for which more than one of the indices ν_i are 2, vanishes. Thus only those terms remain in which exactly one of the indices ν_i is equal to 2, all the others being 1. Hence there are n summands of the form

---

[6] Or alternately, for each vector $\mathfrak{b}_i^1$ we have

$$\mathfrak{b}_i^1 = \sum_{k=1}^{n-1} a_{ik}\,\mathfrak{e}_k, \qquad i = 1, 2, \cdots, n.$$

Thus the vectors $\mathfrak{b}_i^1$ all are linear combinations of the $n - 1$ vectors $\mathfrak{e}_1, \mathfrak{e}_2, \cdots \mathfrak{e}_{n-1}$, so that by Theorem 2 of § 4, any set of more than $n - 1$ of them must be linearly dependent.

[7] We also see that for $i, k = 1, 2, \ldots, n$,

$$a_{kn} \cdot \mathfrak{b}_i^2 - a_{in} \cdot \mathfrak{b}_k^2 = 0.$$

$$D(\mathfrak{b}_1^1, \cdots, \mathfrak{b}_{k-1}^1, \mathfrak{b}_k^2, \mathfrak{b}_{k+1}^1, \cdots, \mathfrak{b}_n^1).$$

so that we may write

$$D(\mathfrak{a}_1, \mathfrak{a}_2, \cdots, \mathfrak{a}_n) = \sum_{k=1}^{n} D(\mathfrak{b}_1^1, \cdots, \mathfrak{b}_{k-1}^1, \mathfrak{b}_k^2, \mathfrak{b}_{k+1}^1, \cdots, \mathfrak{b}_n^1).$$

If we successively interchange $\mathfrak{b}_k^2$ and $\mathfrak{b}_{k+1}^1, \mathfrak{b}_{k+2}^1, \cdots, \mathfrak{b}_n^1$, in the individual summands, then by Theorem 5, the sign of the k-th summand is changed $n - k$ times. Thus,

$$D(\mathfrak{b}_1^1, \cdots, \mathfrak{b}_{k-1}^1, \mathfrak{b}_k^2, \mathfrak{b}_{k+1}^1, \cdots, \mathfrak{b}_n^1) = (-1)^{n-k} \cdot D(\mathfrak{b}_1^1, \cdots, \mathfrak{b}_{k-1}^1, \mathfrak{b}_{k+1}^1, \cdots, \mathfrak{b}_n^1, \mathfrak{b}_k^2).$$

Recalling that $\mathfrak{b}_k^2 = \{0, 0, \cdots, 0, a_{kn}\} = a_{kn} \cdot \mathfrak{e}_n$ we have by *ii*) that

$$D(\mathfrak{b}_1^1, \cdots, \mathfrak{b}_{k-1}^1, \mathfrak{b}_{k+1}^1, \cdots, \mathfrak{b}_n^1, \mathfrak{b}_k^2) = a_{kn} \cdot D(\mathfrak{b}_1^1, \cdots, \mathfrak{b}_{k-1}^1, \mathfrak{b}_{k+1}^1, \cdots, \mathfrak{b}_n^1, \mathfrak{e}_n).$$

Thus, we have

$$D(\mathfrak{a}_1, \mathfrak{a}_2, \cdots, \mathfrak{a}_n) = \sum_{k=1}^{n} (-1)^{n-k} \cdot a_{kn} \cdot D(\mathfrak{b}_1^1, \cdots, \mathfrak{b}_{k-1}^1, \mathfrak{b}_{k+1}^1, \cdots, \mathfrak{b}_n^1, \mathfrak{e}_n).$$

We shall now employ the previously introduced abbreviation

$$D(\mathfrak{a}_1, \mathfrak{a}_2, \cdots, \mathfrak{a}_n) = \begin{vmatrix} a_{11} & a_{12} & \cdots & a_{1n} \\ a_{21} & a_{22} & \cdots & a_{2n} \\ \cdot & \cdot & \cdot & \cdot \\ a_{n1} & a_{n2} & \cdots & a_{nn} \end{vmatrix}$$

in order to get a better picture of what is going on. The components of the i-th vector $\mathfrak{a}_i$ occur in the i-th row of this array. What is the appearance of the expressions

$$D(\mathfrak{b}_1^1, \cdots, \mathfrak{b}_{k-1}^1, \mathfrak{b}_{k+1}^1, \cdots, \mathfrak{b}_n^1, \mathfrak{e}_n)$$

when written in this form? If we recall that the last components of the vectors $\mathfrak{b}_i^1$ vanish, and that $\mathfrak{e}_n = \{0, 0, \ldots, 0, 1\}$, then we see that each of these expressions is of the form

$$\begin{vmatrix} c_{11} & c_{12} & \cdots & c_{1,n-1} & 0 \\ c_{21} & c_{22} & \cdots & c_{2,n-1} & 0 \\ \cdot & \cdot & \cdot & \cdot & \cdot \\ c_{n-1,1} & c_{n-1,2} & \cdots & c_{n-1,n-1} & 0 \\ 0 & 0 & \cdots & 0 & 1 \end{vmatrix}$$

A determinant of this form is a function of the $(n-1)^2$ quantities

c_{ik}, $i, k = 1, 2, \ldots, n-1$. Using the first $n-1$ elements of the i-th row $(1 \leqq i \leqq n-1)$ we form the vectors

$$\mathfrak{c}_i = \{c_{i1}, c_{i2}, \cdots, c_{i,n-1}\}, \quad i = 1, 2, \cdots, n-1.$$

We may thus consider our determinant as a function of these $n-1$ vectors of R_{n-1}, and we therefore set, say,

$$\bar{D}(\mathfrak{c}_1, \mathfrak{c}_2, \cdots, \mathfrak{c}_{n-1}) = \begin{vmatrix} c_{11} & c_{12} & \cdots & c_{1,n-1} & 0 \\ c_{21} & c_{22} & \cdots & c_{2,n-1} & 0 \\ \cdot & \cdot & \cdot & \cdot & \cdot \\ c_{n-1,1} & c_{n-1,2} & \cdots & c_{n-1,n-1} & 0 \\ 0 & 0 & \cdots & 0 & 1 \end{vmatrix}$$

We now assert that this function $\bar{D}(\mathfrak{c}_1, \mathfrak{c}_2, \cdots, \mathfrak{c}_{n-1})$ as a function of vectors of R_{n-1}, actually satisfies properties *i*), *ii*), and *iii*). We had $n \geqq 2$. If $n = 2$, then property *i*) holds vacuously, for the function D, since there is only one argument vector in this case. However, if $n > 2$, then in $\bar{D}$ let us replace the vector $\mathfrak{c}_i$ by $\mathfrak{c}_i + \mathfrak{c}_k$ $(i \neq k, 1 \leqq i \leqq n-1, 1 \leqq k \leqq n-1)$. For the corresponding n-by-n determinant on the right-hand side, this means that the i-th row $c_{i1}, c_{i2}, \ldots, c_{i,n-1}, 0$ $(i \leqq n-1)$ is replaced by $c_{i1} + c_{k1}, c_{i2} + c_{k2}, \ldots, c_{i,n-1} + c_{k,n-1}$, 0. But by property *i*) this does not alter the value of the n-by-n determinant on the right, and hence the value of the function $\bar{D}(\mathfrak{c}_1, \mathfrak{c}_2, \cdots, \mathfrak{c}_{n-1})$ is left unaltered. Furthermore, if we replace a vector $\mathfrak{c}_i$ by $\lambda \mathfrak{c}_i$ $(1 \leqq i \leqq n-1)$, then this involves replacing the i-th row $c_{i1}, c_{i2}, \cdots, c_{i,n-1}$, 0 of the corresponding n-by-n determinant by $\lambda c_{i1}, \lambda c_{i2}, \cdots, \lambda c_{i,n-1}$, 0. By *ii*), the value of the n-by-n determinant goes over into its product by λ. Thus

$$\bar{D}(\mathfrak{c}_1, \cdots, \lambda \mathfrak{c}_i, \cdots, \mathfrak{c}_{n-1}) = \lambda \cdot \bar{D}(\mathfrak{c}_1, \cdots, \mathfrak{c}_i, \cdots, \mathfrak{c}_{n-1}).$$

Finally, if we consider $\bar{D}(\mathfrak{e}'_1, \mathfrak{e}'_2, \cdots, \mathfrak{e}'_{n-1})$, where $\mathfrak{e}'_1, \mathfrak{e}'_2, \cdots, \mathfrak{e}'_{n-1}$ are the $n-1$ unit vectors of R_{n-1}, then we have, by substitution in the equation before last, that

$$\bar{D}(\mathfrak{e}'_1, \mathfrak{e}'_2, \cdots, \mathfrak{e}'_{n-1}) = \underbrace{\begin{vmatrix} 1 & 0 & \cdots & 0 \\ 0 & 1 & \cdots & 0 \\ \cdot & \cdot & \cdot & \cdot \\ 0 & 0 & \cdots & 1 \end{vmatrix}}_{n\text{-by-}n} = D(\mathfrak{e}_1, \mathfrak{e}_2, \cdots, \mathfrak{e}_n) = 1,$$

which proves that *iii*) holds for $\bar{D}(\mathfrak{c}_1, \mathfrak{c}_2, \cdots, \mathfrak{c}_{n-1})$. But, by induction hypothesis, there is for dimension $n-1$ only one function which satisfies *i*), *ii*), *iii*), namely the function $D(\mathfrak{c}_1, \mathfrak{c}_2, \cdots, \mathfrak{c}_{n-1})$. [8] Thus,

$$\bar{D}(\mathfrak{c}_1, \mathfrak{c}_2, \cdots, \mathfrak{c}_{n-1}) = D(\mathfrak{c}_1, \mathfrak{c}_2, \cdots, \mathfrak{c}_{n-1})$$

or written differently,

$$\begin{vmatrix} c_{11} & c_{12} & \cdots & c_{1,n-1} & 0 \\ c_{21} & c_{22} & \cdots & c_{2,n-1} & 0 \\ \cdot & \cdot & \cdot & \cdot & \cdot \\ c_{n-1,1} & c_{n-1,2} & \cdots & c_{n-1,n-1} & 0 \\ 0 & 0 & \cdots & 0 & 1 \end{vmatrix} = \begin{vmatrix} c_{11} & c_{12} & \cdots & c_{1,n-1} \\ c_{21} & c_{22} & \cdots & c_{2,n-1} \\ \cdot & \cdot & \cdot & \cdot \\ c_{n-1,1} & c_{n-1,2} & \cdots & c_{n-1,n-1} \end{vmatrix}$$

If we apply this result to the expressions

$$D(\mathfrak{b}_1^1, \cdots, \mathfrak{b}_{k-1}^1, \mathfrak{b}_{k+1}^1, \cdots, \mathfrak{b}_n^1; \mathfrak{e}_n)$$

from the above sum, it follows that

$$D(\mathfrak{b}_1^1, \cdots, \mathfrak{b}_{k-1}^1, \mathfrak{b}_{k+1}^1, \cdots, \mathfrak{b}_n^1, \mathfrak{e}_n) = \begin{vmatrix} a_{11} & a_{12} & \cdots & a_{1,n-1} \\ \cdot & \cdot & \cdot & \cdot \\ a_{k-1,1} & a_{k-1,2} & \cdots & a_{k-1,n-1} \\ a_{k+1,1} & a_{k+1,2} & \cdots & a_{k+1,n-1} \\ \cdot & \cdot & \cdot & \cdot \\ a_{n1} & a_{n2} & \cdots & a_{n,n-1} \end{vmatrix}$$

The $(n-1)$-by-$(n-1)$ determinant on the right is obtained from the n-by-n determinant

$$\begin{vmatrix} a_{11} & a_{12} & \cdots & a_{1n} \\ a_{21} & a_{22} & \cdots & a_{2n} \\ \cdot & \cdot & \cdot & \cdot \\ a_{n1} & a_{n2} & \cdots & a_{nn} \end{vmatrix}$$

by crossing out the last column and the k-th row. If we denote this $(n-1)$-by-$(n-1)$ determinant by D_k, then we have

$$D(\mathfrak{a}_1, \mathfrak{a}_2, \cdots, \mathfrak{a}_n) = \sum_{k=1}^{n} (-1)^{n-k} \cdot a_{kn} \cdot D_k,$$

[8] Indeed, we have been able to prove the fact that the function D satisfies property *i*) only for $n > 2$. But for $n-1=1$ the function D has the form $D(\mathfrak{c}_1)$ and is a function of one vector of R_1. In this case, as we saw above (cf. footnote 5 of this section), it follows from *ii*) and *iii*) alone that $\bar{D} = D$.

where the determinants D_k on the right have $(n-1)$ rows.

This last equation holds for any function $D(\mathfrak{a}_1, \mathfrak{a}_2, \cdots, \mathfrak{a}_n)$ which satisfies conditions *i*), *ii*), *iii*). This proves:

If there is any function $D(\mathfrak{a}_1, \mathfrak{a}_2, \cdots, \mathfrak{a}_n)$ *whatever which satisfies conditions i), ii), and iii), then this is necessarily the function:*

$$\sum_{k=1}^{n} (-1)^{n-k} \cdot a_{kn} \cdot D_k.$$

This expression is a well-defined function. For our induction hypothesis gives the existence and uniqueness of the $(n-1)$-by-$(n-1)$ determinants D_k. Further, since this expression depends only on the n^2 quantities a_{ik}, it is a function of the n vectors $\mathfrak{a}_1, \mathfrak{a}_2, \cdots, \mathfrak{a}_n$. If we further show that as a function of these n vectors of R_n, it satisfies conditions *i*), *ii*), *iii*), then the existence of a function $D(\mathfrak{a}_1, \mathfrak{a}_2, \cdots, \mathfrak{a}_n)$ for dimension n is proved. Moreover, since the above expression is the only possible function of this sort, this would also show that the determinant $D(\mathfrak{a}_1, \mathfrak{a}_2, \cdots, \mathfrak{a}_n)$ is uniquely determined.

Let us observe what occurs if a vector $\mathfrak{a}_i$ is replaced by $\mathfrak{a}_i + \mathfrak{a}_j$, $j \neq i$, in the expression $\sum_{k=1}^{n}(-1)^{n-k} \cdot a_{kn} \cdot D_k$. To replace $\mathfrak{a}_i$ by $\mathfrak{a}_i + \mathfrak{a}_j$ may be expressed as follows in terms of the components: The quantities a_{ir} are to be replaced by $a_{ir} + a_{jr}$ for $r = 1, 2, \ldots, n$. We first note that for $k \neq i, j$, the $(n-1)$-by-$(n-1)$ determinant D_k remains unchanged. For, such a determinant is of the form

$$D_k = \begin{vmatrix} a_{11} & a_{12} & \cdots & a_{1,n-1} \\ \cdot & \cdot & \cdot & \cdot \\ a_{k-1,1} & a_{k-1,2} & \cdots & a_{k-1,n-1} \\ a_{k+1,1} & a_{k+1,2} & \cdots & a_{k+1,n-1} \\ \cdot & \cdot & \cdot & \cdot \\ a_{n1} & a_{n2} & \cdots & a_{n,n-1} \end{vmatrix}$$

The rows $a_{i1}, a_{i2}, \cdots, a_{i,n-1}$ and $a_{j1}, a_{j2}, \cdots, a_{j,n-1}$ certainly occur among the $n-1$ rows of this determinant, since we supposed $k \neq i, j$. Our substitution results in replacing the row $a_{i1}, a_{i2}, \cdots, a_{i,n-1}$ by the row $a_{i1} + a_{j1}, a_{i2} + a_{j2}, \cdots, a_{i,n-1} + a_{j,n-1}$ in the determinant D_k. By property *i*), which by induction hypothesis holds for $(n-1)$-by-$(n-1)$ determinants, D_k remains indeed unchanged in this case.[9]

[9] Property *i*) is vacuous for 1-by-1 determinants. But D^k is 1-by-1 only if $n = 2$. However, in this case there are no determinants D_k for which $k \neq i$ and $k \neq j$. For only the 1-by-1 determinants D_i and D_j are available. ($\mathfrak{a}_i$ was replaced by $\mathfrak{a}_i + \mathfrak{a}_j$).

Furthermore, our substitution also leaves the value of the determinant D_i unchanged. For D_i is independent of the values of $a_{i1}, a_{i2}, \ldots, a_{i,n-1}$ and is therefore unchanged by the substitution.

Finally, what is the situation with respect to D_j? The determinant D_j contains the row $a_{i1}, a_{i2}, \ldots, a_{i,n-1}$, which is to be replaced by $a_{i1} + a_{j1}, a_{i2} + a_{j2}, \ldots, a_{i,n-1} + a_{j,n-1}$. But D_j does not contain the row $a_{j1}, a_{j2}, \ldots, a_{j,n-1}$, so that we can not make use of the fact that property i) holds for D_j. However, we may apply Theorem 6 of this section. For, consider the determinant D_j^* which is obtained by our substitution from D_j, as a function of its $n-1$ row vectors. If we set $\bar{\mathfrak{a}}_k = \{a_{k1}, a_{k2}, \cdots, a_{k,n-1}\}$ then

$$\begin{aligned} D_j &= D(\bar{\mathfrak{a}}_1, \cdots, \bar{\mathfrak{a}}_{j-1}, \bar{\mathfrak{a}}_{j+1}, \cdots, \bar{\mathfrak{a}}_n), \\ D_j^* &= D(\bar{\mathfrak{a}}_1, \cdots, \bar{\mathfrak{a}}_i + \bar{\mathfrak{a}}_j, \cdots, \bar{\mathfrak{a}}_{j-1}, \bar{\mathfrak{a}}_{j+1}, \cdots, \bar{\mathfrak{a}}_n) \end{aligned}$$

Now, by Theorem 6, it follows that

$$\begin{aligned} D_j^* &= D(\bar{\mathfrak{a}}_1, \cdots, \bar{\mathfrak{a}}_i, \cdots, \bar{\mathfrak{a}}_{j-1}, \bar{\mathfrak{a}}_{j+1}, \cdots, \bar{\mathfrak{a}}_n) \\ &\quad + D(\bar{\mathfrak{a}}_1, \cdots, \bar{\mathfrak{a}}_j, \cdots, \bar{\mathfrak{a}}_{j-1}, \bar{\mathfrak{a}}_{j+1}, \cdots, \bar{\mathfrak{a}}_n). \end{aligned}$$

The first summand on the right has as arguments all the vectors $\bar{\mathfrak{a}}_k$ except for $\bar{\mathfrak{a}}_j$, and in their natural order. It is therefore equal to D_j. The second summand has as arguments all vectors $\bar{\mathfrak{a}}_k$ other than $\bar{\mathfrak{a}}_i$, but these vectors are not in their natural order, for the vector $\bar{\mathfrak{a}}_j$ occupies the position that $\bar{\mathfrak{a}}_i$ does in D_j. In order to have the arguments of the second summand also in their natural order, we must successively interchange $\bar{\mathfrak{a}}_j$ with $\bar{\mathfrak{a}}_{i+1}, \bar{\mathfrak{a}}_{i+2}, \cdots, \bar{\mathfrak{a}}_{j-1}$ if $i < j$. If $i > j$, we must successively interchange it with $\bar{\mathfrak{a}}_{i-1}, \bar{\mathfrak{a}}_{i-2}, \cdots, \bar{\mathfrak{a}}_{j+1}$. That is, there are to be made $j - i - 1$ interchanges in the first case, and $i - j - 1$ interchanges in the second case. The second summand thus has its sign changed $j - i - 1$ or $i - j - 1$ times, and then becomes D_i. However, $i - j - 1 = j - i - 1 + 2(i - j)$, which gives

$$(-1)^{i-j-1} = (-1)^{j-i-1} \cdot (-1)^{2(i-j)} = (-1)^{j-i-1}$$

since $2(i - j)$ is an even number so that $(-1)^{2(i-j)} = 1$. In any case, we thus have

$$D_j^* = D_j + (-1)^{j-i-1} \cdot D_i.$$

We may now see what happens to the expression $\sum_{k=1}^{n} (-1)^{n-k} \cdot a_{kn} \cdot D_k$

[10] Of course, it is also possible that $i > j$. In this case $\bar{\mathfrak{a}}_i + \bar{\mathfrak{a}}_j$ would come to be between $\bar{\mathfrak{a}}_{j+1}$ and $\bar{\mathfrak{a}}_n$.

upon replacement of $\mathfrak{a}_i$ by $\mathfrak{a}_i + \mathfrak{a}_j$. Among the factors a_{kn}, only a_{in} need be changed; a_{in} is to be replaced by $a_{in} + a_{jn}$. Thus all summands $(-1)^{n-k} \cdot a_{kn} \cdot D_k$ for which $k \neq i, j$ remain unchanged. The summand $(-1)^{n-i} \cdot a_{in} \cdot D_i$ goes over into

$$(-1)^{n-i} \cdot a_{in} \cdot D_i + (-1)^{n-i} \cdot a_{jn} \cdot D_i,$$

while $(-1)^{n-j} \cdot a_{jn} \cdot D_j$ goes over into

$$(-1)^{n-j} \cdot a_{jn} \cdot D_j + (-1)^{n-j} \cdot a_{jn} \cdot (-1)^{j-i-1} \cdot D_i.$$

Thus the entire sum becomes

$$[(-1)^{n-i} + (-1)^{n-i-1}] \cdot a_{jn} \cdot D_i + \sum_{k=1}^{n} [(-1)^{n-k} \cdot a_{kn} \cdot D_k].$$

Now the number $n-i$ and $n-i-1$ differ by precisely 1, so that one of them must be even and the other odd. Thus of the two values $(-1)^{n-i}$ and $(-1)^{n-i-1}$, one must be -1 and the other $+1$, so that their sum is 0. Hence the first part of the last expression vanishes. Thus we have proved that $\sum_{k=1}^{n} (-1)^{n-k} \cdot a_{kn} \cdot D_k$ has the property that it remains unchanged upon replacement of $\mathfrak{a}_i$ by $\mathfrak{a}_i + \mathfrak{a}_j$, i.e. we have proved property *i*).

We next verify *ii*). Let a vector $\mathfrak{a}_i$ be replaced by $\lambda\mathfrak{a}_i$, i.e. the numbers a_{ik} are to be replaced by λa_{ik} for $k = 1, 2, \ldots, n$ (for fixed i). The determinant D_i which is independent of the a_{ik} is therefore again un-unchanged. In each determinant D_k with $k \neq i$, however, the row $a_{i1}, a_{i2}, \ldots, a_{i,n-1}$ is replaced by $\lambda a_{i1}, \lambda a_{i2}, \ldots, \lambda a_{i,n-1}$. Since the $(n-1)$-by-$(n-1)$ determinants D_k satisfy condition *ii*) by induction hypothesis, D_k goes over into $\lambda \cdot D_k$ for $k \neq i$. The summands $(-1)^{n-k} \cdot a_{kn} \cdot D_k$ for $k \neq i$ are thus multiplied by λ. But $(-1)^{n-i} \cdot a_{in} \cdot D_i$ is also multiplied by λ since a_{in} is replaced by λa_{in}. Hence, the entire sum $\sum_{k=1}^{n} (-1)^{n-k} \cdot a_{kn} \cdot D_k$ goes over into its product by λ, which proves property *ii*).

It remains only to verify *iii*). Each vector $\mathfrak{a}_i$ is to be taken equal to the corresponding $\mathfrak{e}_i$ $(i = 1, 2, \ldots, n)$. That is, we set $a_{ik} = 0$ for $i \neq k$, $a_{ii} = 1$ for $i = 1, 2, \ldots, n$. Thus only the final summand $(-1)^{n-n} \cdot a_{nn} \cdot D_n = D_n$ remains. But D_n now has the form

$$\underbrace{\begin{vmatrix} 1 & 0 & \cdots & 0 \\ 0 & 1 & \cdots & 0 \\ \cdot & \cdot & \cdot & \cdot \\ 0 & 0 & \cdots & 1 \end{vmatrix}}_{(n-1)\text{-by-}(n-1)}.$$

By property *iii*) for $(n-1)$-by-$(n-1)$ determinants, we thus have $D_n = 1$. Therefore the value of our sum is precisely 1, which was to be proved. Our result is now completely proved.

It should also be noted that the formula

$$D(\mathfrak{a}_1, \mathfrak{a}_2, \cdots, \mathfrak{a}_n) = \sum_{k=1}^{n} (-1)^{n-k} \cdot a_{kn} \cdot D_k$$

actually enables us to calculate the value of a determinant. For it reduces the calculation of an n-by-n determinant to that of $(n-1)$-by-$(n-1)$ determinants. In the same way, the calculation of $(n-1)$-by-$(n-1)$ determinants is reduced to that of $(n-2)$-by-$(n-2)$ determinants, etc. This reduction may be continued until we reach one-rowed determinants, whose values we know.

Before we can return to our consideration of the question of determining volumes, we must prove one further property of determinants. Namely, we shall prove the following converse of Theorem 4:

THEOREM 8. *If the vectors* $\mathfrak{a}_1, \mathfrak{a}_2, \cdots, \mathfrak{a}_n$ *are linearly independent, then the determinant* $D(\mathfrak{a}_1, \mathfrak{a}_2, \cdots, \mathfrak{a}_n)$ *is not equal to* 0.

By § 4, any n linearly independent vectors of R_n form a basis of R_n. Thus, the unit vectors $\mathfrak{e}_1, \mathfrak{e}_2, \cdots, \mathfrak{e}_n$ must be representable as linear combinations of the n vectors $\mathfrak{a}_1, \mathfrak{a}_2, \cdots, \mathfrak{a}_n$. Hence, we may write, say,

$$\mathfrak{e}_k = b_{k1}\mathfrak{a}_1 + b_{k2}\mathfrak{a}_2 + \cdots + b_{kn}\mathfrak{a}_n, \qquad k = 1, 2, \cdots, n.$$

We set $\mathfrak{b}_k^i = b_{ki}\mathfrak{a}_i$. Then

$$\mathfrak{e}_k = \sum_{i=1}^{n} \mathfrak{b}_k^i.$$

Applying Theorem 7 to the determinant $D(\mathfrak{e}_1, \mathfrak{e}_2, \cdots, \mathfrak{e}_n)$ we have

$$D(\mathfrak{e}_1, \mathfrak{e}_2, \cdots, \mathfrak{e}_n) = \sum_{\nu_1, \nu_2, \cdots, \nu_n = 1}^{n} D(b_{1\nu_1}\mathfrak{a}_{\nu_1}, b_{2\nu_2}\mathfrak{a}_{\nu_2}, \cdots, b_{n\nu_n}\mathfrak{a}_{\nu_n}).$$

If we take the factors $b_{1\nu_1}, b_{2\nu_2}, \cdots, b_{n\nu_n}$ in front of the determinant in each summand on the right, which we may do by *ii*), we obtain

$$D(\mathfrak{e}_1, \mathfrak{e}_2, \cdots, \mathfrak{e}_n) = \sum_{\nu_1, \nu_2, \cdots, \nu_n = 1}^{n} b_{1\nu_1} \cdot b_{2\nu_2} \cdots b_{n\nu_n} \cdot D(\mathfrak{a}_{\nu_1}, \mathfrak{a}_{\nu_2}, \cdots, \mathfrak{a}_{\nu_n}).$$

If two of the indices ν_i are equal in one of the summands

$$b_{1\nu_1} \cdot b_{2\nu_2} \cdots b_{n\nu_n} \cdot D(\mathfrak{a}_{\nu_1}, \mathfrak{a}_{\nu_2}, \cdots, \mathfrak{a}_{\nu_n})$$

then

$$D(\mathfrak{a}_{\nu_1}, \mathfrak{a}_{\nu_2}, \cdots, \mathfrak{a}_{\nu_n}) = 0.$$

Thus, only those terms for which all of the indices are distinct, remain. However, a determinant of the form $D(\mathfrak{a}_{\nu_1}, \mathfrak{a}_{\nu_2}, \cdots, \mathfrak{a}_{\nu_n})$ with all of the indices distinct, can be obtained from $D(\mathfrak{a}_1, \mathfrak{a}_2, \cdots, \mathfrak{a}_n)$ by successive interchanges of pairs of vectors $\mathfrak{a}_i$. For, we may first bring $\mathfrak{a}_1$ into the position which it has in $D(\mathfrak{a}_{\nu_1}, \mathfrak{a}_{\nu_2}, \cdots, \mathfrak{a}_{\nu_n})$, next do the same for $\mathfrak{a}_2$, etc. By Theorem 5, $D(\mathfrak{a}_{\nu}, \mathfrak{a}_{\nu_2}, \cdots, \mathfrak{a}_{\nu_n})$ must thus be equal to $\pm D(\mathfrak{a}_1, \mathfrak{a}_2, \cdots, \mathfrak{a}_n)$. If now we had $D(\mathfrak{a}_1, \mathfrak{a}_2, \cdots, \mathfrak{a}_n) = 0$, then each term of the sum

$$\sum_{\nu_1, \nu_2, \cdots, \nu_n = 1}^{n} b_{1\nu_1} b_{2\nu_2} \cdots b_{n\nu_n} \cdot D(\mathfrak{a}_{\nu_1}, \mathfrak{a}_{\nu_2}, \cdots, \mathfrak{a}_{\nu_n})$$

would vanish. Then we should have $D(\mathfrak{e}_1, \mathfrak{e}_2, \cdots, \mathfrak{e}_n) = 0$, which contradicts property *iii*). It thus follows that

$$D(\mathfrak{a}_1, \mathfrak{a}_2, \cdots, \mathfrak{a}_n) \neq 0,$$

which was to be proved.

Volumes

We are now in a position to settle the question of determining a function $V(\mathfrak{a}_1, \mathfrak{a}_2, \cdots, \mathfrak{a}_n)$ which satisfies properties 1., 2., 3., and 4., on p. 68. We indeed can produce such a function. *In fact, the function* $|D(\mathfrak{a}_1, \mathfrak{a}_2, \cdots, \mathfrak{a}_n)|$ *i.e. the absolute value of the determinant, has these properties.* First, we note that any absolute value is a non-negative number so that condition 1. is satisfied. Property 2. is clearly satisfied, since anything which does not alter the determinant will not alter its absolute value. So far as property 3. is concerned, replacement of $\mathfrak{a}_i$ by $\lambda \mathfrak{a}_i$ results in multiplying the determinant by λ. Thus, for its absolute value $|\lambda \cdot D(\mathfrak{a}_1, \mathfrak{a}_2, \cdots, \mathfrak{a}_n)|$ we have

$$|\lambda \cdot D(\mathfrak{a}_1, \mathfrak{a}_2, \cdots, \mathfrak{a}_n)| = |\lambda| \cdot |D(\mathfrak{a}_1, \mathfrak{a}_2, \cdots, \mathfrak{a}_n)|,$$

i.e. the absolute value is multiplied by $|\lambda|$ as a result of this replacement; this is property 3. Finally, property 4. is satisfied since the absolute value of 1 is itself 1.

Moreover, we will show that *the absolute value of the determinant is the only function which satisfies properties* 1. — 4. *For, let*

$$V(\mathfrak{a}_1, \mathfrak{a}_2, \cdots, \mathfrak{a}_n)$$

be any such function. Let "sgn D" be used to indicate the sign of D, i.e. let

$$\operatorname{sgn} D = 1 \text{ if } D > 0,$$
$$\operatorname{sgn} D = -1 \text{ if } D < 0,$$
$$\operatorname{sgn} D = 0 \text{ if } D = 0.$$

Then it follows that the function

$$V(\mathfrak{a}_1, \mathfrak{a}_2, \cdots, \mathfrak{a}_n) \cdot \operatorname{sgn} D(\mathfrak{a}_1, \mathfrak{a}_2, \cdots, \mathfrak{a}_n)$$

satisfies properties *i*), *ii*), *iii*). For, since $V(\mathfrak{a}_1, \mathfrak{a}_2, \cdots, \mathfrak{a}_n)$ satisfies property 2., and since $D(\mathfrak{a}_1, \mathfrak{a}_2, \cdots, \mathfrak{a}_n)$ satisfies property *i*), neither $V(\mathfrak{a}_1, \mathfrak{a}_2, \cdots, \mathfrak{a}_n)$ nor $\operatorname{sgn} D(\mathfrak{a}_1, \mathfrak{a}_2, \cdots, \mathfrak{a}_n)$ is changed by replacing a vector $\mathfrak{a}_i$ by $\mathfrak{a}_i + \mathfrak{a}_k$ $(i \neq k)$. Hence their product also remains unchanged under this replacement. If we further note that for any two real numbers a, b, we have

$$(\operatorname{sgn} a) \cdot (\operatorname{sgn} b) = \operatorname{sgn}(ab),$$

we see at once that upon replacement of a vector $\mathfrak{a}_i$ by $\lambda\mathfrak{a}_i$, the product

$$V(\mathfrak{a}_1, \mathfrak{a}_2, \cdots, \mathfrak{a}_n) \cdot \operatorname{sgn} D(\mathfrak{a}_1, \mathfrak{a}_2, \cdots, \mathfrak{a}_n)$$

is multiplied by $|\lambda| \cdot \operatorname{sgn} \lambda$. Now it is obvious that

$$|\lambda| \cdot \operatorname{sgn} \lambda = \lambda,$$

so that the function $V(\mathfrak{a}_1, \mathfrak{a}_2, \cdots, \mathfrak{a}_n) \cdot \operatorname{sgn} D(\mathfrak{a}_1, \mathfrak{a}_2, \cdots, \mathfrak{a}_n)$ also satisfies property *ii*). Finally, *iii*) is clear, since

$$D(\mathfrak{e}_1, \mathfrak{e}_2, \cdots, \mathfrak{e}_n) = V(\mathfrak{e}_1, \mathfrak{e}_2, \cdots, \mathfrak{e}_n) = 1.$$

Since there exists only one function of n vectors of R_n which has properties *i*), *ii*), and *iii*), namely the determinant $D(\mathfrak{a}_1, \mathfrak{a}_2, \cdots, \mathfrak{a}_n)$, we must have

$$V(\mathfrak{a}_1, \mathfrak{a}_2, \cdots, \mathfrak{a}_n) \cdot \operatorname{sgn} D(\mathfrak{a}_1, \mathfrak{a}_2, \cdots, \mathfrak{a}_n) = D(\mathfrak{a}_1, \mathfrak{a}_2, \cdots, \mathfrak{a}_n).$$

We further observe that for $D \neq 0$, we always have $(\operatorname{sgn} D)^2 = 1$. Thus, assuming that $D(\mathfrak{a}_1 . \mathfrak{a}_2, \cdots, \mathfrak{a}_n) \neq 0$, and multiplying the last equation by sgn $D(\mathfrak{a}_1, \mathfrak{a}_2, \cdots, \mathfrak{a}_n)$ we have

$$V(\mathfrak{a}_1, \mathfrak{a}_2, \cdots, \mathfrak{a}_n) = D(\mathfrak{a}_1, \mathfrak{a}_2, \cdots, \mathfrak{a}_n) \cdot \operatorname{sgn} D(\mathfrak{a}_1, \mathfrak{a}_2, \cdots, \mathfrak{a}_n).$$

That is,

$$V(\mathfrak{a}_1, \mathfrak{a}_2, \cdots, \mathfrak{a}_n) = |D(\mathfrak{a}_1, \mathfrak{a}_2, \cdots, \mathfrak{a}_n)|.$$

If, however, $D(\mathfrak{a}_1, \mathfrak{a}_2, \cdots, \mathfrak{a}_n) = 0$, then by Theorem 8, the vectors $\mathfrak{a}_1, \mathfrak{a}_2, \cdots, \mathfrak{a}_n$ are linearly dependent. By the remark made in connection with Theorem 4, in this case we have also that

$$V(\mathfrak{a}_1, \mathfrak{a}_2, \cdots, \mathfrak{a}_n) = 0,$$

so that the equation

$$V(\mathfrak{a}_1, \mathfrak{a}_2, \cdots, \mathfrak{a}_n) = |D(\mathfrak{a}_1, \mathfrak{a}_2, \cdots, \mathfrak{a}_n)|$$

is valid without restriction. We have thus proved that

$$|D(\mathfrak{a}_1, \mathfrak{a}_2, \cdots, \mathfrak{a}_n)|$$

is the only function with properties 1. — 4.

We have now arrived at the end of our investigation. It remains only to make the following definition:

An n-dimensional parallelotope in euclidean R_n with edge vectors $\mathfrak{a}_1, \mathfrak{a}_2, \cdots, \mathfrak{a}_n$ has the **volume** $|D(\mathfrak{a}_1, \mathfrak{a}_2, \cdots, \mathfrak{a}_n)|$.

We have thus given a definition of n-dimensional volume which has the essential properties of ordinary area and volume. We have moreover seen that it is the only such definition possible.

Let us take a final glance at the special cases of R_1, R_2, and R_3. In R_1, a one-dimensional parallelotope is nothing but a segment, and its volume is the length of the segment. For, if $\mathfrak{a} = \{a\}$, we have $D(\mathfrak{a}) = a$, so that $V(\mathfrak{a}) = |a|$. In the case of the plane or of ordinary space, we once again introduce a Cartesian coordinate system. We again consider ordinary areas and volumes of parallelograms and parallelepipeds, respectively, as functions of their edge vectors. We recall that for linearly dependent vectors $\mathfrak{a}_1, \mathfrak{a}_2$ in the plane (or $\mathfrak{a}_1, \mathfrak{a}_2, \mathfrak{a}_3$ in space), $V(\mathfrak{a}_1, \mathfrak{a}_2)$ (or $V(\mathfrak{a}_1, \mathfrak{a}_2, \mathfrak{a}_3)$) vanishes. Then, as we have seen above, ordinary area and volume satisfy conditions 1., 2., 3., and 4.[11]

[11] It is also clear that the use of a Cartesian coordinate system is not so essential here. Properties 1, 2, and 3 are satisfied in an arbitrary linear coordinate system, and property 4 then states that the unit of volume is not a square (or a cube) of side 1, but rather a parallelogram with edge vectors $\mathfrak{e}_1, \mathfrak{e}_2$ in the case of the plane, and a parallelepiped with edge vectors $\mathfrak{e}_1, \mathfrak{e}_2, \mathfrak{e}_3$ in the case of space.

(This is also easily seen for the cases $V(\mathfrak{a}_1, \mathfrak{a}_2) = 0$ or

$$V(\mathfrak{a}_1, \mathfrak{a}_2, \mathfrak{a}_3) = 0).$$

Now for each n, there is only one function $V(\mathfrak{a}_1, \mathfrak{a}_2, \cdots, \mathfrak{a}_n)$ with properties 1.-4., namely $|D(\mathfrak{a}_1, \mathfrak{a}_2, \cdots, \mathfrak{a}_n)|$. Hence, the area of a parallelogram in the plane with edge vectors $\mathfrak{a}_1$, $\mathfrak{a}_2$ is precisely equal to $|D(\mathfrak{a}_1, \mathfrak{a}_2)|$. Also, the volume of a parallelepiped with edge vectors $\mathfrak{a}_1, \mathfrak{a}_2, \mathfrak{a}_3$ is precisely equal to $|D(\mathfrak{a}_1, \mathfrak{a}_2, \mathfrak{a}_3)|$. Thus our definition of volume agrees with the intuitive notions of area and volume for ordinary two- and three-dimensional space in which a Cartesian coordinate system has been introduced.

Exercises

1. Using the recursion formula on page 82, show that the equalities

$$\begin{vmatrix} a_{11} & a_{12} \\ a_{21} & a_{22} \end{vmatrix} = a_{11}\, a_{22} - a_{12}\, a_{21},$$

$$\begin{vmatrix} a_{11} & a_{12} & a_{13} \\ a_{21} & a_{22} & a_{23} \\ a_{31} & a_{32} & a_{33} \end{vmatrix} = a_{11}\, a_{22}\, a_{33} + a_{12}\, a_{23}\, a_{31} + a_{13}\, a_{21}\, a_{32} - a_{31}\, a_{22}\, a_{13} - a_{32}\, a_{23}\, a_{11} - a_{33}\, a_{21}\, a_{12}$$

hold.

2. What are the values of the determinants:

$$\begin{vmatrix} 1 & 2 & 6 & -2 \\ 7 & 4 & -1 & 19 \\ 3 & 5 & -3 & 14 \\ 1 & 1 & 2 & 1 \end{vmatrix} \quad \text{and} \quad \begin{vmatrix} 1 & 6 & 8 & 2 & 0 \\ 3 & 0 & 1 & 0 & 0 \\ 4 & -2 & -3 & 3 & 0 \\ 8 & 4 & 6 & 5 & 0 \\ 1 & 1 & -1 & -1 & 1 \end{vmatrix}?$$

3. Show by repeated application of Theorem 1 and by using Theorem 3 that the following determinants vanish:

$$\begin{vmatrix} 1 & 6 & -5 & 3 & 5 \\ 7 & 3 & -8 & 2 & 4 \\ -1 & 2 & 3 & -1 & 3 \\ 0 & 5 & 2 & 1 & 8 \\ 2 & -3 & 6 & -5 & 0 \end{vmatrix}, \quad \begin{vmatrix} a+d & 3a & b+2a & b+d \\ 2b & d+b & c-b & c-d \\ a+c & c-2d & d & a+3d \\ b-d & c-d & a+c & a+b \end{vmatrix}$$

4. Let a Cartesian coordinate system be introduced in the plane. Evaluate the area of the triangle ABC, whose vertices have the coordinates

a) $A = (-1,\ 1)$, $B = (2,\ 14)$, $C = (4,\ 6)$, b) $A = (-3,\ -4)$, $B = (5,\ -1)$, $C = (1,\ 3)$.

What is the area of the general triangle with vertices $P_i = (x_1^{(i)}, x_2^{(i)})$, $i = 1, 2, 3$?

5. Let a Cartesian coordinate system be introduced into ordinary space. Evaluate the volume of the tetrahedron A, B, C, D whose vertices have the coordinates

a) $A = (0, 0, 0)$, $B = (7, 1, -3)$, $C = (5, 0, 1)$, $D = (2, 1, 1)$,

b) $A = (1, -2, 1)$, $B = (2, -2, 5)$, $C = (4, 0, 1)$, $D = (2, -1, 0)$.

What is the volume of the general tetrahedron with vertices

$$P_i = (x_1^{(i)}, x_2^{(i)}, x_3^{(i)}), \quad i = 1, 2, 3, 4?$$

§ 9. The Principal Theorems of Determinant Theory

We shall now derive some additional important theorems on determinants, with a view to the many applications of determinant theory. In so doing we shall also see what role is played by determinants in the solution of systems of linear equations.

The Complete Development of a Determinant

We begin by deriving an explicit expression for the determinant

$$D(\mathfrak{a}_1, \mathfrak{a}_2, \cdots, \mathfrak{a}_n) = \begin{vmatrix} a_{11} & a_{12} & \cdots & a_{1n} \\ a_{21} & a_{22} & \cdots & a_{2n} \\ \cdot & \cdot & \cdot & \cdot \\ a_{n1} & a_{n2} & \cdots & a_{nn} \end{vmatrix}.$$

If $\mathfrak{e}_1, \mathfrak{e}_2, \cdots, \mathfrak{e}_n$ are the unit vectors of R_n, then we have for the vector $\mathfrak{a}_i = \{a_{i1}, a_{i2}, \cdots, a_{in}\}$ the following identity, which has already been employed in § 4:

$$\mathfrak{a}_i = \sum_{k=1}^{n} a_{ik}\, \mathfrak{e}_k.$$

Setting $\mathfrak{b}_i^k = a_{ik}\, \mathfrak{e}_k$, we thus have

$$\mathfrak{a}_i = \sum_{k=1}^{n} \mathfrak{b}_i^k, \qquad i = 1, 2, \cdots, n.$$

By Theorem 7 of § 8, this yields

$$(1) \qquad D(\mathfrak{a}_1, \mathfrak{a}_2, \cdots, \mathfrak{a}_n) = \sum_{\nu_1, \nu_2, \cdots, \nu_n = 1}^{n} D(\mathfrak{b}_1^{\nu_1}, \mathfrak{b}_2^{\nu_2}, \cdots, \mathfrak{b}_n^{\nu_n}).$$

Since $\mathfrak{b}_i^{\nu_k} = a_{i\nu_k}\, \mathfrak{e}_{\nu_k}$, we have by property *ii)* of determinants that

$$(2) \quad D(\mathfrak{b}_1^{\nu_1}, \mathfrak{b}_2^{\nu_2}, \cdots, \mathfrak{b}_n^{\nu_n}) = a_{1\nu_1} \cdot a_{2\nu_2} \cdots a_{n\nu_n}\, D(\mathfrak{e}_{\nu_1}, \mathfrak{e}_{\nu_2}, \cdots, \mathfrak{e}_{\nu_n}).$$

If two of the vectors $\mathfrak{e}_{\nu_1}, \mathfrak{e}_{\nu_2}, \cdots, \mathfrak{e}_{\nu_n}$ are equal to each other, then by Theorem 4 of § 8, $D(\mathfrak{e}_{\nu_1}, \mathfrak{e}_{\nu_2}, \cdots, \mathfrak{e}_{\nu_n}) = 0$. Thus, in the sum of (1), we need sum only over all those ordered n-tuples $(\nu_1, \nu_2, \cdots, \nu_n)$

of indices for which no two of the indices $\nu_1, \nu_2, \cdots, \nu_n$ are equal. Such an ordered n-tuple of indices is called a *permutation* of the indices $1, 2, \ldots, n$, since it is obtained from the n-tuple $(1, 2, \ldots, n)$ by some rearrangement.

Let us consider one of the determinants $D(\mathfrak{e}_{\nu_1}, \mathfrak{e}_{\nu_2}, \cdots, \mathfrak{e}_{\nu_n})$ for which the n-tuple $(\nu_1, \nu_2, \cdots, \nu_n)$ is a permutation of $(1, 2, \ldots, n)$. Then $\mathfrak{e}_1$ certainly appears among the vectors $\mathfrak{e}_{\nu_1}, \mathfrak{e}_{\nu_2}, \cdots, \mathfrak{e}_{\nu_n}$. Let f_1 be the number of vectors which precede $\mathfrak{e}_1$ in the sequence $\mathfrak{e}_{\nu_1}, \mathfrak{e}_{\nu_2}, \cdots, \mathfrak{e}_{\nu_n}$. If we then successively interchange $\mathfrak{e}_1$ with the f_1 vectors preceding it, the sign of $D(\mathfrak{e}_{\nu_1}, \mathfrak{e}_{\nu_2}, \cdots, \mathfrak{e}_{\nu_n})$ is changed f_1 times. $\mathfrak{e}_1$ is now in the first place. Next, we bring $\mathfrak{e}_2$ into the second place by successively interchanging it with all vectors, with the exception of $\mathfrak{e}_1$, which precede it. If f_2 interchanges were necessary to accomplish this, then the determinant has changed sign another f_2 times. f_2 is precisely equal to the number of indices which are > 2 and which appear to the left of the index 2 in the permutation $(\nu_1, \nu_2, \cdots, \nu_n)$. In the same way, we successively bring the vectors $\mathfrak{e}_3, \mathfrak{e}_4, \ldots, \mathfrak{e}_n$ into the 3-rd, 4-th, $\ldots$, n-th places, employing $f_3, f_4, \ldots, f_n$ interchanges, respectively.[1] Then f_i $(i = 3, 4, \ldots, n)$ is precisely the number of indices which are $> i$ and appear before the index i in the permutation $(\nu_1, \nu_2, \cdots, \nu_n)$. Thus the sign of the determinant has been changed in all $f_1 + f_2 + \ldots + f_n$ times. In the final result, the unit vectors appear in their natural order. Thus if we let $f = f_1 + f_2 + \ldots + f_n$, we have

$$(3) \qquad D(\mathfrak{e}_{\nu_1}, \mathfrak{e}_{\nu_2}, \cdots, \mathfrak{e}_{\nu_n}) = (-1)^f \cdot D(\mathfrak{e}_1, \mathfrak{e}_2, \cdots, \mathfrak{e}_n) = (-1)^f.$$

For, $D(\mathfrak{e}_1, \mathfrak{e}_2, \cdots, \mathfrak{e}_n)$ equals 1.

The number $f = f_1 + f_2 + \ldots + f_n$ is called the *number of inversions* of the permutation $(\nu_1, \nu_2, \cdots, \nu_n)$, since every occurrence in $(\nu_1, \nu_2, \cdots, \nu_n)$ of a larger index preceding[2] a smaller one is referred to as an *inversion*. We further set

$$(4) \qquad \operatorname{sgn}(\nu_1, \nu_2, \cdots, \nu_n) = (-1)^f,$$

where f is the number of inversions of $(\nu_1, \nu_2, \cdots, \nu_n)$. Hence sgn $(\nu_1, \nu_2, \cdots, \nu_n)$ is $+1$ or -1, according to whether the number of inversions of $(\nu_1, \nu_2, \cdots, \nu_n)$ is even or odd. Comparing (2), (3), and (4), we have by (1) that

---

[1] In particular f_n is necessarily equal to 0. However, for the sake of symmetry, f_n has been retained.

[2] "preceding" does *not* mean "immediately preceding" here. There may be other indices in between.

$$(5)\quad \begin{vmatrix} a_{11} & a_{12} & \cdots & a_{1n} \\ a_{21} & a_{22} & \cdots & a_{2n} \\ \cdot & \cdot & \cdot & \cdot \\ a_{n1} & a_{n2} & \cdots & a_{nn} \end{vmatrix} = \sum_{(\nu_1, \nu_2, \cdots, \nu_n)} \operatorname{sgn}(\nu_1, \nu_2, \cdots, \nu_n) \cdot a_{1\nu_1} \cdot a_{2\nu_2} \cdots a_{n\nu_n}.$$

The summation on the right is to be carried out over all permutations $(\nu_1, \nu_2, \cdots, \nu_n)$ of the indices $(1, 2, \ldots, n)$.

The Determinant As a Function of Its Column Vectors

In what follows, we shall employ functions which are somewhat more general than determinants. We shall require the following result:

THEOREM 1. *Let a function* $F(\mathfrak{a}_1, \mathfrak{a}_2, \cdots, \mathfrak{a}_n)$ *of* n *vectors* $\mathfrak{a}_1, \mathfrak{a}_2, \cdots, \mathfrak{a}_n$ *of* R_n *be given, and let it satisfy conditions i) and ii). Then*

$$F(\mathfrak{a}_1, \mathfrak{a}_2, \cdots, \mathfrak{a}_n) = F(\mathfrak{e}_1, \mathfrak{e}_2, \cdots, \mathfrak{e}_n) \cdot D(\mathfrak{a}_1, \mathfrak{a}_2, \cdots, \mathfrak{a}_n).$$

This means that such a function is completely determined by the value of $F(\mathfrak{e}_1, \mathfrak{e}_2, \cdots, \mathfrak{e}_n)$.

In fact, if $F(\mathfrak{e}_1, \mathfrak{e}_2, \cdots, \mathfrak{e}_n) = 1$, then this function also satisfies *iii*), and so, by the uniqueness of the determinant, is identical with the determinant $D(\mathfrak{a}_1, \mathfrak{a}_2, \cdots, \mathfrak{a}_n)$. Thus our assertion is correct in this case.

If however, $F(\mathfrak{e}_1, \mathfrak{e}_2, \cdots, \mathfrak{e}_n) \neq 1$, then the expression

$$\frac{F(\mathfrak{a}_1, \mathfrak{a}_2, \cdots, \mathfrak{a}_n) - D(\mathfrak{a}_1, \mathfrak{a}_2, \cdots, \mathfrak{a}_n)}{F(\mathfrak{e}_1, \mathfrak{e}_2, \cdots, \mathfrak{e}_n) - 1}$$

is a well-defined function since its denominator is a fixed non-zero number. This function of the vectors $\mathfrak{a}_1, \mathfrak{a}_2, \cdots, \mathfrak{a}_n$ satisfies *i*), *ii*), and *iii*). For, *i*) and *ii*) are satisfied, since they hold for each term of the numerator. But, for $\mathfrak{a}_i = \mathfrak{e}_i$, $(i = 1, 2, \ldots, n)$, the numerator and denominator are equal, so that *iii*) is also satisfied. This function must then, since it satisfies *i*), *ii*), and *iii*), be identical with the determinant $D(\mathfrak{a}_1, \mathfrak{a}_2, \cdots, \mathfrak{a}_n)$. But from

$$\frac{F(\mathfrak{a}_1, \mathfrak{a}_2, \cdots, \mathfrak{a}_n) - D(\mathfrak{a}_1, \mathfrak{a}_2, \cdots, \mathfrak{a}_n)}{F(\mathfrak{e}_1, \mathfrak{e}_2, \cdots, \mathfrak{e}_n) - 1} = D(\mathfrak{a}_1, \mathfrak{a}_2, \cdots, \mathfrak{a}_n)$$

we have by an easy calculation that

$$F(\mathfrak{a}_1, \mathfrak{a}_2, \cdots, \mathfrak{a}_n) = F(\mathfrak{e}_1, \mathfrak{e}_2, \cdots, \mathfrak{e}_n) \cdot D(\mathfrak{a}_1, \mathfrak{a}_2, \cdots, \mathfrak{a}_n),$$

which was to be proved.

Let us consider the determinant $D(\mathfrak{a}_1, \mathfrak{a}_2, \cdots, \mathfrak{a}_n)$, written in the form

$$D(\mathfrak{a}_1, \mathfrak{a}_2, \cdots, \mathfrak{a}_n) = \begin{vmatrix} a_{11} & a_{12} & \cdots & a_{1n} \\ a_{21} & a_{22} & \cdots & a_{2n} \\ \cdot & \cdot & \cdot & \cdot \\ a_{n1} & a_{n2} & \cdots & a_{nn} \end{vmatrix}.$$

The components of the vector $\mathfrak{a}_i = \{a_{i1}, a_{i2}, \cdots, a_{in}\}$ appear in the i-th row of this square array. It is clear that the determinant, which has heretofore been considered as a function of its row vectors, may also be considered as a function of its column vectors. Let us denote the column vectors by $\bar{\mathfrak{a}}_1, \bar{\mathfrak{a}}_2, \cdots, \bar{\mathfrak{a}}_n$, so that $\bar{\mathfrak{a}}_i = \{a_{1i}, a_{2i}, \cdots, a_{ni}\}$. However, we have no information concerning whether the determinant, when considered as a function of its column vectors $\bar{\mathfrak{a}}_1, \bar{\mathfrak{a}}_2, \cdots, \bar{\mathfrak{a}}_n$, also satisfies *i*), *ii*), and *iii*). In order to decide this, we investigate the more general question of how the value of the determinant is changed if we replace the column vectors by linear combinations of them. Thus, let there be given a second determinant

$$\begin{vmatrix} c_{11} & c_{12} & \cdots & c_{1n} \\ c_{21} & c_{22} & \cdots & c_{2n} \\ \cdot & \cdot & \cdot & \cdot \\ c_{n1} & c_{n2} & \cdots & c_{nn} \end{vmatrix}$$

whose row vectors will be denoted by $\mathfrak{c}_1, \mathfrak{c}_2, \cdots, \mathfrak{c}_n$, and column vectors by $\bar{\mathfrak{c}}_1, \bar{\mathfrak{c}}_2, \cdots, \bar{\mathfrak{c}}_n$. Thus,

$$\mathfrak{c}_i = \{c_{i1}, c_{i2}, \cdots, c_{in}\}, \quad \bar{\mathfrak{c}}_i = \{c_{1i}, c_{2i}, \cdots, c_{ni}\}.$$

The column vectors $\bar{\mathfrak{c}}_i$ are to be linear combinations of the column vectors $\bar{\mathfrak{a}}_i$ of the first determinant. Thus let

$$(6) \qquad \bar{\mathfrak{c}}_k = b_{1k}\bar{\mathfrak{a}}_1 + b_{2k}\bar{\mathfrak{a}}_2 + \cdots + b_{nk}\bar{\mathfrak{a}}_n, \qquad k = 1, 2, \cdots, n.$$

The b_{ik} are certain real numbers which we consider constant in the following. The i-th components of the vectors $\bar{\mathfrak{c}}_k, \bar{\mathfrak{a}}_1, \bar{\mathfrak{a}}_2, \cdots, \bar{\mathfrak{a}}_n$ are $c_{ik}, a_{i1}, a_{i2}, \cdots, a_{in}$ respectively. Thus the above n vector equations are equivalent to the following n^2 equations in the vector components:

$$(7) \qquad c_{ik} = a_{i1}b_{1k} + a_{i2}b_{2k} + \cdots + a_{in}b_{nk}, \qquad i, k = 1, 2, \cdots, n.$$

The elements c_{ik} are represented as functions of the a_{ik} by these equations, and thus, for constant b_{ik}, the determinant[3] $|c_{ik}|$ may be considered as a function of the a_{ik}, or what amounts to the same thing, of the n vectors $\mathfrak{a}_i = \{a_{i1}, a_{i2}, \cdots, a_{in}\}$ $(i = 1, 2, \ldots, n)$. We accordingly set

(8) $$|c_{ik}| = F(\mathfrak{a}_1, \mathfrak{a}_2, \cdots, \mathfrak{a}_n).$$

Moreover, by definition,

(9) $$|c_{ik}| = D(\mathfrak{c}_1, \mathfrak{c}_2, \cdots, \mathfrak{c}_n),$$

where $D(\mathfrak{c}_1, \mathfrak{c}_2, \cdots, \mathfrak{c}_n)$ satisfies conditions *i*), *ii*), and *iii*).

We now assert that the function $F(\mathfrak{a}_1, \mathfrak{a}_2, \cdots, \mathfrak{a}_n)$ satisfies properties *i*) and *ii*). To verify *i*), $\mathfrak{a}_j$ is to be replaced by $\mathfrak{a}_j + \mathfrak{a}_h$ $(j \neq h)$, i.e. the elements $a_{j1}, a_{j2}, \cdots, a_{jn}$ are to be replaced by $a_{j1} + a_{h1}$, $a_{j2} + a_{h2}$, $\cdots$, $a_{jn} + a_{hn}$, respectively. By (7), this substitution does not alter those c_{ik} for which $i \neq j$, since these in no way depend on $a_{j1}, a_{j2}, \cdots, a_{jn}$. On the other hand $c_{j1}, c_{j2}, \cdots, c_{jn}$ are changed. In fact, for $k = 1, 2, \ldots, n$, the expression

$$a_{j1} b_{1k} + a_{j2} b_{2k} + \cdots + a_{jn} b_{nk}$$

goes over into

$$(a_{j1} + a_{h1}) b_{1k} + (a_{j2} + a_{h2}) b_{2k} + \cdots + (a_{jn} + a_{hn}) b_{nk}.$$

But by (7), this is precisely $c_{jk} + c_{hk}$. Thus the elements $c_{j1}, c_{j2}, \cdots, c_{jn}$ go over into $c_{j1} + c_{h1}$, $c_{j2} + c_{h2}$, $\cdots$, $c_{jn} + c_{hn}$, respectively. Thus, under our substitution, the vector $\mathfrak{c}_j$ is replaced by $\mathfrak{c}_j + \mathfrak{c}_h$, while for $i \neq j$, the vector $\mathfrak{c}_i$ remains unchanged. By property *i*) applied to (9), the determinant $|c_{ik}|$ remains unchanged by our substitution. Thus $F(\mathfrak{a}_1, \mathfrak{a}_2, \cdots, \mathfrak{a}_n)$, which by (8) is only another notation for $|c_{ik}|$ remains unchanged.

To verify *ii*), the elements $a_{j1}, a_{j2}, \cdots, a_{jn}$, for some fixed j, are to be replaced by $\lambda a_{j1}, \lambda a_{j2}, \cdots, \lambda a_{jn}$, respectively. Then by (7), of the elements c_{ik}, only $c_{j1}, c_{j2}, \cdots, c_{jn}$ are altered, and indeed, as is easily verified, they go over into $\lambda c_{j1}, \lambda c_{j2}, \cdots, \lambda c_{jn}$ respectively. That is:

[3] Where the meaning is clear and there is no danger of confusion, we also write for a determinant of the form

$$\begin{vmatrix} c_{11} & c_{12} & \cdots & c_{1n} \\ c_{21} & c_{22} & \cdots & c_{2n} \\ \cdot & \cdot & \cdot & \cdot \\ c_{n1} & c_{n2} & \cdots & c_{nn} \end{vmatrix}$$

the shorter and more convenient symbol $|c_{ik}|$.

Under our substitution, the vectors $\mathfrak{c}_i$ remain unchanged for $i \neq j$, while $\mathfrak{c}_j$ goes over into $\lambda \mathfrak{c}_j$. Thus, property *ii*) applied to (9) yields that $|c_{ik}|$ goes over into $\lambda \cdot |c_{ik}|$. Hence, by (8), we must have that $F(\mathfrak{a}_1, \mathfrak{a}_2, \cdots, \mathfrak{a}_n)$ goes over into $\lambda \cdot F(\mathfrak{a}_1, \mathfrak{a}_2, \cdots, \mathfrak{a}_n)$, as was to be proved.

We now apply Theorem 1. Since our function $F(\mathfrak{a}_1, \mathfrak{a}_2, \cdots, \mathfrak{a}_n)$ satisfies the hypotheses of Theorem 1, we must have

$$F(\mathfrak{a}_1, \mathfrak{a}_2, \cdots, \mathfrak{a}_n) = F(\mathfrak{e}_1, \mathfrak{e}_2, \cdots, \mathfrak{e}_n) \cdot D(\mathfrak{a}_1, \mathfrak{a}_2, \cdots, \mathfrak{a}_n)$$

or by (8) and (9),

$$D(\mathfrak{c}_1, \mathfrak{c}_2, \cdots, \mathfrak{c}_n) = F(\mathfrak{e}_1, \mathfrak{e}_2, \cdots, \mathfrak{e}_n) \cdot D(\mathfrak{a}_1, \mathfrak{a}_2, \cdots, \mathfrak{a}_n). \tag{10}$$

However, the value of $F(\mathfrak{e}_1, \mathfrak{e}_2, \cdots, \mathfrak{e}_n)$ may easily be determined. To this end, we must evaluate the c_{ik} for $\mathfrak{a}_i = \mathfrak{e}_i$ $(i = 1, 2, \ldots, n)$ from (6) and (7). $\mathfrak{a}_i = \mathfrak{e}_i$ means that the i-th component of $\mathfrak{a}_i$ (i.e. a_{ii}) is 1, while all the others are 0. Thus, in (7), we set $a_{ik} = 0$ for $i \neq k$, and $a_{11} = a_{22} = \cdots = a_{nn} = 1$. This immediately yields for $i, k = 1, 2, \ldots, n$, that $c_{ik} = b_{ik}$. Hence by (8),

$$F(\mathfrak{e}_1, \mathfrak{e}_2, \cdots, \mathfrak{e}_n) = \begin{vmatrix} b_{11} & b_{12} & \cdots & b_{1n} \\ b_{21} & b_{22} & \cdots & b_{2n} \\ \cdot & \cdot & \cdot & \cdot \\ b_{n1} & b_{n2} & \cdots & b_{nn} \end{vmatrix}.$$

Thus (10) may also be written

$$|c_{ik}| = |b_{ik}| \cdot |a_{ik}|. \tag{11}$$

This formula tells us how the value of the determinant $|a_{ik}|$ is changed when its column vectors $\bar{\mathfrak{a}}_i$ are replaced by the linear combinations (6). However, (11) will also make clear the nature of the functional dependence of a determinant on its column vectors.

In order to make explicit the fact that we are now considering the determinant as a function of its column vectors, we set:

$$\begin{vmatrix} a_{11} & a_{12} & \cdots & a_{1n} \\ a_{21} & a_{22} & \cdots & a_{2n} \\ \cdot & \cdot & \cdot & \cdot \\ a_{n1} & a_{n2} & \cdots & a_{nn} \end{vmatrix} = G(\bar{\mathfrak{a}}_1, \bar{\mathfrak{a}}_2, \cdots, \bar{\mathfrak{a}}_n). \tag{12}$$

We now assert that the function $G(\bar{\mathfrak{a}}_1, \bar{\mathfrak{a}}_2, \cdots, \bar{\mathfrak{a}}_n)$ also satisfies properties *i*), *ii*), and *iii*).

First, *iii*) is clear. For by (12), we have

$$G(\mathfrak{e}_1, \mathfrak{e}_2, \cdots, \mathfrak{e}_n) = \begin{vmatrix} 1 & 0 & \cdot & \cdot & 0 \\ 0 & 1 & \cdot & \cdot & 0 \\ 0 & 0 & \cdot & \cdot & \vdots \\ \vdots & \vdots & \cdot & \cdot & 0 \\ 0 & 0 & \cdot & \cdot & 1 \end{vmatrix} = D(\mathfrak{e}_1, \mathfrak{e}_2, \cdots, \mathfrak{e}_n) = 1.$$

In order to verify *i*) and *ii*), we employ formula (11). We wish to choose the numbers b_{ik} in (6) so that for some definite vector $\bar{\mathfrak{c}}_j$,

$$\bar{\mathfrak{c}}_j = \bar{\mathfrak{a}}_j + \bar{\mathfrak{a}}_h, \qquad h \neq j,$$

holds, while for all $k \neq j$,

$$\bar{\mathfrak{c}}_k = \bar{\mathfrak{a}}_k,$$

That is, the determinant $|c_{ik}|$ is obtained from $|a_{ik}|$, i.e. from $G(\bar{\mathfrak{a}}_1, \bar{\mathfrak{a}}_2, \cdots, \bar{\mathfrak{a}}_n)$, upon replacement of the column vector $\bar{\mathfrak{a}}_j$ by $\bar{\mathfrak{a}}_j + \bar{\mathfrak{a}}_h$. In order to see how this alters the value of $G(\bar{\mathfrak{a}}_1, \bar{\mathfrak{a}}_2, \cdots, \bar{\mathfrak{a}}_n)$, it is only necessary, by (11), to determine the value of the determinant $|b_{ik}|$. But by (6), we now have $b_{kk} = 1$ for $k \neq j$, and $b_{ik} = 0$ for $i \neq k$. For $k = j$, we have $b_{jj} = 1$, $b_{hj} = 1$, and $b_{ij} = 0$ if $i \neq j, h$. In order to evaluate $|b_{ik}|$, we insert the above values of b_{ik} for a_{ik} in (5). Then we see that only one of the summands on the right of (5) is non-zero, namely sgn $(1, 2, \ldots, n) \cdot b_{11} \cdot b_{22} \cdots b_{nn}$. For, with the exception of the element b_{hj}, we have $b_{ik} = 0$ for all $i \neq k$. Thus, if the product $b_{1\nu_1} \cdot b_{2\nu_2} \cdots b_{n\nu_n}$ is not to be equal to 0, then the factor $b_{i\nu_i}$ must be b_{ii} for $i \neq h$, i.e. for $i \neq h$ we must have $\nu_i = i$. Since $(\nu_1, \nu_2, \cdots, \nu_n)$ was to have been a permutation of $(1, 2, \ldots, n)$, the only possible value that remains for ν_h is h itself, so that $\nu_h = h$ also holds. Thus the only product of the form $b_{1\nu_1} \cdot b_{2\nu_2} \cdots b_{n\nu_n}$ which does not vanish is $b_{11} \cdot b_{22} \cdots b_{nn}$. If we further observe that sgn$(1, 2, \ldots, n) = (-1)^0 = 1$, since there are no inversions in this case, we have at once that

$$|b_{ik}| = 1.$$

Thus by (11), $|c_{ik}| = |a_{ik}|$. But this states that $G(\bar{\mathfrak{a}}_1, \bar{\mathfrak{a}}_2, \cdots, \bar{\mathfrak{a}}_n)$ remains unchanged upon replacement of the vector $\bar{\mathfrak{a}}_j$ by $\bar{\mathfrak{a}}_j + \bar{\mathfrak{a}}_h$.

Property *ii*) may be verified in an analogous manner. Here, a vector $\bar{\mathfrak{a}}_j$ is to be replaced by $\lambda\bar{\mathfrak{a}}_j$. Thus the equations (6) must have the following form: For $k \neq j$,

$$\bar{\mathfrak{c}}_k = \bar{\mathfrak{a}}_k,$$

while for j,

$$\bar{\mathfrak{c}}_j = \lambda \bar{\mathfrak{a}}_j.$$

Thus $b_{ik} = 0$ for $i \neq k$. On the other hand, $b_{kk} = 1$ for $k \neq j$, while $b_{jj} = \lambda$. The development of the determinant $|b_{ik}|$ by equation (5) involves only a single non-zero term, namely $\operatorname{sgn}(1, 2, \ldots, n) \cdot b_{11} \cdot b_{22} \cdots b_{nn}$. For, since $b_{ik} = 0$ if $i \neq k$, $b_{1\nu_1} \cdot b_{2\nu_2} \cdots b_{n\nu_n}$ can only be non-zero if $\nu_1 = 1$, $\nu_2 = 2, \ldots, \nu_n = n$. Thus

$$|b_{ik}| = \operatorname{sgn}(1, 2, \cdots, n) \cdot b_{11} \cdot b_{22} \cdots b_{nn} = \lambda.$$

In this case, equation (11) therefore takes on the form $|c_{ik}| = \lambda \cdot |a_{ik}|$. That is, $|a_{ik}| = G(\bar{\mathfrak{a}}_1, \bar{\mathfrak{a}}_2, \cdots, \bar{\mathfrak{a}}_n)$ is multiplied by λ if a vector $\mathfrak{a}_j$ is replaced by $\lambda\bar{\mathfrak{a}}_j$.

The function $G(\bar{\mathfrak{a}}_1, \bar{\mathfrak{a}}_2, \cdots, \bar{\mathfrak{a}}_n)$ is thus a function of n vectors of R_n which satisfies conditions *i*), *ii*), and *iii*). By § 8, there is only one such function, namely the n-by-n determinant. Thus we must have

$$G(\bar{\mathfrak{a}}_1, \bar{\mathfrak{a}}_2, \cdots, \bar{\mathfrak{a}}_n) = D(\bar{\mathfrak{a}}_1, \bar{\mathfrak{a}}_2, \cdots, \bar{\mathfrak{a}}_n) \tag{13}$$

But, by equation (12) of this section, this yields

$$D(\mathfrak{a}_1, \mathfrak{a}_2, \cdots, \mathfrak{a}_n) = D(\bar{\mathfrak{a}}_1, \bar{\mathfrak{a}}_2, \cdots, \bar{\mathfrak{a}}_n)$$

or

$$\begin{vmatrix} a_{11} & a_{12} & \cdots & a_{1n} \\ a_{21} & a_{22} & \cdots & a_{2n} \\ \cdot & \cdot & \cdot & \cdot \\ a_{n1} & a_{n2} & \cdots & a_{nn} \end{vmatrix} = \begin{vmatrix} a_{11} & a_{21} & \cdots & a_{n1} \\ a_{12} & a_{22} & \cdots & a_{n2} \\ \cdot & \cdot & \cdot & \cdot \\ a_{1n} & a_{2n} & \cdots & a_{nn} \end{vmatrix}.$$

The columns of the determinant on the left are the rows of the determinant on the right. This may also be stated as follows: The determinant on the left goes over into the one on the right by *reflection in its principal diagonal.* (In such a square array, the diagonal leading from the upper left-hand corner to the lower right-hand corner is called the *principal diagonal* of the array.) In fact, if the determinant on the left is rotated through an angle of 180° about its principal diagonal, every element a_{ik} is brought into the position which it occupies in the right-hand determinant. The terms in the principal diagonal remain fixed under this transformation. The above result may then also be expressed as follows:

THEOREM 2. *The value of a determinant remains unchanged under rotation of the determinant about its principal diagonal.*[4]

[4] Theorem 2 can also be easily deduced from formula (5). This is the more usual mode of procedure.

From this point on we shall nearly always employ the notation

$$\begin{vmatrix} a_{11} & a_{12} & \cdots & a_{1n} \\ a_{21} & a_{22} & \cdots & a_{2n} \\ \cdot & \cdot & \cdot & \cdot \\ a_{n1} & a_{n2} & \cdots & a_{nn} \end{vmatrix}$$

for determinants. This is the usual notation and is also the most useful one. Instead of row vectors, column vectors, addition of row or column vectors, etc., we shall simply speak of rows, columns, addition of rows or columns, etc. Thus, adding the rows $a_{i1}, a_{i2}, \ldots, a_{in}$ and $a_{k1}, a_{k2}, \ldots, a_{kn}$ will mean construction of the row $a_{i1} + a_{k1}, a_{i2} + a_{k2}, \cdots, a_{in} + a_{kn}$. To multiply a row (or a column) by a number means to multiply each element of the row (or column) by the number. The notions of linear combination of rows or of columns and of linear dependence or independence are to be understood similarly.

We shall derive some consequences of Theorem 2. This result (or the equivalent statement of equation (13)) states that the functional dependence of a determinant on its rows is of precisely the same nature as the functional dependence on its columns. Now, since the determinant, when considered as a function of its column vectors, likewise satisfies the fundamental properties *i*), *ii*), and *iii*), all of the consequences of these three properties which we have derived for row vectors hold equally for column vectors. In particular, Theorems 1 through 8 of the preceding section hold word for word if the row vectors $\mathfrak{a}_i$ are replaced by the column vectors $\overline{\mathfrak{a}_i}$. For example, corresponding to Theorem 2 of § 8, we have

The value of determinant remains unchanged if we add to one of its columns a linear combination of the remaining columns.

Or, by analogy with Theorems 4, 5, and 6 of § 8:

A determinant vanishes if its columns are linearly dependent, and hence, in particular, if

1. *the elements of one column are all* 0, *or*
2. *two columns are equal.*

The sign of a determinant is changed if two of its columns are interchanged.

The sum of two n-by-n determinants which coincide for $n-1$ *columns, is itself a determinant which agrees with the summands in* *these $n-1$ columns, and whose remaining column is the sum of the corresponding columns of the summands. That is:*

$$\begin{vmatrix} a_{11} & \cdots & a_{1,k-1} & b_1 & a_{1,k+1} & \cdots & a_{1n} \\ a_{21} & \cdots & a_{2,k-1} & b_2 & a_{2,k+1} & \cdots & a_{2n} \\ \cdot & \cdot & \cdot & \cdot & \cdot & \cdot & \cdot \\ a_{n1} & \cdots & a_{n,k-1} & b_n & a_{n,k+1} & \cdots & a_{nn} \end{vmatrix} + \begin{vmatrix} a_{11} & \cdots & a_{1,k-1} & c_1 & a_{1,k+1} & \cdots & a_{1n} \\ a_{21} & \cdots & a_{2,k-1} & c_2 & a_{2,k+1} & \cdots & a_{2n} \\ \cdot & \cdot & \cdot & \cdot & \cdot & \cdot & \cdot \\ a_{n1} & \cdots & a_{n,k-1} & c_n & a_{n,k+1} & \cdots & a_{nn} \end{vmatrix}$$

$$= \begin{vmatrix} a_{11} & \cdots & a_{1,k-1} & b_1+c_1 & a_{1,k+1} & \cdots & a_{1n} \\ a_{21} & \cdots & a_{2,k-1} & b_2+c_2 & a_{2,k+1} & \cdots & a_{2n} \\ \cdot & \cdot & \cdot & \cdot & \cdot & \cdot & \cdot \\ a_{n1} & \cdots & a_{n,k-1} & b_n+c_n & a_{n,k+1} & \cdots & a_{nn} \end{vmatrix}.$$

The Multiplication Theorem

Formula (11) has yet another important interpretation. Since, as is clear from its proof, it holds for arbitrary quantities a_{ik} and b_{ik}, it enables us to write the product of two n-by-n determinants $|a_{ik}|$, $|b_{ik}|$ as another n-by-n determinant $|c_{ik}|$, where the quantities c_{ik} are determined from the a_{ik} and b_{ik} by equation (7). Substituting the value of c_{ik} from (7) into (11), we obtain

$$|a_{ik}| \cdot |b_{ik}| = \left| \sum_{\nu=1}^{n} a_{i\nu} b_{\nu k} \right|.$$

This is the so-called *multiplication theorem* for determinants. The determinant on the right is, of course, to be understood as follows: The element $\sum_{\nu=1}^{n} a_{i\nu} b_{\nu k}$ occurs in the i-th row and the k-th column. Again denoting the row vectors of the determinant $|a_{ik}|$ by $\mathfrak{a}_i$ ($i=1, 2, \ldots, n$), and those of $|b_{ik}|$ by $\mathfrak{b}_i$ ($i=1, 2, \ldots, n$), the column vectors of $|a_{ik}|$ by $\bar{\mathfrak{a}}_i$ ($i=1, 2, \ldots, n$), and those of $|b_{ik}|$ by $\bar{\mathfrak{b}}_i$ ($i=1, 2, \ldots, n$), our product formula may be written

$$|a_{ik}| \cdot |b_{ik}| = |\mathfrak{a}_i \cdot \bar{\mathfrak{b}}_k|.$$

For, we have $\sum_{\nu=1}^{n} a_{i\nu} b_{\nu k} = \mathfrak{a}_i \cdot \bar{\mathfrak{b}}_k$. Thus the element of the i-th row and the k-th column is the scalar product of the i-th row of $|a_{ik}|$ by the k-th column of $|b_{ik}|$. If we now denote by $|a_{ik}|'$ and $|b_{ik}|'$ the determinants which arise from $|a_{ik}|$ and $|b_{ik}|$, respectively, by reflection about their principal diagonals, then by the rule we have just formulated, we have

$$|a_{ik}|'\cdot|b_{ik}| = |\bar{\mathfrak{a}}_i\,\bar{\mathfrak{b}}_k|,\quad |a_{ik}|\cdot|b_{ik}|' = |\mathfrak{a}_i\cdot\mathfrak{b}_k|,\quad |a_{ik}|'\cdot|b_{ik}|' = |\bar{\mathfrak{a}}_i\cdot\mathfrak{b}_k|.$$

However, $|a_{ik}|' = |a_{ik}|$, $|b_{ik}|' = |b_{ik}|$. Thus, we have

$$|a_{ik}|\cdot|b_{ik}| = |\mathfrak{a}_i\cdot\mathfrak{b}_k| = |\mathfrak{a}_i\cdot\bar{\mathfrak{b}}_k| = |\bar{\mathfrak{a}}_i\cdot\mathfrak{b}_k| = |\bar{\mathfrak{a}}_i\cdot\bar{\mathfrak{b}}_k|.$$

These are essentially all the methods for calculating the product of two determinants.[5]

---

[5] The multiplication theorem may also easily be proved by means of Theorem 7 of § 8 and formula (5) of this section. For, suppose there are given n vectors $\mathfrak{c}_1, \mathfrak{c}_2, \cdots, \mathfrak{c}_n$ as linear combinations of the vectors $\mathfrak{a}_1, \mathfrak{a}_2, \cdots, \mathfrak{a}_n$, say

$$\mathfrak{c}_i = \sum_{k=1}^{n} b_{ik}\,\mathfrak{a}_k.$$

If we then set $\mathfrak{b}_i^k = b_{ik}\,\mathfrak{a}_k$, we have $\mathfrak{c}_i = \sum_{k=1}^{n}\mathfrak{b}_i^k$, so that by Theorem 7 of § 8, we have

$$D(\mathfrak{c}_1, \mathfrak{c}_2, \cdots, \mathfrak{c}_n) = \sum_{\nu_1,\nu_2,\cdots,\nu_n=1}^{n} D(b_{1\nu_1}\mathfrak{a}_{\nu_1}, b_{2\nu_2}\mathfrak{a}_{\nu_2}, \cdots, b_{n\nu_n}\mathfrak{a}_{\nu_n}).$$

Applying property *ii*), we infer

$$D(\mathfrak{c}_1, \mathfrak{c}_2, \cdots, \mathfrak{c}_n) = \sum_{\nu_1,\nu_2,\cdots,\nu_n=1}^{n} b_{1\nu_1}\cdot b_{2\nu_2}\cdots b_{n\nu_n}\cdot D(\mathfrak{a}_{\nu_1}, \mathfrak{a}_{\nu_2}, \cdots, \mathfrak{a}_{\nu_n}).$$

In the sum on the right all the summands with two of the indices ν_i equal, are $= 0$, for in such a case $D(\mathfrak{a}_{\nu_1}, \mathfrak{a}_{\nu_2}, \cdots, \mathfrak{a}_{\nu_n})$ vanishes. We therefore need only sum over all permutations $(\nu_1, \nu_2, \cdots, \nu_n)$ of the integers $(1, 2, \ldots, n)$. Let us recall formula (3). It yields, using (4),

$$D(\mathfrak{e}_{\nu_1}, \mathfrak{e}_{\nu_2}, \cdots, \mathfrak{e}_{\nu_n}) = \operatorname{sgn}(\nu_1, \nu_2, \cdots, \nu_n)\, D(\mathfrak{e}_1, \mathfrak{e}_2, \cdots, \mathfrak{e}_n).$$

As is easily seen, we made no use of the fact that the unit vectors were involved in the proof of this formula. In fact, our proof remains valid without change if $\mathfrak{e}_1, \mathfrak{e}_2, \cdots, \mathfrak{e}_n$ are replaced by arbitrary vectors $\mathfrak{a}_1, \mathfrak{a}_2, \cdots, \mathfrak{a}_n$ throughout. Thus,

$$D(\mathfrak{a}_{\nu_1}, \mathfrak{a}_{\nu_2}, \cdots, \mathfrak{a}_{\nu_n}) = \operatorname{sgn}(\nu_1, \nu_2, \cdots, \nu_n)\, D(\mathfrak{a}_1, \mathfrak{a}_2, \cdots, \mathfrak{a}_n).$$

Employing this, we obtain

$$D(\mathfrak{c}_1, \mathfrak{c}_2, \cdots, \mathfrak{c}_n) = D(\mathfrak{a}_1, \mathfrak{a}_2, \cdots, \mathfrak{a}_n)\cdot \sum_{(\nu_1,\nu_2,\cdots,\nu_n)} \operatorname{sgn}(\nu_1, \nu_2, \cdots, \nu_n)\, b_{1\nu_1}\cdot b_{2\nu_2}\cdots b_{n\nu_n}.$$

If we now set $\mathfrak{b}_i = \{b_{i1}, b_{i2}, \cdots, b_{in}\}$, then by (5), it follows that

$$D(\mathfrak{c}_1, \mathfrak{c}_2, \cdots, \mathfrak{c}_n) = D(\mathfrak{a}_1, \mathfrak{a}_2, \cdots, \mathfrak{a}_n)\cdot D(\mathfrak{b}_1, \mathfrak{b}_2, \cdots, \mathfrak{b}_n).$$

This is again the multiplication theorem, as the definition of $\mathfrak{c}_i$ shows.

The Development of a Determinant by Rows or Columns

In the preceding section, we have derived the recursion formula

$$|a_{ik}| = \sum_{k=1}^{n} (-1)^{n-k} \cdot a_{kn} \cdot D_k .$$

The right-hand side of this equation is called *the development of the determinant* $|a_{ik}|$ *by its last column.* Now, there is an analogous development with respect to each column and also with respect to each row. Let us recall the meaning of D_k. D_k was used to denote the $(n-1)$-by-$(n-1)$ determinant which is obtained from $|a_{ik}|$ by crossing out the k-th row and the n-th column. We now consider $(-1)^{n-k}D_k$ as a single entity, and introduce the abbreviation [6]

$$A_{kn} = (-1)^{n-k} D_k = (-1)^{n+k} D_k .$$

More generally the $(n-1)$-by-$(n-1)$ determinant obtained by crossing out the i-th row and the k-th column of $|a_{ik}|$ is called the *minor* with respect to the i-th row and k-th column of $|a_{ik}|$. We then employ the notation A_{ik} for the product of this minor by $(-1)^{i+k}$. A_{ik} is called the *cofactor* or *algebraic complement* of a_{ik}. We now assert that the following equations hold:

$$(14)\qquad \begin{aligned} |a_{ik}| &= \sum_{i=1}^{n} a_{ik} A_{ik}, \qquad 1 \leqq k \leqq n, \\ |a_{ik}| &= \sum_{k=1}^{n} a_{ik} A_{ik}, \qquad 1 \leqq i \leqq n. \end{aligned}$$ [7]

The first of these equations represents a *development by the k-th column,* while the second represents a *development by the i-th row.* It will suffice to verify this development for columns, since by Theorem 2 the result for rows would then follow. For, if $|a_{ik}|$ is reflected about its principal diagonal, and if the resulting determinant is developed by its i-th column, then this immediately yields a development of $|a_{ik}|$ by its i-th row.

---

[6] Since $2k$ is even, we have $(-1)^{2k} = 1$ so that

$$(-1)^{n-k} = (-1)^{n-k}(-1)^{2k} = (-1)^{n+k}.$$

[7] The indices i, k in the symbol $|a_{ik}|$ have, of course, nothing to do with indices i, k which occur on the right-hand sides of these equations. $|a_{ik}|$ is merely an abbreviation for the determinant.

In the determinant $|a_{ik}|$, let us successively interchange the k-th column with the $(k+1)$-st, $(k+2)$-nd, ..., n-th columns. In the process, the sign of the determinant is changed $n-k$ times. Thus

$$\begin{vmatrix} a_{11} & a_{12} & \cdots & a_{1n} \\ a_{21} & a_{22} & \cdots & a_{2n} \\ \cdot & \cdot & \cdot & \cdot \\ a_{n1} & a_{n2} & \cdots & a_{nn} \end{vmatrix} = (-1)^{n-k} \begin{vmatrix} a_{11} & \cdots & a_{1,k-1} & a_{1,k+1} & \cdots & a_{1n} & a_{1k} \\ a_{21} & \cdots & a_{2,k-1} & a_{2,k+1} & \cdots & a_{2n} & a_{2k} \\ \cdot & \cdot & \cdot & \cdot & \cdot & \cdot & \cdot \\ a_{n1} & \cdots & a_{n,k-1} & a_{n,k+1} & \cdots & a_{nn} & a_{nk} \end{vmatrix}.$$

Let D_i^* be the minor with respect to the i-th row and the last column of the determinant on the right. We develop the determinant on the right with respect to its last column (as may be done for any determinant), and obtain:

$$|a_{ik}| = (-1)^{n-k}\left(\sum_{i=1}^{n}(-1)^{n-i}\, a_{ik}\, D_i^*\right).$$

Now, $(-1)^{n-k}\cdot(-1)^{n-i} = (-1)^{2n}\cdot(-1)^{-(i+k)} = (-1)^{i+k}$ and D_i^* may also be obtained from $|a_{ik}|$ by crossing out the i-th row and k-th column. Thus by the definition of A_{ik}, we have

$$|a_{ik}| = \sum_{i=1}^{n} a_{ik}\, A_{ik},$$

as was to be proved.

Let us now consider the determinant which arises from $|a_{ik}|$ by replacement of the i-th row by the k-th row $(i \neq k)$, while all the remaining rows (including the k-th) are left unchanged; that is, the determinant

$$\begin{vmatrix} a_{11} & a_{12} & \cdots & a_{1n} \\ \cdot & \cdot & \cdot & \cdot \\ a_{i-1,1} & a_{i-1,2} & \cdots & a_{i-1,n} \\ a_{k1} & a_{k2} & \cdots & a_{kn} \\ a_{i+1,1} & a_{i+1,2} & \cdots & a_{i+1,n} \\ \cdot & \cdot & \cdot & \cdot \\ a_{n1} & a_{n2} & \cdots & a_{nn} \end{vmatrix}.$$

This determinant is equal to 0, since its i-th and k-th rows are now identical. If on the other hand we develop this determinant by its i-th row, we obtain

(15) $$\sum_{j=1}^{n} a_{kj}\, A_{ij} = 0.$$

For, the cofactors of the elements of the i-th row of this determinant are the same as those of the elements of the i-th row of $|a_{ik}|$. Equations (15) are valid for $k \neq i$. For $k = i$ however, we have (14). Similarly, we have for the cofactors of a column of $|a_{ik}|$:

$$\sum_{j=1}^{n} a_{jk} A_{ji} = 0, \tag{15a}$$

where $k \neq i$. The pair of equations (14) and (15), and the pair (14) and (15a), may each be combined into a single equation if we employ the so-called *Kronecker delta*, δ_{ik}. This symbol is defined by

$$\delta_{ik} = \begin{cases} 0 \text{ for } i \neq k \\ 1 \text{ for } i = k. \end{cases}$$

Then we may write

$$\begin{aligned} \sum_{j=1}^{n} a_{ij} A_{kj} &= \delta_{ik} \cdot |a_{ik}|, \\ \sum_{j=1}^{n} a_{ji} A_{jk} &= \delta_{ik} \cdot |a_{ik}|. \end{aligned} \tag{16}$$

Determinants and Linear Equations

Formulas (16) have an important application to the theory of linear equations. Let there be given a system of n linear equations in n unknowns $x_1, x_2, \ldots, x_n$,

$$\sum_{k=1}^{n} a_{ik} x_k = b_i, \qquad i = 1, 2, \cdots, n. \tag{17}$$

To begin with, we assume that the matrix of the coefficients

$$\begin{pmatrix} a_{11} & a_{12} & \cdots & a_{1n} \\ a_{21} & a_{22} & \cdots & a_{2n} \\ \cdot & \cdot & \cdot & \cdot \\ a_{n1} & a_{n2} & \cdots & a_{nn} \end{pmatrix}$$

of the system (17) of equations is of rank n, since all other cases may be reduced to this one. Now if the n column vectors of this matrix are linearly independent, then the augmented matrix

$$\begin{pmatrix} a_{11} & a_{12} & \cdots & a_{1n} & b_1 \\ a_{21} & a_{22} & \cdots & a_{2n} & b_2 \\ \cdot & \cdot & \cdot & \cdot & \cdot \\ a_{n1} & a_{n2} & \cdots & a_{nn} & b_n \end{pmatrix}$$

contains n linearly independent column vectors, and so its rank is at least n. The rank of the augmented matrix can not, however, be greater than n, since the matrix has only n rows. Hence, its rank is precisely n. By Theorem 2 of § 6, system (17) is therefore solvable, and moreover, by Theorem 9 of § 6, it has precisely one solution $x_1, x_2, \ldots, x_n$. We are now in a position to determine this solution. Let us first observe that by our hypotheses, and Theorem 8 of § 8, it follows that the determinant $|a_{ik}|$ is not 0. To evaluate x_h, we now multiply the i-th equation of (17) by A_{ih} (h fixed), where, as above, A_{ih} is the cofactor of a_{ih} in the determinant $|a_{ik}|$. We then add all the n resulting equations. We thus obtain

$$\sum_{i=1}^{n}\left(A_{ih}\sum_{k=1}^{n} a_{ik}\,x_k\right) = \sum_{i=1}^{n} A_{ih}\,b_i.$$

However

$$\sum_{i=1}^{n}\left(A_{ih}\sum_{k=1}^{n} a_{ik}\,x_k\right) = \sum_{i,k=1}^{n} A_{ih}\,a_{ik}\,x_k = \sum_{k=1}^{n}\left(x_k\sum_{i=1}^{n} A_{ih}\,a_{ik}\right).$$

But by (16), we have $\sum_{i=1}^{n} A_{ih}\,a_{ik} = \delta_{hk}\cdot|a_{ik}|$, so that only one of the n summands $x_k\sum_{i=1}^{n} A_{ih}\,a_{ik}$ $(k = 1, 2, \ldots, n)$ is non-zero, namely $x_h\sum_{i=1}^{n} A_{ih}\,a_{ih} = x_h\cdot|a_{ik}|$. Hence, since $|a_{ik}|$ is not 0,

$$x_h = \frac{\sum_{i=1}^{n} A_{ih}\,b_i}{|a_{ik}|}, \qquad h = 1, 2, \cdots, n. \tag{18}$$

This result is known as **Cramer's Rule.** Equations (18) have been deduced from equations (17). That is, we have proved: *The system* x_h $(h = 1, 2, \ldots, n)$ *which solves equations* (17) *and whose existence and uniqueness has already been proved, must necessarily be given by* (18). We could also have verified easily that the quantities x_h determined by (18) really do satisfy (17), by substitution and employment of (16).

Next, in order to show how to determine the solutions of an *arbitrary* system of linear equations, we must first show how to evaluate the rank of a matrix. Determinant theory enables us to solve this problem also. Let us consider a matrix with m rows and n columns:

$$(19) \qquad \begin{pmatrix} a_{11} & a_{12} & \cdots & a_{1n} \\ a_{21} & a_{22} & \cdots & a_{2n} \\ \cdot & \cdot & \cdot & \cdot \\ a_{m1} & a_{m2} & \cdots & a_{mn} \end{pmatrix}$$

Let k be an integer > 1, which is $\leqq m$ and $\leqq n$. If we cross out any $n - k$ columns and $m - k$ rows, then precisely k^2 elements a_{ik} remain, arranged in a square array of k rows and k columns. The determinant associated with this square array is called a *(k-by-k) sub-determinant* of the matrix. For example, if in the matrix

$$\begin{pmatrix} a_{11} & a_{12} & a_{13} & a_{14} & a_{15} \\ a_{21} & a_{22} & a_{23} & a_{24} & a_{25} \\ a_{31} & a_{32} & a_{33} & a_{34} & a_{35} \end{pmatrix}$$

we cross out the first, third, and fifth columns, and the first row, we obtain the sub-determinant

$$\begin{vmatrix} a_{22} & a_{24} \\ a_{32} & a_{34} \end{vmatrix}.$$

Let us consider the totality of all sub-determinants of our matrix. Let r be that integer which has the following property: There exists an r-by-r sub-determinant which is not 0, but every sub-determinant with more than r rows (and columns) is equal to 0. We assert that this integer r is precisely the rank of the matrix. That is,

THEOREM 3. *The rank of a matrix is precisely the largest integer r for which some r-by-r sub-determinant is unequal to* 0.

We first prove that the rank of the matrix is at least r. Let us consider some r-by-r sub-determinant D which is not 0. It is obtained from the matrix by crossing out $m - r$ rows and $n - r$ columns. Let the rows which were not crossed out be the i_1-st, i_2-nd, . . . , and i_r-th rows. Then we form the matrix

$$(20) \qquad \begin{pmatrix} a_{i_1,1} & a_{i_1,2} & a_{i_1,3} & \cdots & a_{i_1,n} \\ a_{i_2,1} & a_{i_2,2} & a_{i_2,3} & \cdots & a_{i_2,n} \\ \cdot & \cdot & \cdot & \cdot & \cdot \\ a_{i_r,1} & a_{i_r,2} & a_{i_r,3} & \cdots & a_{i_r,n} \end{pmatrix},$$

which consists of these r rows of our original matrix (19). The sub-determinant D which we have chosen is also a sub-determinant of the matrix (20). Since $D \neq 0$, the r column vectors of D are linearly independent. However, the column vectors of D are also column vectors of (20). Therefore the rank of (20) is at least r. But since the matrix (20) has only r rows, its rank must be precisely r, and hence its row vectors must be linearly independent. Therefore, the matrix (19) also has r linearly independent row vectors, and its rank is thus certainly $\geqq r$.

We next show that the rank of (19) is at most r, which will complete the proof. It clearly suffices to prove that if the matrix (19) has k linearly independent rows, then there is a k-by-k sub-determinant of (19) which is $\neq 0$. For it would then follow that if the rank of (19) were $> r$, the matrix (19) would have a non-vanishing sub-determinant with more than r rows and columns, contrary to hypothesis.

Let there then be given k linearly independent rows of (19), say the i_1-st, i_2-nd, ..., i_k-th rows. We then form the matrix

$$(21) \qquad \begin{pmatrix} a_{i_1,1} & a_{i_1,2} & a_{i_1,3} & \cdots & a_{i_1,n} \\ a_{i_2,1} & a_{i_2,2} & a_{i_2,3} & \cdots & a_{i_2,n} \\ \cdot & \cdot & \cdot & \cdots & \cdot \\ a_{i_k,1} & a_{i_k,2} & a_{i_k,3} & \cdots & a_{i_k,n} \end{pmatrix},$$

from these rows. The matrix (21) has rank k; hence there are k linearly independent columns. Choose k such columns in (21) and cross out the remaining ones. Corresponding to the array which is thus obtained there is a k-by-k determinant, which is certainly $\neq 0$ since its columns are linearly independent (Theorem 8 of § 8). Since this sub-determinant of (21) is also a sub-determinant of (19), our assertion is proved.

We next discuss the application of our methods to the solution of arbitrary systems of linear equations. Of course we must first determine the rank of the coefficient matrix and of the augmented matrix in order to decide the question of solvability. Theorem 3 provides us with a practicable method of accomplishing this. Let the system of equations consist, say, of m equations in n unknowns, of the form

$$(22) \qquad \sum_{k=1}^{n} a_{ik}\, x_k = b_i, \qquad i = 1, 2, \cdots, m.$$

Once we have established the solvability of this system, and in the process have determined the ranks of the coefficient matrix and of the augmented matrix of the system to be, say, r, we proceed to find linearly independent row vectors in the coefficient matrix (which has the form (19)). This too can be accomplished with the aid of Theorem 3, as follows: We choose some non-vanishing r-by-r sub-determinant of (19). The corresponding r rows of the matrix (19) form an r-rowed matrix of rank r by Theorem 3, and so are linearly independent.

We now assume that the first r rows of (19) are linearly independent. At worst, this assumption involves a rearrangement of the equations. Then, in order to solve (22), it is only necessary to consider the first r equations

$$\sum_{k=1}^{n} a_{ik} x_k = b_i, \qquad i = 1, 2, \cdots, r \tag{23}$$

and to determine their solutions. For, (23) is certainly solvable since every solution of (22) is also a solution of (23). The totality of all points constituting a solution of (22) forms a linear space L (Theorem 9, § 6); the corresponding totality for (23) is a linear space L'. As has just been stated, L is contained in L'. The matrices of (22) and (23) have the same rank r, and therefore by Theorem 9 of § 6, the linear spaces L and L' have the same dimension, and so are identical.

By Theorem 6 of § 6, we need determine only *one* solution of (23) and the totality of all solutions of the corresponding system of homogeneous equations. The coefficient matrix of (23) has rank r; hence there are r linearly independent column vectors. We assume that the first r of them are linearly independent. This assumption involves nothing worse than a possible renumbering of the unknowns. In order to find a solution of (23) we then set $x_{r+1} = x_{r+2} = \cdots = x_n = 0$. The equations (23) then take on the form

$$\sum_{k=1}^{r} a_{ik} x_k = b_i, \qquad i = 1, 2, \cdots, r.$$

These are r equations in r unknowns whose determinant $|a_{ik}|$ is non-zero, and so they may be solved by Cramer's rule. Finally, to solve the system of homogeneous equations

$$\sum_{k=1}^{n} a_{ik} x_k = 0, \qquad i = 1, 2, \cdots, r$$

we recall the method of proof of Theorem 3, § 6. In the course of this proof a basis $\mathfrak{y}_1, \mathfrak{y}_2, \cdots, \mathfrak{y}_{n-r}$ for the vector space of all solution vectors was set up. In our case, this procedure amounts to representing each column vector $\bar{\mathfrak{a}}_h = \{a_{1h}, a_{2h}, \cdots, a_{rh}\}$ for $h = r+1, r+2, \ldots, n$ as a linear combination of the first r column vectors $\mathfrak{a}_1, \mathfrak{a}_2, \ldots, \mathfrak{a}_r$ of the coefficient matrix of (19). This means determining the solution, for each $h = r + 1, r + 2, \ldots, n$, of a system of equations of the form

$$\sum_{k=1}^{r} a_{ik} x_k = a_{ih}, \qquad i = 1, 2, \cdots, r.$$

Since this is, for each h, a system of r equations in r unknowns with non-vanishing determinant $|a_{ik}|$, Cramer's rule once again suffices. Thus we are through.

One special case is of great importance, namely n linear homogeneous equations in n unknowns. Let the equations be, say,

$$\sum_{k=1}^{n} a_{ik} x_k = 0, \qquad i = 1, 2, \cdots, n.$$

The matrix of this system has n rows and n columns, and so is *square*. By Theorem 4 of § 6, the equations have a non-trivial solution if and only if the rank of the matrix is less than n. But by Theorem 3 of the present section (or by Theorems 4 and 8 of § 8) this is the case if and only if the (n-by-n) determinant $|a_{ik}|$ vanishes. Thus, we have

THEOREM 4. *n linear homogeneous equations in n unknowns have a non-trivial solution if and only if the determinant of the system vanishes.*

Laplace's Expansion Theorem

As the final topic of this section, we prove the Laplace expansion theorem (Equation (34)). It provides us with new methods for evaluating a determinant. We derive the theorem in several steps. We begin by settling two special cases. Let us consider an n-by-n determinant of the following form:

$$(24) \qquad \left|\begin{array}{cccc|cccc} b_{11} & b_{12} & \cdots & b_{1p} & 0 & 0 & \cdots & 0 \\ b_{21} & b_{22} & \cdots & b_{2p} & 0 & 0 & \cdots & 0 \\ \cdot & \cdot & \cdot & \cdot & \cdot & \cdot & \cdot & \cdot \\ b_{p1} & b_{p2} & \cdots & b_{pp} & 0 & 0 & \cdots & 0 \\ \hline 0 & 0 & \cdots & 0 & c_{11} & c_{12} & \cdots & c_{1q} \\ 0 & 0 & \cdots & 0 & c_{21} & c_{22} & \cdots & c_{2q} \\ \cdot & \cdot & \cdot & \cdot & \cdot & \cdot & \cdot & \cdot \\ 0 & 0 & \cdots & 0 & c_{q1} & c_{q2} & \cdots & c_{qq} \end{array}\right|$$

In this determinant, the last q elements in the first p rows ($p + q = n$) are 0, and the first p elements of the last q rows are also 0. The elements of the p-by-p square in the upper left-hand corner and those of the q-by-q square in the lower right-hand corner are arbitrary real numbers. They are denoted by b_{ik} and c_{ik} respectively.

In the determinant (24), let us consider the c_{ik} as constants and the b_{ik} as variables, so that the determinant is a function of the p-dimensional vectors $\mathfrak{b}_i = \{b_{i1}, b_{i2}, \cdots, b_{ip}\}$ $(i = 1, 2, \ldots, p)$. We denote this function by $F(\mathfrak{b}_1, \mathfrak{b}_2, \cdots, \mathfrak{b}_p)$. Now, we easily see that $F(\mathfrak{b}_1, \mathfrak{b}_2, \cdots, \mathfrak{b}_p)$ satisfies properties *i*) and *ii*) of § 8. For, replacement of a vector $\mathfrak{b}_i$ by $\mathfrak{b}_i + \mathfrak{b}_k$ $(i \neq k)$ can be interpreted as follows for (24) : To the row $b_{i1}, b_{i2}, \cdots, b_{ip}, 0, 0, \ldots, 0$, the row $b_{k1}, b_{k2}, \cdots, b_{kp}, 0, 0, \ldots, 0$ is to be added. Similarly, replacement of $\mathfrak{b}_i$ by $\lambda\mathfrak{b}_i$ may be interpreted for (24) as multiplication of the row $b_{i1}, b_{i2}, \cdots, b_{ip}, 0, 0, \ldots, 0$ by λ. But (24) remains unchanged under the first of these operations and is multiplied by λ under the second, and hence the same is true of $F(\mathfrak{b}_1, \mathfrak{b}_2, \cdots, \mathfrak{b}_p)$. Hence, by Theorem 1 of § 9, we have

$$F(\mathfrak{b}_1, \mathfrak{b}_2, \cdots, \mathfrak{b}_p) =$$

$$(25) \qquad = \left|\begin{array}{cccc|cccc} 1 & 0 & \cdots & 0 & 0 & 0 & \cdots & 0 \\ 0 & 1 & \cdots & 0 & 0 & 0 & \cdots & 0 \\ \cdot & \cdot & \cdot & \cdot & \cdot & \cdot & \cdot & \cdot \\ 0 & 0 & \cdots & 1 & 0 & 0 & \cdots & 0 \\ \hline 0 & 0 & \cdots & 0 & c_{11} & c_{12} & \cdots & c_{1q} \\ 0 & 0 & \cdots & 0 & c_{21} & c_{22} & \cdots & c_{2q} \\ \cdot & \cdot & \cdot & \cdot & \cdot & \cdot & \cdot & \cdot \\ 0 & 0 & \cdots & 0 & c_{q1} & c_{q2} & \cdots & c_{qq} \end{array}\right| \cdot \left|\begin{array}{cccc} b_{11} & b_{12} & \cdots & b_{1p} \\ b_{21} & b_{22} & \cdots & b_{2p} \\ \cdot & \cdot & \cdot & \cdot \\ b_{p1} & b_{p2} & \cdots & b_{pp} \end{array}\right|.$$

Now let us consider the elements c_{ik} as variables. Then the first factor on the right in (25) is a function of the elements c_{ik}, and we consider it as a function of the q-dimensional vectors

$$\mathfrak{c}_i = \{c_{i1}, c_{i2}, \cdots, c_{iq}\},$$

$i = 1, 2, \ldots, q$. As above, we can easily verify that this factor, as a function of the vectors $\mathfrak{c}_1, \mathfrak{c}_2, \cdots, \mathfrak{c}_q$, satisfies conditions *i*) and *ii*). However, it also satisfies *iii*). For if we replace each $\mathfrak{c}_i$ $(i = 1, 2, \ldots, q)$ by the i-th unit vector of q-dimensional space R_q, then the first factor on the right of (25) becomes

$$\left|\begin{array}{cccc|cccc} 1 & 0 & \cdots & 0 & 0 & 0 & \cdots & 0 \\ 0 & 1 & \cdots & 0 & 0 & 0 & \cdots & 0 \\ \cdot & \cdot & \cdot & \cdot & \cdot & \cdot & \cdot & \cdot \\ 0 & 0 & \cdots & 1 & 0 & 0 & \cdots & 0 \\ \hline 0 & 0 & \cdots & 0 & 1 & 0 & \cdots & 0 \\ 0 & 0 & \cdots & 0 & 0 & 1 & \cdots & 0 \\ \cdot & \cdot & \cdot & \cdot & \cdot & \cdot & \cdot & \cdot \\ 0 & 0 & \cdots & 0 & 0 & 0 & \cdots & 1 \end{array}\right|$$

and so is $= 1$. Hence this factor must be the q-by-q determinant $|\, c_{ik} \,|$, so that

$$\left|\begin{array}{cccc|cccc} b_{11} & b_{12} & \cdots & b_{1p} & 0 & 0 & \cdots & 0 \\ b_{21} & b_{22} & \cdots & b_{2p} & 0 & 0 & \cdots & 0 \\ \cdot & \cdot & \cdot & \cdot & \cdot & \cdot & \cdot & \cdot \\ b_{p1} & b_{p2} & \cdots & b_{pp} & 0 & 0 & \cdots & 0 \\ \hline 0 & 0 & \cdots & 0 & c_{11} & c_{12} & \cdots & c_{1q} \\ 0 & 0 & \cdots & 0 & c_{21} & c_{22} & \cdots & c_{2q} \\ \cdot & \cdot & \cdot & \cdot & \cdot & \cdot & \cdot & \cdot \\ 0 & 0 & \cdots & 0 & c_{q1} & c_{q2} & \cdots & c_{qq} \end{array}\right| = \tag{26}$$

$$= \begin{vmatrix} b_{11} & b_{12} & \cdots & b_{1p} \\ b_{21} & b_{22} & \cdots & b_{2p} \\ \cdot & \cdot & \cdot & \cdot \\ b_{p1} & b_{p2} & \cdots & b_{pp} \end{vmatrix} \cdot \begin{vmatrix} c_{11} & c_{12} & \cdots & c_{1q} \\ c_{21} & c_{22} & \cdots & c_{2q} \\ \cdot & \cdot & \cdot & \cdot \\ c_{q1} & c_{q2} & \cdots & c_{qq} \end{vmatrix}.$$

We shall soon make use of this formula.

We now return to the consideration of a general n-by-n determinant of the form

$$\begin{vmatrix} a_{11} & a_{12} & \cdots & a_{1n} \\ a_{21} & a_{22} & \cdots & a_{2n} \\ \cdot & \cdot & \cdot & \cdot \\ a_{n1} & a_{n2} & \cdots & a_{nn} \end{vmatrix}.$$

We divide the columns of this determinant into two systems. The first is to consist of the first p columns, the other of the last q columns $(p + q = n)$. We furthermore set

$$\mathfrak{b}_i^1 = \sum_{k=1}^{p} a_{ik}\,\mathfrak{e}_k, \quad \mathfrak{b}_i^2 = \sum_{k=p+1}^{n} a_{ik}\,\mathfrak{e}_k.$$

If we denote the row vectors of $|a_{ik}|$ by $\mathfrak{a}_1, \mathfrak{a}_2, \cdots, \mathfrak{a}_n$ as before, then $\mathfrak{b}_i^1$ results from $\mathfrak{a}_i$ upon setting the $(p+1)$-st, $(p+2)$-nd, ..., n-th components of $\mathfrak{a}_i$ equal to 0, and leaving the remaining components unchanged; and $\mathfrak{b}_i^2$ results from $\mathfrak{a}_i$ upon setting the 1-st, 2-nd, ..., p-th components of $\mathfrak{a}_i$ equal to zero. Thus

$$\mathfrak{a}_i = \mathfrak{b}_i^1 + \mathfrak{b}_i^2 .$$

Then by Theorem 7 of § 8, we have

$$(27) \qquad |a_{ik}| = \sum_{\nu_1, \nu_2, \cdots, \nu_n = 1}^{2} D(\mathfrak{b}_1^{\nu_1}, \mathfrak{b}_2^{\nu_2}, \cdots, \mathfrak{b}_n^{\nu_n}).$$

The vectors $\mathfrak{b}_i^1$ all are linear combinations of the p vectors $\mathfrak{e}_1, \mathfrak{e}_2, \ldots, \mathfrak{e}_p$, and the vectors $\mathfrak{b}_i^2$ are, correspondingly, linear combinations of $\mathfrak{e}_{p+1}, \mathfrak{e}_{p+2}, \cdots, \mathfrak{e}_n$. Hence, by Theorem 2 of § 4, any $p+1$ of the vectors $\mathfrak{b}_i^1$ as well as any $q+1$ of the vectors $\mathfrak{b}_i^2$ are linearly dependent. Recalling Theorem 1 of § 3, it follows from Theorem 4 of § 8 that in the sum of (27), the terms $D(\mathfrak{b}_1^{\nu_1}, \mathfrak{b}_2^{\nu_2}, \cdots, \mathfrak{b}_n^{\nu_n})$ having more than p of the indices $\nu_1, \nu_2, \cdots, \nu_n$ equal to 1, or more than q of the indices equal to 2, vanish. Hence we need only sum over n-tuples $(\nu_1, \nu_2, \cdots, \nu_n)$ for which precisely p of the indices are $=1$ and precisely q are $=2$. Let us consider such a summand

$$D(\mathfrak{b}_1^{\nu_1}, \mathfrak{b}_2^{\nu_2}, \cdots, \mathfrak{b}_n^{\nu_n}).$$

Let the p indices which are equal to 1 be, say

$$\nu_{\varrho_1}, \nu_{\varrho_2}, \cdots, \nu_{\varrho_p},$$

where we may take $\varrho_1 < \varrho_2 < \cdots < \varrho_p$. The remaining q indices, which are, say, $\nu_{\sigma_1}, \nu_{\sigma_2}, \cdots, \nu_{\sigma_q}$, are all equal to 2, where we may take $\sigma_1 < \sigma_2 < \cdots < \sigma_q$. The first vector in the sequence

$$\mathfrak{b}_1^{\nu_1}, \mathfrak{b}_2^{\nu_2}, \cdots, \mathfrak{b}_n^{\nu_n},$$

whose upper index is equal to 1 is thus $\mathfrak{b}_{\varrho_1}^1$ and is therefore in the ϱ_1-st place in the sequence. There are precisely $\varrho_1 - 1$ vectors in front of it, namely $\mathfrak{b}_1^2, \mathfrak{b}_2^2, \cdots, \mathfrak{b}_{\varrho_1-1}^2$ (the upper indices here are $=2$, since ν_{ϱ_1} was taken to be the first upper index which was equal to 1). We successively interchange $\mathfrak{b}_{\varrho_1}^1$ with the vectors $\mathfrak{b}_{\varrho_1-1}^2, \mathfrak{b}_{\varrho_1-2}^2, \cdots, \mathfrak{b}_1^2$. Thus $\mathfrak{b}_{\varrho_1}^1$ is brought into the first place, while the relative positions of the other vectors remain unaltered. In the process, the sign of the determinant $D(\mathfrak{b}_1^{\nu_1}, \mathfrak{b}_2^{\nu_2}, \cdots, \mathfrak{b}_n^{\nu_n})$ is changed $\varrho_1 - 1$ times. In the same way, we bring the vector $\mathfrak{b}^1_{\varrho_2}$ into the second place by successively interchanging it with all vectors which precede it, with the exception of $\mathfrak{b}^1_{\varrho_1}$. This involves $\varrho_2 - 2$ interchanges, so that the sign of the determinant is changed another $\varrho_2 - 2$ times. Continuing this process, we successively bring the vectors $\mathfrak{b}^1_{\varrho_3}, \mathfrak{b}^1_{\varrho_4}, \cdots, \mathfrak{b}^1_{\varrho_p}$ into the 3-rd, 4-th, ..., p-th places, respectively. This involves $\varrho_3 - 3$, $\varrho_4 - 4$, ..., $\varrho_p - p$ interchanges, respectively, so that these numbers also represent the number of changes in sign of the determinant during the corresponding process. At the conclusion of the process, the vectors $\mathfrak{b}^{\nu_i}_i$ appear in the order $\mathfrak{b}^1_{\varrho_1}, \mathfrak{b}^1_{\varrho_2}, \cdots, \mathfrak{b}^1_{\varrho_p}, \mathfrak{b}^2_{\sigma_1}, \mathfrak{b}^2_{\sigma_2}, \cdots, \mathfrak{b}^2_{\sigma_q}$, so that we have

$$D(\mathfrak{b}^{\nu_1}_1, \mathfrak{b}^{\nu_2}_2, \cdots, \mathfrak{b}^{\nu_n}_n) = (-1)^{(\varrho_1-1)+(\varrho_2-2)+\cdots+(\varrho_p-p)} \cdot$$
$$\cdot D(\mathfrak{b}^1_{\varrho_1}, \mathfrak{b}^1_{\varrho_2}, \cdots, \mathfrak{b}^1_{\varrho_p}, \mathfrak{b}^2_{\sigma_1}, \mathfrak{b}^2_{\sigma_2}, \cdots, \mathfrak{b}^2_{\sigma_q}).$$

Substituting this in (27), we obtain

$$(28) \qquad |a_{ik}| = \sum_{\substack{(\varrho_1, \varrho_2, \cdots, \varrho_p) \\ \varrho_1 < \varrho_2 < \cdots < \varrho_p}} (-1)^{\varrho_1+\varrho_2+\cdots+\varrho_p - \frac{p(p+1)}{2}} \cdot$$
$$\cdot D(\mathfrak{b}^1_{\varrho_1}, \mathfrak{b}^1_{\varrho_2}, \cdots, \mathfrak{b}^1_{\varrho_p}, \mathfrak{b}^2_{\sigma_1}, \mathfrak{b}^2_{\sigma_2}, \cdots, \mathfrak{b}^2_{\sigma_q}).$$

The summation on the right is taken over all p-tuples

$$(\varrho_1, \varrho_2, \cdots, \varrho_p)$$

of numbers from among $1, 2, \ldots, n$, where

$$\varrho_1 < \varrho_2 < \cdots < \varrho_p .$$

The remaining q integers, in order of magnitude, are

$$\sigma_1, \sigma_2, \cdots, \sigma_q$$

What do the rows of a determinant

$$D(\mathfrak{b}^1_{\varrho_1}, \mathfrak{b}^1_{\varrho_2}, \cdots, \mathfrak{b}^1_{\varrho_p}, \mathfrak{b}^2_{\sigma_1}, \mathfrak{b}^2_{\sigma_2}, \cdots, \mathfrak{b}^2_{\sigma_q})$$

look like? Recalling the special form of the vectors $\mathfrak{b}^1_i$ and $\mathfrak{b}^2_i$, we see that for $1 \leqq k \leqq p$, the first p elements of the k-th row are

$$a_{\varrho_k,1}, \ a_{\varrho_k,2}, \ \cdots, \ a_{\varrho_k,p}$$

while the last q elements vanish; and for $1 \leqq k \leqq q$, the first p elements of the $(p+k)$-th row are 0, while the last q elements are $a_{\sigma_k,p+1}, \ a_{\sigma_k,p+2}, \cdots, \ a_{\sigma_k,n}$. The determinant in question thus has the form

$$\left|\begin{array}{cccc|cccc} a_{\varrho_1 1} & a_{\varrho_1 2} & \cdots & a_{\varrho_1 p} & 0 & 0 & \cdots & 0 \\ a_{\varrho_2 1} & a_{\varrho_2 2} & \cdots & a_{\varrho_2 p} & 0 & 0 & \cdots & 0 \\ \cdot & \cdot & \cdot & \cdot & \cdot & \cdot & \cdot & \cdot \\ a_{\varrho_p 1} & a_{\varrho_p 2} & \cdots & a_{\varrho_p p} & 0 & 0 & \cdots & 0 \\ \hline 0 & 0 & \cdots & 0 & a_{\sigma_1, p+1} & a_{\sigma_1, p+2} & \cdots & a_{\sigma_1, n} \\ 0 & 0 & \cdots & 0 & a_{\sigma_2, p+1} & a_{\sigma_2, p+2} & \cdots & a_{\sigma_2, n} \\ \cdot & \cdot & \cdot & \cdot & \cdot & \cdot & \cdot & \cdot \\ 0 & 0 & \cdots & 0 & a_{\sigma_q, p+1} & a_{\sigma_q, p+2} & \cdots & a_{\sigma_q, n} \end{array}\right|.$$

Applying (26), we obtain

$$D(\mathfrak{b}^1_{\varrho_1}, \mathfrak{b}^1_{\varrho_2}, \cdots, \mathfrak{b}^1_{\varrho_p}, \mathfrak{b}^2_{\sigma_1}, \mathfrak{b}^2_{\sigma_2}, \cdots, \mathfrak{b}^2_{\sigma_q}) =$$

$$= \begin{vmatrix} a_{\varrho_1 1} & a_{\varrho_1 2} & \cdots & a_{\varrho_1 p} \\ a_{\varrho_2 1} & a_{\varrho_2 2} & \cdots & a_{\varrho_2 p} \\ \cdot & \cdot & \cdot & \cdot \\ a_{\varrho_p 1} & a_{\varrho_p 2} & \cdots & a_{\varrho_p p} \end{vmatrix} \cdot \begin{vmatrix} a_{\sigma_1, p+1} & a_{\sigma_1, p+2} & \cdots & a_{\sigma_1 n} \\ a_{\sigma_2, p+1} & a_{\sigma_2, p+2} & \cdots & a_{\sigma_2 n} \\ \cdot & \cdot & \cdot & \cdot \\ a_{\sigma_q, p+1} & a_{\sigma_q, p+2} & \cdots & a_{\sigma_q n} \end{vmatrix}.$$

Finally, substituting this into (28), we have

$$|a_{ik}| = \sum_{\substack{(\varrho_1, \varrho_2, \cdots, \varrho_p) \\ \varrho_1 < \varrho_2 < \cdots < \varrho_p}} (-1)^{\varrho_1 + \varrho_2 + \cdots + \varrho_p + \frac{p(p+1)}{2}} \cdot$$

(29) $$\begin{vmatrix} a_{\varrho_1 1} & a_{\varrho_1 2} & \cdots & a_{\varrho_1 p} \\ a_{\varrho_2 1} & a_{\varrho_2 2} & \cdots & a_{\varrho_2 p} \\ \cdot & \cdot & \cdot & \cdot \\ a_{\varrho_p 1} & a_{\varrho_p 2} & \cdots & a_{\varrho_p p} \end{vmatrix} \cdot \begin{vmatrix} a_{\sigma_1, p+1} & a_{\sigma_1, p+2} & \cdots & a_{\sigma_1 n} \\ a_{\sigma_2, p+1} & a_{\sigma_2, p+2} & \cdots & a_{\sigma_2 n} \\ \cdot & \cdot & \cdot & \cdot \\ a_{\sigma_q, p+1} & a_{\sigma_q, p+2} & \cdots & a_{\sigma_q n} \end{vmatrix}.$$ [8]

Let us try to get a clear idea of the meaning of this formula. Each summand on the right-hand side of (29) is the product of two subdeterminants, with a suitable sign prefixed. However, the two subdeterminants which appear in a given term are in a simple relation to one another. In fact, the p-by-p determinant $|a_{\varrho_i, k}|$ results from $|a_{ik}|$ by the crossing out of the σ_1-st, σ_2-nd, ..., σ_q-th rows, and the $(p+1)$-st, $(p+2)$-nd, ..., and n-th columns; while the q-by-q determinant $|a_{\sigma_i, p+k}|$ results from $|a_{ik}|$ by crossing out just those rows and columns which were not crossed out in the process of obtaining

[8] We have

$$(-1)^{\varrho_1 + \varrho_2 + \cdots + \varrho_p - \frac{p(p+1)}{2}} = (-1)^{\varrho_1 + \varrho_2 + \cdots + \varrho_p + \frac{p(p+1)}{2}}$$

$|a_{\varrho_i, k}|$, namely the ϱ_1-st, ϱ_2-nd, ..., ϱ_p-th rows, and the 1-st, 2-nd, ..., p-th columns. Two such sub-determinants are called *complementary* to each other. Furthermore, the sum (29) is taken over all p-tuples $(\varrho_1, \varrho_2, \cdots, \varrho_p)$ for which $\varrho_1 < \varrho_2 < \cdots < \varrho_p$, while the column indices 1, 2, ..., p are the same for all summands. Thus if we consider the matrix which consists of the first p columns of $|a_{ik}|$, i.e. the matrix

$$\begin{pmatrix} a_{11} & a_{12} & \cdots & a_{1p} \\ a_{21} & a_{22} & \cdots & a_{2p} \\ \cdot & \cdot & \cdot & \cdot \\ a_{n1} & a_{n2} & \cdots & a_{np} \end{pmatrix}, \tag{30}$$

we see that the determinants $|a_{\varrho_i, k}|$ are precisely the p-by-p sub-determinants of this matrix, and that indeed each such sub-determinant occurs in the sum precisely once. In order to evaluate the determinant $|a_{ik}|$, by (29) we have only to place in front of each p-by-p sub-determinant $|a_{\varrho_i, k}|$ of (30), the sign $(-1)^{\varrho_1+\varrho_2+\cdots+\varrho_p+\frac{p(p+1)}{2}}$, and then to multiply it by its complementary sub-determinant $|a_{\sigma_i, p+k}|$ with respect to $|a_{ik}|$, and finally to sum all products of this form.

We also see at once, by transposing the determinant $|a_{ik}|$ so that its columns become rows and its rows, columns, that an analogous expansion holds with respect to the rows of a determinant, as follows. We form the matrix consisting of the first p rows of $|a_{ik}|$. If we then prefix each p-by-p sub-determinant $|a_{i, \varrho_k}|$ of this matrix by the sign $(-1)^{\frac{p(p+1)}{2}+\varrho_1+\varrho_2+\cdots+\varrho_p}$, and next multiply it by its complementary sub-determinant $|a_{p+i, \sigma_k}|$ with respect to $|a_{ik}|$, and finally sum all products of this form, then we obtain the value of the determinant $|a_{ik}|$. That is,

$$|a_{ik}| = \sum_{\substack{(\varrho_1, \varrho_2, \cdots, \varrho_p) \\ \varrho_1 < \varrho_2 < \cdots < \varrho_p}} (-1)^{\frac{p(p+1)}{2}+\varrho_1+\varrho_2+\cdots+\varrho_p} \cdot \begin{vmatrix} a_{1\varrho_1} & a_{1\varrho_2} & \cdots & a_{1\varrho_p} \\ a_{2\varrho_1} & a_{2\varrho_2} & \cdots & a_{2\varrho_p} \\ \cdot & \cdot & \cdot & \cdot \\ a_{p\varrho_1} & a_{p\varrho_2} & \cdots & a_{p\varrho_p} \end{vmatrix} \cdot \begin{vmatrix} a_{p+1, \sigma_1} & a_{p+1, \sigma_2} & \cdots & a_{p+1, \sigma_q} \\ a_{p+2, \sigma_1} & a_{p+2, \sigma_2} & \cdots & a_{p+2, \sigma_q} \\ \cdot & \cdot & \cdot & \cdot \\ a_{n, \sigma_1} & a_{n, \sigma_2} & \cdots & a_{n, \sigma_q} \end{vmatrix}. \tag{31}$$

We now proceed to generalize (31). To this end, we divide the vectors $\mathfrak{a}_1, \mathfrak{a}_2, \cdots, \mathfrak{a}_n$ into two systems. Let the first consist of the p vectors $\mathfrak{a}_{\alpha_1}, \mathfrak{a}_{\alpha_2}, \cdots, \mathfrak{a}_{\alpha_p}$ $(\alpha_1 < \alpha_2 < \cdots < \alpha_p)$, the second of the q remaining vectors

$$\mathfrak{a}_{\beta_1}, \mathfrak{a}_{\beta_2}, \cdots, \mathfrak{a}_{\beta_q} \; (\beta_1 < \beta_2 < \cdots < \beta_q, \quad p + q = n).$$

We then interchange $\mathfrak{a}_{\alpha_1}$ with all vectors which precede it in the determinant $D(\mathfrak{a}_1, \mathfrak{a}_2, \cdots, \mathfrak{a}_n)$. This involves $\alpha_1 - 1$ interchanges, and brings $\mathfrak{a}_{\alpha_1}$ into the first place. In the same way we bring the vectors $\mathfrak{a}_{\alpha_2}, \mathfrak{a}_{\alpha_3}, \cdots, \mathfrak{a}_{\alpha_p}$ into the 2-nd, 3-rd, . . . , p-th places, respectively; this involves $\alpha_2 - 2$, $\alpha_3 - 3$, . . . , $\alpha_p - p$ interchanges, respectively. Then

$$\begin{aligned} &D(\mathfrak{a}_1, \mathfrak{a}_2, \cdots, \mathfrak{a}_n) = \\ (32)\qquad &= (-1)^{\alpha_1+\alpha_2+\cdots+\alpha_p-\frac{p(p+1)}{2}} \cdot D(\mathfrak{a}_{\alpha_1}, \mathfrak{a}_{\alpha_2}, \cdots, \mathfrak{a}_{\alpha_p}, \mathfrak{a}_{\beta_1}, \mathfrak{a}_{\beta_2}, \cdots, \mathfrak{a}_{\beta_q}). \end{aligned}$$

We apply (31) to the determinant $D(\mathfrak{a}_{\alpha_1}, \mathfrak{a}_{\alpha_2}, \cdots, \mathfrak{a}_{\alpha_p}, \mathfrak{a}_{\beta_1}, \mathfrak{a}_{\beta_2}, \cdots, \mathfrak{a}_{\beta_q})$ and obtain

$$D(\mathfrak{a}_{\alpha_1}, \cdots, \mathfrak{a}_{\alpha_p}, \mathfrak{a}_{\beta_1}, \cdots, \mathfrak{a}_{\beta_q}) = \sum_{\substack{(\varrho_1, \varrho_2, \cdots, \varrho_p) \\ \varrho_1 < \varrho_2 < \cdots < \varrho_p}} (-1)^{\varrho_1+\varrho_2+\cdots+\varrho_p+\frac{p(p+1)}{2}} \cdot$$

$$(33) \qquad \cdot \begin{vmatrix} a_{\alpha_1\varrho_1} & a_{\alpha_1\varrho_2} & \cdots & a_{\alpha_1\varrho_p} \\ a_{\alpha_2\varrho_1} & a_{\alpha_2\varrho_2} & \cdots & a_{\alpha_2\varrho_p} \\ \cdot & \cdot & \cdot & \cdot \\ a_{\alpha_p\varrho_1} & a_{\alpha_p\varrho_2} & \cdots & a_{\alpha_p\varrho_p} \end{vmatrix} \cdot \begin{vmatrix} a_{\beta_1\sigma_1} & a_{\beta_1\sigma_2} & \cdots & a_{\beta_1\sigma_q} \\ a_{\beta_2\sigma_1} & a_{\beta_2\sigma_2} & \cdots & a_{\beta_2\sigma_q} \\ \cdot & \cdot & \cdot & \cdot \\ a_{\beta_q\sigma_1} & a_{\beta_q\sigma_2} & \cdots & a_{\beta_q\sigma_q} \end{vmatrix}.$$

$\alpha_1, \alpha_2, \cdots, \alpha_p, \beta_1, \beta_2, \cdots, \beta_q$ were defined to be fixed indices. The summation is taken over all p-tuples $(\varrho_1, \varrho_2, \cdots, \varrho_p)$ from among the numbers 1, 2, . . . , n for which $\varrho_1 < \varrho_2 < \cdots < \varrho_p$ where

$$\sigma_1 < \sigma_2 < \cdots < \sigma_q$$

are the remaining q integers. The two sub-determinants $|a_{\alpha_i\varrho_k}|$ and $|a_{\beta_i\sigma_k}|$ are also called complementary to each other. ($|a_{\beta_i\sigma_k}|$ results from $|a_{ik}|$ by crossing out those rows and columns which remained in $|a_{\alpha_i\varrho_k}|$) If we substitute (33) into (32), we finally obtain

$$|a_{ik}| = \sum_{\substack{(\varrho_1, \varrho_2, \cdots, \varrho_p) \\ \varrho_1 < \varrho_2 < \cdots < \varrho_p}} (-1)^{\alpha_1+\alpha_2+\cdots+\alpha_p+\varrho_1+\varrho_2+\cdots+\varrho_p} \cdot$$

$$(34) \qquad \cdot \begin{vmatrix} a_{\alpha_1\varrho_1} & a_{\alpha_1\varrho_2} & \cdots & a_{\alpha_1\varrho_p} \\ a_{\alpha_2\varrho_1} & a_{\alpha_2\varrho_2} & \cdots & a_{\alpha_2\varrho_p} \\ \cdot & \cdot & \cdot & \cdot \\ a_{\alpha_p\varrho_1} & a_{\alpha_p\varrho_2} & \cdots & a_{\alpha_p\varrho_p} \end{vmatrix} \cdot \begin{vmatrix} a_{\beta_1\sigma_1} & a_{\beta_1\sigma_2} & \cdots & a_{\beta_1\sigma_q} \\ a_{\beta_2\sigma_1} & a_{\beta_2\sigma_2} & \cdots & a_{\beta_2\sigma_q} \\ \cdot & \cdot & \cdot & \cdot \\ a_{\beta_q\sigma_1} & a_{\beta_q\sigma_2} & \cdots & a_{\beta_q\sigma_q} \end{vmatrix}.$$

This is *Laplace's general expansion theorem*. The meaning of (34) may also be expressed as follows.

We consider the matrix which is formed of the α_1-st, α_2-nd, . . . , α_p-th rows of $|a_{ik}|$, i.e.

$$\begin{pmatrix} a_{\alpha_1 1} & a_{\alpha_1 2} & \cdots & a_{\alpha_1 n} \\ a_{\alpha_2 1} & a_{\alpha_2 2} & \cdots & a_{\alpha_2 n} \\ \cdot & \cdot & \cdot & \cdot \\ a_{\alpha_p 1} & a_{\alpha_p 2} & \cdots & a_{\alpha_p n} \end{pmatrix}.$$

If we prefix each p-by-p sub-determinant $|a_{\alpha_i \varrho_k}|$ of this matrix by the sign $(-1)^{\alpha_1+\alpha_2+\cdots+\alpha_p+\varrho_1+\varrho_2+\cdots+\varrho_p}$, and then multiply it by its complementary sub-determinant $|a_{\beta_i \sigma_k}|$ with respect to $|a_{ik}|$, and finally sum over all products of this form, we obtain the value of $|a_{ik}|$.

Of course, we have an analogous result for the columns of the determinant.

Exercises

1. Let n points $P_i = (a_1^{(i)}, a_2^{(i)}, \cdots, a_n^{(i)})\ i = 1, 2, \ldots, n$ which do not all lie in the same linear space of dimension less than $n-1$, be given in R_n. Prove that

$$\begin{vmatrix} x_1 & x_2 & \cdots & x_n & 1 \\ a_1^{(1)} & a_2^{(1)} & \cdots & a_n^{(1)} & 1 \\ a_1^{(2)} & a_2^{(2)} & \cdots & a_n^{(2)} & 1 \\ \cdot & \cdot & \cdot & \cdot & \cdot \\ a_1^{(n)} & a_2^{(n)} & \cdots & a_n^{(n)} & 1 \end{vmatrix} = 0$$

is a linear equation in the n variables $x_1, x_2, \cdots, x_n$ (the $a_k^{(i)}$ are considered to be constants). Thus, by § 6, Theorem 9, this equation represents a hyperplane. This hyperplane contains the n points $P_1, P_2, \cdots, P_n$. Hence, what is the criterion that $n+1$ given points of R_n lie in a hyperplane?

2. Employing exercise 1, determine the equation of the plane in R_3 which passes through the points $P_1 = (0, 1, 7)$, $P_2 = (3, 1, -1)$, $P_3 = (-1, -1, -2)$. Also the equations of the lines in R_2 through the points a) $(0, 1)$, $(-5, 10)$; b) $(-4, 1)$, $(11, 9)$. Do the points $(1, 2)$, $(4, 1)$, and $(-2, -4)$ of R_2 lie on a line? The points $(2, 2)$, $(-1, 3)$, $(8, 0)$? Do the points $(1, 6, -4)$, $(0, 0, 1)$, $(2, -3, 0)$, $(1, 1, -1)$ of R_3 lie in a plane? Do the points $(1, 1, 1)$, $(2, -1, 0)$, $(0, 3, 2)$ of R_3 lie on a line?

3. Determine the rank of the following matrices:

$$\begin{pmatrix} 1 & -1 & 1 \\ 2 & 3 & 1 \\ 4 & 1 & 3 \end{pmatrix}, \quad \begin{pmatrix} 1 & 3 & 7 & -1 \\ 4 & -1 & 2 & -2 \\ 4 & 11 & 17 & 1 \end{pmatrix}, \quad \begin{pmatrix} 1 & 3 & 2 & 2 \\ 2 & -1 & 1 & 0 \\ 1 & -1 & 2 & -2 \\ 0 & 1 & 2 & -1 \end{pmatrix}.$$

4. Given three lines in R_3. Let them pass through the points

a) $(-1,\ 7,\ 3)$, $(0,\ \frac{7}{2},\ 2)$,
b) $(4,\ 5,\ -2)$, $(-2,\ -5,\ 4)$,
c) $(2,\ 2,\ 1)$, $(-4,\ 12,\ 5)$.

Which of these lines are skew, and which are intersecting?

5. Let four hyperplanes in R_4 be given by the equations

$$\begin{aligned}
&\text{a)}\quad x_1 + x_2 + 4x_4 = 3,\\
&\text{b)}\quad x_2 - x_3 + 3x_4 = 1,\\
&\text{c)}\quad x_1 - 2x_2 + 3x_3 - 5x_4 = 0,\\
&\text{d)}\quad 3x_1 - x_2 + 4x_3 = 5.
\end{aligned}$$

Do these four hyperplanes have any points of intersection in common? What is the dimension of their intersection? Determine the points of intersection.

6. Let there be given $n-1$ linear homogeneous equations in n unknowns,

$$\sum_{k=1}^{n} a_{ik} x_k = 0, \qquad i = 1, 2, \cdots, n-1.$$

The matrix of this system of equations is

$$\begin{pmatrix} a_{11} & a_{12} & \cdots & a_{1n} \\ a_{21} & a_{22} & \cdots & a_{2n} \\ \cdot & \cdot & \cdot & \cdot \\ a_{n-1,1} & a_{n-1,2} & \cdots & a_{n-1,n} \end{pmatrix}.$$

We denote by A_k the $(n-1)$-by-$(n-1)$ determinant which results from this matrix by crossing out the k-th column. Show that the equations are satisfied by $x_k = (-1)^k A_k$ or by $x_k = (-1)^{k+1} A_k$. If the matrix has rank $n-1$, this provides a useful method for determining the solutions of this system of equations. n linear equations in n unknowns with non-vanishing determinant may also be solved by use of this method. For, instead of seeking a solution of the system of equations

$$\sum_{k=1}^{n} a_{ik} x_k = b_i, \qquad i = 1, 2, \cdots, n,$$

we seek a solution of the homogeneous system

$$\sum_{k=1}^{n} a_{ik} x_k - b_i x_{n+1} = 0, \qquad i = 1, 2, \cdots, n,$$

for which $x_{n+1} = 1$. Use these remarks to give another proof of Cramer's rule.

7. Prove the following identity:

$$\begin{vmatrix} 1 & x_1 & x_1^2 & \cdots & x_1^{n-1} \\ 1 & x_2 & x_2^2 & \cdots & x_2^{n-1} \\ \cdot & \cdot & \cdot & \cdot & \cdot \\ 1 & x_n & x_n^2 & \cdots & x_n^{n-1} \end{vmatrix} = \begin{vmatrix} (x_2-x_1) & (x_2-x_1)x_2 & (x_2-x_1)x_2^2 & \cdots & (x_2-x_1)x_2^{n-2} \\ (x_3-x_1) & (x_3-x_1)x_3 & (x_3-x_1)x_3^2 & \cdots & (x_3-x_1)x_3^{n-2} \\ \cdot & \cdot & \cdot & \cdot & \cdot \\ (x_n-x_1) & (x_n-x_1)x_n & (x_n-x_1)x_n^2 & \cdots & (x_n-x_1)x_n^{n-2} \end{vmatrix}$$

The n-by-n determinant which appears on the left is known as the *Vandermonde determinant*. The determinant on the right has $n-1$ rows. From this equation, it easily follows by mathematical induction that

$$\begin{vmatrix} 1 & x_1 & x_1^2 & \cdots & x_1^{n-1} \\ 1 & x_2 & x_2^2 & \cdots & x_2^{n-1} \\ \cdot & \cdot & \cdot & \cdot & \cdot \\ 1 & x_n & x_n^2 & \cdots & x_n^{n-1} \end{vmatrix} = \begin{aligned} &(x_2-x_1)(x_3-x_1)(x_4-x_1)\cdots(x_n-x_1)\\ &\cdot(x_3-x_2)(x_4-x_2)\cdots(x_n-x_2)\\ &\cdot(x_4-x_3)\cdots(x_n-x_3)\\ &\cdots\cdots\\ &(x_n-x_{n-1}). \end{aligned}$$

This result is known as *Vandermonde's determinant theorem.* The expression which appears on the right is the product of all differences $x_i - x_k$ with $i > k$ and

$$1 \leqq i \leqq n, \quad 1 \leqq k \leqq n-1.$$

8. Generalizing (4) of this section somewhat, we define

$$\operatorname{sgn}(\nu_1, \nu_2, \cdots, \nu_n) = D(\mathfrak{e}_{\nu_1}, \mathfrak{e}_{\nu_2}, \cdots \mathfrak{e}_{\nu_n}).$$

Then (5) may be written

$$|a_{ik}| = \sum_{\nu_1, \nu_2, \cdots, \nu_n = 1}^{n} \operatorname{sgn}(\nu_1, \nu_2, \cdots, \nu_n)\, a_{1\nu_1} a_{2\nu_2} \cdots a_{n\nu_n}.$$

Prove that

$$\operatorname{sgn}(\alpha_1, \alpha_2, \cdots, \alpha_n) \cdot |a_{ik}| = \sum_{\nu_1, \nu_2, \cdots, \nu_n = 1}^{n} \operatorname{sgn}(\nu_1, \nu_2, \cdots, \nu_n)\, a_{\alpha_1\nu_1} a_{\alpha_2\nu_2} \cdots a_{\alpha_n\nu_n}.$$

In this expression $\alpha_1, \alpha_2, \cdots, \alpha_n$ are n fixed positive integers with $1 \leqq \alpha_i \leqq n$. Furthermore,

$$\operatorname{sgn}(\alpha_1, \alpha_2, \cdots, \alpha_n) \cdot |a_{ik}| = \sum_{\nu_1, \nu_2, \cdots, \nu_n = 1}^{n} \operatorname{sgn}(\nu_1, \nu_2, \cdots, \nu_n)\, a_{\nu_1\alpha_1} a_{\nu_2\alpha_2} \cdots a_{\nu_n\alpha_n}.$$

9. The notation introduced in the course of the preceding exercise leads to an easy proof of the multiplication theorem. As on page 90 (or 96), let there be given three n-by-n determinants $|a_{ik}|, |b_{ik}|, |c_{ik}|$ whose elements satisfy the relation

$$c_{ik} = \sum_{\nu=1}^{n} a_{i\nu} b_{\nu k}.$$

It easily follows that

$$\begin{aligned}
|a_{ik}| \cdot |b_{ik}| &= \sum_{\nu_1, \nu_2, \cdots, \nu_n = 1}^{n} (|a_{ik}| \cdot \operatorname{sgn}(\nu_1, \nu_2, \cdots, \nu_n)\, b_{\nu_1 1} \cdot b_{\nu_2 2} \cdots b_{\nu_n n}) \\
&= \sum_{\nu_1, \nu_2, \cdots, \nu_n = 1}^{n} \Bigg(\sum_{\mu_1, \mu_2, \cdots, \mu_n = 1}^{n} \operatorname{sgn}(\mu_1, \mu_2, \cdots, \mu_n) \cdot \\
&\qquad \cdot a_{\mu_1\nu_1} \cdot a_{\mu_2\nu_2} \cdots a_{\mu_n\nu_n} \cdot b_{\nu_1 1} \cdot b_{\nu_2 2} \cdots b_{\nu_n n} \Bigg) \\
&= \sum_{\mu_1, \mu_2, \cdots, \mu_n = 1}^{n} \Bigg[\operatorname{sgn}(\mu_1, \mu_2, \cdots, \mu_n) \left(\sum_{\nu_1=1}^{n} a_{\mu_1\nu_1} b_{\nu_1 1} \right) \cdot \\
&\qquad \cdot \left(\sum_{\nu_2=1}^{n} a_{\mu_2\nu_2} b_{\nu_2 2} \right) \cdots \left(\sum_{\nu_n=1}^{n} a_{\mu_n\nu_n} b_{\nu_n n} \right) \Bigg] \\
&= \sum_{\mu_1, \mu_2, \cdots, \mu_n = 1}^{n} \operatorname{sgn}(\mu_1, \mu_2, \cdots, \mu_n)\, c_{\mu_1 1} \cdot c_{\mu_2 2} \cdots c_{\mu_n n} \\
&= |c_{ik}|.
\end{aligned}$$

10. Let

$$(a_{ik}) = \begin{pmatrix} a_{11} & a_{12} & \cdots & a_{1n} \\ a_{21} & a_{22} & \cdots & a_{2n} \\ \cdot & \cdot & \cdot & \cdot \\ a_{m1} & a_{m2} & \cdots & a_{mn} \end{pmatrix}, \qquad (b_{ik}) = \begin{pmatrix} b_{11} & b_{12} & \cdots & b_{1n} \\ b_{21} & b_{22} & \cdots & b_{2n} \\ \cdot & \cdot & \cdot & \cdot \\ b_{m1} & b_{m2} & \cdots & b_{mn} \end{pmatrix}.$$

be two m-by-n matrices. Employing these matrices, we form the determinant

$$D = \left|\begin{array}{cccc|cccc} 0 & 0 & \cdots & 0 & a_{11} & a_{12} & \cdots & a_{1n} \\ 0 & 0 & \cdots & 0 & a_{21} & a_{22} & \cdots & a_{2n} \\ \cdot & \cdot & \cdot & \cdot & \cdot & \cdot & \cdot & \cdot \\ 0 & 0 & \cdots & 0 & a_{m1} & a_{m2} & \cdots & a_{mn} \\ \hline b_{11} & b_{21} & \cdots & b_{m1} & 1 & 0 & \cdots & 0 \\ b_{12} & b_{22} & \cdots & b_{m2} & 0 & 1 & \cdots & 0 \\ \cdot & \cdot & \cdot & \cdot & \cdot & \cdot & \cdot & \cdot \\ b_{1n} & b_{2n} & \cdots & b_{mn} & 0 & 0 & \cdots & 1 \end{array}\right|.$$

In this determinant, the m-by-m square array in the upper left corner contains only zeros. The n-by-n square array in the lower right corner contains only zeros except for its principal diagonal which consists entirely of ones. The m-by-n rectangular array in the upper right corner contains the entries of the matrix (a_{ik}) in the given arrangement. The n-by-m rectangular array in the lower left corner contains the entries of the matrix (b_{ik}), but arranged so that the rows of (b_{ik}) become columns of this rectangle.

We denote the column vectors of the matrix (a_{ik}) by $\mathfrak{a}_1, \mathfrak{a}_2, \cdots, \mathfrak{a}_n$, those of the matrix (b_{ik}) by $\mathfrak{b}_1, \mathfrak{b}_2, \cdots, \mathfrak{b}_n$. Thus $\mathfrak{a}_i = \{a_{1i}, a_{2i}, \cdots, a_{mi}\}$, $\mathfrak{b}_i = \{b_{1i}, b_{2i}, \cdots, b_{mi}\}$. By successive application of Laplace's general expansion theorem, prove that

$$D = (-1)^{m^2} \sum_{\substack{\nu_1, \nu_2, \cdots, \nu_m = 1 \\ \nu_1 < \nu_2 < \cdots < \nu_m}}^{n} D(\mathfrak{a}_{\nu_1}, \mathfrak{a}_{\nu_2}, \cdots, \mathfrak{a}_{\nu_m}) \cdot D(\mathfrak{b}_{\nu_1}, \mathfrak{b}_{\nu_2}, \cdots, \mathfrak{b}_{\nu_m}).$$

The individual summands of the sum on the right are each the product of two m-by-m sub-determinants of the matrices (a_{ik}) and (b_{ik}), of which the first consists of the ν_1-st, ν_2-nd, ..., ν_n-th columns of (a_{ik}), and the second of the same columns of the matrix (b_{ik}).

We denote the $(m+i)$-th row of the determinant D by $\mathfrak{z}_i$ $(i = 1, 2, \ldots, n)$. We now successively subtract the vectors $\sum_{i=1}^{n} a_{ki}\,\mathfrak{z}_i$ from the k-th row of the determinant D, for $k = 1, 2, \ldots, m$. By a suitable expansion of the determinant thus obtained, show that

$$D = (-1)^m \left| \sum_{\nu=1}^{n} a_{i\nu}\, b_{k\nu} \right|.$$

The determinant which appears on the right has m rows. In its i-th row and k-th column the sum $\sum_{\nu=1}^{n} a_{i\nu}\, b_{k\nu}$ appears, i.e. the scalar product of the i-th row of (a_{ik}) and the k-th row of (b_{ik}).

Comparison of the last two equations yields the *general Lagrange identity*:

$$\sum_{\substack{\nu_1, \nu_2, \cdots, \nu_n = 1 \\ \nu_1 < \nu_2 < \cdots < \nu_n}}^{n} D(\mathfrak{a}_{\nu_1}, \mathfrak{a}_{\nu_2}, \cdots, \mathfrak{a}_{\nu_n}) \cdot D(\mathfrak{b}_{\nu_1}, \mathfrak{b}_{\nu_2}, \cdots, \mathfrak{b}_{\nu_n}) = \left| \sum_{\nu=1}^{n} a_{i\nu}\, b_{k\nu} \right|.$$

§ 10. Transformation of Coordinates

General Linear Coordinate Systems

In § 5 we have shown how so-called general linear coordinates could be introduced into an arbitrary linear space. In particular, this may be done for R_n, which is nothing but an (n-dimensional) linear space. A (linear) coordinate system in R_n is determined by the choice of a point Q as an origin and of n linearly independent vectors $\mathfrak{v}_1, \mathfrak{v}_2, \cdots, \mathfrak{v}_n$ as basis vectors. If P is an arbitrary point and if

$$\overrightarrow{QP} = x_1^* \mathfrak{v}_1 + x_2^* \mathfrak{v}_2 + \cdots + x_n^* \mathfrak{v}_n, \tag{1}$$

then $x_1^*, x_2^*, \ldots, x_n^*$ are the coordinates of P in our coordinate system. The point Q thus has the coordinates $0, 0, \ldots, 0$.

The usual coordinates $x_1, x_2, \ldots, x_n$ of the point $P = (x_1, x_2, \ldots, x_n)$ also may be considered as coordinates if we choose the point $O = (0, 0, \ldots, 0)$ as origin and the unit vectors $\mathfrak{e}_1, \mathfrak{e}_2, \cdots, \mathfrak{e}_n$ as our basis vectors in R_n. Indeed we have

$$\overrightarrow{OP} = x_1 \mathfrak{e}_1 + x_2 \mathfrak{e}_2 + \cdots + x_n \mathfrak{e}_n.$$

We shall agree to write $P = (x_1, x_2, \ldots, x_n)$ only when $x_1, x_2, \ldots, x_n$ are the coordinates of P in the special coordinate system having O as origin and $\mathfrak{e}_1, \mathfrak{e}_2, \cdots, \mathfrak{e}_n$ as basis vectors. In other words, $P = (x_1, x_2, \ldots, x_n)$ shall mean that P is the n-tuple $(x_1, x_2, \ldots, x_n)$.

We shall denote the coordinate system having Q as origin and $\mathfrak{v}_1, \mathfrak{v}_2, \cdots, \mathfrak{v}_n$ as basis vectors by $[Q; \mathfrak{v}_1, \mathfrak{v}_2, \cdots, \mathfrak{v}_n]$. If

$$\mathfrak{a} = \{a_1, a_2, \cdots, a_n\}$$

is any vector of R_n, we may write it as a linear combination of the vectors $\mathfrak{v}_1, \mathfrak{v}_2, \cdots, \mathfrak{v}_n$; say

$$\mathfrak{a} = \sum_{i=1}^{n} a_i^* \mathfrak{v}_i.$$

We call the uniquely determined numbers $a_1^*, a_2^*, \ldots, a_n^*$ the *component of* $\mathfrak{a}$ *in the coordinate system* $[Q; \mathfrak{v}_1, \mathfrak{v}_2, \cdots, \mathfrak{v}_n]$ or *the components with respect to the basis* $\mathfrak{v}_1, \mathfrak{v}_2, \cdots, \mathfrak{v}_n$. These vector components are independent of the choice of the origin Q. In addition, we shall write $\mathfrak{a} = \{a_1, a_2, \ldots, a_n\}$ *only* if the numbers $a_1, a_2, \ldots, a_n$ are the components of $\mathfrak{a}$ with respect to the special basis $\mathfrak{e}_1, \mathfrak{e}_2, \cdots, \mathfrak{e}_n$.

Let there be given two points P and R having the coordinates $x_1^*, x_2^*, \ldots, x_n^*$ and $y_1^*, y_2^*, \ldots, y_n^*$ respectively in the coordinate system $[Q; \mathfrak{v}_1, \mathfrak{v}_2, \cdots, \mathfrak{v}_n]$. Then

$$\overrightarrow{PR} = \overrightarrow{PQ} + \overrightarrow{QR} = -\sum_{i=1}^{n} x_i^* \mathfrak{v}_i + \sum_{i=1}^{n} y_i^* \mathfrak{v}_i = \sum_{i=1}^{n} (y_i^* - x_i^*) \mathfrak{v}_i .$$

Thus $\overrightarrow{PR}$ has the components $y_i^* - x_i^*$ $(i = 1, 2, \ldots, n)$ in the coordinate system $[Q; \mathfrak{v}_1, \mathfrak{v}_2, \cdots, \mathfrak{v}_n]$.

By multiplying the vector $\mathfrak{a} = \sum_{i=1}^{n} a_i^* \mathfrak{v}_i$ by λ we obtain

$$\lambda \mathfrak{a} = \sum_{i=1}^{n} (\lambda a_i^*) \mathfrak{v}_i .$$

Thus, *if we multiply the components of* $\mathfrak{a}$ *in the coordinate system* $[Q; \mathfrak{v}_1, \mathfrak{v}_2, \cdots, \mathfrak{v}_n]$ *by* λ *we obtain the components of the vector* $\lambda\mathfrak{a}$ *in this system.*

Furthermore, if $\mathfrak{b} = \sum_{i=1}^{n} b_i^* \mathfrak{v}_i$ is another vector, then

$$\mathfrak{a} + \mathfrak{b} = \sum_{i=1}^{n} (a_i^* + b_i^*) \mathfrak{v}_i .$$

Thus, *if we add the corresponding components of* $\mathfrak{a}$ *and* $\mathfrak{b}$ *in the coordinate system* $[Q; \mathfrak{v}_1, \mathfrak{v}_2, \cdots, \mathfrak{v}_n]$ *we obtain the components of the vector* $\mathfrak{a} + \mathfrak{b}$. Of course the same holds for addition of more than two vectors.

Now let $\mathfrak{a}_1, \mathfrak{a}_2, \cdots, \mathfrak{a}_m$ be m vectors of R_n, and suppose that

$$\mathfrak{a}_i = \sum_{k=1}^{n} a_{ik}^* \mathfrak{v}_k, \qquad i = 1, 2, \cdots, m.$$

Consider the matrix of the components a_{ik}^*,

$$\begin{pmatrix} a_{11}^* & a_{12}^* & \cdots & a_{1n}^* \\ a_{21}^* & a_{22}^* & \cdots & a_{2n}^* \\ \cdot & \cdot & \cdot & \cdot \\ a_{m1}^* & a_{m2}^* & \cdots & a_{mn}^* \end{pmatrix}$$

If there is a linear relation which holds among the row vectors

$$\mathfrak{a}_i^* = \{a_{i1}^*, a_{i2}^*, \cdots, a_{in}^*\}, \qquad i = 1, 2, \cdots, m,$$

of this matrix, then the same linear relation holds among the vectors $\mathfrak{a}_i$ $(i = 1, 2, \ldots, m)$, and conversely. For suppose that $\sum_{i=1}^{m} \lambda_i \mathfrak{a}_i^* = 0$, i.e.

$$\sum_{i=1}^{m} \lambda_i a_{ik}^* = 0, \qquad k = 1, 2, \cdots, n.$$

It then follows that

$$\sum_{i=1}^{m} \lambda_i \mathfrak{a}_i = \sum_{i=1}^{m} \left(\lambda_i \sum_{k=1}^{n} a_{ik}^* \mathfrak{v}_k\right) = \sum_{k=1}^{n} \left(\mathfrak{v}_k \sum_{i=1}^{m} \lambda_i a_{ik}^*\right) = 0.$$

Conversely, if we assume that $\sum_{i=1}^{m} \lambda_i \mathfrak{a}_i = 0$, then by the last equation we also have

$$\sum_{k=1}^{n} \left(\sum_{i=1}^{m} \lambda_i a_{ik}^*\right) \mathfrak{v}_k = 0.$$

But, since the vectors $\mathfrak{v}_1, \mathfrak{v}_2, \cdots, \mathfrak{v}_n$ are linearly independent, all of their coefficients in this expression must vanish. Thus

$$\sum_{i=1}^{m} \lambda_i a_{ik}^* = 0,$$

for $k = 1, 2, \ldots, n$, so that

$$\sum_{i=1}^{m} \lambda_i \mathfrak{a}_i^* = 0.$$

Thus, if several of the vectors $\mathfrak{a}_i$ are linearly independent, then the same is true of the corresponding vectors $\mathfrak{a}_i^*$, for otherwise we should have a contradiction to the result we have just obtained. Of course, for the same reasons we also have, conversely, that if some vectors $\mathfrak{a}_i^*$ are linearly independent, then the same is true of the corresponding vectors $\mathfrak{a}_i$.

Hence, we clearly have

THEOREM 1. *The maximal number of linearly independent vectors among* $\mathfrak{a}_i$ *is equal to the maximal number of linearly independent vectors among the* $\mathfrak{a}_i^*$, *and thus equals the rank of the matrix* (a_{ik}^*).[1]

Now let $[Q'; \mathfrak{v}_1, \mathfrak{v}_2, \cdots, \mathfrak{v}_n]$ and $[Q''; \mathfrak{u}_1, \mathfrak{u}_2, \cdots, \mathfrak{u}_n]$ be two coordinate systems. If the coordinates of an arbitrary point P are given in one of the coordinate systems, P is uniquely determined, and therefore so

[1] Of course, the symbol (a_{ik}^*) denotes the matrix

$$\begin{pmatrix} a_{11}^* & a_{12}^* & \cdots & a_{1n}^* \\ a_{21}^* & a_{22}^* & \cdots & a_{2n}^* \\ \cdot & \cdot & \cdot & \cdot \\ a_{m1}^* & a_{m2}^* & \cdots & a_{mn}^* \end{pmatrix}.$$

are its coordinates in the other coordinate system. We shall show how to calculate them. First write the vector $\overrightarrow{Q'Q''}$ as a linear combination of the vectors $\mathfrak{v}_1, \mathfrak{v}_2, \cdots, \mathfrak{v}_n$, and the vector $\overrightarrow{Q'Q''}$ as a linear combination of the vectors $\mathfrak{u}_1, \mathfrak{u}_2, \cdots, \mathfrak{u}_n$, say

$$\overrightarrow{Q'Q''} = \sum_{i=1}^{n} s_i \mathfrak{v}_i, \tag{2}$$

$$\overrightarrow{Q''Q'} = \sum_{i=1}^{n} t_i \mathfrak{u}_i. \tag{3}$$

Now each of the vectors $\mathfrak{v}_k$ may be written as a linear combination of the vectors $\mathfrak{u}_1, \mathfrak{u}_2, \cdots, \mathfrak{u}_n$, and each of the vectors $\mathfrak{u}_k$ as a linear combination of $\mathfrak{v}_1, \mathfrak{v}_2, \cdots, \mathfrak{v}_n$, say

$$\mathfrak{v}_k = \sum_{i=1}^{n} v_{ik} \mathfrak{u}_i, \qquad k = 1, 2, \cdots, n, \tag{4}$$

$$\mathfrak{u}_k = \sum_{i=1}^{n} u_{ik} \mathfrak{v}_i, \qquad k = 1, 2, \cdots n. \tag{5}$$

Now, if $x_1, x_2, \ldots, x_n$ are the coordinates of the point P in the coordinate system $[Q'; \mathfrak{v}_1, \mathfrak{v}_2, \cdots, \mathfrak{v}_n]$ and $y_1, y_2, \ldots, y_n$ its coordinates with respect to $[Q''; \mathfrak{u}_1, \mathfrak{u}_2, \cdots, \mathfrak{u}_n]$ then by (1), we have

$$\overrightarrow{Q'P} = \sum_{i=1}^{n} x_i \mathfrak{v}_i, \tag{6}$$

$$\overrightarrow{Q''P} = \sum_{i=1}^{n} y_i \mathfrak{u}_i. \tag{7}$$

Now

$$\overrightarrow{Q''P} = \overrightarrow{Q''Q'} + \overrightarrow{Q'P},$$

or by (3), (6) and (7)

$$\sum_{i=1}^{n} y_i \mathfrak{u}_i = \sum_{i=1}^{n} t_i \mathfrak{u}_i + \sum_{k=1}^{n} x_k \mathfrak{v}_k.$$

Substituting for $\mathfrak{v}_k$ its value as given by (4), we obtain

$$\sum_{i=1}^{n} y_i \mathfrak{u}_i = \sum_{i=1}^{n} t_i \mathfrak{u}_i + \sum_{k=1}^{n} \sum_{i=1}^{n} x_k v_{ik} \mathfrak{u}_i = \sum_{i=1}^{n} t_i \mathfrak{u}_i + \sum_{i=1}^{n} \left(\sum_{k=1}^{n} v_{ik} x_k \right) \mathfrak{u}_i,$$

or

$$\sum_{i=1}^{n} \left(y_i - t_i - \sum_{k=1}^{n} v_{ik} x_k \right) \mathfrak{u}_i = 0.$$

Since the vectors $\mathfrak{u}_1, \mathfrak{u}_2, \cdots, \mathfrak{u}_n$ are linearly independent, we must have

$$(8) \qquad y_i = t_i + \sum_{k=1}^{n} v_{ik}\, x_k, \qquad i = 1, 2, \cdots, n.$$

In the same way, it follows from the equation

$$\overrightarrow{Q'P} = \overrightarrow{Q'Q''} + \overrightarrow{Q''P}$$

using equations (2), (6), (7), and (5), that

$$\sum_{i=1}^{n} x_i\, \mathfrak{v}_i = \sum_{i=1}^{n} s_i\, \mathfrak{v}_i + \sum_{k=1}^{n} y_k\, \mathfrak{u}_k = \sum_{i=1}^{n} s_i\, \mathfrak{v}_i + \sum_{i=1}^{n} \left(\sum_{k=1}^{n} u_{ik}\, y_k \right) \mathfrak{v}_i$$

so that, by the linear independence of the vectors $\mathfrak{v}_1, \mathfrak{v}_2, \cdots, \mathfrak{v}_n$, we obtain

$$(9) \qquad x_i = s_i + \sum_{k=1}^{n} u_{ik}\, y_k, \qquad i = 1, 2, \cdots, n.$$

Equations (8) show us how to calculate the coordinates $y_1, y_2, \ldots, y_n$ of a point P with respect to $[Q''; \mathfrak{u}_1, \mathfrak{u}_2, \cdots, \mathfrak{u}_n]$ if its coordinates $x_1, x_2, \ldots, x_n$ in the coordinate system $[Q'; \mathfrak{v}_1, \mathfrak{v}_2, \cdots, \mathfrak{v}_n]$ are known. Equations (9) show us how to carry out the inverse calculation. Thus, the coordinates of a point in one coordinate system depend linearly on the coordinates of the point in the other. Equations of the form (8) or (9) are called *equations of transformation*, and the change from one coordinate system to another which they represent is called a **transformation of coordinates.**

How do the components of a vector change under such a transformation of coordinates? Let $\mathfrak{a}$ be a vector of R_n; $a_1, a_2, \ldots, a_n$ its components with respect to $[Q'; \mathfrak{v}_1, \mathfrak{v}_2, \cdots, \mathfrak{v}_n]$; $b_1, b_2, \cdots, b_n$ its components with respect to $[Q''; \mathfrak{u}_1, \mathfrak{u}_2, \cdots, \mathfrak{u}_n]$ Then,

$$(10) \qquad \mathfrak{a} = \sum_{k=1}^{n} a_k\, \mathfrak{v}_k = \sum_{k=1}^{n} b_k\, \mathfrak{u}_k.$$

Using (4), this yields

$$\sum_{i=1}^{n} \left(\sum_{k=1}^{n} v_{ik}\, a_k \right) \mathfrak{u}_i = \sum_{i=1}^{n} b_i\, \mathfrak{u}_i.$$

By the linear independence of the $\mathfrak{u}_i$, we have

$$(11) \qquad b_i = \sum_{k=1}^{n} v_{ik}\, a_k, \qquad i = 1, 2, \cdots, n.$$

Correspondingly,

$$\sum_{i=1}^{n} a_i \mathfrak{v}_i = \sum_{i=1}^{n} \left(\sum_{k=1}^{n} u_{ik} \, b_k \right) \mathfrak{v}_i$$

follows from (5) and (10), so that

$$a_i = \sum_{k=1}^{n} u_{ik} \, b_k, \qquad i = 1, 2, \cdots, n. \tag{12}$$

Finally, the determinants $| u_{ik} |$ and $| v_{ik} |$ formed from the coefficients of (4) and (5) are certainly not 0. In fact, we have the same kind of relation between the vectors $\mathfrak{v}_i$ and $\mathfrak{u}_i$ as we had between the vectors $\mathfrak{a}_i$ and $\mathfrak{v}_i$ on page 118. By Theorem 1, the rank of the matrix (v_{ik}) is the maximal number of linearly independent vectors among the vectors $\mathfrak{v}_i$. But this number is n, and so $| v_{ik} | \neq 0$. Similarly we see that $| u_{ik} | \neq 0$.

Equations (4) and (5) are inverses of one another. If (4) is solved for the $\mathfrak{u}_i$, then (5) is obtained; and if (5) is solved for the $\mathfrak{v}_i$, then (4) is obtained. The same is true for the pairs of systems (8), (9) and (11), (12).

Now suppose that only the one coordinate system $[Q'; \mathfrak{v}_1, \mathfrak{v}_2, \cdots, \mathfrak{v}_n]$ is given, and that a system of equations of the form (8) with determinant $| v_{ik} | \neq 0$ is also given. This system of equations assigns to a point of R_n which has the coordinates $x_1, x_2, \ldots, x_n$ with respect to $[Q'; \mathfrak{v}_1, \mathfrak{v}_2, \cdots, \mathfrak{v}_n]$, a new coordinate n-tuple $y_1, y_2, \ldots, y_n$. We may easily find a coordinate system in which the point P has precisely the coordinates $y_1, y_2, \ldots, y_n$. For this purpose, we must solve equations (8) for the x_k. By Cramer's rule, we obtain

$$x_k = \frac{\sum_{i=1}^{n} (y_i - t_i) V_{ik}}{| v_{ik} |}; \tag{9a}$$

where V_{ik} denotes the cofactor of v_{ik} in the determinant $| v_{ik} |$. Now, if we set

$$s_k = \frac{-\sum_{i=1}^{n} t_i \, V_{ik}}{| v_{ik} |}, \qquad u_{ki} = \frac{V_{ik}}{| v_{ik} |},$$

we obtain a system of equations of the form (9). We then determine the point Q'' for which

$$\overrightarrow{Q' Q''} = \sum_{i=1}^{n} s_i \, \mathfrak{v}_i$$

and introduce the vectors $\mathfrak{u}_1, \mathfrak{u}_2, \cdots, \mathfrak{u}_n$ defined by the equations

$$\mathfrak{u}_k = \sum_{i=1}^{n} u_{ik}\, \mathfrak{v}_i,$$

then the coordinate system $[Q''; \mathfrak{u}_1, \mathfrak{u}_2, \cdots, \mathfrak{u}_n]$ is the one desired. In fact, the coordinate change from $[Q''; \mathfrak{u}_1, \mathfrak{u}_2, \cdots, \mathfrak{u}_n]$ to

$$[Q'; \mathfrak{v}_1, \mathfrak{v}_2, \cdots, \mathfrak{v}_n]$$

is given by the equations (9a), and, as a consequence, that from $[Q'; \mathfrak{v}_1, \mathfrak{v}_2, \cdots, \mathfrak{v}_n]$ to $[Q''; \mathfrak{u}_1, \mathfrak{u}_2, \cdots, \mathfrak{u}_n]$, is given by our system of equations (8), which is the inverse of (9a).

In the same way, given a basis $\mathfrak{v}_1, \mathfrak{v}_2, \cdots, \mathfrak{v}_n$ and a system of equations of the form (11), we can find a second basis $\mathfrak{u}_1, \mathfrak{u}_2, \cdots, \mathfrak{u}_n$ such that (11) represents the equations of transformation for vector components under the transition from the basis $\mathfrak{v}_1, \mathfrak{v}_2, \cdots, \mathfrak{v}_n$ to the basis

$$\mathfrak{u}_1, \mathfrak{u}_2, \cdots, \mathfrak{u}_n.$$

We shall now use the equations of transformation to find how a linear space is represented analytically in an arbitrary linear coordinate system. We have shown in § 6 that every linear space of R_n is representable by a system of linear equations, in the sense that the linear space consists precisely of the points which are the solutions of the system of equations. For the derivation of this result we used the coordinate system $[O; \mathfrak{e}_1, \mathfrak{e}_2, \cdots, \mathfrak{e}_n]$ whose origin is $O = (0, 0, \ldots, 0)$ and whose basis vectors are the unit vectors. What is the situation when coordinates are taken with respect to an *arbitrary* linear coordinate system? Do the coordinates of the points of a linear space again satisfy some system of linear equations?

Let $[Q'; \mathfrak{v}_1, \mathfrak{v}_2, \cdots, \mathfrak{v}_n]$ be a coordinate system in which every linear space of dimension p is representable by a system of equations of rank[2] $n - p$ and such that, conversely, every such system represents a p-dimensional linear space. Such coordinate systems exist, since $[O; \mathfrak{e}_1, \mathfrak{e}_2, \cdots, \mathfrak{e}_n]$ is one such. Then let the p-dimensional linear space L be given by the system of equations

I. $$\sum_{k=1}^{n} a_{ik} x_k = b_i, \qquad i = 1, 2, \cdots, m,$$

[2] A solvable system of linear equations the rank of whose matrix is $n - p$, is itself said to be of rank $n - p$.

whose rank is $n - p$. Now let $[Q''; \mathfrak{u}_1, \mathfrak{u}_2, \cdots, \mathfrak{u}_n]$ be another, arbitrary, coordinate system. Let the equations of transformation from $[Q''; \mathfrak{u}_1, \mathfrak{u}_2, \cdots, \mathfrak{u}_n]$ to $[Q'; \mathfrak{v}_1, \mathfrak{v}_2, \cdots, \mathfrak{v}_n]$ be of the form (9). In order to simplify calculations, define $\mathfrak{w}_i = \{u_{i1}, u_{i2}, \cdots, u_{in}\}$ for $i = 1, 2, \ldots, n$ and put $\mathfrak{y} = \{y_1, y_2, \cdots, y_n\}$. Then $\sum_{k=1}^{n} u_{ik} y_k = \mathfrak{w}_i \mathfrak{y}$, and equations (9) take on the form

$$x_i = s_i + \mathfrak{w}_i \mathfrak{y}.$$

After substituting this in I, we obtain by an easy calculation:

$$\text{II.} \qquad \left(\sum_{k=1}^{n} a_{ik} \mathfrak{w}_k\right) \mathfrak{y} = b_i - \sum_{k=1}^{n} a_{ik} s_k, \qquad i = 1, 2, \cdots, n.$$

This is also a system of linear equations, but in the quantities $y_1, y_2, \ldots, y_n$. Now let P be a point of the linear space L; $x_1, x_2, \ldots, x_n$ its coordinates with respect to $[Q'; \mathfrak{v}_1, \mathfrak{v}_2, \cdots, \mathfrak{v}_n]$; $y_1, y_2, \cdots, y_n$ its coordinates with respect to $[Q''; \mathfrak{u}_1, \mathfrak{u}_2, \cdots, \mathfrak{u}_n]$. Then the coordinates x_i satisfy equations I. But since $x_i = s_i + \mathfrak{w}_i \mathfrak{y}$ by virtue of the equations of transformation, equations I remain valid if the x_i are replaced by the quantities $s_i + \mathfrak{w}_i \mathfrak{y}$. But then, I goes into II, and thus the coordinates $y_1, y_2, \ldots, y_n$ of the point P satisfy the system II.

Conversely, let $y_1, y_2, \ldots, y_n$ be the coordinates of a point P with respect to $[Q''; \mathfrak{u}_1, \mathfrak{u}_2, \cdots, \mathfrak{u}_n]$. Then if the y_i satisfy equations II, P is in L. For, the coordinates $x_1, x_2, \ldots, x_n$, of P with respect to $[Q, \mathfrak{v}_1, \mathfrak{v}_2, \cdots, \mathfrak{v}_n]$ may be calculated in terms of the y_i from the equations $x_i = s_i + \mathfrak{w}_i \mathfrak{y}$. But by II we have

$$\sum_{k=1}^{n} a_{ik} (s_k + \mathfrak{w}_k \mathfrak{y}) = b_i,$$

and so

$$\sum_{k=1}^{n} a_{ik} x_k = b_i,$$

which proves that P is in L.

Thus the system of linear equations II represents the linear space L, with respect to the coordinate system $[Q''; \mathfrak{u}_1, \mathfrak{u}_2, \cdots, \mathfrak{u}_n]$. What is the rank of II? Since II is certainly solvable, it suffices to consider its coefficient matrix. Its row vectors are the vectors $\mathfrak{a}_i = \sum_{k=1}^{n} a_{ik} \mathfrak{w}_k$ $(i = 1, 2, \ldots, n)$. Since the vectors $\mathfrak{a}_i$ are linear combinations of the linearly independent vectors $\mathfrak{w}_1, \mathfrak{w}_2, \cdots, \mathfrak{w}_n$, the maximal number of linearly independent vectors among them is, by Theorem 1, equal to the rank of the matrix (a_{ik}). But this, by hypothesis, is equal to $n - p$. Since $[Q''; \mathfrak{u}_1, \mathfrak{u}_2, \cdots, \mathfrak{u}_n]$ is an arbitrary linear coordinate system, we have proved

THEOREM 2. *A linear space of dimension p is representable in any linear coordinate system by a system of linear equations of rank* $n - p$.

Of course, every system of linear equations of rank $n - p$ represents a p-dimensional linear space, in any coordinate system

$$[Q''; \mathfrak{u}_1, \mathfrak{u}_2, \cdots, \mathfrak{u}_n].$$

In point of fact, such a system is transformed by the inverse equations $y_i = t_i + \sum_{k=1}^{n} v_{ik} x_k$ of transformation into a system of linear equations of the same rank where the transformed system is now referred to the coordinate system $[Q'; \mathfrak{v}_1, \mathfrak{v}_2, \cdots, \mathfrak{v}_n]$. But in this coordinate system every such system of equations represents a p-dimensional linear space.

An analogous result can be proved, in the same way, for vector spaces. In this case the system I is homogeneous, so that all $b_i = 0$. The equations of transformation for the vector components read: $x_i = \mathfrak{w}_i \mathfrak{y}$, i.e. $s_i = 0$ in II. Thus, equations II are homogeneous. The remarks concerning rank apply without change. We thus have

THEOREM 3. *A p-dimensional vector space is represented in every linear coordinate system by a homogeneous system of linear equations of rank* $n - p$. *Conversely, any such system of equations represents a vector space of dimension p.*

Next, let n vectors $\mathfrak{a}_1, \mathfrak{a}_2, \cdots, \mathfrak{a}_n$ be given by their components in a coordinate system $[Q; \mathfrak{v}_1, \mathfrak{v}_2, \cdots, \mathfrak{v}_n]$. How can we calculate the volume of the parallelotope whose edge vectors are $\mathfrak{a}_i$? Let

$$\mathfrak{a}_i = \{a_{i1}, a_{i2}, \cdots, a_{in}\}$$

for $i = 1, 2, \ldots, n$, and let $a^*_{i1}, a^*_{i2}, \cdots, a^*_{in}$ be the components of $\mathfrak{a}_i$ with respect to the basis $\mathfrak{v}_1, \mathfrak{v}_2, \cdots, \mathfrak{v}_n$, so that

$$\mathfrak{a}_i = \sum_{\nu=1}^{n} a^*_{i\nu} \mathfrak{v}_\nu .$$

Let $v_{i1}, v_{i2}, \cdots, v_{in}$ be the components of the vector $\mathfrak{v}_i$ with respect to the basis $\mathfrak{e}_1, \mathfrak{e}_2, \cdots, \mathfrak{e}_n$, so that

$$\mathfrak{v}_i = \{v_{i1}, v_{i2}, \cdots, v_{in}\} = \sum_{k=1}^{n} v_{ik} \mathfrak{e}_k.$$

If we observe that $\mathfrak{a}_i = \sum_{k=1}^{n} a_{ik}\, \mathfrak{e}_k$ we have by the above equations that

$$\sum_{k=1}^{n} a_{ik}\, \mathfrak{e}_k = \sum_{\nu=1}^{n} \left(a_{i\nu}^{*} \sum_{k=1}^{n} v_{\nu k}\, \mathfrak{e}_k \right) = \sum_{k=1}^{n} \mathfrak{e}_k \left(\sum_{\nu=1}^{n} a_{i\nu}^{*}\, v_{\nu k} \right).$$

Since the vectors $\mathfrak{e}_i$ are linearly independent, we therefore have

$$a_{ik} = \sum_{\nu=1}^{n} a_{i\nu}^{*}\, v_{\nu k}, \qquad i, k = 1, 2, \cdots, n.$$

The sum on the right is the scalar product of the i-th row of the determinant a_{ik}^{*} and the k-th column of the determinant $| v_{ik} |$. Hence, by the multiplication theorem for determinants, we have

$$(13) \qquad | a_{ik} | = | a_{ik}^{*} | \cdot | v_{ik} |.$$

The required volume is the absolute value of the determinant $| a_{ik} |$. Formula (13) shows that it may be calculated from the basis vectors $\mathfrak{v}_i = \{v_{i1}, v_{i2}, \cdots, v_{in}\}$ of the coordinate system $[Q; \mathfrak{v}_1, \mathfrak{v}_2, \cdots, \mathfrak{v}_n]$ and the components of the edge vectors $\mathfrak{a}_i$ in this system.

Cartesian Coordinate Systems

At the beginning of this section we saw, in connection with Theorems 1, 2, and 3, that the vectors of R_n behave in essentially the same way whether their components be taken relative to an arbitrary linear coordinate system or, as before, relative to the basis $\mathfrak{e}_1, \mathfrak{e}_2, \cdots, \mathfrak{e}_n$. How does the scalar product of two vectors behave in this respect?

Let $\mathfrak{a} = \{a_1, a_2, \cdots, a_n\}$, $\mathfrak{b} = \{b_1, b_2, \cdots, b_n\}$ be two vectors of R_n. Now let $[Q; \mathfrak{v}_1, \mathfrak{v}_2, \cdots, \mathfrak{v}_n]$ be some coordinate system, and let $\mathfrak{a}$ have the components $a_1^{*}, a_2^{*}, \cdots, a_n^{*}$, and $\mathfrak{b}$ the components $b_1^{*}, b_2^{*}, \cdots, b_n^{*}$, in this coordinate system. Then

$$\mathfrak{a} = \sum_{i=1}^{n} a_i^{*}\, \mathfrak{v}_i, \quad \mathfrak{b} = \sum_{i=1}^{n} b_i^{*}\, \mathfrak{v}_i.$$

For the scalar product $\mathfrak{a} \cdot \mathfrak{b} = \sum_{i=1}^{n} a_i b_i$ we accordingly obtain

$$\mathfrak{a} \cdot \mathfrak{b} = \left(\sum_{i=1}^{n} a_i^{*}\, \mathfrak{v}_i \right) \cdot \left(\sum_{k=1}^{n} b_k^{*}\, \mathfrak{v}_k \right) = \sum_{i,k=1}^{n} a_i^{*}\, b_k^{*}\, \mathfrak{v}_i \mathfrak{v}_k.$$

We see that, in general, the scalar product is calculated from the components a_i^{*}, b_i^{*} in a very different way than from the components

a_i, b_i.[3] However, in special cases, this difference may again disappear, namely when the coordinate system $[Q; \mathfrak{v}_1, \mathfrak{v}_2, \cdots, \mathfrak{v}_n]$ has the property that for $i \neq k$ we have $\mathfrak{v}_i \cdot \mathfrak{v}_k = 0$ while for $i = k$, $\mathfrak{v}_i \cdot \mathfrak{v}_i = 1$. In this case we have from the preceding equation that

$$(14) \qquad \mathfrak{a} \cdot \mathfrak{b} = \sum_{i=1}^{n} a_i^* b_i^*.$$

The condition $\mathfrak{v}_i \cdot \mathfrak{v}_k = \delta_{ik}$ (where δ_{ik} is the Kronecker symbol defined in § 9) is moreover necessary if (14) is to hold for all pairs of vectors, since the truth of (14) implies $\mathfrak{v}_i \cdot \mathfrak{v}_k = \delta_{ik}$. To establish this, put $\mathfrak{a} = \mathfrak{v}_i$ and $\mathfrak{b} = \mathfrak{v}_k$ in (14). Noting that only the i-th component of $\mathfrak{v}_i$ in the system $[Q; \mathfrak{v}_1, \mathfrak{v}_2, \cdots, \mathfrak{v}_n]$ is non-zero and is, in fact, equal to 1, we conclude from (14), with $\mathfrak{a} = \mathfrak{v}_i$, $\mathfrak{b} = \mathfrak{v}_k$, that the equation $\mathfrak{v}_i \cdot \mathfrak{v}_k = \delta_{ik}$ holds.

We define a system $\mathfrak{b}_1, \mathfrak{b}_2, \cdots, \mathfrak{b}_p$ of finitely many vectors of R_n to be a *normal orthogonal system* if we have $\mathfrak{b}_i \cdot \mathfrak{b}_k = \delta_{ik}$, for $i, k = 1, 2, \ldots, p$. This terminology may be justified by noting that if we introduce euclidean length into R_n, the vanishing of the scalar product $\mathfrak{b}_i \cdot \mathfrak{b}_k$ for $i \neq k$ means nothing but that $\mathfrak{b}_i$ is perpendicular to $\mathfrak{b}_k$. On the other hand, $\mathfrak{b}_i^2 = 1$ means that each vector $\mathfrak{b}_i$ is of length 1, a property which is expressed in the word "normal."

Every normal orthogonal system $\mathfrak{b}_1, \mathfrak{b}_2, \cdots, \mathfrak{b}_p$ *consists of linearly independent vectors*. For, let

$$\lambda_1 \mathfrak{b}_1 + \lambda_2 \mathfrak{b}_2 + \cdots + \lambda_p \mathfrak{b}_p = 0$$

be a linear relation which holds among these vectors. We form the scalar product of each of the sides of this equation with $\mathfrak{b}_k$ $(1 \leq k \leq p)$. Since $\mathfrak{b}_i \cdot \mathfrak{b}_k = 0$ for $i \neq k$, only the term $\lambda_k \mathfrak{b}_k^2$ remains on the left, and since $\mathfrak{b}_k^2 = 1$, it follows that $\lambda_k = 0$ $(k = 1, 2, \ldots, p)$, i.e. the vectors are linearly independent.

The coordinate systems $[Q; \mathfrak{v}_1, \mathfrak{v}_2, \cdots, \mathfrak{v}_n]$ considered above, for which the basis $\mathfrak{v}_1, \mathfrak{v}_2, \cdots, \mathfrak{v}_n$ is a normal orthogonal system, have, because of

[3] In particular, note that *the condition (in the coordinate system*

$$[Q; \mathfrak{v}_1, \mathfrak{v}_2, \cdots, \mathfrak{v}_n])$$

that two vectors $\mathfrak{a}, \mathfrak{b}$ *be orthogonal to one another, is that the expression*

$$\sum_{i=1}^{n} a_i^* b_k^* \mathfrak{v}_i \mathfrak{v}_k$$

vanish.

their importance, been given a special name. They are called **Cartesian coordinate systems.** The question as to whether such exist is settled by the remark that every coordinate system $\{Q; \mathfrak{e}_1, \mathfrak{e}_2, \cdots, \mathfrak{e}_n]$ which has the unit vectors as a basis, is Cartesian.

Let us now determine how the transformation from one Cartesian coordinate system to another is expressed in formulas. In this case, the systems of vectors $\mathfrak{v}_1, \mathfrak{v}_2, \cdots, \mathfrak{v}_n$ and $\mathfrak{u}_1, \mathfrak{u}_2, \cdots, \mathfrak{u}_n$ which occur in (4) and (5) are normal orthogonal systems. If we multiply the k-th equation of (4) by the vector $\mathfrak{u}_j$ and note that $\mathfrak{u}_i \mathfrak{u}_j = 0$ if $i \neq j$ and $= 1$ if $i = j$, we obtain

$$\mathfrak{v}_k \mathfrak{u}_j = v_{jk}. \tag{15}$$

In the same way, by multiplying (5) by $\mathfrak{v}_j$, we obtain

$$\mathfrak{v}_j \mathfrak{u}_k = u_{jk}. \tag{16}$$

Equations (15) and (16) hold for any two indices j, k. Thus, for every i and k it follows that

$$u_{ik} = v_{ki}.$$

Under our present assumptions equations (5) take on the form

$$\mathfrak{u}_k = \sum_{i=1}^{n} v_{ki} \mathfrak{v}_i. \tag{5a}$$

Since the vectors $\mathfrak{u}_1, \mathfrak{u}_2, \cdots, \mathfrak{u}_n$ form a normal orthogonal system, we have from (4) and (14) that

$$\mathfrak{v}_k \mathfrak{v}_j = \sum_{i=1}^{n} v_{ik} v_{ij} = \delta_{kj}, \qquad k, j = 1, 2, \cdots, n, \tag{17}$$

and analogously, it results from (5a) that

$$\mathfrak{u}_k \mathfrak{u}_j = \sum_{i=1}^{n} v_{ki} v_{ji} = \delta_{kj}, \qquad k, j = 1, 2, \cdots, n. \tag{18}$$

However, this says that both the row vectors and the column vectors of the square matrix

$$\begin{pmatrix} v_{11} & v_{12} & \cdots & v_{1n} \\ v_{21} & v_{22} & \cdots & v_{2n} \\ \cdot & \cdot & \cdot & \cdot \\ v_{n1} & v_{n2} & \cdots & v_{nn} \end{pmatrix} \tag{19}$$

form normal orthogonal systems. Such a matrix is called an **orthogonal matrix.**

From (17) we draw yet another conclusion. Let V_{ik} be the cofactor of v_{ik} in the determinant $|v_{ik}|$. We multiply the j-th equation of (17) $(j=1,2,\ldots,n)$ by V_{hj}, where h is a fixed number between 1 and n. We then add the n equations which are obtained from (17) with k fixed and $j=1,2,\ldots,n$. We thus obtain

$$\sum_{j=1}^{n}\left(\sum_{i=1}^{n} v_{ik}\, v_{ij}\, V_{hj}\right) = \sum_{j=1}^{n} \delta_{kj}\, V_{hj},$$

or

$$\sum_{i=1}^{n}\left(\sum_{j=1}^{n} v_{ij}\, V_{hj}\right)\cdot v_{ik} = V_{hk}. \tag{20}$$

However, from (16) of § 9 we obtain $\sum_{j=1}^{n} v_{ij}\, V_{hj} = \delta_{ih}\cdot|v_{ik}|$. If we substitute this into (20) and note that the determinant $|v_{ik}|$ is independent of the index of summation i, it follows that

$$|v_{ik}|\cdot v_{hk} = V_{hk}.$$

Since by (17) the column vectors of (19) form a normal orthogonal system, and are thus linearly independent, we have $|v_{ik}| \neq 0$, and we may write

$$v_{hk} = \frac{V_{hk}}{|v_{ik}|}. \tag{21}$$

Equation (21) is valid for arbitrary indices h and k, as is clear from its derivation.

Conversely, relation (21) *characterizes an orthogonal matrix.* In fact, if it holds for arbitrary indices h and k, then by the use of equations (16) of § 9, we have at once that

$$\sum_{i=1}^{n} v_{ik}\, v_{ij} = \frac{\sum_{i=1}^{n} v_{ik}\, V_{ij}}{|v_{ik}|} = \delta_{kj},$$

$$\sum_{i=1}^{n} v_{ki}\, v_{ji} = \frac{\sum_{i=1}^{n} v_{ki}\, V_{ji}}{|v_{ik}|} = \delta_{kj}.$$

These are equations (17) and (18).

Note that (21) follows from equations (17) alone. However, (18) also follows from (21). That is to say:

If the column vectors of a matrix form a normal orthogonal system, so do the row vectors.

On the other hand, if the row vectors of the matrix (19) are known to form a normal orthogonal system, then the column vectors of the transposed matrix $(v_{ik})'$ (cf. § 6 page 43) form a normal orthogonal system. By what has just been proved, the row vectors of the transposed matrix, i.e., the column vectors of (19), form a normal orthogonal system. Thus, we have also:

If the row vectors of a matrix form a normal orthogonal system, so do the column vectors.

The value of the determinant $|v_{ik}|$ may easily be determined if (v_{ik}) is an orthogonal matrix. By the multiplication theorem of determinants, it follows that

$$|v_{ik}| \cdot |v_{ik}| = \left| \sum_{\nu=1}^{n} v_{i\nu} v_{k\nu} \right|.$$

However, the element $\sum_{\nu=1}^{n} v_{i\nu} v_{k\nu}$ of the i-th row and k-th column of the right-hand determinant is δ_{ik} by (18). Thus we have

$$\left| \sum_{\nu=1}^{n} v_{i\nu} v_{k\nu} \right| = \begin{vmatrix} 1 & 0 & \cdots & 0 \\ 0 & 1 & \cdots & 0 \\ \cdot & \cdot & \cdot & \cdot \\ 0 & 0 & \cdots & 1 \end{vmatrix} = 1.$$

As a consequence of this we have

$$|v_{ik}|^2 = 1.$$

Thus, we must have

$$|v_{ik}| = \pm 1.$$

There exist orthogonal matrices whose determinant is $+1$ as well as such with determinant -1, for example,

$$\begin{pmatrix} 1 & 0 & \cdots & 0 & 0 \\ 0 & 1 & \cdots & 0 & 0 \\ \cdot & \cdot & \cdot & \cdot & \cdot \\ 0 & 0 & \cdots & 1 & 0 \\ 0 & 0 & \cdots & 0 & 1 \end{pmatrix} \text{ and } \begin{pmatrix} 1 & 0 & \cdots & 0 & 0 \\ 0 & 1 & \cdots & 0 & 0 \\ \cdot & \cdot & \cdot & \cdot & \cdot \\ 0 & 0 & \cdots & 1 & 0 \\ 0 & 0 & \cdots & 0 & -1 \end{pmatrix}.$$

The family of orthogonal matrices is thus divided into two classes; one contains all the orthogonal matrices with determinant $+1$, and the other, all those with determinant -1.

Finally, let n vectors $\mathfrak{a}_1, \mathfrak{a}_2, \cdots, \mathfrak{a}_n$ be given by specification of their components in a Cartesian coordinate system $[Q; \mathfrak{v}_1, \mathfrak{v}_2, \cdots, \mathfrak{v}_n]$. We wish to determine the volume of the parallelotope which has the $\mathfrak{a}_i$ as edge vectors. Let $a^*_{i1}, a^*_{i2}, \cdots, a^*_{in}$ be the components of the vector $\mathfrak{a}_i$ with respect to the basis $\mathfrak{v}_1, \mathfrak{v}_2, \cdots, \mathfrak{v}_n$, so that

$$\mathfrak{a}_i = \sum_{k=1}^{n} a^*_{ik}\, \mathfrak{v}_k,$$

and let $v_{i1}, v_{i2}, \cdots, v_{in}$ be the components of the vector $\mathfrak{v}_i$ with respect to the basis $\mathfrak{e}_1, \mathfrak{e}_2, \cdots, \mathfrak{e}_n$. Then, by formula (13), the desired volume is the absolute value of the following product of determinants:

$$|a^*_{ik}| \cdot |v_{ik}|$$

However, since the vectors $\mathfrak{v}_i = \{v_{i1}, v_{i2}, \cdots, v_{in}\}$ form a normal orthogonal system, (v_{ik}) is an orthogonal matrix, and therefore $|v_{ik}| = \pm 1$. *As a consequence, the volume of a parallelotope with edge vectors* $\mathfrak{a}_1, \mathfrak{a}_2, \cdots, \mathfrak{a}_n$ *is equal to the absolute value of the determinant* $|a^*_{ik}|$.

Continuous Deformation of a Linear Coordinate System

We return once more to the consideration of a general linear coordinate system $[Q; \mathfrak{v}_1, \mathfrak{v}_2, \cdots, \mathfrak{v}_n]$. Since the basis vectors $\mathfrak{v}_i$ of such a system are linearly independent, the determinant $D(\mathfrak{v}_1, \mathfrak{v}_2, \cdots, \mathfrak{v}_n)$ is $\neq 0$ by Theorem 8 of § 8. On the other hand, this determinant can be made to take on any given real value but 0 by proper choice of the basis. In order to show this, note that

$$D(\lambda\mathfrak{v}_1, \mathfrak{v}_2, \cdots, \mathfrak{v}_n) = \lambda \cdot D(\mathfrak{v}_1, \mathfrak{v}_2, \cdots, \mathfrak{v}_n).$$

Thus we need only choose λ suitably in order to have in $\lambda\mathfrak{v}_1, \mathfrak{v}_2, \mathfrak{v}_3, \mathfrak{v}_4, \ldots, \mathfrak{v}_n$ a basis whose determinant will have a given, non-zero, real value. Since $D(\mathfrak{v}_1, \mathfrak{v}_2, \cdots, \mathfrak{v}_n)$ cannot be zero, the coordinate systems $[Q; \mathfrak{v}_1, \mathfrak{v}_2, \cdots, \mathfrak{v}_n]$ may be divided into two classes: those for which the determinant $D(\mathfrak{v}_1, \mathfrak{v}_2, \cdots, \mathfrak{v}_n)$ is greater than 0, and those for which this determinant is less than 0. It is a highly noteworthy fact that any two coordinate systems of the same class may be continuously deformed into one another without the determinant vanishing at any stage, while two of different classes may not be so deformed into one another. Before we attempt the proof, let us make the statement more precise.

Let $\mathfrak{v} = \{v_1, v_2, \cdots, v_n\}$, $\mathfrak{u} = \{u_1, u_2, \cdots, u_n\}$ be two vectors of

R_n, and let $f_1(t), f_2(t), \ldots, f_n(t)$ be n continuous[4] (real) functions defined in a closed interval $c \leqq t \leqq d$, such that for $i = 1, 2, \ldots, n$ we have

$$f_i(c) = v_i, \qquad f_i(d) = u_i.$$

If we let the parameter t run continuously over the given interval from c to d, then $f_1(t), f_2(t), \ldots, f_n(t)$ run continuously from the initial values $v_1, v_2, \ldots, v_n$ (the components of the vector $\mathfrak{v}$) to the final values $u_1, u_2, \ldots, u_n$ (the components of the vector $\mathfrak{u}$). We then say that *the vector* $\mathfrak{v}$ *is continuously deformed into the vector* $\mathfrak{u}$.[5] If we let the parameter t go through the interval in the opposite direction, from d to c, then $\mathfrak{u}$ is continuously deformed into $\mathfrak{v}$. Incidentally, the particular interval $c \leqq t \leqq d$ that we use is of no significance. Indeed, let a second finite interval, with end-points c' and d', be given, where we do not specify whether $c' \gtreqless d'$. If we then put

$$t = \frac{(c-d)\,t' + d\,c' - c\,d'}{c' - d'},$$

and if we let t' run through the interval (c', d') from c' to d', then t describes the interval (c, d) from c to d. If we then substitute this expression for t into the $f_i(t)$, the functions $f_i\left(\frac{(c-d)\,t' + d\,c' - c\,d'}{c' - d'}\right)$, $(i = 1, 2, \ldots, n)$ which we obtain, are functions of the parameter t' which serve the same purpose for our interval (c', d') as the $f_i(t)$ did for the interval (c, d).

Let there now be given two linear coordinate systems

$$[Q; \mathfrak{v}_1, \mathfrak{v}_2, \cdots, \mathfrak{v}_n]$$

and $[Q^*; \mathfrak{u}_1, \mathfrak{u}_2, \cdots, \mathfrak{u}_n]$. It is quite easy to deform the point Q into the point Q^*. We need only let it run continuously through the segment QQ^*.[6] It only remains to be shown that the system of vectors

[4] We must here assume as known the concept of continuity and several fundamental theorems concerning continuous functions.

[5] The parameter t symbolizes time. As t traverses the interval (c, d), the vector $\mathfrak{v}$ is continuously transformed into $\mathfrak{u}$.

[6] If $Q = (x_1, x_2, \cdots, x_n)$, $Q^* = (y_1, y_2, \cdots, y_n)$, then the general point

$$(z_1, z_2, \cdots, z_n)$$

of the segment QQ^* is given by

$$z_i = x_i + \lambda(y_i - x_i), \qquad 0 \leqq \lambda \leqq 1,\ i = 1, 2, \cdots, n.$$

As λ increases continuously from 0 to 1, $(z_1, z_2, \cdots, z_n)$ traverses the segment QQ^* continuously.

$\mathfrak{v}_1, \mathfrak{v}_2, \cdots, \mathfrak{v}_n$ can be deformed continuously into the system of vectors $\mathfrak{u}_1, \mathfrak{u}_2, \cdots, \mathfrak{u}_n$. This is also trivial if no restriction is put on the deformation. But we must take heed of just such a restriction; in fact, it is essential that the linear independence of the system of vectors be preserved during the deformation. Thus, if $\mathfrak{v}_i = \{v_{i1}, v_{i2}, \cdots, v_{in}\}$, $\mathfrak{u}_i = \{u_{i1}, u_{i2}, \cdots, u_{in}\}$ for $i = 1, 2, \ldots, n$, then we must find n^2 functions $f_{ik}(t)$ $(i, k = 1, 2, \ldots, n)$ such that for the real number c we have $f_{ik}(c) = v_{ik}$, while for some other number d we have $f_{ik}(d) = u_{ik}$, and such that $f_{ik}(t)$ varies continuously from v_{ik} to u_{ik} as t runs continuously from c to d. *But, for all values of t which are thus taken on, the determinants $f_{ik}(t)$ are to be always non-zero,* as is certainly the case for $t = c$ and $t = d$. We see immediately that we can never transform two systems of vectors $\mathfrak{v}_1, \mathfrak{v}_2, \cdots, \mathfrak{v}_n$ and

$$\mathfrak{u}_1, \mathfrak{u}_2, \cdots, \mathfrak{u}_n$$

into one another if $D(\mathfrak{v}_1, \mathfrak{v}_2, \cdots, \mathfrak{v}_n) = |v_{ik}|$ and

$$D(\mathfrak{u}_1, \mathfrak{u}_2, \cdots, \mathfrak{u}_n) = |u_{ik}|$$

have opposite signs. This is because the determinant $|f_{ik}(t)|$ is a continuous function of t,[7] and if its value varied continuously from $|v_{ik}|$ to $|u_{ik}|$ it would have to take on the value 0 at some point.

Thus, we shall assume that $|v_{ik}|$ and $|u_{ik}|$ have the same sign. Then, in order to show that the system $\mathfrak{v}_1, \mathfrak{v}_2, \cdots, \mathfrak{v}_n$ may be continuously deformed into the system $\mathfrak{u}_1, \mathfrak{u}_2, \cdots, \mathfrak{u}_n$ we proceed by choosing one of the systems of vectors with positive determinant, say $\mathfrak{e}_1, \mathfrak{e}_2, \cdots, \mathfrak{e}_n$, as a representative of this class of systems, and one of the other sort, say $\mathfrak{e}_1, \mathfrak{e}_2, \cdots, \mathfrak{e}_{n-1}, -\mathfrak{e}_n$, which is obtained from the preceding system by the substitution of $-\mathfrak{e}_n$ for $\mathfrak{e}_n$, as a representative of its class. We shall show that each system of vectors of a particular class may be continuously deformed as described above into the representative system of that class. From this it will follow immediately that two systems of the same class may be continuously deformed into one another. For if, say, $\mathfrak{v}_1, \mathfrak{v}_2, \cdots, \mathfrak{v}_n$ and $\mathfrak{u}_1, \mathfrak{u}_2, \cdots, \mathfrak{u}_n$ are two systems which may each be deformed in this way into $\mathfrak{e}_1, \mathfrak{e}_2, \cdots, \mathfrak{e}_n$, then $\mathfrak{e}_1, \mathfrak{e}_2, \cdots, \mathfrak{e}_n$ may similarly be deformed into

---

[7] Sums and products of continuous functions are themselves continuous, and hence the determinant $|f_{ik}(t)|$ is a continuous function of t, since by § 9 it is a sum of products of the $f_{ik}(t)$.

$\mathfrak{u}_1, \mathfrak{u}_2, \cdots, \mathfrak{u}_n$, and thus $\mathfrak{v}_1, \mathfrak{v}_2, \cdots, \mathfrak{v}_n$ may be deformed, via $\mathfrak{e}_1, \mathfrak{e}_2, \cdots, \mathfrak{e}_n$ into $\mathfrak{u}_1, \mathfrak{u}_2, \cdots, \mathfrak{u}_n$. Thus, we need only prove

THEOREM 4. *If* $D(\mathfrak{v}_1, \mathfrak{v}_2, \cdots, \mathfrak{v}_n) > 0$, *the system of vectors* $\mathfrak{v}_1, \mathfrak{v}_2, \cdots, \mathfrak{v}_n$ *may be continuously deformed into* $\mathfrak{e}_1, \mathfrak{e}_2, \cdots, \mathfrak{e}_n$ *without the determinant of the system of vectors vanishing at any stage of this process. In the same way,* $\mathfrak{v}_1, \mathfrak{v}_2, \cdots, \mathfrak{v}_n$ *may be deformed into* $\mathfrak{e}_1, \mathfrak{e}_2, \cdots, \mathfrak{e}_{n-1}, -\mathfrak{e}_n$ *if only* $D(\mathfrak{v}_1, \mathfrak{v}_2, \cdots, \mathfrak{v}_n) < 0$.

The proof is given by induction on the dimension n. If $n = 1$, our system of vectors consists of a single vector $\mathfrak{v}_1 = \{v\}$ whose determinant is equal to v. If $v > 0$, we need only allow v to run continuously through the interval $(1, v)$ from v to 1; this represents a deformation of $\mathfrak{v}_1 = \{v\}$ into $\mathfrak{e}_1 = \{1\}$. If $v < 0$, we let v run continuously through the interval $(-1, v)$ from v to -1. Thus, for $n = 1$, Theorem 4 is trivial.

Let us assume it to be proven for dimension $n - 1$. We must show that its truth for dimension n follows from this, where we may assume $n \geqq 2$. We first prove:

A. *The system of vectors* $\mathfrak{v}_1, \mathfrak{v}_2, \cdots, \mathfrak{v}_n$ *may be continuously deformed into the system arising from it by replacing* $\mathfrak{v}_i$ *by* $\mathfrak{v}_i + \lambda\mathfrak{v}_k$, $i \neq k$, λ *real. The determinant of the system remains constant during this deformation.*

To carry out this deformation, we have only to let the parameter t in $\mathfrak{v}_i + t\mathfrak{v}_k$ vary continuously from 0 to λ, while the vectors $\mathfrak{v}_j$ with $j \neq i$ are left fixed. Since

$$D(\mathfrak{v}_1, \cdots, \mathfrak{v}_{i-1}, \mathfrak{v}_i + t\mathfrak{v}_k, \mathfrak{v}_{i+1}, \cdots, \mathfrak{v}_n) = D(\mathfrak{v}_1, \mathfrak{v}_2, \cdots, \mathfrak{v}_n)$$

the determinant has a constant value during this process.

B. *The system of vectors* $\mathfrak{v}_1, \mathfrak{v}_2, \cdots, \mathfrak{v}_n$ *may be deformed continuously, without changing the value of its determinant, into any system which arises from it by the simultaneous change of sign of two vectors, i.e., by the substitution of* $-\mathfrak{v}_i, -\mathfrak{v}_k$ *for* $\mathfrak{v}_i, \mathfrak{v}_k$.

This operation B may actually be regarded as a multiple application of operation A. In this latter, the vectors $\mathfrak{v}_j$ with $j \neq i, k$ are held constant. By writing the initial and final values of the vectors $\mathfrak{v}_i$ and $\mathfrak{v}_k$, we may also write an operation of type A as follows:

$$\mathfrak{v}_i \to \mathfrak{v}_i + \lambda\mathfrak{v}_k$$
$$\mathfrak{v}_k \to \mathfrak{v}_k.$$

We now carry out the following four operations of type A:

$$\begin{array}{lllll} \mathfrak{v}_i \to & \mathfrak{v}_i + 2\mathfrak{v}_k \to & \mathfrak{v}_i + 2\mathfrak{v}_k \to & -\mathfrak{v}_i & \to -\mathfrak{v}_i \\ \mathfrak{v}_k \to & \mathfrak{v}_k & \to -\mathfrak{v}_i - \mathfrak{v}_k \to & -\mathfrak{v}_i - \mathfrak{v}_k & \to -\mathfrak{v}_k. \end{array}$$

In the first operation, $\mathfrak{v}_i$ is transformed into $\mathfrak{v}_i + 2\mathfrak{v}_k$, in the next, $\mathfrak{v}_k$ is transformed into $\mathfrak{v}_k - (\mathfrak{v}_i + 2\mathfrak{v}_k) = -\mathfrak{v}_i - \mathfrak{v}_k$, in the third, $\mathfrak{v}_i + 2\mathfrak{v}_k$ is changed to $(\mathfrak{v}_i + 2\mathfrak{v}_k) + 2(-\mathfrak{v}_i - \mathfrak{v}_k) = -\mathfrak{v}_i$, and in the fouth, $-\mathfrak{v}_i - \mathfrak{v}_k$ becomes $(-\mathfrak{v}_i - \mathfrak{v}_k) - (-\mathfrak{v}_i) = -\mathfrak{v}_k$. Summing up, we see that the vectors $\mathfrak{v}_i$ and $\mathfrak{v}_k$ have each changed their sign, i.e., our operation B has been carried out.

We again let $\mathfrak{v}_i$ $(1 \leqq i \leqq n)$ have the components $v_{i1}, v_{i2}, \cdots, v_{in}$. For at least one of the vectors $\mathfrak{v}_i$, the last component v_{in} must be non-zero, since otherwise the determinant $|v_{ik}|$ would vanish, contrary to our assumption. Thus if, say $v_{nn} = 0$, we can find a vector $\mathfrak{v}_i$ whose last component v_{in} is non-zero, and using operation A, replace $\mathfrak{v}_n$ by $\mathfrak{v}_n + \mathfrak{v}_i$, whose last component is obviously non-zero. Thus, in order to avoid the introduction of new notation, we will assume $v_{nn} \neq 0$. Then, by another application of operation A, we transform the vector $\mathfrak{v}_1$ into $\mathfrak{v}_1 - \frac{v_{1n}}{v_{nn}}\mathfrak{v}_n$, thus transforming its last component into zero. In the same way, we transform the vectors $\mathfrak{v}_2, \mathfrak{v}_3, \cdots, \mathfrak{v}_{n-1}$ in order, by transforming the vector $\mathfrak{v}_i$ into $\mathfrak{v}_i - \frac{v_{in}}{v_{nn}}\mathfrak{v}_n$ $(1 \leqq i \leqq n-1)$. Our determinant $|v_{ik}|$ thus takes on the form

$$\begin{vmatrix} b_{11} & b_{12} & \cdots & b_{1,n-1} & 0 \\ b_{21} & b_{22} & \cdots & b_{2,n-1} & 0 \\ \cdot & \cdot & \cdot & \cdot & \cdot \\ b_{n-1,1} & b_{n-1,2} & \cdots & b_{n-1,n-1} & 0 \\ v_{n1} & v_{n2} & \cdots & v_{n,n-1} & v_{nn} \end{vmatrix},$$

and our system of vectors is transformed into the row vectors of this determinant. (The value of the determinant is still $|v_{ik}|$.) Let us now consider the column vectors of this determinant. A continuous deformation of the column vectors also represents a continuous deformation of the row vectors. However, operation A may be carried out for any n vectors, and thus also for the system of column vectors of our determinant. If we then subtract $\frac{v_{ni}}{v_{nn}}$ times the last column vector, i.e., $\frac{v_{ni}}{v_{nn}}\{0, 0, \cdots, 0, v_{nn}\}$, from the i-th column vector

$$\{b_{1i}, b_{2i}, \cdots, b_{n-1,i}, v_{ni}\},$$

$i = 1, 2, \ldots, n-1$, by a series of applications of operation A, we cause the last components of our column vectors to vanish, and our determinant takes on the form

$$\begin{vmatrix} b_{11} & b_{12} & \cdots & b_{1,n-1} & 0 \\ b_{21} & b_{22} & \cdots & b_{2,n-1} & 0 \\ \cdot & \cdot & \cdot & \cdot & \cdot \\ b_{n-1,1} & b_{n-1,2} & \cdots & b_{n-1,n-1} & 0 \\ 0 & 0 & \cdots & 0 & v_{nn} \end{vmatrix}.$$

Now our original system of vectors $\mathfrak{v}_1, \mathfrak{v}_2, \cdots, \mathfrak{v}_n$ has been transformed into the system of row vectors of this determinant. We shall now hold the last row and column of this determinant fixed, and vary the elements b_{ik} continuously. If we expand the determinant by its last row or column (§ 9), we see that it is equal to the product

$$v_{nn} \cdot \begin{vmatrix} b_{11} & b_{12} & \cdots & b_{1,n-1} \\ b_{21} & b_{22} & \cdots & b_{2,n-1} \\ \cdot & \cdot & \cdot & \cdot \\ b_{n-1,1} & b_{n-1,2} & \cdots & b_{n-1,n-1} \end{vmatrix}.$$

Since, on the other hand, its value is still $= |v_{ik}| \neq 0$, neither of the factors v_{nn} or $|b_{ik}|$ can vanish. We now denote the unit vectors of R_{n-1} by $\mathfrak{e}'_1, \mathfrak{e}'_2, \cdots, \mathfrak{e}'_{n-1}$. Then, by our induction assumption, the $n-1$ row vectors of the $(n-1)$-by-$(n-1)$ determinant $|b_{ik}|$ can be continuously deformed into one of the two systems of vectors

$$\mathfrak{e}'_1, \mathfrak{e}'_2, \cdots, \mathfrak{e}'_{n-2}, \pm\mathfrak{e}'_{n-1}$$

depending on whether $|b_{ik}| \gtrless 0$, and, in fact, this may be carried out in such a way that the determinant does not change sign and pass through the value 0. The determinant $|b_{ik}|$ then takes on the form

$$\begin{vmatrix} 1 & 0 & \cdots & 0 \\ 0 & 1 & \cdots & 0 \\ \cdot & \cdot & \cdot & \cdot \\ 0 & 0 & \cdots & \pm 1 \end{vmatrix},$$

and our determinant D is thus transformed into

$$\begin{vmatrix} 1 & 0 & \cdots & 0 & 0 \\ 0 & 1 & \cdots & 0 & 0 \\ \cdot & \cdot & \cdot & \cdot & \cdot \\ 0 & 0 & \cdots & \pm 1 & 0 \\ 0 & 0 & \cdots & 0 & v_{nn} \end{vmatrix}.$$

Finally, we transform v_{nn} continuously into $+1$ or -1 according to whether it is > 0 or < 0, in such a way that it does not take on the value 0. If the element in the next to the last row and the next to the last column is -1, we simultaneously change the sign of the next to the last and the last row vectors by an operation of type B, so as to have our determinant take on the final form

$$\begin{vmatrix} 1 & 0 & \cdots & 0 & 0 \\ 0 & 1 & \cdots & 0 & 0 \\ \cdot & \cdot & \cdot & \cdot & \cdot \\ 0 & 0 & \cdots & 1 & 0 \\ 0 & 0 & \cdots & 0 & \pm 1 \end{vmatrix}.$$

The value of this determinant is $+1$ or -1, according to whether the element in the last row and last column is $+1$ or -1, as we easily see by the use of the expansion formulas of § 9. During the continuous deformation, the value of the determinant has not changed its sign, and thus it is $+1$ or -1 according to whether $|v_{ik}| \gtrless 0$. Our system of vectors $\mathfrak{v}_1, \mathfrak{v}_2, \cdots, \mathfrak{v}_n$ has been transformed into the system of row vectors of the above determinant, i.e., into $\mathfrak{e}_1, \mathfrak{e}_2, \cdots, \mathfrak{e}_{n-1}, \pm \mathfrak{e}_n$, depending on whether $|v_{ik}| \gtrless 0$. Thus Theorem 4 is proved.

Exercises

1. Let there be given in R_3 the point $O' = (1, 1, 1)$ and the vectors

$$\mathfrak{a}_1 = \{0, 1, 7\}, \qquad \mathfrak{a}_2 = \{-1, -2, 1\}, \qquad \mathfrak{a}_3 = \{3, 4, -1\}.$$

What are the equations of the planes $x_i = 0$ $(i = 1, 2, 3)$; of the planes

$$x_1 + 3x_2 = 0, \; 15x_1 + 8x_2 + x_3 + 9 = 0;$$

and the equations of the line through the points $(1, 1, 1)$, $(-1, -1, -1)$ of R_3, in the coordinate system $[O'; \mathfrak{a}_1, \mathfrak{a}_2, \mathfrak{a}_3]$?

2. Let n vectors $\mathfrak{a}_1, \mathfrak{a}_2, \cdots, \mathfrak{a}_n$ of R_n be given in terms of their components in a coordinate system $[Q; \mathfrak{v}_1, \mathfrak{v}_2, \cdots, \mathfrak{v}_n]$, say by $\mathfrak{a}_i = \sum_{k=1}^{n} a_{ik} \mathfrak{v}_k$. We consider a vector $\mathfrak{b} = \sum_{k=1}^{n} b_k \mathfrak{v}_k$, whose components $b_1, b_2, \ldots, b_n$ (with respect to $[Q; \mathfrak{v}_1, \mathfrak{v}_2, \cdots, \mathfrak{v}_n]$)

are calculated from the components of the vectors $\mathfrak{a}_i$ as follows:

$$b_k = \sum_{i=1}^{n} \lambda_i a_{ik},$$

where $\lambda_1, \lambda_2, \cdots, \lambda_n$ are arbitrary real numbers between 0 and 1, i.e., $0 \leq \lambda_i \leq 1$. Show that if we draw all vectors $\mathfrak{b}$ of this sort from a fixed point, we obtain a parallelotope whose edge vectors are $\mathfrak{a}_1, \mathfrak{a}_2, \cdots, \mathfrak{a}_n$.

3. A matrix whose row and column vectors each form a normal orthogonal system is necessarily square (i.e., has as many rows as columns).

4. Let the end points of the unit vectors $\mathfrak{e}_1, \mathfrak{e}_2$ in the plane, drawn from the origin, be E_1, E_2 (Fig. 21). The order of the points O, E_1, E_2 then defines a *sense of*

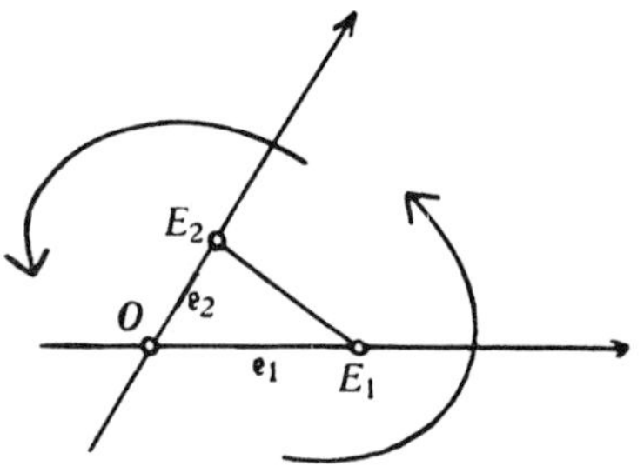

Fig. 21

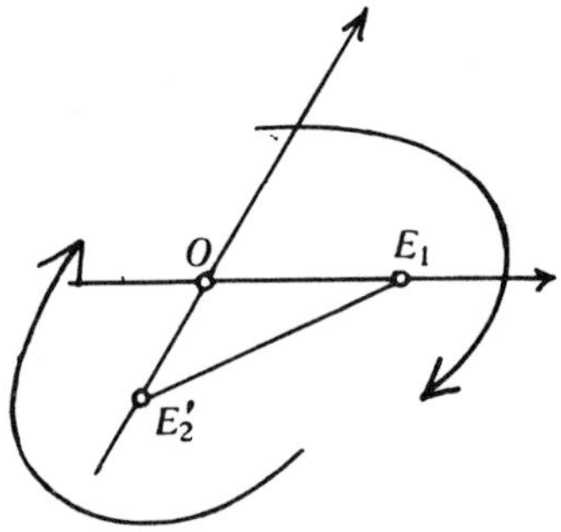

Fig. 22

rotation in the plane which is obtained by going around the triangle OE_1E_2 from O to E_1 to E_2 and back to O. (Indicated in Fig. 21 by arrows.) In addition, let E_2' be the end point of the vector $-\mathfrak{e}_2$, when this is drawn from the origin (Fig. 22). Then the order of the points O, E_1, E_2' also defines a sense of rotation, namely, the sense opposite to the first. The first sense is called the *positive* sense, the second the *negative*. The negative sense of rotation is also defined by the circuit O, E_2, E_1, O in Fig. 21.

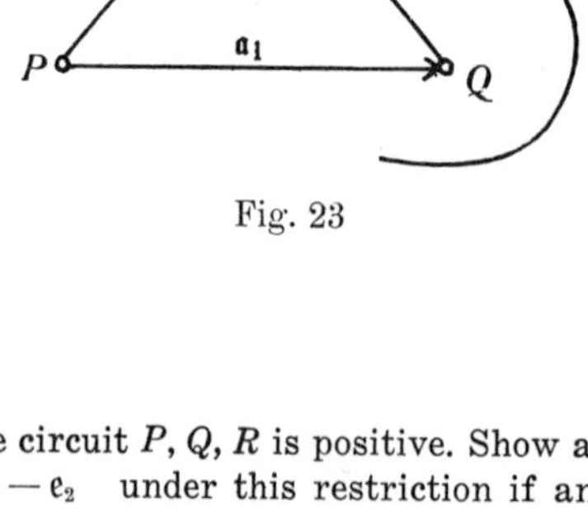

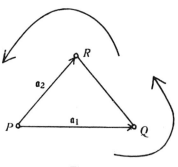

Fig. 23

In addition, let $\mathfrak{a}_1, \mathfrak{a}_2$ be two linearly independent vectors in the plane. If from an arbitrary point P of the plane we draw the vectors $\mathfrak{a}_1$ and $\mathfrak{a}_2$, these extending to the points Q and R respectively, the order of the points P, Q, R defines a sense of rotation in the plane (Fig. 23). Show that the system of vectors $\mathfrak{a}_1, \mathfrak{a}_2$ can be continuously deformed into the system $\mathfrak{e}_1, \mathfrak{e}_2$ under the conditions of Theorem 4 if and only if the sense of rotation defined by the circuit P, Q, R is positive. Show also that it may be deformed continuously into $\mathfrak{e}_1, -\mathfrak{e}_2$ under this restriction if and only if this sense is negative.

5. Let there be given a triangle PQR in the plane,

$$P = (x_1, x_2),\ Q = (y_1, y_2),\ R = (z_1, z_2).$$

Twice the area of the triangle is equal to the absolute value of the determinant

$$\begin{vmatrix} 1 & x_1 & x_2 \\ 1 & y_1 & y_2 \\ 1 & z_1 & z_2 \end{vmatrix}$$

(cf. exercise 4, § 8). Show (using 4) that this determinant is positive if the sense of the circuit P, Q, R is positive and negative if this sense is negative.

6. The unit vectors $\mathfrak{e}_1,\ \mathfrak{e}_2,\ \mathfrak{e}_3$ in R_3 (Fig. 24) constitute a so-called "right-handed system" if we think of the vectors $\mathfrak{e}_2,\ \mathfrak{e}_3$ as lying in the plane of the page while $\mathfrak{e}_1$ is directed toward the reader; for in this order they assume the same sort of orientation as the thumb, index finger, and middle finger of the right hand. On the other hand, $\mathfrak{e}_1, \mathfrak{e}_2, -\mathfrak{e}_3$ constitute a "left-handed system," since in this order they stand in the same orientation as the thumb, index finger, and middle finger of the left hand.

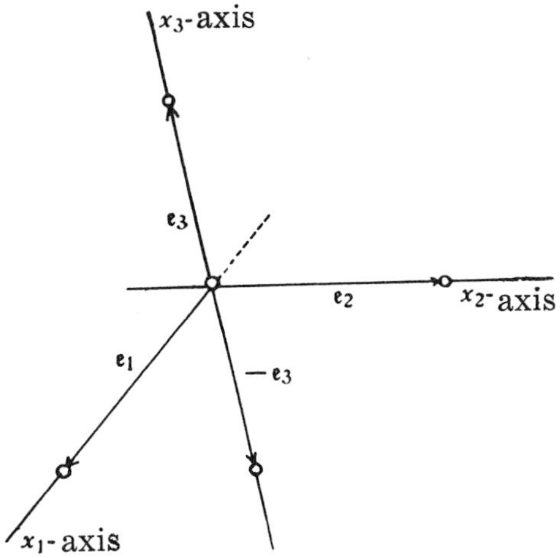

Fig. 24

Let $\mathfrak{a}_1, \mathfrak{a}_2, \mathfrak{a}_3$ be three linearly independent vectors. We have then that if $\mathfrak{a}_1,\ \mathfrak{a}_2,\ \mathfrak{a}_3$ and $\mathfrak{e}_1,\ \mathfrak{e}_2,\ \mathfrak{e}_3$ are systems of similar orientation (either both right-handed or both left-handed), then the vectors $\mathfrak{a}_1, \mathfrak{a}_2, \mathfrak{a}_3$ may be continuously deformed into $\mathfrak{e}_1, \mathfrak{e}_2, \mathfrak{e}_3$ under the conditions of Theorem 4. In the other case, they may be continuously deformed in the same way into $\mathfrak{e}_1, \mathfrak{e}_2, -\mathfrak{e}_3$.

7. Let P, Q, R, S be the vertices of a tetrahedron in R_3,

$$P = (u_1, u_2, u_3),\quad Q = (v_1, v_2, v_3),\quad R = (x_1, x_2, x_3),\quad S = (y_1, y_2, y_3).$$

Six times the volume of the tetrahedron $PQRS$ is given by the absolute value of the determinant

$$\begin{vmatrix} 1 & u_1 & u_2 & u_3 \\ 1 & v_1 & v_2 & v_3 \\ 1 & x_1 & x_2 & x_3 \\ 1 & y_1 & y_2 & y_3 \end{vmatrix}.$$

Show (using exercise 6) that the sign of the determinant is positive or negative according to whether the vectors $\overrightarrow{PQ}, \overrightarrow{PR}, \overrightarrow{PS}$, taken in this order are oriented in a similar or in an opposite way to $\mathfrak{e}_1,\ \mathfrak{e}_2,\ \mathfrak{e}_3$.

§ 11. Construction of Normal Orthogonal Systems and Applications

The considerations of this section are concerned with R_n in which euclidean length has been introduced. To begin with, let there be given a vector space L of dimension $p > 0$ and a basis $\mathfrak{a}_1, \mathfrak{a}_2, \cdots, \mathfrak{a}_p$ of L. We shall decide the question of whether it is possible to choose a normal orthogonal system as a basis of L. It is certainly clear that we may determine a *single* vector of L which forms a normal orthogonal system, i.e. has length 1. For the vector $\frac{\mathfrak{a}_1}{|\mathfrak{a}_1|}$ certainly is such.[1] It is thus also clear that every vector space of dimension 1 has a basis which forms a normal orthogonal system. Now, in order to prove this for vector spaces of dimension $p > 1$, we may employ mathematical induction, and assume the existence of a normal orthogonal basis for vector spaces of dimension $p - 1$. Let us denote by L′, the vector space spanned by the vectors $\mathfrak{a}_1, \mathfrak{a}_2, \cdots, \mathfrak{a}_{p-1}$. By induction hypothesis, there is a basis $\mathfrak{v}_1, \mathfrak{v}_2, \cdots, \mathfrak{v}_{p-1}$ of L′ which forms a normal orthogonal system. We seek to determine a vector $\mathfrak{v}_p$ of L which is of length 1 and which is orthogonal to the vectors $\mathfrak{v}_1, \mathfrak{v}_2, \cdots, \mathfrak{v}_{p-1}$.

The vector $\mathfrak{a}_p$ is certainly not in L′, since the vectors $\mathfrak{a}_1, \mathfrak{a}_2, \cdots, \mathfrak{a}_p$ are linearly independent. Hence it is not representable as a linear combination of the vectors $\mathfrak{v}_1, \mathfrak{v}_2, \cdots, \mathfrak{v}_{p-1}$. Hence, by Theorem 6 of § 3, the vectors $\mathfrak{v}_1, \mathfrak{v}_2, \cdots, \mathfrak{v}_{p-1}, \mathfrak{a}_p$ must be linearly independent, and hence must form a basis of L. The vector $\mathfrak{v}_p$ which we are seeking must then be a linear combination of this last system of vectors:

$$\mathfrak{v}_p = \lambda_1 \mathfrak{v}_1 + \lambda_2 \mathfrak{v}_2 + \cdots + \lambda_{p-1} \mathfrak{v}_{p-1} + \lambda_p \mathfrak{a}_p. \tag{1}$$

If we multiply both sides of this equation by $\mathfrak{v}_i$ $(1 \leqq i \leqq p-1)$, then by the orthogonality of $\mathfrak{v}_p$ and $\mathfrak{v}_i$ for $i \leqq p - 1$, the left-hand side of the equation becomes 0. In calculating the right-hand side we need only observe that for $i, k = 1, 2, \ldots, p-1$, $\mathfrak{v}_i \mathfrak{v}_k = \delta_{ik}$. We thus obtain

$$0 = \lambda_i + \lambda_p \cdot (\mathfrak{a}_p \cdot \mathfrak{v}_i),$$
$$\lambda_i = -\lambda_p \cdot (\mathfrak{a}_p \cdot \mathfrak{v}_i), \qquad i = 1, 2, \cdots, p-1.$$

Substituting this in (1), it follows that

$$\mathfrak{v}_p = \lambda_p \left(\mathfrak{a}_p - \sum_{i=1}^{p-1} (\mathfrak{a}_p \cdot \mathfrak{v}_i) \cdot \mathfrak{v}_i\right).$$

---

[1] $|\mathfrak{a}|$ is the length of a vector $\mathfrak{a}$ (§ 7).

Now, we also wanted $\mathfrak{v}_p^2$ to be equal to 1. Applied to the right-hand side, this condition yields

$$\lambda_p^2 \left(\mathfrak{a}_p - \sum_{i=1}^{p-1} (\mathfrak{a}_p \cdot \mathfrak{v}_i) \cdot \mathfrak{v}_i\right)^2 = 1 .$$

Since the vectors $\mathfrak{v}_1, \mathfrak{v}_2, \cdots, \mathfrak{v}_{p-1}, \mathfrak{a}_p$ were linearly independent, $\mathfrak{a}_p - \sum_{i=1}^{p-1} (\mathfrak{a}_p \cdot \mathfrak{v}_i) \cdot \mathfrak{v}_i \neq 0$ and therefore also $\left(\mathfrak{a}_p - \sum_{i=1}^{p-1} (\mathfrak{a}_p \cdot \mathfrak{v}_i) \cdot \mathfrak{v}_i\right)^2 \neq 0$. Hence there exists a number λ_p which satisfies the last equation, namely

$$\lambda_p = \pm \frac{1}{\left|\mathfrak{a}_p - \sum_{i=1}^{p-1} (\mathfrak{a}_p \cdot \mathfrak{v}_i) \cdot \mathfrak{v}_i\right|} .$$

Therefore, we must have for $\mathfrak{v}_p$ that

$$\mathfrak{v}_p = \pm \frac{\mathfrak{a}_p - \sum_{i=1}^{p-1} (\mathfrak{a}_p \cdot \mathfrak{v}_i) \cdot \mathfrak{v}_i}{\left|\mathfrak{a}_p - \sum_{i=1}^{p-1} (\mathfrak{a}_p \cdot \mathfrak{v}_i) \cdot \mathfrak{v}_i\right|} . \tag{2}$$

However, either of these two vectors does actually fulfil our requirements as can be verified immediately by calculation. If then, for definiteness, we choose one of the signs in (2) $\mathfrak{v}_1, \mathfrak{v}_2, \cdots, \mathfrak{v}_p$ is the desired normal orthogonal basis for L.

Let us observe that the proof we have just carried out provides us with a recursive procedure which actually enables us to obtain the normal orthogonal basis. For, if we let the space spanned by the first i vectors $\mathfrak{a}_1, \mathfrak{a}_2, \cdots, \mathfrak{a}_i$ $(1 \leq i \leq p)$ of the given basis of L be denoted by L_i, then $L_p = L$ while L_1 is one-dimensional. Beginning with a vector $\mathfrak{v}_1$ of L_1 whose length is 1, we may obtain, using (2), a vector $\mathfrak{v}_2$ such that $\mathfrak{v}_1, \mathfrak{v}_2$ is a normal orthogonal basis of L_2. In exactly the same way, we obtain such a basis for L_3, and continuing the process, we finally arrive at one for $L_p = L$.

Before we discuss the applications of the above, we remark briefly on certain properties of a normal orthogonal basis of R_n. If we are given a Cartesian coordinate system $[O'; \mathfrak{v}_1, \mathfrak{v}_2, \cdots, \mathfrak{v}_n]$ in R_n then the components $a_1, a_2, \ldots, a_n$ of a vector $\mathfrak{a}$ with respect to this coordinate system may easily be calculated. In fact,

$$\mathfrak{a} = a_1 \mathfrak{v}_1 + a_2 \mathfrak{v}_2 + \cdots + a_n \mathfrak{v}_n .$$

Multiplying both sides of this equation by $\mathfrak{v}_i$ $(1 \leq i \leq n)$, and observing that $\mathfrak{v}_i \mathfrak{v}_k = \delta_{ik}$, we obtain:

$$(3) \qquad a_i = \mathfrak{a}\,\mathfrak{v}_i.$$

Since the scalar product of two vectors may be computed from their components with respect to the Cartesian coordinate system

$$[O'; \mathfrak{v}_1, \mathfrak{v}_2, \cdots, \mathfrak{v}_n]$$

in exactly the same way as from their components in R_n, by (3) we obtain for the length of the vector $\mathfrak{a}$,

$$(4) \qquad |\mathfrak{a}| = {}_{+}\sqrt{\mathfrak{a}^2} = {}_{+}\sqrt{\sum_{i=1}^{n} a_i^2} = {}_{+}\sqrt{\sum_{i=1}^{n} (\mathfrak{a}\,\mathfrak{v}_i)^2}.$$

We shall now apply our previous discussion to the determination of the perpendicular which may be drawn to a given linear space L from a point outside L. We assume that L contains more than one point, but not all points of R_n. Thus, if p is the dimension of L, we must have $0 < p < n$. L is obtained from any one of its points by applying all the vectors of some vector space L of dimension p. We determine a normal orthogonal basis $\mathfrak{v}_1, \mathfrak{v}_2, \cdots, \mathfrak{v}_p$ of L. This can be extended to a basis of R_n (i.e. to a basis of R_n considered as a vector space; cf. § 4, Theorem 6). We may perform this extension by the method described above in such a manner that we obtain a normal orthogonal basis for R_n. Let this be, say, $\mathfrak{v}_1, \mathfrak{v}_2, \cdots, \mathfrak{v}_p, \mathfrak{v}_{p+1}, \cdots, \mathfrak{v}_n$; thus we again have $\mathfrak{v}_i \mathfrak{v}_k = \delta_{ik}$ for $i, k = 1, 2, \ldots, n$.

We now consider the vector space P which is spanned by the vectors $\mathfrak{v}_{p+1}, \mathfrak{v}_{p+2}, \cdots, \mathfrak{v}_n$. *Every vector of* P *is orthogonal to every vector of* L. For, a vector of P may be written in the form $\sum_{i=p+1}^{n} \lambda_i \mathfrak{v}_i$, while a vector of L may be written in the form $\sum_{i=1}^{p} \mu_i \mathfrak{v}_i$. Let us observe that for $i \neq k$, we have $\mathfrak{v}_i \mathfrak{v}_k = 0$, so that

$$\left(\sum_{i=1}^{p} \mu_i \mathfrak{v}_i\right) \cdot \left(\sum_{i=p+1}^{n} \lambda_i \mathfrak{v}_i\right) = 0.$$

Furthermore, the intersection of P *and* L *consists of the null vector alone.* For if $\mathfrak{a}$ is a vector which P and L have in common, then $\mathfrak{a}$ may be written as a linear combination of $\mathfrak{v}_1, \mathfrak{v}_2, \cdots, \mathfrak{v}_p$ and also as a linear combination of $\mathfrak{v}_{p+1}, \mathfrak{v}_{p+2}, \cdots, \mathfrak{v}_n$, say

$$\mathfrak{a} = \sum_{i=1}^{p} \mu_i \mathfrak{v}_i = \sum_{i=p+1}^{n} \lambda_i \mathfrak{v}_i .$$

We thus have

$$\sum_{i=1}^{p} \mu_i \mathfrak{v}_i - \sum_{i=p+1}^{n} \lambda_i \mathfrak{v}_i = 0 .$$

By the linear independence of the vectors $\mathfrak{v}_1, \mathfrak{v}_2, \cdots, \mathfrak{v}_n$, this is possible only if

$$\mu_1 = \mu_2 = \cdots = \mu_p = \lambda_{p+1} = \lambda_{p+2} = \cdots = \lambda_n = 0 .$$

Hence $\mathfrak{a}$ must be the null vector. Furthermore, every vector which is orthogonal to all vectors of L belongs to P. For if $\mathfrak{a} = \sum_{i=1}^{n} a_i \mathfrak{v}_i$ is such a vector of R_n, then it must in particular be orthogonal to the basis vectors $\mathfrak{v}_1, \mathfrak{v}_2, \cdots, \mathfrak{v}_p$ of L, i.e. $\mathfrak{a}\mathfrak{v}_i = 0$ for $i = 1, 2, \ldots, p$. By (3) it follows that $a_i = 0$ for $i = 1, 2, \ldots, p$. Hence $\mathfrak{a}$ is a linear combination of the vectors $\mathfrak{v}_{p+1}, \mathfrak{v}_{p+2}, \cdots, \mathfrak{v}_n$ alone, i.e. it belongs to P. P *is therefore the totality of all vectors which are orthogonal to* L (cf. § 6, proof of Theorem 8).

Now, let $Q = (y_1, y_2, \ldots, y_n)$ be a point of R_n which does not belong to L. Does there exist a point P in L such that $\overrightarrow{PQ}$ is orthogonal to all vectors of L? Since L consists of all vectors which join two points of L, we also call such a vector $\overrightarrow{PQ}$ *orthogonal to* L. To answer the question, let P_0 be an arbitrary point of L. The vector $\overrightarrow{P_0Q}$, being a vector of R_n, is a linear combination of $\mathfrak{v}_1, \mathfrak{v}_2, \cdots, \mathfrak{v}_n$, say:

$$\overrightarrow{P_0 Q} = \sum_{i=1}^{n} \lambda_i \mathfrak{v}_i . \tag{5}$$

Now, let us form the vector $\mathfrak{b} = \sum_{i=1}^{p} \lambda_i \mathfrak{v}_i$, where the coefficients

$$\lambda_1, \lambda_2, \cdots, \lambda_p$$

are the first p coefficients from equation (5). Let the vector $\mathfrak{b}$ carry the point P_0 into, say, P. Then

$$\overrightarrow{P_0 P} = \sum_{i=1}^{p} \lambda_i \mathfrak{v}_i ,$$

and P is a point of L, since $\sum_{i=1}^{p} \lambda_i \mathfrak{v}_i$ is a vector of L. Furthermore $\overrightarrow{P_0 Q} = \overrightarrow{P_0 P} + \overrightarrow{PQ}$, so that by (5),

(6) $$\overrightarrow{PQ} = \sum_{i=p+1}^{n} \lambda_i \mathfrak{v}_i.$$

$\overrightarrow{PQ}$ is thus a linear combination of $\mathfrak{v}_{p+1}, \mathfrak{v}_{p+2}, \cdots, \mathfrak{v}_n$, i.e. a vector of P. However, it must therefore be orthogonal to all vectors of L. We have thus obtained a point P of the desired sort.

However, P is the only point of this sort. For suppose that P' were another such point of L. Then let

$$\overrightarrow{P'Q} = \sum_{i=1}^{n} \mu_i \mathfrak{v}_i.$$

Since by our assumption $\overrightarrow{P'Q}$ was to be orthogonal to all vectors of L, we must have for $i = 1, 2, \ldots, p$ that $(\overrightarrow{P'Q}) \cdot \mathfrak{v}_i = 0$, so that, by (3), $\mu_i = 0$ for $i = 1, 2, \ldots, p$. However, $\overrightarrow{P'Q} = \overrightarrow{P'P} + \overrightarrow{PQ}$, so that by (6), we have

$$\overrightarrow{P'P} = \overrightarrow{P'Q} - \overrightarrow{PQ} = \sum_{i=p+1}^{n} (\mu_i - \lambda_i)\mathfrak{v}_i.$$

Thus $\overrightarrow{P'P}$ is a vector of P. On the other hand, P' and P are two points of L. Hence, $\overrightarrow{P'P}$ belongs also to L. However, since the intersection of P and L consists of the null vector alone, we must have $\overrightarrow{P'P} = 0$, i.e. the points P and P' coincide. Therefore there are no points of the desired sort in L other than P itself.

The segment PQ (or the vector $\overrightarrow{PQ}$, or $\overrightarrow{QP}$) is called the *perpendicular from Q to L. P* is called the *foot* of the perpendicular. The length of the perpendicular, by (4), (5), and (6), is given by

(7) $$\overline{PQ} = +\sqrt{\sum_{i=p+1}^{n} \lambda_i^2} = +\sqrt{\sum_{i=p+1}^{n} [(\overrightarrow{P_0Q}) \cdot \mathfrak{v}_i]^2}.$$

The point P_0 was an arbitrary point of L. Hence by (4) and (5), we have the following formula for the distance between the points P_0 and Q:

$$\overline{P_0Q} = +\sqrt{\sum_{i=1}^{n} [(\overrightarrow{P_0Q}) \cdot \mathfrak{v}_i]^2}.$$

Comparison with (7) immediately yields:

$$\overline{P_0Q} \geq \overline{PQ},$$

where equality holds only if $(\overrightarrow{P_0Q}) \cdot \mathfrak{v}_i = 0$ for $i = 1, 2, \ldots, p$. But, by (3) and (5), this implies that P_0Q belongs to P and so is orthogonal to L, which is only possible if P_0 coincides with P. *The length of the segment PQ is thus the shortest distance from the point Q to the linear space L. And conversely, if P_0 is a point of L for which $\overrightarrow{P_0Q}$ is the shortest distance from Q to the space L, then $\overrightarrow{P_0Q} = \overrightarrow{PQ}$ is the perpendicular from Q to L.*

We shall next consider how we may calculate the perpendicular if the linear space L is given by a system of linear equations, say by the equations

$$\begin{aligned} a_{11}x_1 + a_{12}x_2 + \cdots + a_{1n}x_n &= b_1, \\ a_{21}x_1 + a_{22}x_2 + \cdots + a_{2n}x_n &= b_2, \\ \cdots\cdots\cdots\cdots\cdots & \\ a_{r1}x_1 + a_{r2}x_2 + \cdots + a_{rn}x_n &= b_r. \end{aligned} \tag{8}$$

Then, in the terminology of § 6, the linear space L consists of all points which are solutions of this system of equations. If q is the rank of the matrices[2] of (8), then by § 9, page 104, it is sufficient to consider q linearly independent equations of the system (8), which themselves also represent all of L. We assume that this reduction has already been accomplished, and that accordingly the rank of (8) is exactly r, the number of equations occurring in (8). By § 6, $r + p = n$, where p is the dimension of L. The vector space L associated with L is now represented by the system of homogeneous equations

$$\begin{aligned} a_{11}x_1 + a_{12}x_2 + \cdots + a_{1n}x_n &= 0, \\ a_{21}x_1 + a_{22}x_2 + \cdots + a_{2n}x_n &= 0, \\ \cdots\cdots\cdots\cdots\cdots & \\ a_{r1}x_1 + a_{r2}x_2 + \cdots + a_{rn}x_n &= 0. \end{aligned} \tag{9}$$

That is, L is the totality of vector solutions of (9) (cf. § 6, Theorems 8 and 9). The row vectors $\mathfrak{a}_1, \mathfrak{a}_2, \cdots, \mathfrak{a}_r$ of the coefficient matrix of (9) are therefore orthogonal to all vector solutions of (9), i.e. orthogonal to L. The vector space P which is orthogonal to L is however of dimension $n - p = r$. Since the vectors $\mathfrak{a}_1, \mathfrak{a}_2, \cdots, \mathfrak{a}_r$ are linearly independent (the rank of the matrix of (9) was r), they form a basis of P.

Now by the procedure introduced at the beginning of this section, we may construct a normal orthogonal basis of P from $\mathfrak{a}_1, \mathfrak{a}_2, \cdots, \mathfrak{a}_r$.

---

[2] The coefficient matrix of the system (8) must have the same rank as the augmented matrix of this system, since the system represents a linear space L, and so must be solvable.

We again denote this normal orthogonal basis by $\mathfrak{v}_{p+1}, \mathfrak{v}_{p+2}, \cdots, \mathfrak{v}_n$. Let the components of the vector $\mathfrak{v}_{p+i}$ be $v_{i1}, v_{i2}, \cdots, v_{in}$ for $i = 1, 2, \ldots, r$. If we now choose an arbitrary (but fixed) point $P_0 = (z_1, z_2, \ldots, z_n)$ of L, and form the equations

$$(10) \qquad \sum_{k=1}^{n} v_{ik} x_k = \sum_{k=1}^{n} v_{ik} z_k, \qquad i = 1, 2, \cdots, r,$$

then by the proof of Theorem 9 of § 6, this system of r linear equations in the variables $x_1, x_2, \ldots, x_n$ also represents the linear space L. We write the system (10) in the more useful form

$$(11) \qquad \sum_{k=1}^{n} v_{ik}(x_k - z_k) = 0, \qquad i = 1, 2, \cdots, r.$$

Now let $Q = (y_1, y_2, \ldots, y_n)$ be an arbitrary point not in L. For the scalar product $(\overrightarrow{P_0 Q}) \cdot \mathfrak{v}_{p+i}$ we have by an easy calculation,

$$(\overrightarrow{P_0 Q}) \cdot \mathfrak{v}_{p+i} = \sum_{k=1}^{n} v_{ik}(y_k - z_k).$$

By (7), we thus have the following formula for the length of the perpendicular PQ from Q to L:

$$(12) \qquad \overline{PQ}^2 = \sum_{i=1}^{r} \left[\sum_{k=1}^{n} v_{ik}(y_k - z_k) \right]^2.$$

That is, *if we substitute the coordinates* $y_1, y_2, \ldots, y_n$ *of the point* Q *in the left-hand sides of equations* (11) *for the variables* $x_1, x_2, \ldots, x_n$, *and if we square each of the resulting quantities and add them, then we obtain precisely the square of the perpendicular distance from the point* Q *to the space* L.

In particular, let us consider the special case for which L is a hyperplane, and so has dimension $p = n - 1$. Then the system (8) of linear equations consists of the single equation

$$(8a) \qquad a_1 x_1 + a_2 x_2 + \cdots + a_n x_n = b.$$

The vector space P which is orthogonal to L is then one-dimensional, and the vector $\mathfrak{a} = \{a_1, a_2, \cdots, a_n\}$ alone forms a basis of P. Thus a normal orthogonal basis of P is given by the vector

$$\mathfrak{a}^* = \frac{\mathfrak{a}}{|\mathfrak{a}|}.$$

If we denote the components of $\mathfrak{a}^*$ by $a_1^*, a_2^*, \cdots, a_n^*$, then

$$a_i^* = \frac{a_i}{+\sqrt{a_1^2 + a_2^2 + \cdots + a_n^2}}.$$

Hence, we shall have for an arbitrary point $P_0 = (z_1, z_2, \cdots, z_n)$ of L, since its coordinates satisfy equation (8a), that

$$\sum_{i=1}^{n} a_i^* z_i = \frac{1}{+\sqrt{a_1^2 + a_2^2 + \cdots + a_n^2}} \cdot \sum_{i=1}^{n} a_i z_i = \frac{b}{+\sqrt{a_1^2 + a_2^2 + \cdots + a_n^2}}.$$

Thus, the system (11) now consists of the single equation

$$\text{(11a)} \quad \sum_{i=1}^{n} \left(\frac{a_i}{+\sqrt{a_1^2 + a_2^2 + \cdots + a_n^2}} x_i \right) - \frac{b}{+\sqrt{a_1^2 + a_2^2 + \cdots + a_n^2}} = 0.$$

Thus, by (12), the perpendicular distance of a point $Q = (y_1, y_2, \ldots, y_n)$ from L is given by

$$\overline{PQ} = \left| \sum_{k=1}^{n} \frac{a_i y_i}{+\sqrt{a_1^2 + a_2^2 + \cdots + a_n^2}} - \frac{b}{+\sqrt{a_1^2 + a_2^2 + \cdots + a_n^2}} \right|.$$

Equation (11a) is called the **Hesse normal form** of the equation of the hyperplane L. *The absolute value of the left-hand side of the Hesse normal form yields precisely the perpendicular distance of the point Q from L if we replace the variables x_i by the coordinates y_i of Q.*

We now wish to determine a somewhat more general problem. Namely, we wish to determine the *common perpendiculars* (if indeed such exist) *to two linear spaces* L_1 and L_2. By such a common perpendicular we mean a vector $\overrightarrow{PQ}$ whose initial point P lies in one of the two given linear spaces, say L_1, and whose terminal point Q lies in the other space L_2, and which is orthogonal to both L_1 and L_2. Let $\mathfrak{L}_1$ be the vector space corresponding to L_1 (i.e. the totality of all vectors which lie in L_1), $\mathfrak{L}_2$, that corresponding to L_2. We form the sum $\mathfrak{S}$ of $\mathfrak{L}_1$ and $\mathfrak{L}_2$.[3] Let the dimension of $\mathfrak{S}$ be s. We assume that $s > 0$, that is, that $\mathfrak{L}_1$ and $\mathfrak{L}_2$ are not both of dimension 0, so that L_1 and L_2 do not both consist of only one point. This case is immediately settled because of its extreme simplicity. Now, let $\mathfrak{v}_1, \mathfrak{v}_2, \cdots, \mathfrak{v}_s$ be a normal orthogonal basis of $\mathfrak{S}$. If now $s = n$, the vector space orthogonal to $\mathfrak{S}$ is of dimension 0, i.e. the null vector is the only vector which is orthogonal to all vectors of $\mathfrak{S}$. Since

[3] $\mathfrak{S}$ consists of all vectors of the form $\mathfrak{a}_1 + \mathfrak{a}_2$, where $\mathfrak{a}_1$ belongs to $\mathfrak{L}_1$ and $\mathfrak{a}_2$ belongs to $\mathfrak{L}_2$ (cf. § 4, p. 25).

a common perpendicular $\overrightarrow{PQ}$ must be orthogonal to all vectors of L_1 and L_2, it must also be orthogonal to all vectors of S. Hence in the present case such a perpendicular $\overrightarrow{PQ}$ can only be the null vector, i.e. the points P and Q must coincide. P belongs to L_1, and since P and Q are identical, also to L_2. P is thus a point of the intersection of L_1 and L_2. Moreover the intersection of L_1 and L_2 is now actually non-empty. For if P_0 is an arbitrary point of L_1, Q_0 one of L_2, then $\overrightarrow{P_0Q_0}$ belongs to S since $s = n$. Thus by definition of S, there exist two vectors $\mathfrak{a}_1$ and $\mathfrak{a}_2$ such that $\mathfrak{a}_1$ is a vector of L_1 and $\mathfrak{a}_2$ is a vector of L_2, and such that

$$\overrightarrow{P_0 Q_0} = \mathfrak{a}_1 + \mathfrak{a}_2 .$$

If the vector $\mathfrak{a}_1$ carries P_0 to P and the vector $(-\mathfrak{a}_1)$ carries Q_0 to Q, then

$$\overrightarrow{P_0 P} = \mathfrak{a}_1 , \qquad \overrightarrow{Q Q_0} = \mathfrak{a}_2 .$$

On the other hand,

$$\overrightarrow{P_0 Q_0} = \overrightarrow{P_0 P} + \overrightarrow{PQ} + \overrightarrow{Q Q_0} = \mathfrak{a}_1 + \mathfrak{a}_2 .$$

Hence we must have $\overrightarrow{PQ} = 0$, so that P and Q are identical. However, P is, by construction, a point of L_1, Q a point of L_2, so that P is a point of their intersection, which is thus non-empty. Thus the case $s = n$ is completely settled. We shall later see that the results thus obtained may also be considered as special cases of the results we shall obtain for $s < n$.

Thus, let $s < n$ in what follows. Then, once again, we may extend the basis $\mathfrak{v}_1, \mathfrak{v}_2, \cdots, \mathfrak{v}_s$ of S to a normal orthogonal basis of R_n by the addition of suitably selected vectors $\mathfrak{v}_{s+1}, \mathfrak{v}_{s+2}, \cdots, \mathfrak{v}_n$. Let P be the vector space which is spanned by $\mathfrak{v}_{s+1}, \mathfrak{v}_{s+2}, \cdots, \mathfrak{v}_n$. As we have already seen, P is then the totality of all vectors which are orthogonal to S, and the intersection of P and S consists of the null vector alone.

Now let P_0 be an arbitrary point of L_1, Q_0 an arbitrary point of L_2. Let us write the vector $\overrightarrow{P_0Q_0}$ as a linear combination of $\mathfrak{v}_1, \mathfrak{v}_2, \cdots, \mathfrak{v}_n$, say

$$(13) \qquad \overrightarrow{P_0 Q_0} = \sum_{i=1}^{n} \lambda_i \mathfrak{v}_i .$$

Then let us consider the vector $\sum_{i=1}^{s} \lambda_i \mathfrak{v}_i$, where the coefficients $\lambda_1, \lambda_2, \ldots, \lambda_s$ are the first s coefficients of (13). As a linear combination of $\mathfrak{v}_1, \mathfrak{v}_2, \cdots, \mathfrak{v}_s$, it is a vector of S and hence certainly the sum of a vector $\mathfrak{a}_1$ of L_1 and a vector $\mathfrak{a}_2$ of L_2:

$$\sum_{i=1}^{s} \lambda_i \mathfrak{v}_i = \mathfrak{a}_1 + \mathfrak{a}_2. \tag{14}$$

Let the vector $\mathfrak{a}_1$ carry P_0 to P, and let the vector $(-\mathfrak{a}_2)$ carry Q_0 to Q. Thus,

$$\overrightarrow{P_0 P} = \mathfrak{a}_1, \qquad \overrightarrow{Q Q_0} = \mathfrak{a}_2. \tag{15}$$

Hence P is a point of L_1, since P_0 is a point of L_1 and $\mathfrak{a}_1$ is a vector of L_1. Similarly, Q is a point of L_2. However,

$$\overrightarrow{P_0 Q_0} = \overrightarrow{P_0 P} + \overrightarrow{PQ} + \overrightarrow{Q Q_0}.$$

On the other hand, by (13), (14), and (15), we have

$$\overrightarrow{P_0 Q_0} = \overrightarrow{P_0 P} + \sum_{i=s+1}^{n} \lambda_i \mathfrak{v}_i + \overrightarrow{Q Q_0}.$$

Thus the relation

$$\overrightarrow{PQ} = \sum_{i=s+1}^{n} \lambda_i \mathfrak{v}_i \tag{16}$$

must hold. Moreover, $\overrightarrow{PQ}$ as a linear combination of $\mathfrak{v}_{s+1}, \mathfrak{v}_{s+2}, \cdots, \mathfrak{v}_n$, is a vector of P and as such is orthogonal to all vectors of S, and hence also orthogonal to all vectors of L_1 and L_2, which are themselves subspaces of S. $\overrightarrow{PQ}$ is thus a common perpendicular of L_1 and L_2. P and Q are each called a *foot* of the perpendicular.

In general, P and Q will not be the only points of this sort. If, however, P', Q' is another pair of points of this sort, that is, if P' is a point of L_1 and Q' a point of L_2 and if, moreover, $\overrightarrow{P'Q'}$ is orthogonal to L_1 and to L_2, then we must necessarily have $\overrightarrow{PQ} = \overrightarrow{P'Q'}$. That is, *two common perpendiculars to L_1 and L_2 are always parallel and of equal length.* For, the vector $\overrightarrow{P'Q'}$ must then belong to P since it is orthogonal to all vectors of S. Hence, $\overrightarrow{P'Q'}$ may be written as a linear combination of $\mathfrak{v}_{s+1}, \mathfrak{v}_{s+2}, \cdots, \mathfrak{v}_n$,

$$\overrightarrow{P'Q'} = \sum_{i=s+1}^{n} \mu_i \mathfrak{v}_i.$$

Since however, by (16), we had $\overrightarrow{PQ} = \sum_{i=s+1}^{n} \lambda_i \mathfrak{v}_i$, it follows that the vector

$$\overrightarrow{PQ} - \overrightarrow{P'Q'} = \sum_{i=s+1}^{n} (\lambda_i - \mu_i) \mathfrak{v}_i$$

is also a vector of P. On the other hand $\overrightarrow{PQ} = \overrightarrow{PP'} + \overrightarrow{P'Q'} + \overrightarrow{Q'Q}$, or

$$\overrightarrow{PQ} - \overrightarrow{P'Q'} = \overrightarrow{PP'} + \overrightarrow{Q'Q}. \tag{17}$$

P and P' are points of L_1, Q and Q' are points of L_2, so that $\overrightarrow{PP'}$ is a vector of L_1 and $\overrightarrow{Q'Q}$ is a vector of L_2. By (17), the vector $\overrightarrow{PQ} - \overrightarrow{P'Q'}$ is also a vector of S, and so must be the null vector since the intersection of P and S consists of the null vector alone. Thus,

$$\overrightarrow{PQ} = \overrightarrow{P'Q'},$$

as was to be proved.

By equation (17) we then also have $\overrightarrow{PP'} + \overrightarrow{Q'Q} = 0$, i.e.

$$\overrightarrow{PP'} = \overrightarrow{QQ'}.$$

Since $\overrightarrow{PP'}$ is a vector of L_1, and $\overrightarrow{QQ'}$ a vector of L_2, $\overrightarrow{PP'} = \overrightarrow{QQ'}$ is a vector of the intersection D of L_1 and L_2. The converse also holds. For, let $\mathfrak{d}$ be an arbitrary vector of D which carries P into P' and Q into Q'; then $\overrightarrow{P'Q'}$ is necessarily a common perpendicular to L_1 and L_2. In fact, P' is certainly a point of L_1 and Q', a point of L_2, since $\overrightarrow{PP'} = \overrightarrow{QQ'} = \mathfrak{d}$ belongs to both L_1 and L_2. Since $\overrightarrow{PP'} = \overrightarrow{QQ'}$, we have $\overrightarrow{PP'} + \overrightarrow{Q'Q} = 0$, or by (17),

$$\overrightarrow{PQ} = \overrightarrow{P'Q'}.$$

Thus, $\overrightarrow{P'Q'}$ is indeed orthogonal to L_1 and L_2. *Thus, let P and Q be the feet of a common perpendicular to L_1 and L_2, and let* D *be the intersection of* L_1 *and* L_2. *Let P, Q be carried into P' and Q' respectively, by some arbitrary vector of* D. *Then P' and Q' are the feet of a new common perpendicular to L_1 and L_2, and moreover all common perpendiculars are obtained in this manner.*

Let us return to equation (13). There, P_0 was taken to be an arbitrary preassigned point of L_1, and Q_0 one of L_2. By (15), we then obtained two points P of L_1 and Q of L_2 such that $\overrightarrow{PQ}$ was a common perpendicular to L_1 and L_2, and such that $\overrightarrow{P_0Q_0}$ and $\overrightarrow{PQ}$ are in the relation given by equations (13) and (16). By (4), we thus have the following formulas for the lengths of P_0Q_0 and PQ:

$$\overline{P_0Q_0} = {}_{+}\sqrt{\sum_{i=1}^{n} \lambda_i^2}, \quad \overline{PQ} = {}_{+}\sqrt{\sum_{i=s+1}^{n} \lambda_i^2}. \tag{18}$$

It follows that

$$\overline{P_0Q_0} \geqq \overline{PQ}. \tag{19}$$

That is, the distance between two arbitrary points P_0 and Q_0 of L_1 and L_2 respectively, is at least as great as the length of a suitably chosen common perpendicular. But, since all common perpendiculars have the same length, *the length of a common perpendicular is the shortest possible distance between points of L_1 and L_2.*

When does equality hold in (19)? By (18), this is possible only if $\lambda_i = 0$ for $i = 1, 2, \ldots, s$. However, the vector $\overrightarrow{P_0Q_0}$, being in this case a linear combination of $\mathfrak{v}_{s+1}, \mathfrak{v}_{s+2}, \cdots, \mathfrak{v}_n$ only, must belong to P, i.e. it is a common perpendicular to L_1 and L_2. Thus, *a segment connecting a point of L_1 with a point of L_2 is the shortest distance between L_1 and L_2 only if it is a common perpendicular to L_1 and L_2.*

We now gather together the various results obtained concerning the common perpendiculars to L_1 and L_2. We have proved

1. *There is at least one common perpendicular to L_1 and L_2.*
2. *The totality of all feet of common perpendiculars which lie in L_1 forms a linear subspace of L_1. Its dimension is that of the intersection* D *of* L_1 *and* L_2. *For it may be obtained from any one of its points by applying all the vectors of* D. *The same holds for the totality of all feet which lie in L_2.*
3. *All common perpendiculars are parallel and have the same length.*
4. *The common perpendiculars, and they only, yield the shortest distance between L_1 and L_2.*

The results proved earlier concerning the perpendiculars from a point to a linear space are contained in these propositions as a special case, namely the case in which one of the two spaces L_1, L_2 is of dimension 0. We also see that, as was mentioned earlier, the case $s = n$ (s was the dimension of S) also appears as a special case of the above four propositions. For in this case, the common perpendicular consists of but a single point of the intersection (which in this case is non-empty) of L_1 and L_2, so that propositions 1 through 4 remain valid.

Finally, it is suggested that the reader clarify the meaning of these propositions for himself for the special cases which are accessible to geometric intuition.

Exercises

1. The procedure for the construction of a normal orthogonal basis can also be used to determine the linear dependence or independence of a system of vectors. For, if $\mathfrak{a}_1, \mathfrak{a}_2, \cdots, \mathfrak{a}_p$ are arbitrary vectors of R_n, we treat them as though they were the basis of a vector space and attempt to derive a normal orthogonal basis

for this fictitious vector space. The reader should convince himself that the procedure can not be carried out if the vectors are linearly dependent. In this way, determine the maximal number of linearly independent vectors among the following vectors of R_5:

$$\begin{aligned}
\mathfrak{a}_1 &= \{\ 2, & -1, && 3, && -1, && 1\ \},\\
\mathfrak{a}_2 &= \{\ 3, & 2, && -2, && -2, && 1\ \},\\
\mathfrak{a}_3 &= \{\ 0, & -7, && 13, && 1, && 1\ \},\\
\mathfrak{a}_4 &= \{-1, & 4, && -8, && 0, && -1\},\\
\mathfrak{a}_5 &= \{\ 5, & 1, && 1, && 2, && -2\}.
\end{aligned}$$

2. Prove that the equation of a hyperplane

$$a_1 x_1 + a_2 x_2 + \cdots + a_n x_n = b$$

is in Hesse normal form if and only if $a_1^2 + a_2^2 + \cdots + a_n^2 = 1$. Furthermore, the Hesse normal form is uniquely determined up to a simultaneous change in the sign of all of the coefficients.

3. Let the line g_1 pass through the points $(1, 1, 1)$ and $(4, 5, 3)$ in euclidean R_3. Let the line g_2 pass through the points $(-1, -10, -1)$ and $(8, 2, 2)$. Determine the common perpendiculars to g_1 and g_2. What is the shortest distance between points of g_1 and g_2?

4. In euclidean R_3, determine the distances of the points $(0, 0, 0)$, $(3, 2, 1)$, $(2, 1, 2)$ from the plane

$$3x_1 - 4x_2 + 12x_3 = 13.$$

Do these points lie on the same or on opposite sides of the plane? (Cf. § 6, exercise 7.)

5. Let there be given an arbitrary set M of points of R_n, and a linear space L of dimension $p < n$. Let the perpendicular from each point of M to L be constructed. Then, the totality of all points which are feet of these perpendiculars is called the *orthogonal projection of M on L.*

If, in particular, M itself is a linear space, then let M be the corresponding vector space. Furthermore, let L be the vector space which corresponds to L, and let P be the vector space which is orthogonal to L. Let S be the sum of P and M. The totality of all points which are obtained by applying to any fixed point of M all vectors of S, forms a linear space S which contains M. Prove that the orthogonal projection of M on L is precisely the intersection of S and L, and therefore is a linear space Q. If m is the dimension of M, and d is the dimension of the intersection of M and P, then the dimension of Q is $m - d$.

Discuss the interpretation of these results in ordinary two- and three-dimensional space.

6. Let L be a linear space in euclidean R_n; let P be the vector space of all vectors which are orthogonal to L. Let $\mathfrak{v}_1, \mathfrak{v}_2, \cdots, \mathfrak{v}_r$ be a normal orthogonal basis of P. Let us construct the perpendiculars to L from two arbitrary points P and Q of R_n. Let the feet of these perpendiculars be P^* and Q^*, respectively. Prove that we then have

$$\overrightarrow{P^* Q^*} = \overrightarrow{PQ} + \sum_{i=1}^{r} (\overrightarrow{QP} \cdot \mathfrak{v}_i)\, \mathfrak{v}_i .$$

From this we easily see that if $\overrightarrow{P_1 Q_1}, \overrightarrow{P_2 Q_2}, \cdots, \overrightarrow{P_s Q_s}$ are vectors of R_n and $\overrightarrow{P_1^* Q_1^*}, \overrightarrow{P_2^* Q_2^*}, \cdots, \overrightarrow{P_s^* Q_s^*}$ are their orthogonal projections on L, then any linear relation $\sum_{i=1}^{s} \lambda_i \cdot \overrightarrow{P_i Q_i} = 0$ which holds among the vectors $\overrightarrow{P_i Q_i}$ also holds among the vectors $\overrightarrow{P_i^* Q_i^*}$, so that $\sum_{i=1}^{s} \lambda_i \cdot \overrightarrow{P_i^* Q_i^*} = 0$.

7. Let P_0 be a point and $\mathfrak{a}_1, \mathfrak{a}_2, \cdots, \mathfrak{a}_p$ be p linearly independent vectors of euclidean R_n. The totality of all points which are obtained from P_0 by applying all the vectors $\lambda_1 \mathfrak{a}_1 + \lambda_2 \mathfrak{a}_2 + \cdots + \lambda_p \mathfrak{a}_p$ with $0 \leqq \lambda_i \leqq 1$ is called a *p-dimensional parallelotope*. If $P_1, P_2, \cdots, P_p$, are obtained similarly from P_0 by applying $\mathfrak{a}_1, \mathfrak{a}_2, \cdots, \mathfrak{a}_p$ respectively, then the vectors $\overrightarrow{P_0 P_1}, \overrightarrow{P_0 P_2}, \cdots, \overrightarrow{P_0 P_p}$ are the edge vectors of the parallelotope which emanate from P_0. We form the orthogonal projection of the parallelotope on a linear space L. Let the projections of the points $P_0, P_1, \cdots, P_p$ be $P_0^*, P_1^*, \cdots, P_p^*$ respectively. Prove that if the vectors $\overrightarrow{P_0^* P_1^*}, \overrightarrow{P_0^* P_2^*}, \cdots, \overrightarrow{P_0^* P_p^*}$ are linearly independent, then the orthogonal projection of the given parallelotope on L is also a p-dimensional parallelotope.

§ 12. Rigid Motions

Coordinate transformations have a very definite relation to certain mappings of R_n on itself. A (*single-valued*) *mapping* of R_n into itself is determined if a rule is given which associates with each point of R_n a uniquely determined *image point* in R_n. Such a correspondence is, of course, possible in many ways. From the totality of such mappings, we now choose a particularly important class for our discussion. We assume that euclidean length has been defined in R_n, and consider mappings with the following property. If P, Q are two arbitrary points of euclidean R_n, and P^*, Q^* are their image points, then the distance from P^* to Q^* is to be the same as from P to Q, i.e.

$$\overline{P^* Q^*} = \overline{PQ}.$$

Mappings which satisfy this condition are called **rigid motions.** We shall justify this name below.

Let there be given a rigid motion. Let P, Q, R be three points of R_n, and let P^*, Q^*, R^* be their image points under the rigid motion. We wish to investigate whether there is any relation between the scalar product $\overrightarrow{PQ} \cdot \overrightarrow{PR}$ and the scalar product $\overrightarrow{P^*Q^*} \cdot \overrightarrow{P^*R^*}$ of the image vectors. We certainly have $\overrightarrow{QR} = \overrightarrow{QP} + \overrightarrow{PR}$. If we take the scalar product of the right-hand side of this equation with itself, and likewise of the left-hand side with itself, we obtain

$$\overrightarrow{QR}^2 = \overrightarrow{PQ}^2 + 2\,\overrightarrow{QP} \cdot \overrightarrow{PR} + \overrightarrow{PR}^2.$$

Now we have, for the absolute value of a vector $\mathfrak{a}$, $|\mathfrak{a}| = {}_{+}\sqrt{\mathfrak{a}^2}$. Thus in our case,

$$\overrightarrow{QR}^2 = \overline{QR}^2, \qquad \overrightarrow{PQ}^2 = \overline{PQ}^2, \qquad \overrightarrow{PR}^2 = \overline{PR}^2.$$

Substituting this in the above equation, it follows that

$$\overrightarrow{PQ} \cdot \overrightarrow{PR} = \tfrac{1}{2}(\overline{PQ}^2 + \overline{PR}^2 - \overline{QR}^2).$$

What we have just proved for the points P, Q, R, clearly holds also for P^*, Q^*, R^*, so that

$$\overrightarrow{P^*Q^*} \cdot \overrightarrow{P^*R^*} = \tfrac{1}{2}(\overline{P^*Q^*}^2 + \overline{P^*R^*}^2 - \overline{Q^*R^*}^2).$$

Since our mapping was a rigid motion, we must have

$$\overline{PQ} = \overline{P^*Q^*}, \quad \overline{PR} = \overline{P^*R^*}, \quad \overline{QR} = \overline{Q^*R^*}.$$

Hence the right-hand sides of the last two equations are equal to each other, and it follows that

$$\overrightarrow{PQ} \cdot \overrightarrow{PR} = \overrightarrow{P^*Q^*} \cdot \overrightarrow{P^*R^*}. \tag{1}$$

This is the desired relation. The scalar products are equal to each other. One also says that *the scalar product of two vectors $\overrightarrow{PQ}$ and $\overrightarrow{PR}$ is invariant under a rigid motion.*

This result gives us an insight into the nature of a rigid motion. For, let $[O; \mathfrak{v}_1, \mathfrak{v}_2, \cdots, \mathfrak{v}_n]$ be a Cartesian coordinate system in R_n.[1] Then $\mathfrak{v}_i \mathfrak{v}_k = \delta_{ik}$. Let the vector $\mathfrak{v}_i$, when applied to the origin O, have the endpoint P_i; thus $\overrightarrow{OP_i} = \mathfrak{v}_i$ $(i = 1, 2, \ldots, n)$. Let the rigid motion under consideration map the point O onto O^*, the point P_i onto P_i^* $(i = 1, 2, \ldots, n)$. Let us denote the vector $\overrightarrow{O^*P_i^*}$ by $\mathfrak{v}_i^*$. By (1), we then have

$$\mathfrak{v}_i^* \cdot \mathfrak{v}_k^* = \overrightarrow{O^*P_i^*} \cdot \overrightarrow{O^*P_k^*} = \overrightarrow{OP_i} \cdot \overrightarrow{OP_k} = \mathfrak{v}_i \cdot \mathfrak{v}_k = \delta_{ik}.$$

Thus, $[O^*; \mathfrak{v}_1^*, \mathfrak{v}_2^*, \cdots, \mathfrak{v}_n^*]$ *is also a Cartesian coordinate system.*

Further, let P be an arbitrary point of R_n, and let P^* be its image point. Let P have the coordinates $x_1, x_2, \ldots, x_n$ in the coordinate system $[O; \mathfrak{v}_1, \mathfrak{v}_2, \cdots, \mathfrak{v}_n]$, and let the image point P^* have the coordinates $x_1^*, x_2^*, \cdots, x_n^*$ in the coordinate system $[O^*; \mathfrak{v}_1^*, \mathfrak{v}_2^*, \cdots, \mathfrak{v}_n^*]$.

[1] Of course in this, O need not be the point $(0, 0, \ldots, 0)$.

By the definition of coordinates, we then have

$$\overrightarrow{OP} = \sum_{i=1}^{n} x_i \mathfrak{v}_i, \quad \overrightarrow{O^*P^*} = \sum_{i=1}^{n} x_i^* \mathfrak{v}_i^*.$$

Hence, (by equation (3) of § 11), we have

$$x_i = \overrightarrow{OP} \cdot \mathfrak{v}_i = \overrightarrow{OP} \cdot \overrightarrow{OP_i}$$

and analogously

$$x_i^* = \overrightarrow{O^*P^*} \cdot \mathfrak{v}_i^* = \overrightarrow{O^*P^*} \cdot \overrightarrow{O^*P_i^*}.$$

But since we have from (1) that

$$\overrightarrow{OP} \cdot \overrightarrow{OP_i} = \overrightarrow{O^*P^*} \cdot \overrightarrow{O^*P_i^*},$$

it finally follows that

$$x_i = x_i^*, \qquad i = 1, 2, \cdots, n.$$

That is, the point P has the same coordinates in $[O; \mathfrak{v}_1, \mathfrak{v}_2, \cdots, \mathfrak{v}_n]$ *as its image point P^* has in the coordinate system* $[O^*; \mathfrak{v}_1^*, \mathfrak{v}_2^*, \cdots, \mathfrak{v}_n^*]$. Thus, if we know the coordinate system $[O^*; \mathfrak{v}_1^*, \mathfrak{v}_2^*, \cdots, \mathfrak{v}_n^*]$ into which the given coordinate system $[O; \mathfrak{v}_1, \mathfrak{v}_2, \cdots, \mathfrak{v}_n]$ is transformed by the rigid motion, then we can immediately find the image point corresponding to any given point P. We also see that every point of R_n occurs as an image point, and indeed as the image point of precisely one point. For, if Q^* is any point, whose coordinates in the coordinate system $[O^*; \mathfrak{v}_1^*, \mathfrak{v}_2^*, \cdots, \mathfrak{v}_n^*]$ are, say, $y_1, y_2, \ldots, y_n$, then it is the image of that point Q whose coordinates are $y_1, y_2, \ldots, y_n$ in the coordinate system $[O; \mathfrak{v}_1, \mathfrak{v}_2, \cdots, \mathfrak{v}_n]$ and of that point only. A mapping under which every point has precisely one image point and every image point precisely one "pre-image" point, will be called (as before) a *one-to-one* (or *one-one*) mapping. Thus, *a rigid motion is a one-to-one mapping of R_n onto itself.*

Conversely, if we start with two arbitrary Cartesian coordinate systems $[O; \mathfrak{v}_1, \mathfrak{v}_2, \cdots, \mathfrak{v}_n]$ and $[O^*; \mathfrak{v}_1^*, \mathfrak{v}_2^*, \cdots, \mathfrak{v}_n^*]$ of R_n, then we may use them to define a mapping of the sort just obtained. For, we have simply to define the image of any point P of R_n to be that point P^* whose coordinates in the system $[O^*; \mathfrak{v}_1^*, \mathfrak{v}_2^*, \cdots, \mathfrak{v}_n^*]$ are the same as those of the point P in the coordinate system $[O; \mathfrak{v}_1, \mathfrak{v}_2, \cdots, \mathfrak{v}_n]$. It is clear that the image point is uniquely determined. The mapping thus defined is indeed a rigid motion. For, let P, Q be two points whose coordinates in the system $[O; \mathfrak{v}_1, \mathfrak{v}_2, \cdots, \mathfrak{v}_n]$ are $x_1, x_2, \ldots, x_n$ and $y_1, y_2, \ldots, y_n$, respectively. Then their image points P^*, Q^* have the same coordinates in the system $[O^*; \mathfrak{v}_1^*, \mathfrak{v}_2^*, \cdots, \mathfrak{v}_n^*]$. Hence, by § 10, the vector $\overrightarrow{PQ}$ has the components $y_1 - x_1, y_2 - x_2, \cdots, y_n - x_n$ in the coordinate system $[O; \mathfrak{v}_1, \mathfrak{v}_2, \cdots, \mathfrak{v}_n]$ and $\overrightarrow{P^*Q^*}$ has the same components in $[O^*; \mathfrak{v}_1^*, \mathfrak{v}_2^*, \cdots, \mathfrak{v}_n^*]$. By (14) of § 10, it furthermore follows that

$$\overline{PQ} = {}_+\sqrt{\overrightarrow{PQ}^2} = {}_+\sqrt{\sum_{i=1}^{n} (y_i - x_i)^2},$$

$$\overline{P^*Q^*} = {}_+\sqrt{\overrightarrow{P^*Q^*}^2} = {}_+\sqrt{\sum_{i=1}^{n} (y_i - x_i)^2}.$$

Hence $\overline{PQ} = \overline{P^*Q^*}$. But this is precisely the characteristic property of a rigid motion.[2]

By the *image* L^* *of a linear space* L under a rigid motion, we mean the totality of all image points of L. We shall also say that L is mapped onto L^* by the rigid motion. L^* is also a linear space. In fact,

Under a rigid motion, a linear space is transformed into another linear space of the same dimension.

For, by § 10, a linear space of dimension p may be represented in the coordinate system $[O; \mathfrak{v}_1, \mathfrak{v}_2 \cdots, \mathfrak{v}_n]$ by a solvable system of linear equations of rank $n - p$. Let us consider the totality of all image points of points of the linear space. Each has the same coordinates in the system $[O^*; \mathfrak{v}_1^*, \mathfrak{v}_2^*, \cdots, \mathfrak{v}_n^*]$ as its pre-image has in the system

$$[O; \mathfrak{v}_1, \mathfrak{v}_2, \cdots, \mathfrak{v}_n].$$

It thus follows that the totality of all image points also consists of all points which are solutions of the system of equations under consideration if we now refer the coordinates to the coordinate system $[O^*; \mathfrak{v}_1^*, \mathfrak{v}_2^*, \cdots, \mathfrak{v}_n^*]$. Hence the totality of image points is a linear space of dimension p.

Let L_1, L_2 be two linear spaces, D their intersection, so that D is either empty or is itself a linear space. Let the rigid motion under consideration map L_1 onto L_1^*, L_2 onto L_2^*, and D onto D^*. *Then* D^* *is the intersection of* L_1^* *and* L_2^*. For, L_1^* consists of the images of all points of L_1, and L_2^* of the images of all points of L_2. Thus, if P is a point of D, i.e. of both L_1 and L_2, then its image point P^* belongs to both L_1^* and L_2^*, and hence to their intersection. Conversely, if P^*

[2] The above method of producing rigid motions justifies their name. Later we shall recognize these mappings as actual rigid motions in the case of the ordinary spaces ($n = 1, 2, 3$).

is a point of the intersection of L_1^* and L_2^*, then there is one and only one point P whose image is P^* (since a rigid motion is a one-one mapping). P must be in L_1, since P^* belongs to L_1^*, and similarly P must be in L_2, since P^* also belongs to L_2^*. That is, P lies in D. It follows that P^* also lies in D^*. It has thus been proved that every point of the intersection of L_1^* and L_2^* also belongs to D^*. We have already verified the converse. Hence, D^* is identical with the intersection of L_1^* and L_2^*.

In particular, if D is empty then D^* is also empty. Furthermore, if L_1 is contained in L_2, then $D = L_1$, and then we also have $D^* = L_1^*$. That is, L_1^* is contained in L_2^*. This could also have easily been seen directly.

A rigid motion also induces a one-one mapping of the vector space R_n onto itself. This mapping may be defined as follows:

If $\mathfrak{a}$ is an arbitrary vector of R_n, let $\mathfrak{a}$ carry an arbitrary point P to, say, Q. Let P^*, Q^* be the images of P, Q respectively under the given mapping. Then it is quite natural to speak of the vector $\mathfrak{a}^* = \overrightarrow{P^*Q^*}$ as the *image vector* of $\mathfrak{a}$.[3] However, we must first show that this mapping is single-valued, i.e. that it is independent of the choice of the value of the initial point P. Thus, let us choose another arbitrary point P_1 as the initial point of $\mathfrak{a}$, so that for suitable Q_1, $\overrightarrow{PQ} = \overrightarrow{P_1Q_1}$. Let P_1^*, Q_1^* be the images of P_1 and Q_1 respectively. Let us recall that, by § 10, the components of a vector with respect to a coordinate system are given by the differences of the coordinates of the initial and the terminal points of the vector in this coordinate system. However, the points P. Q, P_1, Q_1 have the same coordinates in the system $[O; \mathfrak{v}_1, \mathfrak{v}_2, \ldots, \mathfrak{v}_n]$ as their image points P^*, Q^*, P_1^*, Q_1^* have in the system $[O^*; \mathfrak{v}_1^*, \mathfrak{v}_2^*, \cdots, \mathfrak{v}_n^*]$. Thus the vectors $\overrightarrow{PQ}$, $\overrightarrow{P_1Q_1}$ must have the same components in the system $[O; \mathfrak{v}_1, \mathfrak{v}_2, \cdots, \mathfrak{v}_n]$ as their image vectors $\overrightarrow{P^*Q^*}$, $\overrightarrow{P_1^*Q_1^*}$ have in the system $[O^*; \mathfrak{v}_1^*, \mathfrak{v}_2^*, \cdots, \mathfrak{v}_n^*]$. Since, however, $\overrightarrow{PQ}$ and $\overrightarrow{P_1Q_1}$ are equal, it follows that $\overrightarrow{P^*Q^*}$ and $\overrightarrow{P_1^*Q_1^*}$ are also equal. These considerations have moreover shown that $\mathfrak{a}^*$ has the same components in the system $[O^*; \mathfrak{v}_1^*, \mathfrak{v}_2^*, \cdots, \mathfrak{v}_n^*]$ as $\mathfrak{a}$ does in $[O; \mathfrak{v}_1, \mathfrak{v}_2, \cdots, \mathfrak{v}_n]$. Thus again it is clear that not only does every vector have precisely one image, but that moreover every image vector

[3] The segment P^*Q^* consists precisely of all images of points of the segment PQ. We shall however make no use of this fact, and we leave the proof to the reader. (Cf. § 10, exercise 2.)

is the image of precisely one pre-image vector, so that *the mapping of the vector space also is one-one.*

Let there be given a rigid motion and some *fixed* Cartesian coordinate system, and let us investigate the problem of determining the coordinates of the image point P^* if those of its pre-image point P are given. Let $[O; \mathfrak{v}_1, \mathfrak{v}_2, \cdots, \mathfrak{v}_n]$ be the Cartesian coordinate system and let the coordinates of P be $x_1, x_2, \ldots, x_n$. We know that under a rigid motion $[O; \mathfrak{v}_1, \mathfrak{v}_2, \cdots, \mathfrak{v}_n]$ is transformed into another Cartesian coordinate system $[O^*; \mathfrak{v}_1^*, \mathfrak{v}_2^*, \cdots, \mathfrak{v}_n^*]$ in which the coordinates of the image point P^* are precisely $x_1, x_2, \ldots, x_n$. This enables us to evaluate the coordinates of P^* in $[O; \mathfrak{v}_1, \mathfrak{v}_2, \cdots, \mathfrak{v}_n]$ with ease. For, this is a problem which we have solved in § 10, namely the transformation of coordinates under the transition from the coordinate system $[O^*; \mathfrak{v}_1^*, \mathfrak{v}_2^*, \cdots, \mathfrak{v}_n^*]$ to the coordinate system $[O; \mathfrak{v}_1, \mathfrak{v}_2, \cdots, \mathfrak{v}_n]$. Thus, by analogy with equation (3) of § 10, we must determine the quantities $t_1, t_2, \ldots, t_n$ for which

$$\overrightarrow{OO^*} = \sum_{i=1}^{n} t_i \mathfrak{v}_i. \tag{2}$$

Furthermore, let the vector $\mathfrak{v}_k{}^*$ have the coordinates $a_{1k}, a_{2k}, \cdots, a_{nk}$ in the coordinate system $[O; \mathfrak{v}_1, \mathfrak{v}_2, \cdots, \mathfrak{v}_n]$; then by analogy with equation (4) of § 10, we have

$$\mathfrak{v}_k^* = \sum_{i=1}^{n} a_{ik} \mathfrak{v}_i. \tag{3}$$

It then follows by (8), § 10, that, if $y_1, y_2, \ldots, y_n$ denote the coordinates of the point P^* in the coordinate system $[O; \mathfrak{v}_1, \mathfrak{v}_2, \cdots, \mathfrak{v}_n]$, then

$$y_i = t_i + \sum_{k=1}^{n} a_{ik} x_k, \qquad i = 1, 2, \cdots, n. \tag{4}$$

Since the coordinate systems $[O; \mathfrak{v}_1, \mathfrak{v}_2, \cdots, \mathfrak{v}_n]$ and

$$[O^*; \mathfrak{v}_1^*, \mathfrak{v}_2^*, \cdots, \mathfrak{v}_n^*]$$

are Cartesian, equations (17) and (18) of § 10 also hold for the a_{ik}, i.e. (a_{ik}) is an orthogonal matrix. Equations (4) give a method for calculating the coordinates $y_1, y_2, \ldots, y_n$ of the point P^*, given those of P with respect to the given coordinate system

$$[O; \mathfrak{v}_1, \mathfrak{v}_2, \cdots, \mathfrak{v}_n].$$

Conversely, a system of linear equations of the form (4) always defines a mapping. We need simply associate with the point P, whose coordinates in some fixed coordinate system are $x_1, x_2, \ldots, x_n$, the point P^* whose coordinates in this same coordinate system are $y_1, y_2, \ldots, y_n$, as given by (4). If the fixed coordinate system is Cartesian, and if moreover the matrix (a_{ik}) of the system (4) is orthogonal, then the mapping thus obtained is a rigid motion. For, if Q is another point, whose coordinates are $x'_1, x'_2, \cdots, x'_n$, and Q^*, its image point, has the coordinates $y'_1, y'_2, \cdots, y'_n$, then the quantities y'_i and x'_i also satisfy equations (4), so that

$$(5) \qquad y'_i - y_i = \sum_{k=1}^{n} a_{ik}(x'_k - x_k), \qquad i = 1, 2, \cdots, n.$$

It thus follows that, for $i = 1, 2, \ldots, n$,

$$(y'_i - y_i)^2 = \left[\sum_{k=1}^{n} a_{ik}(x'_k - x_k)\right]^2 = \sum_{k=1}^{n}\sum_{j=1}^{n} a_{ik}\,a_{ij}\,(x'_k - x_k)(x'_j - x_j).$$

Adding these n equations, we obtain

$$\sum_{i=1}^{n}(y'_i - y_i)^2 = \sum_{i=1}^{n}\sum_{k=1}^{n}\sum_{j=1}^{n} a_{ik}\,a_{ij}\,(x'_k - x_k)(x'_j - x_j)$$
$$= \sum_{k=1}^{n}\sum_{j=1}^{n}\left(\sum_{i=1}^{n} a_{ik}\,a_{ij}\right)(x'_k - x_k)(x'_j - x_j).$$

Since (a_{ik}) was assumed to be orthogonal, we must have

$$\sum_{i=1}^{n} a_{ik}\,a_{ij} = \delta_{kj}.$$

Therefore all summands on the left for which $k \neq j$, vanish, and for $k = j$, the coefficient $\sum_{i=1}^{n} a_{ik}\,a_{ik}$ is equal to 1. This yields:

$$\sum_{i=1}^{n}(y'_i - y_i)^2 = \sum_{k=1}^{n}(x'_k - x_k)^2.$$

However, since the given coordinate system is Cartesian, we have

$$\overline{PQ}^2 = \sum_{k=1}^{n}(x'_k - x_k)^2, \quad \overline{P^*Q^*}^2 = \sum_{i=1}^{n}(y'_i - y_i)^2.$$

Thus, $\overline{PQ} = \overline{P^*Q^*}$, i.e. our mapping is a rigid motion.

Since the matrix (a_{ik}) is orthogonal, the value of the determinant $|a_{ik}|$ is $+1$ or -1. The rigid motion defined by (4) is called *proper* if $|a_{ik}| = +1$, and *improper* if $|a_{ik}| = -1$.[4]

In § 10 we have already been introduced to one interpretation of a system of equations of the form (4). There we saw that we may always interpret the system (4) as the equations of transformation of a coordinate transformation. The quantities $x_1, x_2, \ldots, x_n$ and $y_1, y_2, \ldots, y_n$ were in that case the coordinates of the *same* point with respect to two *different* coordinate systems. Under our present interpretation, the equations (4) are regarded as the defining equations of a mapping, and the quantities $x_1, x_2, \ldots, x_n$ and $y_1, y_2, \ldots, y_n$ are considered as the coordinates of two *different* points in the *same* coordinate system.

A rigid motion also defines a mapping of the vector space R_n onto itself. We shall now consider the question of how the components of an image vector in a fixed Cartesian coordinate system may be calculated from those of its pre-image. In equations (5) let the quantities $x_i' - x_i$ be the components of the vector $\overrightarrow{PQ}$ in the Cartesian coordinate system under consideration, $y_i' - y_i$ the corresponding components of the vector $\overrightarrow{P^*Q^*}$. However $\overrightarrow{P^*Q^*}$ is the image vector of $\overrightarrow{PQ}$. Equations (5) thus show how the components $\overrightarrow{P^*Q^*}$ may be calculated from those of PQ. Thus, if we set $u_i^* = y_i' - y_i$, $u_i = x_i' - x_i$ $(i = 1, 2, \ldots, n)$, then the system (5) takes on the form

$$u_i^* = \sum_{k=1}^{n} a_{ik}\, u_k, \qquad i = 1, 2, \cdots, n. \tag{6}$$

Since the determinant $|a_{ik}|$ of the system of equations (4) corresponding to a rigid motion is not zero (being equal to $+1$ or -1), we can solve (4) for the quantities $x_1, x_2, \ldots, x_n$. Thus, by Cramer's rule we obtain

$$x_i = \frac{1}{|a_{ik}|} \sum_{k=1}^{n} A_{ki}(y_k - t_k), \qquad i = 1, 2, \cdots, n. \tag{7}$$

Of course, this system of equations also defines a mapping. Namely, if equations (4) associate with the point P its image P^*, then the

[4] The terms "proper" and "improper" as defined here seem as though they may well depend on the coordinate system employed. For, it is by no means obvious that the determinant $|a_{ik}|$ of a given rigid motion may not take on different values in different coordinate systems. We forégo for the time being the proof that this is impossible, since we shall be able to settle the question later using better methods. In the particular cases of R_2 and R_3 we shall see in this section that the determinant of a rigid motion is independent of the choice of coordinate system.

point P is the image under (7) of the point P^*. The mapping defined by (7) is therefore called *inverse* to that defined by (4). It is clear that the mapping inverse to a rigid motion is itself a rigid motion.

Moreover, we note that the coefficient $\frac{A_{ki}}{|a_{ik}|}$ of y_k in the i-th equation of (7) is equal to a_{ki}, if (a_{ik}) is orthogonal. For, we have shown in equation (21) of § 10 that for an orthogonal matrix (a_{ik}), we always have

$$a_{jh} = \frac{A_{jh}}{|a_{ik}|}. \tag{8}$$

We have already seen, at the beginning of this section, that the scalar product of two vectors is invariant under a rigid motion. To be sure, it was there assumed that the two factors had the same initial point. However, this restriction is superfluous. For if $\mathfrak{a}, \mathfrak{b}$ are two arbitrary vectors, then the image vectors $\mathfrak{a}^*, \mathfrak{b}^*$ are determined quite independently of the choice of the initial points. Thus if we take $\mathfrak{a}$ and $\mathfrak{b}$ with the same initial point P, so that, say, $\mathfrak{a} = \overrightarrow{PQ}$ and $\mathfrak{b} = \overrightarrow{PR}$, then it follows for the image points P^*, Q^*, R^* of P, Q, R that $\mathfrak{a}^* = \overrightarrow{P^*Q^*}$, $\mathfrak{b}^* = \overrightarrow{P^*R^*}$, which by equation (1) yields that $\mathfrak{a}^* \cdot \mathfrak{b}^* = \mathfrak{a} \cdot \mathfrak{b}$.

Another important invariant under rigid motions is volume. Let $\mathfrak{b}_1, \mathfrak{b}_2, \cdots, \mathfrak{b}_n$ be n linearly independent vectors. Then the totality of all points which may be obtained from some fixed point P by applying all the vectors $\sum_{i=1}^{n} \lambda_i \mathfrak{b}_i$ where $0 \leqq \lambda_i \leqq 1$, forms an n-dimensional parallelotope (cf. § 7). Let $\mathfrak{b}_1^*, \mathfrak{b}_2^*, \cdots, \mathfrak{b}_n^*$ be the images of $\mathfrak{b}_1, \mathfrak{b}_2, \ldots, \mathfrak{b}_n$, and let P^* be the image of P. Then the totality of all points which may be obtained from P^* by applying all the vectors $\sum_{i=1}^{n} \lambda_i \mathfrak{b}_i^*$ where $0 \leqq \lambda_i \leqq 1$, forms another parallelotope which we call the *image* of the original parallelotope.[5] Let us seek the relation between the volumes of these two parallelotopes.

Let the vector $\mathfrak{b}_i$ have the components $u_{i1}, u_{i2}, \cdots, u_{in}$ in the Cartesian coordinate system $[O; \mathfrak{v}_1, \mathfrak{v}_2, \cdots, \mathfrak{v}_n]$. Then $\mathfrak{b}_i^*$ has the same components in $[O^*; \mathfrak{v}_1^*, \mathfrak{v}_2^*, \cdots, \mathfrak{v}_n^*]$. Now, by § 10 (p. 131) the volume of the parallelotope whose edge boundary vectors are $\mathfrak{b}_1, \mathfrak{b}_2, \cdots, \mathfrak{b}_n$ is equal to the absolute value of the determinant $|u_{ik}|$. The volume of the parallelo-

[5] The image parallelotope consists of exactly the image points of the points of the given parallelotope, as is easily seen with the aid of the results of exercise 2, § 10.

tope whose edge vectors are $\mathfrak{b}_1^*, \mathfrak{b}_2^*, \cdots, \mathfrak{b}_n^*$ can be evaluated in the same way from the components of the vectors $\mathfrak{b}_i^*$ in the coordinate system $[O^*; \mathfrak{v}_1^*, \mathfrak{v}_2^*, \cdots, \mathfrak{v}_n^*]$. However, since these are equal to the components of the corresponding vectors $\mathfrak{b}_i$ in $[O; \mathfrak{v}_1, \mathfrak{v}_2, \cdots, \mathfrak{v}_n]$, we have that this second volume is also equal to the absolute value of the determinant $| a_{ik} |$. Thus, a parallelotope is transformed into a parallelotope of equal volume under a rigid motion. Otherwise expressed, *the volume of a parallelotope is an invariant under rigid motions.*

We shall now investigate the question of whether the value of the determinant $| u_{ik} |$ is changed if the quantities u_{ik} are replaced by the corresponding components of the image vectors $\mathfrak{b}_i^*$ in this same coordinate system $[O; \mathfrak{v}_1, \mathfrak{v}_2, \cdots, \mathfrak{v}_n]$. Let the vector $\mathfrak{b}_i^*$ have the components $u_{i1}^*, u_{i2}^*, \cdots, u_{in}^*$ in the system $[O; \mathfrak{v}_1, \mathfrak{v}_2, \cdots, \mathfrak{v}_n]$. These may be evaluated from the components $u_{i1}, u_{i2}, \cdots, u_{in}$ by (6), so that

$$u_{ik}^* = \sum_{\nu=1}^{n} a_{k\nu} u_{i\nu}, \qquad i, k = 1, 2, \cdots, n.$$

Hence, for the determinant $|u_{ik}^*|$ we have

$$|u_{ik}^*| = \left| \sum_{\nu=1}^{n} u_{i\nu} a_{k\nu} \right|.$$

The expression $u_{i1} a_{k1} + u_{i2} a_{k2} + \cdots + u_{in} a_{kn}$ occurs in the i-th row and k-th column of the determinant on the right. This expression is nothing but the scalar product of the i-th row vector of the determinant $| u_{ik} |$ by the k-th row vector of the determinant $| a_{ik} |$. Thus, by the multiplication theorem for determinants, we have

$$|u_{ik}^*| = |u_{ik}| \cdot |a_{ik}|.$$

By the orthogonality of (a_{ik}), the determinant $|a_{ik}| = \pm 1$. We thus see that *the determinant $| u_{ik} |$ which is constructed from the components of the vectors $\mathfrak{b}_i$ remains unchanged under a proper rigid motion if the quantities u_{ik} are replaced by the components u_{ik}^* of the image vectors $\mathfrak{b}_i^*$; on the other hand, the determinant changes its sign if this substitution is performed for an improper rigid motion.*

Rigid Motions in R_2

We shall now study rigid motions in R_2 and R_3 (or as we may say, in the plane and in space) somewhat more thoroughly. First, we consider the plane. By (4), a rigid motion is given, with respect to a

Cartesian coordinate system, by a pair of equations of the form

$$(9) \qquad \begin{aligned} y_1 &= t_1 + a_{11} x_1 + a_{12} x_2, \\ y_2 &= t_2 + a_{21} x_1 + a_{22} x_2. \end{aligned}$$

The matrix (a_{ik}) is orthogonal. By (6), the corresponding equations for *vectors* in the plane are

$$(10) \qquad \begin{aligned} u_1^* &= a_{11} u_1 + a_{12} u_2, \\ u_2^* &= a_{21} u_1 + a_{22} u_2. \end{aligned}$$

A vector which is equal to its image vector will be called an *invariant vector*. It is clear by (10) that the null vector is such a vector. Are there any other invariant vectors? For such a vector we must have $u_1^* = u_1$, $u_2^* = u_2$. Thus the vector whose components are u_1, u_2 is an invariant vector if and only if u_1, u_2 satisfy the equations

$$\begin{aligned} u_1 &= a_{11} u_1 + a_{12} u_2, \\ u_2 &= a_{21} u_1 + a_{22} u_2 \end{aligned}$$

or

$$(11) \qquad \begin{aligned} (a_{11} - 1) u_1 + a_{12} u_2 \qquad &= 0, \\ a_{21} u_1 \qquad + (a_{22} - 1) u_2 &= 0. \end{aligned}$$

By § 6, the rank of the matrix

$$(12) \qquad \begin{pmatrix} a_{11} - 1 & a_{12} \\ a_{21} & a_{22} - 1 \end{pmatrix}$$

must be less than 2 if there are to be non-vanishing invariant vectors. We distinguish three cases, according to whether the rank R of the matrix (12) is 0, 1, or 2.

I. $R = 0$. In this case, the totality of all vector solutions of (11) forms a vector space of dimension 2, by Theorem 3 of § 10, i.e. every vector of R_2 is invariant. All elements of the matrix (12) then vanish, so that $a_{11} = a_{22} = 1$, $a_{12} = a_{21} = 0$. A mapping (9) whose matrix has these elements is certainly a rigid motion, since the matrix

$$\begin{pmatrix} 1 & 0 \\ 0 & 1 \end{pmatrix}$$

is orthogonal. In this case, the determinant $|a_{ik}|$ is equal to $+1$. Equations (9) take on the form

$$(13) \qquad \begin{aligned} y_1 &= t_1 + x_1, \\ y_2 &= t_2 + x_2. \end{aligned}$$

Geometrically this means that, by such a rigid motion, every point is moved parallel to the x_1-axis by an amount equal to $|t_1|$, and parallel to the x_2-axis by an amount equal to $|t_2|$; the direction of motion is that of the positive or negative x_i-axis $(i = 1, 2)$ according to whether the corresponding t_i is positive or negative. (Cf. Fig. 25; there t_1 is taken to be negative, and t_2 positive.) We may also express this as follows: If O^* is the image of the the origin O, then each point is moved parallel to the vector $\overrightarrow{OO^*}$ by an amount equal to $\overline{OO^*}$. Such a rigid motion is called a **translation** *along the line* OO^*.

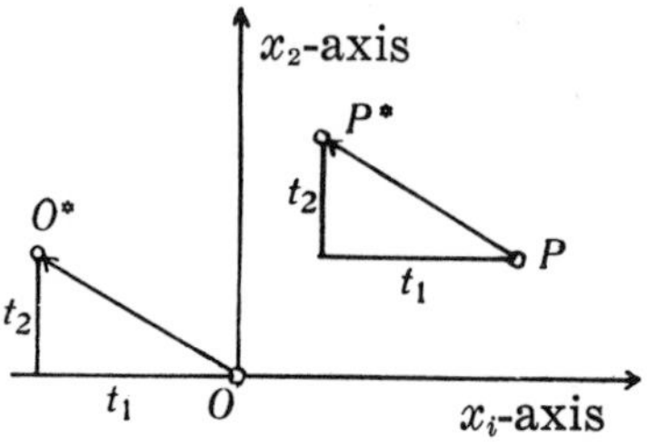

Fig. 25

If $t_1 = t_2 = 0$ in (13), then each point is its own image. In this special case, the rigid motion is called the *identity mapping* or the *identity.*

II. $\boldsymbol{R} = \mathbf{1}$. We must have in this case that

$$(14) \qquad \begin{vmatrix} a_{11}-1 & a_{12} \\ a_{21} & a_{22}-1 \end{vmatrix} = |a_{ik}| + 1 - a_{11} - a_{22} = 0,$$

while not all entries of the matrix (12) vanish. If the determinant $|a_{ik}|$ were equal to $+1$, then it would follow from (14) that $a_{11} + a_{22} = 2$. However, by the orthogonality of (a_{ik}), we have

$$(15) \qquad \begin{aligned} a_{11}^2 + a_{12}^2 &= 1, \\ a_{21}^2 + a_{22}^2 &= 1. \end{aligned}$$

Hence no a_{ik} may have its absolute value > 1. Thus the equation $a_{11} + a_{22} = 2$ can hold only if $a_{11} = a_{22} = 1$. But, by (15), this would yield $a_{12} = a_{21} = 0$. However, this would be precisely the situation of case I above. Hence, in case II, we must have $|a_{ik}| = -1$. Conversely, if the determinant $|a_{ik}|$ of the equations (9) is -1, then by (8), $a_{11} = -a_{22}$, and the right-hand part of (14) must hold. Moreover, not all elements of the matrix (12) can vanish, since in this case we should have case I, which would yield $|a_{ik}| = +1$, contrary to hypothesis. Hence, *case* II *occurs if and only if* $|a_{ik}| = -1$. Note that since the derivation of this result was independent of the particular Cartesian coordinate system involved, the result holds in every Cartesian coordinate system.

In case II, there is a vector space of dimension 1 which consists entirely of invariant vectors. We choose a normal orthogonal basis $\mathfrak{v}_1$ in this space and extend it with, say, $\mathfrak{v}_2$ to such a basis of R_2. Now we choose some arbitrary point Q as our origin and set up the equations of our rigid motion in the Cartesian coordinate system $[Q; \mathfrak{v}_1, \mathfrak{v}_2]$. The equations still have the form (9) but in general with different coefficients a_{ik}. But now, $\mathfrak{v}_1$ is an invariant vector, i.e. if $u_1 = 1$, $u_2 = 0$ in equations (10), then we must have $u_1^* = 1$, $u_2^* = 0$. By substitution, we obtain $a_{11} = 1$, $a_{21} = 0$. By (8) we have furthermore that $a_{22} = -a_{11} = -1$, $a_{12} = a_{21} = 0$. Hence equations (9) must have the form

$$y_1 = t_1 + x_1, \qquad y_2 = t_2 - x_2 \tag{16}$$

in the coordinate system $[Q; \mathfrak{v}_1, \mathfrak{v}_2]$. The point Q was chosen quite arbitrarily. Now, let us consider a point Q_1 whose coordinates in $[Q; \mathfrak{v}_1, \mathfrak{v}_2]$ are as follows: x_1 arbitrary, $x_2 = (1/2)\, t_2$. Then by (16), the image point $Q_1{}^*$ has its second coordinate also equal to $(1/2)\, t_2$. Now let us go over to the coordinate system $[Q; \mathfrak{v}_1, \mathfrak{v}_2]$. The equations of the rigid motion under consideration must also be of the form (16)—of course the new values of t_1, t_2 may be different—since the form of these equations is independent of the choice of origin. In the coordinate system $[Q; \mathfrak{v}_1, \mathfrak{v}_2]$ the second component of the vector $\overrightarrow{Q_1Q_1{}^*}$ was equal to 0. However, the components of vectors depend only on the basis vectors, and are independent of the choice of the origin. Hence the second component of the vector $\overrightarrow{Q_1Q_1{}^*}$ is also equal to 0 in the coordinate system $[Q_1; \mathfrak{v}_1, \mathfrak{v}_2]$. It thus follows, since Q_1 has the coordinates 0, 0 in the coordinate system $[Q_1; \mathfrak{v}_1, \mathfrak{v}_2]$, that the second coordinate of $Q_1{}^*$ must also be equal to 0 in this coordinate system. If in the equations (16) for our rigid motion, taken with respect to the coordinate system $[Q_1; \mathfrak{v}_1, \mathfrak{v}_2]$, we take $x_1 = 0$, $x_2 = 0$, we must also have $y_2 = 0$. Hence, $t_2 = 0$. We thus see that the equations of the given rigid motion must have the form

$$y_1 = t_1 + x_1, \qquad y_2 = -x_2, \tag{17}$$

in the system $[Q_1; \mathfrak{v}_1, \mathfrak{v}_2]$. What does this mean geometrically? The equation $y_1 = t_1 + x_1$ informs us that each point of the plane is moved parallel to the x_1-axis by an amount equal to $| t_1 |$ in the positive or negative direction according to whether $t_1 \gtrless 0$ (Fig. 26). The equation $y_2 = - x_2$ informs us that every point is, at the same time, carried to the opposite side of the x_1-axis, and moreover has the same distance from the x_1-axis as it had before. This last is called **reflection** *in the x_1-axis*. We thus have the following result:

In case II the rigid motion is a reflection in a line combined with a translation along this line.

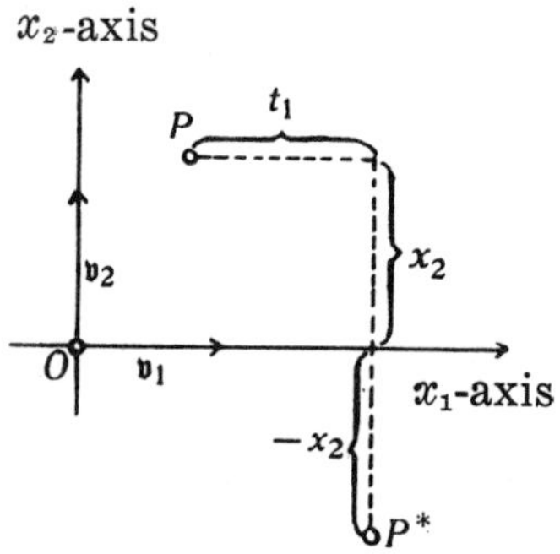

Fig. 26

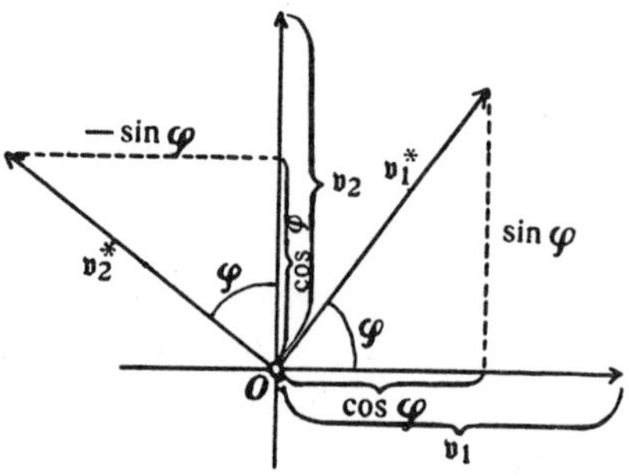

Fig. 27

III. $\boldsymbol{R = 2}$**.** In this case the null vector is the only invariant vector and it is clear that $| a_{ik} | = +1$. For otherwise, we should have case II. We must furthermore have $a_{11} \neq 1$. For otherwise, by (8), we should also have $a_{22} = a_{11} = 1$, so that by (15), $a_{12} = a_{21} = 0$, which would be case I. Conversely, if $| a_{ik} | = +1$ and $a_{11} \neq 1$, then we must have case III, since in case I, $a_{11} = 1$, and in case II, $| a_{ik} | = -1$.

In the present case the rigid motion always has a fixed point, i.e. a point which coincides with its image. For, for a fixed point with coordinates x_1, x_2, we must have $y_1 = x_1$, $y_2 = x_2$ in (9). Thus the coordinates x_1, x_2 must satisfy the equations

$$(18) \qquad \begin{aligned} (a_{11} - 1) x_1 + a_{12} x_2 &= -t_1, \\ a_{21} x_1 + (a_{22} - 1) x_2 &= -t_2 \end{aligned}$$

Since the rank of (12), and hence the rank R of the coefficient matrix of (18), is now 2, the rank of the augmented matrix of (18) must also be 2, so that the system of equations possesses precisely one solution x_1, x_2. That is, there is precisely one fixed point Q with the coordinates x_1, x_2. We now choose some Cartesian coordinate system $[Q; \mathfrak{v}_1, \mathfrak{v}_2]$ whose origin is this fixed point Q. If we take the equations

(9) to represent the rigid motion in this coordinate system, then for $x_1 = x_2 = 0$, we must have also $y_1 = y_2 = 0$. Thus, $t_1 = t_2 = 0$. Since (a_{ik}) is orthogonal, we also have $a_{11}^2 + a_{21}^2 = 1$. Hence there is an angle φ for which the equations

$$\cos \varphi = a_{11}, \qquad \sin \varphi = a_{21}$$

are satisfied. If we require that $0 \leqq \varphi \leqq \pi$, then φ is uniquely determined.[6] Moreover, by (8), we must also have

$$a_{22} = a_{11} = \cos\varphi, \qquad a_{12} = -a_{21} = -\sin\varphi.$$

If we substitute this in (9), then the equations of the rigid motion under consideration with respect to the coordinate system finally become

$$(19) \qquad \begin{aligned} y_1 &= x_1 \cos\varphi - x_2 \sin\varphi, \\ y_2 &= x_1 \sin\varphi + x_2 \cos\varphi. \end{aligned}$$

These equations also have a simple geometrical meaning. For we see that the vector $\mathfrak{v}_1$ goes over into that vector $\mathfrak{v}_1^*$ whose components with respect to $[Q; \mathfrak{v}_1, \mathfrak{v}_2]$ are $\cos\varphi$, $\sin\varphi$ and that similarly $\mathfrak{v}_2$ goes over into $\mathfrak{v}_2^*$ whose components are $-\sin\varphi$, $\cos\varphi$.

Since Q is a fixed point, the coordinate system $[Q; \mathfrak{v}_1, \mathfrak{v}_2]$ goes over into $[Q; \mathfrak{v}_1^*, \mathfrak{v}_2^*]$. It is immediate from Fig. 27 that $\mathfrak{v}_1^*$ is obtained if $\mathfrak{v}_1$ is rotated through an angle φ about Q in the positive sense.[7] (Cf. § 10, exercise 4.) Similarly, this same rotation yields $\mathfrak{v}_2^*$ from $\mathfrak{v}_2$. Thus the coordinate system $[Q; \mathfrak{v}_1^*, \mathfrak{v}_2^*]$ is obtained from $[Q; \mathfrak{v}_1, \mathfrak{v}_2]$ by a rotation in the plane through the angle φ in the positive sense about Q. However, since the image point P^* of an arbitrary point P under the rigid motion given by (19) has the same position in the coordinate system $[Q; \mathfrak{v}_1^*, \mathfrak{v}_2^*]$ as P has in $[Q; \mathfrak{v}_1, \mathfrak{v}_2]$, the point P goes over into P^* under a rotation in the plane through the angle φ. Thus the rigid motion given by (19) is nothing but a **rotation** in the plane through the angle φ and about the fixed point Q.

---

[6] $\varphi = 0$ can not occur in Case III, since R would then also $= 0$.

[7] The angle φ is taken between 0 and $\frac{\pi}{2}$ in the figure. The reader may however easily convince himself that the various relations hold if $\varphi > \frac{\pi}{2}$.

Our results are summarized in the following table:

RIGID MOTIONS IN R_2

	Dimension of Space of Invariant Vectors	Sign of the Rigid Motion	Type of Rigid Motion
I	2	$\mid a_{ik} \mid = +1, \quad a_{ik} = \delta_{ik}$	Translation
II	1	$\mid a_{ik} \mid = -1$	Reflection in a Line Combined with Translation along this Line
III	0	$\mid a_{ik} \mid = +1, \quad a_{11} \neq 1$	Rotation about a Fixed Point

We also see that in R_2 the determinant $|a_{ik}|$ of the equations of a rigid motion must have the same value in all Cartesian coordinate systems. For, this determinant is determined by the dimension of the vector space of invariant vectors. This dimension however, and hence also the value of the determinant, is clearly independent of the choice of the coordinate system.

Rigid Motions in R_3

In order to investigate the rigid motions in R_3, we first introduce an arbitrary Cartesian coordinate system in R_3. The equations of a given rigid motion will then have the form (4) with an orthogonal matrix (a_{ik}). The determinant $|a_{ik}|$ is then equal to $+1$ or -1. We shall first consider the case where $|a_{ik}| = +1$. In this case there certainly exists a non-null invariant vector. To show this, we first observe that such vectors satisfy $u_i^* = u_i$ in (6), i.e. the components of invariant vectors are solutions of the system:

$$\begin{aligned} (a_{11}-1)u_1 + a_{12}u_2 \quad\quad + a_{13}u_3 \quad\quad &= 0, \\ a_{21}u_1 \quad + (a_{22}-1)u_2 + a_{23}u_3 \quad\quad &= 0, \\ a_{31}u_1 \quad + a_{32}u_2 \quad\quad + (a_{33}-1)u_3 &= 0. \end{aligned} \tag{20}$$

We may easily calculate the determinant of this system, obtaining

$$\begin{vmatrix} a_{11}-1 & a_{12} & a_{13} \\ a_{21} & a_{22}-1 & a_{23} \\ a_{31} & a_{32} & a_{33}-1 \end{vmatrix} = |a_{ik}| - A_{11} - A_{22} - A_{33} + a_{11} + a_{22} + a_{33} - 1. \tag{21}$$

Here, as usual, A_{ik} is the cofactor of a_{ik} in $|a_{ik}|$. But $|a_{ik}| = +1$, so that, by (8), $a_{ik} = A_{ik}$. Thus the right-hand side of (21) vanishes.

Hence, determinant (21) is 0. The rank of the matrix of (20) is at most 2, and so the dimension of the vector space of all invariant vectors is at least 1. This proves the existence of a non-zero invariant vector. We further prove that *if* $|a_{ik}| = +1$, *the dimension of the vector space of invariant vectors is either* 1 *or* 3; *it cannot be* 2. In order to show this, we prove that if there is a two-dimensional vector space consisting of invariant vectors, then any vector in R_3 is invariant. For if such a two-dimensional vector space exists, then the rank of (20) is at most 1, and all of its two-by-two sub-determinants vanish. In particular:

$$(22)\qquad \begin{aligned} \begin{vmatrix} a_{11}-1 & a_{12} \\ a_{21} & a_{22}-1 \end{vmatrix} &= A_{33}-a_{11}-a_{22}+1 = 0, \\ \begin{vmatrix} a_{11}-1 & a_{13} \\ a_{31} & a_{33}-1 \end{vmatrix} &= A_{22}-a_{11}-a_{33}+1 = 0, \\ \begin{vmatrix} a_{22}-1 & a_{23} \\ a_{32} & a_{33}-1 \end{vmatrix} &= A_{11}-a_{22}-a_{33}+1 = 0. \end{aligned}$$

Adding the first two of these equations together and observing that $a_{ik} = A_{ik}$, we obtain

$$-2a_{11}+2 = 0,$$

i.e. $a_{11} = 1$. In the same way we obtain $a_{22} = 1$ and $a_{33} = 1$ by adding the first and third equations, and the second and third equations. Since (a_{ik}) is orthogonal, we further have

$$(23)\qquad \begin{aligned} a_{11}^2 + a_{12}^2 + a_{13}^2 &= 1, \\ a_{21}^2 + a_{22}^2 + a_{23}^2 &= 1, \\ a_{31}^2 + a_{32}^2 + a_{33}^2 &= 1. \end{aligned}$$

But since $a_{ii} = 1$, we must have $a_{ik} = 0$ for $i \neq k$. This shows that all of the coefficients in (20) are zero. The dimension of the invariant vectors is thus 3, i.e. every vector of R_3 is invariant, proving our assertion.

Now consider the case $|a_{ik}| = -1$. We do not seek invariant vectors in this case but instead we ask whether there are non-null vectors $\mathfrak{u}$ which map into $-\mathfrak{u}$. Such a $\mathfrak{u}$ satisfies $u_i^* = -u_i$ in (6), i.e. the components of such a vector are solutions of the system of equations

$$\text{(24)} \qquad \begin{aligned} (a_{11}+1)\,u_1 + a_{12}u_2 \qquad\quad + a_{13}u_3 &= 0,\\ a_{21}u_1 \quad + (a_{22}+1)\,u_2 + a_{23}u_3 &= 0,\\ a_{31}u_1 \quad + a_{32}u_2 \qquad + (a_{33}+1)\,u_3 &= 0. \end{aligned}$$

The determinant of this system is, in analogy with (21),

$$\text{(25)} \qquad \begin{vmatrix} a_{11}+1 & a_{12} & a_{13} \\ a_{21} & a_{22}+1 & a_{23} \\ a_{31} & a_{32} & a_{33}+1 \end{vmatrix} = |a_{ik}| + A_{11} + A_{22} + A_{33} + a_{11} + a_{22} + a_{33} + 1 .$$

Since $|a_{ik}| = -1$, we see by (8) that $a_{ik} = -A_{ik}$, so that the right-hand side of (25) vanishes. The dimension of the vector space of all solutions of (24) is thus at least 1. We shall now prove that *this dimension is either* 1 *or* 3 *in the case* $|a_{ik}| = -1$. In order to do this, we shall show that if there is a two-dimensional vector space consisting of vectors $\mathfrak{u}$ whose images are $-\mathfrak{u}$, then every vector of R_3 has this property. For if a two-dimensional vector space of this sort exists, then the rank of the matrix of (24) is at most 1, so that all two-by-two sub-determinants are zero. Thus, in analogy with (22), we have

$$\text{(26)} \qquad \begin{aligned} \begin{vmatrix} a_{11}+1 & a_{12} \\ a_{21} & a_{22}+1 \end{vmatrix} &= A_{33} + a_{11} + a_{22} + 1 = 0,\\ \begin{vmatrix} a_{11}+1 & a_{13} \\ a_{31} & a_{33}+1 \end{vmatrix} &= A_{22} + a_{11} + a_{33} + 1 = 0,\\ \begin{vmatrix} a_{22}+1 & a_{23} \\ a_{32} & a_{33}+1 \end{vmatrix} &= A_{11} + a_{22} + a_{33} + 1 = 0. \end{aligned}$$

If we now add each pair of these equations and use the fact that $a_{ik} = -A_{ik}$, we immediately obtain

$$\text{(27)} \qquad a_{11} = a_{22} = a_{33} = -1 .$$

From (23) it further follows that $a_{ik} = 0$ for $i \neq k$. Thus all of the coefficients in (24) vanish. This proves that every vector of R_3 is a solution of (24), as was to be proved.

Let p be the dimension of the vector space of invariant vectors and q the dimension of the space of the vectors $\mathfrak{u}$ which get mapped into $-\mathfrak{u}$. Both p and q are defined for every rigid motion regardless of whether its determinant is $+1$ or -1. The above results then imply that for any rigid motion in R_3 at least one of the following four equations holds:

$$(28)\qquad \begin{aligned} &\text{I.} \quad p = 1;\\ &\text{II.} \quad p = 3;\\ &\text{III.} \quad q = 1;\\ &\text{IV.} \quad q = 3. \end{aligned}$$

We shall now prove that conversely, *for any given rigid motion in R_3, only one of the above four equations holds; two cannot be simultaneously satisfied.* For if II is satisfied, then every vector of R_3 is invariant and thus none of the other three equations can hold. If the rigid motion satisfies IV then every vector of R_3 is mapped into its negative, eliminating the other three possibilities again. Thus two of the equations (28) can simultaneously hold only if II and IV do not hold. But this would mean that I and III both hold. We will proceed to show that this can not be. For then there would be an invariant vector $\mathfrak{u} \neq 0$ and a vector $\mathfrak{w} \neq 0$ whose image under the given rigid motion is $-\mathfrak{w}$.

$\mathfrak{u}$ and $\mathfrak{w}$ are certainly linearly independent; for otherwise $\mathfrak{w}$ would be a multiple of $\mathfrak{u}$, which is impossible since all multiples of $\mathfrak{u}$ belong to the vector space of invariant vectors. We thus know, from earlier considerations (§ 6 and § 11), that the vectors orthogonal to both $\mathfrak{u}$ and $\mathfrak{w}$ constitute a one-dimensional vector space L. Let $\mathfrak{c} \neq 0$ be a vector of L and $\mathfrak{c}^*$ its image. Then $\mathfrak{c}\mathfrak{u} = \mathfrak{c}\mathfrak{w} = 0$. Since the scalar product of vectors is invariant under a rigid motion, the corresponding scalar products of the image vectors must vanish. Thus

$$\mathfrak{c}^*\mathfrak{u} = \mathfrak{c}^*(-\mathfrak{w}) = 0.$$

This means that $\mathfrak{c}^*$ is orthogonal both to $\mathfrak{u}$ and to $\mathfrak{w}$. Consequently $\mathfrak{c}^*$ is in L and, since L is one-dimensional, $\mathfrak{c}^*$ is a multiple of $\mathfrak{c}$. Since $\mathfrak{c}^*$, as the image vector of $\mathfrak{c}$, has the same length as $\mathfrak{c}$, we must have $\mathfrak{c}^* = \pm\mathfrak{c}$. But the vectors $\mathfrak{c}$, $\mathfrak{u}$, $\mathfrak{w}$ are linearly independent. If $\mathfrak{c}^* = \mathfrak{c}$ then $\mathfrak{c}$ and $\mathfrak{u}$ would be two linearly independent invariant vectors, so that p would be $\geqq 2$. If $\mathfrak{c}^* = -\mathfrak{c}$, then $\mathfrak{c}$ and $\mathfrak{w}$ would be two linearly independent vectors which map into their negatives so that q would be $\geqq 2$. Each of these consequences contradicts the hypothesis that

$p = q = 1$. Hence equations I and III of (28) cannot simultaneously hold.

The rigid motions of R_3 are thus divided into four mutually exclusive classes, namely those satisfying I, II, III, or IV of (28). In cases I and II, the determinant $|a_{ik}| = +1$ and in cases III and IV, $|a_{ik}| = -1$. We now consider each of these cases in turn.

I. $p = 1$. In this case, there is one invariant vector $\mathfrak{v}_3$ of length 1. We now determine two other vectors $\mathfrak{v}_1$, $\mathfrak{v}_2$, such that $\mathfrak{v}_1, \mathfrak{v}_2, \mathfrak{v}_3$ form a normal orthogonal basis of R_3. We further choose an arbitrary point Q and consider the given rigid motion in the Cartesian coordinate system $[Q; \mathfrak{v}_1, \mathfrak{v}_2, \mathfrak{v}_3]$. The equations of the rigid motion have the form (4). But $\mathfrak{v}_3$ is an invariant vector, so that $u_1^* = u_2^* = 0$, $u_3^* = 1$ in (6) for $u_1 = u_2 = 0$, $u_3 = 1$. But this is possible only if $a_{13} = a_{23} = 0$ and $a_{33} = 1$. From (23) we then obtain $a_{31} = a_{32} = 0$. In our coordinate system, equations (4) thus have the form

$$\begin{aligned} y_1 &= t_1 + a_{11} x_1 + a_{12} x_2, \\ y_2 &= t_2 + a_{21} x_1 + a_{22} x_2, \\ y_3 &= t_3 + x_3. \end{aligned} \tag{29}$$

The determinant of this system of equations is

$$\begin{vmatrix} a_{11} & a_{12} & 0 \\ a_{21} & a_{22} & 0 \\ 0 & 0 & 1 \end{vmatrix} = \begin{vmatrix} a_{11} & a_{12} \\ a_{21} & a_{22} \end{vmatrix}. \tag{30}$$

On the other hand we have seen that the value of this determinant is $+1$ for $p = 1$. From (23) it further follows, since $a_{13} = a_{23} = 0$, that

$$\begin{aligned} a_{11}^2 + a_{12}^2 &= 1, \\ a_{21}^2 + a_{22}^2 &= 1. \end{aligned} \tag{31}$$

From $a_{11} a_{21} + a_{12} a_{22} + a_{13} a_{23} = 0$ we obtain similarly that

$$a_{11} a_{21} + a_{12} a_{22} = 0. \tag{32}$$

(31) and (32) together imply that the matrix

$$\begin{pmatrix} a_{11} & a_{12} \\ a_{21} & a_{22} \end{pmatrix} \tag{33}$$

is orthogonal. The matrix (33) is the matrix of the first two equations of (29). These two equations define a mapping in R_2 which is consequently a rigid motion and which by (30) is indeed a proper rigid motion. On the other hand we cannot have $a_{11} = a_{22} = 1$, for otherwise the invariant vectors of the given transformation would have dimension 3, contradicting $p = 1$. The matrix (33), which is the matrix of the rigid motion in R_2 defined by the first two equations of (29), has rank 2, as shown above. But we have already seen that such a motion in R_2 has a fixed point. This means that there are two numbers x_1, x_2 satisfying $y_1 = x_1$, $y_2 = x_2$ in (29). Now let us return to our rigid motion in R_3. Choose a point S of R_3 whose first two coordinates in the system $[Q; \mathfrak{v}_1, \mathfrak{v}_2, \mathfrak{v}_3]$ are x_1 and x_2 as just determined, and whose last coordinate is arbitrary. Its image S^* has, by (29), the coordinates $y_1 = x_1, y_2 = x_2, y_3$. The first two components of the vector $\overrightarrow{SS^*}$ are therefore equal to 0. But vector components are independent of the choice of origin. If we use the coordinate system $[S; \mathfrak{v}_1, \mathfrak{v}_2, \mathfrak{v}_3]$, then the first two components of the vector $\overrightarrow{SS^*}$ are again 0. But this means that the point S has the same first two coordinates as its image S^* in the coordinate system $[S; \mathfrak{v}_1, \mathfrak{v}_2, \mathfrak{v}_3]$ as well. On the other hand, the equations of our rigid motion are of the form (29) in the coordinate system $[S; \mathfrak{v}_1, \mathfrak{v}_2, \mathfrak{v}_3]$ as well (possibly with different coefficients), since this form depended only on the basis vectors $\mathfrak{v}_1, \mathfrak{v}_2, \mathfrak{v}_3$. But now we must have $y_1 = y_2 = 0$ if $x_1 = x_2 = x_3 = 0$, which is only possible if $t_1 = t_2 = 0$. Finally, since (33) is orthogonal, we may write as before

$$a_{11} = \cos\varphi, \quad a_{21} = \sin\varphi, \quad a_{12} = -\sin\varphi, \quad a_{22} = \cos\varphi,$$

where φ is a uniquely determined angle in the interval $0 < \varphi \leqq 2\pi$. Thus the equations of our rigid motion in the coordinate system $[S; \mathfrak{v}_1, \mathfrak{v}_2, \mathfrak{v}_3]$ are of the following form:

$$\begin{aligned} y_1 &= x_1 \cos\varphi - x_2 \sin\varphi, \\ y_2 &= x_1 \sin\varphi + x_2 \cos\varphi, \\ y_3 &= t_3 + x_3. \end{aligned} \tag{34}$$

What does this mean geometrically? A line g parallel to the vector $\mathfrak{v}_3$, i.e. parallel to the x_3-axis of the coordinate system $[S; \mathfrak{v}_1, \mathfrak{v}_2, \mathfrak{v}_3]$

(cf. Fig. 28), is characterized by the fact that all of its points have

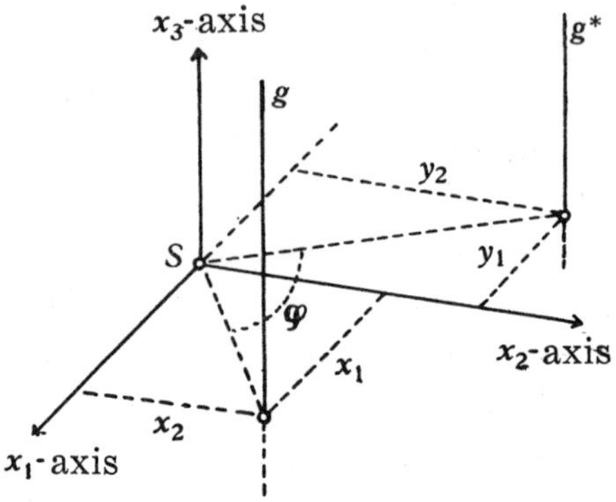

Fig. 28

the same first two coordinates x_1, x_2. The intersection of g with the x_1, x_2-plane has, in particular, the coordinates x_1, x_2, 0. Let us now find the images of the points of g by (34). The first two equations of (34) do not depend on x_3, and so all of the points of the image have the same first two coordinates y_1, y_2, since the points of g have the same first two coordinates x_1, x_2. Thus the images of the points of g all lie on a line g^* parallel to the x_3-axis and hence to g. We call g^* the *image line* of g. The intersection of g^* and the x_1, x_2-plane has the coordinates y_1, y_2, 0, and the first two coordinates y_1, y_2 are given by the first two equations of (34), where x_1, x_2 are the first two coordinates of the intersection of g and the x_1, x_2-plane. On the other hand, these two equations define a mapping in the x_1, x_2-plane which, as we have already seen, is a rotation by the angle φ about the origin. If we now consider the rotation in R_3 about the x_3-axis in the same direction and through the same angle φ, then the foot of the line g in the x_1, x_2-plane goes into the foot of the line g^*. Consequently, the line g will get sent into its image line g^*. Since g was an arbitrary line parallel to the x_3-axis, this is true of all such lines.

In order to complete our geometric interpretation of the given rigid motion, we need only observe that the third of the equations (34) states that every point of R_3 should also be moved a distance $|t_3|$ parallel to the x_3-axis and should be moved along the positive or negative x_3-axis according as t_3 is positive or negative. *Thus our given rigid motion is nothing but a rotation of space about a line (namely about the x_3-axis of the system $[S; \mathfrak{v}_1, \mathfrak{v}_2, \mathfrak{v}_3]$) followed by a translation along this line.*

II. $p = 3$. In this case we have already seen that the determinant of the equations of motion (4) has the value $+1$ in every Cartesian coordinate system, and moreover that $a_{ik} = \delta_{ik}$. The equations then have the form

$$\begin{aligned} y_1 &= t_1 + x_1, \\ y_2 &= t_2 + x_2, \\ y_3 &= t_3 + x_3. \end{aligned}$$

The geometric meaning of these equations is already familiar to us; by such a motion every point of R_3 is translated parallel to the i-th coordinate axis by the distance $| t_i |$. *The motion is a translation.* If in particular, $t_1 = t_2 = t_3 = 0$ then every point is its own image point and the mapping is the *identity mapping.*

III. $q = 1$. In this case $| a_{ik} | = -1$ for every Cartesian coordinate system. There is a vector $\mathfrak{v}_3$ of length 1 which maps into $-\mathfrak{v}_3$. We may find two other vectors $\mathfrak{v}_1, \mathfrak{v}_2$ such that $\mathfrak{v}_1, \mathfrak{v}_2, \mathfrak{v}_3$ form a normal orthogonal system. We now choose an arbitrary point Q as an origin and write the equations of the rigid motion in the coordinate system $[Q; \mathfrak{v}_1, \mathfrak{v}_2, \mathfrak{v}_3]$ in the form (4). Since $\mathfrak{v}_3$ is sent into $-\mathfrak{v}_3$, we must have $\overset{*}{u}_1 = \overset{*}{u}_2 = 0$, $\overset{*}{u}_3 = -1$ if $u_1 = u_2 = 0$, $u_3 = 1$ in (6). But this is possible only if $a_{13} = a_{23} = 0$, $a_{33} = -1$. By the third equation of (23) we then see that $a_{31} = a_{32} = 0$. Thus the equations of our motion in the coordinate system $[Q; \mathfrak{v}_1, \mathfrak{v}_2, \mathfrak{v}_3]$ are of the special form

$$\begin{aligned} y_1 &= t_1 + a_{11} x_1 + a_{12} x_2, \\ y_2 &= t_2 + a_{21} x_1 + a_{22} x_2, \\ y_3 &= t_3 - x_3. \end{aligned} \tag{35}$$

Now let R be any point in R_3 whose third coordinate is $x_3 = (1/2)\,t_3$ in the coordinate system $[Q; \mathfrak{v}_1, \mathfrak{v}_2, \mathfrak{v}_3]$. Its image point R^* then has, as its third coordinate, $y_3 = (1/2)\,t_3$, as can be seen from (35). Then the third component of the vector $\overrightarrow{RR^*}$ in our coordinate system is 0. But vector components are independent of the choice of origin. Thus the third component of $\overrightarrow{RR^*}$ is 0 in the coordinate system $[R; \mathfrak{v}_1, \mathfrak{v}_2, \mathfrak{v}_3]$ also. R now has coordinates 0, 0, 0, so the last coordinate of R^* must also be 0. The equations of our rigid motion are of the form (35) in the system $[R; \mathfrak{v}_1, \mathfrak{v}_2, \mathfrak{v}_3]$ also, since the form (35) depended only on the basis vectors and not on the origin Q. But in this system we must have $y_3 = 0$ if $x_1 = x_2 = x_3 = 0$. Thus $t_3 = 0$.

The determinant of (35) is

$$\begin{vmatrix} a_{11} & a_{12} & 0 \\ a_{21} & a_{22} & 0 \\ 0 & 0 & -1 \end{vmatrix} = -\begin{vmatrix} a_{11} & a_{12} \\ a_{21} & a_{22} \end{vmatrix} = -1. \tag{36}$$

As in case I, it follows that equations (31) and (32) hold, so that the matrix (33) is again orthogonal and indeed by (36) is properly orthogonal.

If $a_{11} = 1$, then by (8) applied to (33), we have $a_{22} = a_{11} = 1$ and so $a_{12} = a_{21} = 0$ by (31). The equations of motion (35) then have the form

$$\begin{aligned} y_1 &= t_1 + x_1, \\ y_2 &= t_2 + x_2, \\ y_3 &= -x_3. \end{aligned} \tag{37}$$

The first two equations of (37) again represent a translation of R_3, and in fact one parallel to the x_1, x_2-plane of the coordinate system $[R; \mathfrak{v}_1, \mathfrak{v}_2, \mathfrak{v}_3]$. The third is a reflection in the x_1, x_2-plane. *Our rigid motion in the present case thus is a reflection in a plane followed by a translation parallel to this plane.*

If, however, $a_{11} \neq 1$, then we see as in case I that there are two numbers x_1, x_2 which, when substituted into the first two equations of (35), yield $y_1 = x_1$, $y_2 = x_2$. Let S be the point of R_3 whose first two coordinates are x_1, x_2 and whose last coordinate is 0 in the coordinate system $[R; \mathfrak{v}_1, \mathfrak{v}_2, \mathfrak{v}_3]$. This point is a fixed point of our rigid motion, for its image point S^* has the coordinates $y_1 = x_1$, $y_2 = x_2$, $y_3 = -x_3 = 0$, by (35) since $t_3 = 0$. If we now employ the coordinate system $[S; \mathfrak{v}_1, \mathfrak{v}_2, \mathfrak{v}_3]$, then the equations of the rigid motion are also of the form (35). Since S is a fixed point, we must in addition have $y_1 = y_2 = y_3 = 0$ if $x_1 = x_2 = x_3 = 0$. This implies that $t_1 = t_2 = t_3 = 0$. As in case I, we may set

$$a_{11} = \cos\varphi, \quad a_{21} = \sin\varphi, \quad a_{12} = -\sin\varphi, \quad a_{22} = \cos\varphi.$$

The equations of our rigid motion will finally be of the form

$$\begin{aligned} y_1 &= x_1 \cos\varphi - x_2 \sin\varphi, \\ y_2 &= x_1 \sin\varphi + x_2 \cos\varphi, \\ y_3 &= -x_3 \end{aligned} \tag{38}$$

in the coordinate system $[S; \mathfrak{v}_1, \mathfrak{v}_2, \mathfrak{v}_3]$. The first two of these equations represent, as in case I, a rotation of angle φ about the x_3-axis of the coordinate system $[S; \mathfrak{v}_1, \mathfrak{v}_2, \mathfrak{v}_3]$. The third equation again represents a reflection in the x_1, x_2-plane. *Our rigid motion is in the present case a reflection in a plane, followed by a rotation about an axis perpendicular to this plane.*

IV. $q = 3$. We already know that for this case $|a_{ik}| = -1$ in every Cartesian coordinate system, and that $a_{11} = a_{22} = a_{33} = -1$ and $a_{ik} = 0$ for $i \neq k$. The equations of the rigid motion hence are of the form

$$
\begin{aligned}
y_1 &= t_1 - x_1, \\
y_2 &= t_2 - x_2, \\
y_3 &= t_3 - x_3.
\end{aligned} \tag{39}
$$

Let Q be the point of R_3 whose coordinates are $\frac{1}{2}t_1, \frac{1}{2}t_2, \frac{1}{2}t_3$. From (39) we see that the image of Q has the same coordinates as Q, and so coincides with Q. Now choose a Cartesian coordinate system having this fixed point Q as its origin, say $[Q; \mathfrak{v}_1, \mathfrak{v}_2, \mathfrak{v}_3]$. In this coordinate system the equations of the rigid motion, being again of the form (39) must yield $y_1 = y_2 = y_3 = 0$ for $x_1 = x_2 = x_3 = 0$. Thus $t_1 = t_2 = t_3 = 0$. The equations hence are of the form

$$
\begin{aligned}
y_1 &= -x_1, \\
y_2 &= -x_2, \\
y_3 &= -x_3.
\end{aligned} \tag{40}
$$

If P is any point whose coordinates are x_1, x_2, x_3, then its image P^* has the coordinates $-x_1, -x_2, -x_3$ by (40). Consequently the line through P and P^* passes through the origin Q, which is the midpoint of the segment $\overline{PP^*}$. We thus call this rigid motion *a reflection through the origin Q.*

These results are collected in the table on p. 178.

It is of course clear that the value of $|a_{ik}|$ for the rigid motions we have considered does not depend on the coordinate system.

Furthermore, their properties in ordinary plane and space justify the name "rigid motion" for the mappings under discussion. For, apart from reflections, our mappings are equivalent to actual rigid motions of plane and space. We may consider the reflections as the *improper* motions. A reflection of the plane in a line may be thought of as obtained by a rotation of this plane about this line. In the same way, a reflection R_3 in a plane may be considered as a rotation of R_3 about the plane in R_4. A reflection of R_3 through a point is reducible to this case. For it is equivalent to a reflection in a plane (say the x_1, x_2-plane of any coordinate system whose origin is this point) combined with a rotation of R_3 about an axis perpendicular to this plane (the x_3-axis) through the angle π.

RIGID MOTIONS IN R_3

	Dimension p of Vector Space of Invariant Vectors	Dimension q of Space of Vectors Mapped into their Negatives	Sign of the Rigid Motion	Type of Motion
I.	1	0 or 2	$\lvert a_{ik}\rvert = +1$, not all a_{ii} equal to 1	Rotation of R_3 about a Line and Translation along this Line
II.	3	0	$\lvert a_{ik}\rvert = +1$, $a_{11} = a_{22} = a_{33} = 1$	Translation
III	0	1	$\lvert a_{ik}\rvert = -1$, $a_{11} \neq 1$, but not all $a_{ii} = -1$	Reflection in a Plane and Simultaneous Rotation about Axis Perpendicular to the Plane
	2	1	$\lvert a_{ik}\rvert = -1$, $a_{11} = 1$	Reflection in a Plane and Simultaneous Translation Parallel to the Plane
IV.	0	3	$\lvert a_{ik}\rvert = -1$, $a_{11} = a_{22} = a_{33} = -1$	Reflection through a Point

Exercises

1. What are the rigid motions of R_1 geometrically?

2. In R_2, determine the dimension of those vectors which get mapped into their negatives by a given rigid motion. Classify the rigid motions of R_2 accordingly.

3. Any p unit vectors $\mathfrak{e}_{\nu_1}, \mathfrak{e}_{\nu_2}, \cdots, \mathfrak{e}_{\nu_p}$ of euclidean R_n, span a p-dimensional vector space L. This vector space when applied to the origin O gives a linear space L, which is called a *p-dimensional coordinate space*. The point $P = (x_1, x_2, \cdots, x_n)$ belongs to L if and only if $x_i = 0$ for all $i \neq \nu_1, \nu_2, \cdots, \nu_p$. A point of L is thus uniquely determined by the p coordinates $x_{\nu_1}, x_{\nu_2}, \cdots, x_{\nu_p}$. L behaves in every way like a p-dimensional euclidean space. Let $\mathfrak{a}_1, \mathfrak{a}_2, \cdots, \mathfrak{a}_p$ be p vectors of L, and let $a_{i1}, a_{i2}, \cdots, a_{in}$ be the components of $\mathfrak{a}_i$ so that $a_{ik} = 0$ for $k \neq \nu_1, \nu_2, \cdots, \nu_p$. Thus the vector $\mathfrak{a}_i$ is determined by the p components $a_{i\nu_1}, a_{i\nu_2}, \cdots, a_{i\nu_p}$. The (*p-dimensional*) *volume* of the p-dimensional parallelotope spanned by the vectors

$$\mathfrak{a}_1, \mathfrak{a}_2, \cdots, \mathfrak{a}_p$$

is the absolute value of the p-by-p determinant

$$\begin{vmatrix} a_{1v_1} & a_{1v_2} & \cdots & a_{1v_p} \\ a_{2v_1} & a_{2v_2} & \cdots & a_{2v_p} \\ \cdot & \cdot & \cdot & \cdot \\ a_{pv_1} & a_{pv_2} & \cdots & a_{pv_p} \end{vmatrix}.$$

This definition will permit us to find the volume of an arbitrary p-dimensional parallelotope in R_n. A *p-dimensional parallelotope* is the totality of points which are obtained from a fixed point by applying all the vectors of the form $\sum_{i=1}^{p} \lambda_i \mathfrak{c}_i$ for $0 \leqq \lambda_i \leqq 1$ where $\mathfrak{c}_1, \mathfrak{c}_2, \cdots, \mathfrak{c}_p$ are the edge vectors of the parallelotope (cf. exercise 7, § 11). Such a p-dimensional parallelotope need not in general lie in a p-dimensional coordinate space. But show that *every p-dimensional parallelotope may be mapped by a suitable rigid motion into one which lies in a p-dimensional coordinate space.* Using this fact, we may find the volume of any parallelotope by the additional requirement that parallelotopes which can be mapped onto each other by rigid motions have the same volume. The volume V of the p-dimensional parallelotope whose edge vectors are $\mathfrak{c}_1, \mathfrak{c}_2, \cdots, \mathfrak{c}_p$ can be calculated by the formula

$$V^2 = \begin{vmatrix} \mathfrak{c}_1^2 & \mathfrak{c}_1\mathfrak{c}_2 & \cdots & \mathfrak{c}_1\mathfrak{c}_p \\ \mathfrak{c}_2\mathfrak{c}_1 & \mathfrak{c}_2^2 & \cdots & \mathfrak{c}_2\mathfrak{c}_p \\ \cdot & \cdot & \cdot & \cdot \\ \mathfrak{c}_p\mathfrak{c}_1 & \mathfrak{c}_p\mathfrak{c}_2 & \cdots & \mathfrak{c}_p^2 \end{vmatrix}.$$

The volume of a p-dimensional parallelotope whose edge vectors are linearly dependent is, accordingly, zero.

4. Project a given p-dimensional parallelotope on all p-dimensional coordinate spaces (cf. exercises 5 and 6 of § 11). Square the (p-dimensional) volumes of the projections and add the squares of these volumes. Then the result is the square of the p-dimensional volume of the parallelotope. (*Hint*: Use the Lagrange identity of exercise 10 of § 9.)

5. A *similarity transformation* is a single-valued mapping of R_n onto itself satisfying $\overline{P^*Q^*} = c \cdot \overline{PQ}$ where c is a fixed real number > 0, (independent of P and Q) and P^* and Q^* are the images of P and Q.

Prove that for any similarity transformation, if P^*, Q^*, R^*, S^* are the images of P, Q, R, S and if $\overrightarrow{PQ} \cdot \overrightarrow{RS} = 0$, then $\overrightarrow{P^*Q^*} \cdot \overrightarrow{R^*S^*} = 0$. Let the coordinates $y_1, y_2, \cdots, y_n$ of the image P^* of P be expressed in terms of the coordinates $x_1, x_2, \cdots, x_n$ of P with respect to a given Cartesian coordinate system by the equations

$$y_i = t_i + \sum_{k=1}^{n} b_{ik} x_k, \qquad i = 1, 2, \cdots, n.$$

The matrix (b_{ik}) has the property that there exists a real number c such that the matrix $\left(\frac{b_{ik}}{c}\right)$ is orthogonal.

An n-dimensional parallelotope is mapped into another n-dimensional parallelotope by a similarity transformation. How is its volume affected?

§ 13. Affine Transformations

Rigid motions are a special case of a more general class of mappings of R_n into itself, namely the class of affine transformations. This section is devoted to a brief discussion of their properties. By an **affine transformation,** we mean a single-valued mapping of R_n into itself which leaves all relations of the form

$$\overrightarrow{RS} = \lambda \cdot \overrightarrow{PQ} \tag{1}$$

invariant. As we already know, the requirement of single-valuedness[1] means that to each point of R_n, there corresponds a uniquely determined image point. By the invariance of relation (1), we mean that if P, Q, R, S are any four points of R_n for which the vector $\overrightarrow{RS}$ is, say, λ times the vector $\overrightarrow{PQ}$, and if P^*, Q^*, R^*, S^* are their respective image points under the given mapping, then the relation

$$\overrightarrow{R^*S^*} = \lambda \cdot \overrightarrow{P^*Q^*} \tag{2}$$

must also hold, that is, $\overrightarrow{R^*S^*}$ must be the product of $\overrightarrow{P^*Q^*}$ by precisely the same λ.

An affine transformation is thus defined as a mapping of the points of R_n. But it also induces a mapping of the vectors of R_n in a natural way. For, let $\mathfrak{v}$ be a vector of R_n, and let $\mathfrak{v}$ carry some arbitrary point P of R_n into Q, so that $\mathfrak{v} = \overrightarrow{PQ}$. Now find the image points P^*, Q^* of P and Q. Now, the segment P^*Q^* consists of all image points of the points of the segment PQ. For, any point R of the segment PQ satisfies a relation of the form $\overrightarrow{PR} = \lambda \bullet \overrightarrow{PQ}$ for $0 \leqq \lambda \leqq 1$. But if R^* denotes the image of R, we have by (1) and (2) that $\overrightarrow{P^*R^*} = \lambda \bullet \overrightarrow{P^*Q^*}$ with the same λ; i.e. R^* is a point of the segment P^*Q^*. It is clear that we obtain all points of P^*Q^* in this way. Thus the vector $\mathfrak{v}^* = \overrightarrow{P^*Q^*}$ is the image vector of $\mathfrak{v} = \overrightarrow{PQ}$. In this way there is assigned to every vector $\mathfrak{v}$ of R_n an image vector $\mathfrak{v}^*$. We assert that $\mathfrak{v}^*$ is uniquely determined by $\mathfrak{v}$. In fact, the only element of arbitrariness in the construction of $\mathfrak{v}^*$ was in the choice of the initial point P of $\mathfrak{v} = \overrightarrow{PQ}$. If, however, we choose another point R as initial point of $\mathfrak{v}$, and if S is the end-point of $\mathfrak{v}$, then we certainly have $\overrightarrow{RS} = \overrightarrow{PQ}$. But by the invariance of (1), we have $\overrightarrow{R^*S^*} = \overrightarrow{P^*Q^*} = \mathfrak{v}^*$, where R^*, S^* are the image

[1] "Single-valued" is not to be confused with "one-to-one." As we shall see later, an affine transformation need not be one-to-one.

points of R, S. Hence, $\mathfrak{v}^*$ is independent of the choice of the initial point of $\mathfrak{v}$. The mapping thus induced in the vector space R_n is therefore single-valued.

The mappings induced by affine transformations on the vectors of R_n in this way have two important characteristic properties, which are expressed by the following equations:

$$(\lambda \mathfrak{v})^* = \lambda \cdot \mathfrak{v}^*, \tag{3}$$

$$(\mathfrak{u} + \mathfrak{v})^* = \mathfrak{u}^* + \mathfrak{v}^*. \tag{4}$$

Equation (3) states that the image vector of the vector $\lambda \mathfrak{v}$ is the product of the image vector of $\mathfrak{v}$ by λ. This condition is only another formulation of the invariance of (1). For if we set $\mathfrak{w} = \lambda \mathfrak{v}$, we have by (2) that

$$\mathfrak{w}^* = \lambda \mathfrak{v}^*.$$

But this is precisely relation (3), if we substitute $\mathfrak{w}$ for $\lambda \cdot \mathfrak{v}$.

Equation (4) states that the image vector of $\mathfrak{u} + \mathfrak{v}$ is precisely the sum of the image vectors of $\mathfrak{u}$ and $\mathfrak{v}$. This may be proved as follows: Let $\mathfrak{u}$ carry P into Q, and then let $\mathfrak{v}$ carry Q into R. Thus, $\mathfrak{u} = \overrightarrow{PQ}$, $\mathfrak{v} = \overrightarrow{QR}$, and $\mathfrak{u} + \mathfrak{v} = \overrightarrow{PR}$. Then by the definition of the vector mapping, we have

$$\mathfrak{u}^* = \overrightarrow{P^*Q^*},\ \mathfrak{v}^* = \overrightarrow{Q^*R^*},\ (\mathfrak{u} + \mathfrak{v})^* = \overrightarrow{P^*R^*}.$$

Furthermore,

$$\overrightarrow{P^*R^*} = \overrightarrow{P^*Q^*} + \overrightarrow{Q^*R^*},$$

from which (4) immediately follows.

A single-valued mapping in a vector space which has properties (3) and (4), is called a **linear transformation.** In this terminology our result is as follows:

Every affine transformation induces a linear transformation in the vector space R_n.

On the other hand, every linear transformation which is defined in the vector space R_n defines an affine transformation in R_n. For, let P_0 and P_0^* be two points of R_n. If P is an arbitrary point of R_n, we determine the image vector $(\overrightarrow{P_0P})^*$ of $\overrightarrow{P_0P}$ under the given linear transformation. Let the vector $(\overrightarrow{P_0P})^*$ carry P_0^* into P^* so that

$$\left(\overrightarrow{P_0P}\right)^* = \overrightarrow{P_0^*P^*}. \tag{5}$$

This point P^* is to be the image point of P. *The mapping thus defined* *is an affine transformation.* In order to see this, we must show that for any four points for which equation (1) is satisfied, equation (2) also holds. If $\mathfrak{a}^*$ is the image vector of $\mathfrak{a}$ under the given linear transformation, then we shall also denote $\mathfrak{a}^*$ by $\sigma(\mathfrak{a})$. In this notation the linear transformation appears as a function σ whose arguments and functional values both are vectors. Equations (3) and (4) then take on the form

$$\sigma(\lambda \mathfrak{v}) = \lambda \sigma(\mathfrak{v}), \tag{6}$$

$$\sigma(\mathfrak{u}+\mathfrak{v}) = \sigma(\mathfrak{u})+\sigma(\mathfrak{v}). \tag{7}$$

Now, by (6) and (1),

$$\sigma(\overrightarrow{RS}) = \sigma(\lambda \cdot \overrightarrow{PQ}) = \lambda \cdot \sigma(\overrightarrow{PQ}). \tag{8}$$

Furthermore, we must have the following relations for P^*, Q^*, R^*, S^* by equation (5):

$$\sigma(\overrightarrow{P_0P}) = \overrightarrow{P_0^*P^*}, \qquad \sigma(\overrightarrow{P_0Q}) = \overrightarrow{P_0^*Q^*},$$
$$\sigma(\overrightarrow{P_0R}) = \overrightarrow{P_0^*R^*}, \qquad \sigma(\overrightarrow{P_0S}) = \overrightarrow{P_0^*S^*}.$$

This yields:

$$\overrightarrow{R^*S^*} = \overrightarrow{P_0^*S^*} - \overrightarrow{P_0^*R^*} = \sigma(\overrightarrow{P_0S}) - \sigma(\overrightarrow{P_0R}). \tag{9}$$

On the other hand, by (6) and (7),

$$-\sigma(\overrightarrow{P_0R}) = \sigma(-\overrightarrow{P_0R}),$$
$$\sigma(\overrightarrow{P_0S}) + \sigma(-\overrightarrow{P_0R}) = \sigma(\overrightarrow{P_0S} - \overrightarrow{P_0R}) = \sigma(\overrightarrow{RS}).$$

Thus, by (9),

$$\overrightarrow{R^*S^*} = \sigma(\overrightarrow{RS}). \tag{10}$$

Quite analogously, we obtain:

$$\overrightarrow{P^*Q^*} = \sigma(\overrightarrow{PQ}). \tag{11}$$

Comparison of (8), (10), and (11) yields (2), which completes the proof.

For what follows, we imagine a linear coordinate system $[P_0; \mathfrak{b}_1, \mathfrak{b}_2, \ldots, \mathfrak{b}_n]$ introduced in R_n. Let the image of P_0 under some given affine transformation be P_0^*, and let that of the vector $\mathfrak{b}_i$, be $\mathfrak{b}_i^*$ $(i = 1, 2, \ldots, n)$. Let $x_1, x_2, \ldots, x_n$ be the coordinates of some arbitrary point P, so that

$$\overrightarrow{P_0P} = \sum_{i=1}^{n} x_i \mathfrak{b}_i.$$

By (4) and (3), this yields:

$$(12) \qquad \overrightarrow{P_0^*P^*} = \left(\sum_{i=1}^{n} x_i \mathfrak{b}_i\right)^* = \sum_{i=1}^{n} (x_i \mathfrak{b}_i)^* = \sum_{i=1}^{n} x_i \mathfrak{b}_i^*.$$

Of course, the symbols P^*, $\left(\sum_{i=1}^{n} x_i \mathfrak{b}_i\right)^*$, $(x_i \mathfrak{b}_i)^*$ mean the image elements of P, $\sum_{i=1}^{n} x_i \mathfrak{b}_i$, $x_i \mathfrak{b}_i$ respectively under the given affine transformation. This enables us to calculate the coordinates of P^* in the system $[P_0; \mathfrak{b}_1, \mathfrak{b}_2, \cdots, \mathfrak{b}_n]$ with ease. For let, say,

$$(13) \qquad \overrightarrow{P_0 P_0^*} = \sum_{i=1}^{n} t_i \mathfrak{b}_i,$$

$$(14) \qquad \mathfrak{b}_k^* = \sum_{i=1}^{n} a_{ik} \mathfrak{b}_i, \qquad k = 1, 2, \cdots, n.$$

Then, since $\overrightarrow{P_0 P^*} = \overrightarrow{P_0 P_0^*} + \overrightarrow{P_0^* P^*}$, we have, if we choose y_1, y_2, ..., y_n to denote the coordinates of P^*, that

$$\sum_{i=1}^{n} y_i \mathfrak{b}_i = \sum_{i=1}^{n} t_i \mathfrak{b}_i + \sum_{k=1}^{n} x_k \mathfrak{b}_k^* = \sum_{i=1}^{n} t_i \mathfrak{b}_i + \sum_{i=1}^{n} \left(\sum_{k=1}^{n} a_{ik} x_k\right) \mathfrak{b}_i,$$

or

$$\sum_{i=1}^{n} \left(y_i - t_i - \sum_{k=1}^{n} a_{ik} x_k\right) \mathfrak{b}_i = 0.$$

By the linear independence of the vectors $\mathfrak{b}_1, \mathfrak{b}_2, \cdots, \mathfrak{b}_n$ we must then have

$$(15) \qquad y_i = t_i + \sum_{k=1}^{n} a_{ik} x_k, \qquad i = 1, 2, \cdots, n.$$

If Q is any other point, say with coordinates $x_1', x_2', \cdots, x_n'$, and if its image point Q^* has coordinates $y_1', y_2', \cdots, y_n'$, then relation (15) also holds between the x_i' and the y_i'. Subtraction yields

$$y_i' - y_i = \sum_{k=1}^{n} a_{ik} (x_k' - x_k), \qquad i = 1, 2, \cdots, n.$$

The quantities $x_k' - x_k$ ($k = 1, 2, \ldots, n$) are however the components of the vector $\overrightarrow{PQ}$, and $y_i' - y_i$ ($i = 1, 2, \ldots, n$) are similarly the components of the image vector $\overrightarrow{P^*Q^*}$. If we set

$$u_k = x_k' - x_k, \; u_i^* = y_i' - y_i,$$

then

(16) $$u_i^* = \sum_{k=1}^{n} a_{ik} u_k, \qquad i = 1, 2, \cdots, n$$

are the equations of the linear transformation which is induced by the-affine transformation on the vector space.

The vectors $\mathfrak{b}_1^*, \mathfrak{b}_2^*, \cdots, \mathfrak{b}_n^*$ need not be linearly independent. By (14) and by Theorem 1 of § 10, this is the case if and only if the determinant $|a_{ik}|$ is non-zero. If $|a_{ik}| = 0$, then we call the affine transformation *singular*, in the other case *non-singular*. If $|a_{ik}| \neq 0$, then equations (15) are uniquely solvable for the x_i. That is, to every image point there is one and only one original point under our affine transformation. *A non-singular affine transformation is thus a one-to-one mapping of R_n itself.* In an analogous manner we have for this case by the solvability of (16) that the linear transformation induced by such an affine transformation is a one-to-one mapping of the vector space R_n onto itself.

The situation is quite different for a singular affine transformation. We may think of all the vectors of R_n as having the same initial point P_0. Then all of the image vectors have the initial point P_0^*. From (12), since $x_1, x_2, \ldots, x_n$ may take on any values, it follows that the totality of image vectors consists of all linear combinations of the vectors $\mathfrak{b}_1^*, \mathfrak{b}_2^*, \cdots, \mathfrak{b}_n^*$. Thus the image vectors form a vector space of dimension r, where r is the maximal number of linearly independent vectors among $\mathfrak{b}_1^*, \mathfrak{b}_2^*, \cdots, \mathfrak{b}_n^*$. If now $|a_{ik}| = 0$, then the vectors $\mathfrak{b}_i^*$ are linearly dependent, that is, we certainly have $r < n$.

Thus not every vector of R_n is an image vector. By (12), the image points are obtained from P_0^* by applying the image vectors. Thus, the image points form a linear space of dimension r. Hence if the affine transformation is singular, then not all points of R_n are image points.

By (14) and Theorem 1 of § 10, the rank of the matrix (a_{ik}) is precisely equal to the maximal number r of linearly independent vectors among $\mathfrak{b}_1^*, \mathfrak{b}_2^*, \cdots, \mathfrak{b}_n^*$. If we wish to determine the totality of vectors whose image vector is the null vector, then we must set $u_1^* = u_2^* = \ldots = u_n^*$ in equations (16) and determine the solutions $u_1, u_2, \ldots, u_n$ of the resulting system of homogeneous linear equations. But by Theorem 3 of § 10, this system of equations represents a vector space of dimension $n - r$. Hence,

The totality of all vectors whose image vector is the null vector forms a vector space of dimension $n - r$, the so-called null space of the linear transformation.

Let us denote this vector space by N. For a non-singular affine transformation, $r = n$. In this case, N consists of the null vector alone. On the other hand, for singular affine transformations, the dimension of N is certainly > 0.

If P, Q are two points whose image points P^*, Q^* are identical, we have

$$(17) \qquad (\overrightarrow{PQ})^* = \overrightarrow{P^*Q^*} = 0.$$

Hence the vector $\overrightarrow{PQ}$ must be an element of N since its image vector is 0. Conversely, if $\overrightarrow{PQ}$ belongs to N, (17) holds, so that P^* and Q^* coincide. Thus, we have proved:

If P is a point of R_n, and if P^* is its image point under the given affine transformation, then the totality of all points which have this same image point P^* form a linear space of dimension $n - r$. Indeed, this linear space consists of all vectors which are obtained from P by applying vectors of N.

Thus, under a singular affine transformation, there are always distinct points which have the same image point, while under a non-singular affine transformation, this can not happen.

An example of a singular transformation is the mapping which sends every point of R_n into the origin.

Finally, we shall prove that every system of equations (15) defines an affine transformation. For, a mapping is certainly defined by associating with the point P whose coordinates are $x_1, x_2, \ldots, x_n$, the point P^* whose coordinates are $y_1, y_2, \ldots, y_n$ as calculated from (15). It is easy to see that this mapping is an affine transformation. For, let the four points P, Q, R, S have the coordinates $x_i, x'_i, \bar{x}_i, \bar{x}'_i$ (for $i = 1, 2, \ldots, n$), while their image points P^*, Q^*, R^*, S^* have the coordinates $y_i, y'_i, \bar{y}_i, \bar{y}'_i$. Then by (15),

$$(18) \qquad y'_i - y_i = \sum_{k=1}^{n} a_{ik}(x'_k - x_k), \qquad i = 1, 2, \cdots, n,$$

$$(19) \qquad \bar{y}'_i - \bar{y}_i = \sum_{k=1}^{n} a_{ik}(\bar{x}'_k - \bar{x}_k), \qquad i = 1, 2, \cdots, n.$$

If $\overrightarrow{RS} = \lambda \cdot \overrightarrow{PQ}$, then $\bar{x}'_k - \bar{x}_k = \lambda(x'_k - x_k)$. Thus by (19),

$$\overline{y}'_i - \overline{y}_i = \lambda \sum_{k=1}^{n} a_{ik}(x'_k - x_k). \tag{20}$$

Comparison of (18) and (20) yields $\overline{y}'_i - \overline{y}_i = \lambda(y'_i - y_i)$. That is, $\overrightarrow{R^*S^*} = \lambda \cdot \overrightarrow{P^*Q^*}$, which proves that the mapping defined by (15) is an affine transformation.

We leave for later a more thorough study of affine transformations and of the closely related linear transformations, since we shall require certain algebraic methods which we have yet to develop.

Exercises

1. Given a linear transformation, what is the totality of all vectors which have the same image vector as some given fixed vector $\mathfrak{a}$?

2. Let r points $P_1, P_2, \cdots, P_r$ be given in R_n; let the point P_i have the coordinates $x_{i1}, x_{i2}, \cdots, x_{in}$. Let a real number m_i, called the *mass* of P_i be associated with each point P_i. We assume that

$$\sum_{i=1}^{r} m_i \neq 0 .$$

By the *centroid* of the points $P_1, P_2, \cdots, P_r$ we mean that point S whose coordinates $s_1, s_2, \ldots, s_n$ are given by the equations

$$s_k \cdot \sum_{i=1}^{r} m_i = \sum_{i=1}^{r} m_i x_{ik}, \qquad k = 1, 2, \cdots, n.$$

Now let there be given an affine transformation. Let the respective image points of $P_1, P_2, \cdots, P_r$ be $P_1^*, P_2^*, \cdots, P_r^*$. Let the point P_i^* be assigned the same mass m_i as P_i. Prove that the centroid of the points $P_1^*, P_2^*, \cdots, P_r^*$ is the image point of the centroid S. In other words, the centroid is invariant under affine transformations.

3. Prove that under an affine transformation, a vector space L goes into another vector space L* and that similarly a linear space L goes into another linear space L^*. If the affine transformation is non-singular, then L and L* have the same dimension; the same is true of L and L^*. How can we determine the dimension of L* (of L^*) if the affine transformation is singular?

4. Let the linear spaces L_1 and L_2 go over into L_1^* and L_2^* respectively under a given affine transformation. Let the intersection D of L_1 and L_2 go over into D^*. Then D^* lies in the intersection of L_1^* and L_2^*. If, furthermore, L_1 is contained in L_2, then L_1^* is also contained in L_2^*. Finally, if L_1 and L_2 are parallel, then so are L_1^* and L_2^*.

5. Under a non-singular affine transformation, an n-dimensional parallelotope in R_n goes over into another n-dimensional parallelotope. How does the volume change under this mapping?

CHAPTER III

FIELD THEORY; THE FUNDAMENTAL THEOREM OF ALGEBRA

§ 14. The Concept of a Field

We have now arrived at a point where we must extend the foundations on which we have so far based our development of mathematical results. Up to this point, the basis of the algebraic part of our development was the real numbers with their laws and properties. It may appear at first glance that the fact that the objects under consideration were real numbers was an essential part of our assumptions. This however is not the case. For example the results of § 6 on linear equations and the discussion of determinant theory in § 8 and § 9 remain valid, without change, in many other domains of mathematical objects, e.g. in the domain of complex numbers—as we shall soon see, and as a matter of fact in domains of functions, of residue classes, and of many other objects whose discussion does not lie within the scope of this book. What is responsible for the fact that the validity of these theorems admits of such wide extension? Let us recall the methods by which we proved these results. In no case did we find it necessary to write down particular real numbers such as 7, 15, $\sqrt{5}$, and to operate upon them. Rather, we used symbols a, b, α, β, etc. which we employed just as though they were actually real numbers. Once this point is understood, we see that the correctness of the results in question depends entirely on the fact that we may calculate with the symbols employed exactly as with real numbers. On the other hand, it was not essential that we regarded these symbols as actually representing real numbers. We could just as well have considered them as representing other objects. For example they may also stand for complex numbers—which indeed we shall soon be considering them to do. Once we are certain that the new objects satisfy all the rules of calculation actually used or assumed in our proofs, then the correctness of our proofs, and thus of all theorems and their consequences, follows without question.

However these results then will have a different content insofar as they concern different objects.

Thus if we wish to determine whether our algebraic results hold for some given domain of mathematical objects, we need only investigate whether they satisfy the algebraic rules used in the proofs of the results. Now it would be quite a tedious job to verify in detail in every such case that all the rules for calculating with real numbers are satisfied. Fortunately, this is not necessary. For, we can extract from the rules of calculation with real numbers a system of particularly simple ones from which the remaining rules may be deduced. The fundamental laws which make up such a system, we call *axioms*. We shall now put down a list of these axioms, and then show that all rules of calculation that we employ do indeed follow from them.

Since we shall later wish to apply our results to domains other than that of the real numbers, we remove the restriction that our symbols represent real numbers. We assume as given a non-empty set F of elements a, b, c, etc. We place no further restrictions on the nature of these elements. Whether they are real numbers or complex numbers or anything else will be of no significance for our developments. Nevertheless, we shall be able to operate with elements of the set F as with real numbers. To this end, we must first assume that an operation which plays the role of *addition* is defined for the elements of the set F. We therefore assume that there is a rule which assigns to every pair a, b of elements of F a uniquely determined element c of F, which is called the *sum* of a and b.[1] Just as for real numbers we shall denote the sum c by $a + b$. Thus we write $c = a + b$.[2] The rules of calculation which this addition is required to satisfy are the following:

I. Laws of Addition

1. *The commutative law:*

$$a + b = b + a.$$

2. *The associative law:*

$$a + (b + c) = (a + b) + c.$$

3. *The reversibility of addition; i.e. the equation*

$$a + x = b$$

is always solvable in F *for* x.

[1] Note that in the sense of this definition the sum c is itself an element of F.

[2] We shall always use the equality symbol in the sense that elements set equal are identical.

It is well known that these laws are satisfied in the case of addition of real numbers. We wish to clarify their meaning and to deduce some consequences from them. Since we can associate a sum with any two elements of F, we can also add any finite number of elements. Let $a_1, a_2, \ldots, a_n$ be arbitrary elements of F. We first determine the sum $a_1 + a_2$, then the sum of the elements $(a_1 + a_2)$ and a_3, next the sum of $((a_1 + a_2) + a_3)$ and a_4, etc., until all n elements have been added. But we can carry out such a successive addition of the n elements in many different ways. We could for example begin with the last element and form, in succession,

$$a_{n-1} + a_n,\quad a_{n-2} + (a_{n-1} + a_n),\quad a_{n-3} + (a_{n-2} + (a_{n-1} + a_n)),$$

etc. Offhand, it is by no means certain that the various ways of adding the n elements necessarily yield the same results. This however is guaranteed by rules 1 and 2. First, let us consider 2. It informs us that when adding the elements a, b, c, parentheses are superfluous. For as long as we do not change the order of the elements, there are only two ways of adding the three elements; namely, we may first form the sum $(b + c)$ and then $a + (b + c)$, or we may first add a to b and then form $(a + b) + c$. Axiom 2, however, states that both are the same element. From this the same result follows easily for any finite set of elements. We proceed to prove this by mathematical induction. Thus we assume as proved that, for less than n elements, the result of addition is independent of the manner of insertion of parentheses as long as one does not change the order of the summands. We must then show that this result follows for n elements. We may assume that $n \geqq 4$.

If we wish to add n elements $a_1, a_2, \ldots, a_n$ *without altering their order,* we must first add two adjacent elements, i.e. replace them by their sum. In the sequence of $n - 1$ elements thus obtained, we must once again replace two adjacent elements by their sum, etc. The last step of this process will consist of adding two elements A and B where, say, A is the sum of certain p elements a_i $(1 \leqq p \leqq n - 1)$, while B is a sum of the remaining $n - p$ elements. But since the order of the elements was to remain unchanged, and since only adjacent elements were to have been added, one of A, B, say A, is a sum of the first p elements $a_1, a_2, \ldots, a_p$ while B is then the sum of the remaining $n - p$ elements $a_{p+1}, \ldots, a_n$. A, B are sums of less than n elements, and so by induction hypothesis their values are independent of the method of parenthesization employed in each. The sum of $a_1, a_2, \ldots, a_n$ is therefore equal to the sum

$$(1) \qquad A+B = (a_1+a_2+\cdots+a_p)+(a_{p+1}+a_{p+2}+\cdots+a_n).$$

These observations show that no matter how we form sums of the n elements $a_1, a_2, \ldots, a_n$, the result is of the form (1). By induction hypothesis, the values of the partial sums A and B are independent of the method of parenthesization used for each. Thus there are *at most* as many different results as there are different decompositions of the form (1). But there are exactly $n-1$ possibilities, since p, the number of summands of A, can take on the values $1, 2, \ldots, n-1$. We denote by S_p the sum

$$(2) \qquad S_p = (a_1+a_2+\cdots+a_p)+(a_{p+1}+a_{p+2}+\cdots+a_n).$$

If we can show further that all these elements $S_1, S_2, \ldots, S_{n-1}$ are equal to one another, then the desired conclusion would immediately follow. In order to verify the equality of the S_i it suffices to show that any two consecutive elements S_p and S_{p+1} are equal. For, we will then have $S_1 = S_2 = S_3 = \cdots = S_{n-1}$. Thus let us compare (2) with the sum

$$(3) \quad S_{p+1} = (a_1+a_2+\cdots+a_p+a_{p+1})+(a_{p+2}+a_{p+3}+\cdots+a_n).$$

Since S_p and S_{p+1} are terms of the sequence $S_1, S_2, \ldots, S_{n-1}$, we have $1 \leqq p < p+1 \leqq n-1$. Therefore the first summand of (3) is a sum of less than n elements, and is thus by induction hypothesis independent of any parenthesization. We may therefore parenthesize at will any partial sums within this summand. Since $p+1 \geqq 2$, we therefore have, say,

$$(4) \qquad a_1+a_2+\cdots+a_{p+1} = (a_1+a_2+\cdots+a_p)+a_{p+1}.$$

Thus we have

$$S_{p+1} = ((a_1+a_2+\cdots+a_p)+a_{p+1})+(a_{p+2}+\cdots+a_n).$$

One may consider the expression on the right as the sum of the three elements

$$(a_1+a_2+\cdots+a_p),\ a_{p+1},\ (a_{p+2}+a_{p+3}+\cdots+a_n).$$

For the sum of three elements, however, the associative holds as an axiom. Using this fact, we obtain

$$S_{p+1} = (a_1 + a_2 + \cdots + a_p) + (a_{p+1} + (a_{p+2} + a_{p+3} + \cdots + a_n)).$$

Now we had $p \geqq 1$, so that the second parenthesis on the right contains less than n elements. Thus by induction hypothesis, we have

$$a_{p+1} + (a_{p+2} + a_{p+3} + \cdots + a_n) = (a_{p+1} + a_{p+2} + \cdots + a_n).$$

Hence finally, we have

$$S_{p+1} = (a_1 + a_2 + \cdots + a_p) + (a_{p+1} + a_{p+2} + a_{p+3} + \cdots + a_n) = S_p,$$

as was to be proved.

Until now we have had to leave the order of the summands in the sum

$$a_1 + a_2 + \ldots + a_n$$

unchanged. But from Axiom 1, the commutative law, the fact that the summands of a sum may be arbitrarily interchanged without changing its value follows easily. As we have just shown, we may introduce or remove parentheses quite arbitrarily in the sum. Hence we may write, say,

$$(5) \quad a_1 + a_2 + \cdots + a_n = (a_1 + a_2 + \cdots + a_{p-1}) + (a_p + a_{p+1}) + (a_{p+2} + \cdots + a_n).$$

However by the commutative law, $a_p + a_{p+1} = a_{p+1} + a_p$. Thus, by (5),

$$\begin{aligned} a_1 + a_2 + \cdots + a_p + a_{p+1} + \cdots + a_n \\ &= (a_1 + a_2 + \cdots + a_{p-1}) + (a_{p+1} + a_p) + (a_{p+2} + \cdots + a_n) \\ &= a_1 + a_2 + \cdots + a_{p-1} + a_{p+1} + a_p + a_{p+2} + \cdots + a_n. \end{aligned}$$

But this means that we may interchange any pair of consecutive summands. It then follows directly that we may arbitrarily interchange summands without changing the value of the sum. For, one may bring each summand into any preassigned position by successive interchanges with adjacent summands. If we wish the summands a_i to appear in the order $a_{\nu_1}, a_{\nu_2}, \cdots, a_{\nu_n}$, we first bring a_{ν_1} into the first place, and then keeping it fixed, bring a_{ν_2} into the second place, etc. As the value of the sum remains unchanged by each single operation, the desired result follows.

We shall now draw some consequences from the above and from Axiom 3. Axiom 3, the reversibility of addition, states that if a and b are arbitrary elements of the set F, then there exists *at least* one element x of F which satisfies the equation $a + x = b$. F was assumed non-empty. Thus we can choose some definite element c of F which will remain fixed in what follows. We then solve the equation

$$c + x = c. \tag{6}$$

By Axiom 3, there is certainly an x in F which satisfies this equation. Single out any one solution of (6), and denote it by 0. For we shall soon see that this element plays the same role in F as zero does in the domain of real numbers. In fact we assert that if a is an *arbitrary* element of F, then we have

$$a + 0 = a. \tag{7}$$

In order to prove this, we determine an element y of F which satisfies the equation

$$c + y = a. \tag{8}$$

The element 0 was a solution of (6). Hence,

$$c + 0 = c. \tag{9}$$

If we add y to both sides of this equation and use the associative law we have

$$(y + c) + 0 = y + c.$$

By (8), this yields

$$a + 0 = a,$$

so that (7) is proved. Of course, the commutative law and (7) yield

$$0 + a = a.$$

Now, we further show that there is only one 0 in F, i.e. only one element which satisfies (7) for all a. For if $0'$ were a second such element, then the equation $a + 0' = a$ would also hold. Setting $a = 0$ in this, we obtain

$$0 + 0' = 0. \tag{10}$$

On the other hand, replacing a by $0'$ in (7), we obtain

(11) $$0' + 0 = 0'.$$

Since the commutative law yields $0 + 0' = 0' + 0$, (10) and (11) give

$$0 = 0'.$$

Thus, the element $0'$ must necessarily be identical with the element 0; *hence there exists only one zero element.*

Axiom 3 postulates the solvability of the equation $a + x = b$, but says nothing concerning the number of solutions. We can now settle this question as follows: *Such an equation always has only one solution.* We first prove this for equations of the form

(12) $$a + x = 0.$$

Let, say, x and x' be two elements which satisfy (12) for a given a. Then $a + x = a + x' = 0$. Thus,

(13) $$x + a + x' = x + (a + x') = x + 0 = x$$

and, on the other hand,

(14) $$x + a + x' = (x + a) + x' = 0 + x' = x'.$$

Comparison of (13) and (14) yields $x = x'$, which proves that (12) can have only one solution. We denote this uniquely determined solution of (12) by $(-a)$, so that for every a we have

(15) $$a + (-a) = 0.$$

We next consider the general equation

(16) $$a + x = b.$$

Upon adding $(-a)$ to both sides of this equation, and using (15), it follows that

(17) $$x = b + (-a).$$

Thus if x is a solution of (16), then x must necessarily be equal to the element $b + (-a)$. But this proves that (16) can have only one solution, namely $b + (-a)$.

We shall write $b - a$ as an abbreviation for $b + (-a)$. Furthermore, it follows from the definition of $-a$ that the equation

$$(-a) + x = 0$$

has $-(-a)$ as a solution. On the other hand, by (15) we have

$$(-a) + a = 0.$$

By the uniqueness of the solution, it then follows that

$$-(-a) = a. \tag{18}$$

Among the fundamental rules of calculation for real numbers, we must include the rules of multiplication. If algebraic laws analogous to those for the real numbers are to hold for the domain F, we must have defined, besides addition, a second operation which will play the role of *multiplication*. We therefore assume that there is a rule which assigns to every pair a, b of elements of F a uniquely determined element c of F, which is then called the *product* of a and b. As usual, we write $c = a \cdot b$. This multiplication must satisfy certain properties. Namely, we must have the following:

II. Laws of Multiplication

1. *The commutative law*:

$$a \cdot b = b \cdot a.$$

2. *The associative law*:

$$a \cdot (b \cdot c) = (a \cdot b) \cdot c.$$

3. *The reversibility of multiplication; i.e. the equation*

$$a \cdot x = b$$

is always solvable in F *for* x, *if* $a \neq 0$.

4. *The existence of an element different from* 0.

From the first two laws we infer, just as we did in the case of addition, that a product $a_1 \cdot a_2 \cdot \ldots \cdot a_n$ of n factors $a_1, a_2, \ldots, a_n$ is independent of both the parenthesization and the order of the factors.

The existence of a unity follows in a manner analogous to that of the zero element for addition. Thus, we have the existence of an element in F which plays the same role as 1 does for the real numbers.

By 4., there is in F an element unequal to 0. Let c be any such element. Axiom 3 states that the equation

$$c \cdot x = c \tag{19}$$

is satisfied by at least one x in F. We denote some definite solution of (19) by 1, so that

$$c \cdot 1 = c. \tag{20}$$

Now let x be a definite solution of the equation

$$c \cdot x = a, \tag{21}$$

where a is an arbitrary element of F. Then, by (20), (21), and the commutative and associative laws, we obtain

$$a \cdot 1 = (c \cdot x) \cdot 1 = x \cdot (c \cdot 1) = x \cdot c = a.$$

Therefore, for every element a of F we have

$$a \cdot 1 = a, \qquad 1 \cdot a = a. \tag{22}$$

Moreover, there is only a single element 1 in F which has the property (22). For, if $1'$ were another such element then for every a of F,

$$a \cdot 1' = a. \tag{23}$$

If we set $a = 1'$ in (22) and $a = 1$ in (23), we have

$$1' \cdot 1 = 1',$$
$$1 \cdot 1' = 1.$$

Thus by the commutative law, we have

$$1 = 1'.$$

Thus there is no element other than 1 which satisfies (22). *There exists only one unity*, namely 1.

Now we may show that if $a \neq 0$, the equation

$$a \cdot x = 1 \tag{24}$$

has only one solution. For if we assume that, in addition to the solution x, there exists a solution x', we easily show that $x = x'$. In any case, we must have

$$(25) \qquad a \cdot x' = 1.$$

Upon application of (22), (24), and (25), we have

$$x \cdot a \cdot x' = (x \cdot a) \cdot x' = 1 \cdot x' = x',$$

$$x \cdot a \cdot x' = x \cdot (a \cdot x') = x \cdot 1 = x.$$

Hence,

$$x = x'.$$

We denote the uniquely determined solution of (24) by $\frac{1}{a}$ or by a^{-1}. Thus we have for $a \neq 0$ that

$$(26) \qquad a \cdot \frac{1}{a} = a \cdot a^{-1} = 1.$$

Furthermore, if we consider the general equation

$$(27) \qquad a \cdot x = b$$

where $a \neq 0$, multiplying it by $\frac{1}{a}$ and using (26), we have

$$(28) \qquad x = b \cdot \frac{1}{a}.$$

That is: Every solution of (27) necessarily has the form (28). Therefore *this equation has only one solution.* We write $\frac{b}{a}$ as an abbreviation of $b \cdot \frac{1}{a}$.

The final axiom which must hold in F is the so-called *distributive law.* It connects the two operations of addition and multiplication.

III. Distributive Law

If a, b, c are any three elements of F, *then*

$$a \cdot (b + c) = a \cdot b + a \cdot c.$$

In words: To multiply a sum by an element, it is merely necessary to multiply each summand by this element. Of course, by the commutative law,

$$(b + c) \cdot a = b \cdot a + b \cdot c.$$

By the distributive law we have at once that, for every a in F,

$$(29) \qquad a \cdot 0 = 0.$$

For by (7), $0 + 0 = 0$, so that

$$(30) \qquad a \cdot (0 + 0) = a \cdot 0.$$

By the distributive law with $b = c = 0$,

$$(31) \qquad a \cdot (0 + 0) = a \cdot 0 + a \cdot 0.$$

Comparison of (30) and (31) yields

$$a \cdot 0 + a \cdot 0 = a \cdot 0.$$

Adding the element $-(a \cdot 0)$ to both sides of the equation, and employing (15), we have at once the desired relation (29).

We may now verify that *the elements* 1 *and* 0 *must be different.* (This was by no means clear at the outset.) For if $1 = 0$, then $a \cdot 1 = 0$ for any a. But by (22), we have for $a \neq 0$ that $a \cdot 1 = a \neq 0$.

If

$$a \cdot b = 0,$$

then at least one of the factors a, b must vanish. For since $0 = a \cdot 0$, we have at once

$$a \cdot b = a \cdot 0.$$

Now if $a \neq 0$, this last relation, upon multiplication by $\frac{1}{a}$, yields

$$b = 0,$$

which proves our assertion.

We may also deduce the *laws of signs*. By (15) and (29), and using the distributive laws,

$$a \cdot 0 = a \cdot (b + (-b)) = a \cdot b + a \cdot (-b) = 0.$$

But we have already agreed to denote the unique solution of the equation $(a \cdot b) + x = 0$ by $-(a \cdot b)$. Thus,

$$(32) \qquad a \cdot (-b) = -(a \cdot b).$$

In the same way we deduce that $(-a)b = -(a \cdot b)$. Now, two applications of (32) yield

$$(-a) \cdot (-b) = -(a \cdot (-b)) = -(-(a \cdot b)).$$

By (18), then,

$$(-a)\cdot(-b)=a\cdot b. \tag{33}$$

By the distributive law,

$$a\cdot(b+(-c)) = a\cdot b+a\cdot(-c) = a\cdot b+(-a\cdot c).$$

But we had agreed to write $d-f$ as an abbreviation for $d+(-f)$. Thus the distributive law also holds in the form

$$a\cdot(b-c)=a\cdot b-a\cdot c. \tag{34}$$

We have defined fractions by the convention that $\frac{b}{a}$ $(a \neq 0)$ is to denote the solution of the equation $a\cdot x=b$. In particular, taking $a=1$, we have $\frac{b}{1}=b$. Now we shall see that the usual *rules for calculating with fractions* hold for our domain F. If the equation $a\cdot x=b$ with $a\neq 0$ holds, then so does the equation $(c\cdot a)\cdot x=c\cdot b$ obtained by multiplying the original equation by an arbitrary element c. If $c\neq 0$, then also $c\cdot a\neq 0$, and so from $(c\cdot a)\cdot x=c\cdot b$ we may infer that

$$x=\frac{c\cdot b}{c\cdot a}.$$

On the other hand, since $a\cdot x=b$, we have

$$x=\frac{b}{a}.$$

Comparison of the last two equations yields

$$\frac{c\cdot b}{c\cdot a}=\frac{b}{a}. \tag{35}$$

That is: A non-zero factor c which is common to the numerator and denominator may be *cancelled*. In other words: We may introduce a new non-zero factor c into both numerator and denominator. If

$$\alpha=\frac{a}{b},\quad \beta=\frac{c}{d}, \qquad (b\neq 0,\ d\neq 0) \tag{36}$$

then by the definition of fraction,

$$b\cdot\alpha=a,\quad d\cdot\beta=c.$$

If we multiply these two equations, we have

$$(b \cdot d) \cdot (\alpha \cdot \beta) = a \cdot c.$$

But, since $b \cdot d \neq 0$, this means that

$$\alpha \cdot \beta = \frac{a \cdot c}{b \cdot d}.$$

Comparison of this equation with (36) yields

$$\left(\frac{a}{b}\right) \cdot \left(\frac{c}{d}\right) = \frac{a \cdot c}{b \cdot d}. \tag{37}$$

This is the *rule of multiplication of fractions.* In order to see how to *divide fractions,* we set

$$x = \frac{\frac{a}{b}}{\frac{c}{d}}. \tag{38}$$

This expression is meaningful only if both b and $\frac{c}{d}$ are unequal to 0. $\frac{c}{d}$ is itself meaningful and different from 0 only if c and d are both different from 0. Then (38) states that

$$\frac{c}{d} \cdot x = \frac{a}{b}.$$

If we multiply this equation by the non-zero element $(b \cdot d)$, and use the cancellation rule that we have just proved, we obtain $(b \cdot c) \cdot x = a \cdot d$. Since $b \cdot c \neq 0$, this yields $x = \dfrac{a \cdot d}{b \cdot c}$, or by (38),

$$\frac{\frac{a}{b}}{\frac{c}{d}} = \frac{a \cdot d}{b \cdot c}. \tag{39}$$

Addition and *subtraction of fractions* may also be carried out as usual. Again, let

$$\alpha = \frac{a}{b}, \quad \beta = \frac{c}{d}, \qquad (b \neq 0, \ d \neq 0) \tag{40}$$

i.e. $b \cdot \alpha = a$, $d \cdot \beta = c$. Thus

$$(b \cdot d) \cdot \alpha = a \cdot d, \qquad (b \cdot d) \cdot \beta = c \cdot b.$$

If we add or subtract these two equations and apply the distributive law we obtain, respectively,

$$b \cdot d \cdot (\alpha + \beta) = a \cdot d + c \cdot b, \qquad b \cdot d \cdot (\alpha - \beta) = a \cdot d - c \cdot b.$$

But, since $b \cdot d \neq 0$, this yields

$$\alpha + \beta = \frac{a \cdot d + c \cdot b}{b \cdot d}, \qquad \alpha - \beta = \frac{a \cdot d - c \cdot b}{b \cdot d},$$

or by (40),

$$(41) \qquad \frac{a}{b} + \frac{c}{d} = \frac{a \cdot d + c \cdot b}{b \cdot d}, \qquad \frac{a}{b} - \frac{c}{d} = \frac{a \cdot d - c \cdot b}{b \cdot d}.$$

These are the familiar rules.

Obviously, we may use the summation sign in dealing with sums of several elements of F. All rules of calculation with the summation sign follow word for word as before.

Further, we may now also define *powers* with integral exponents. We shall denote the product $a \cdot a \cdot \ldots \cdot a$, where a occurs as a factor n times, by a^n. Similarly the product $a^{-1} \cdot a^{-1} \cdot \ldots \cdot a^{-1}$, where $a^{-1} = \frac{1}{a}$ occurs as a factor n times, will be denoted by a^{-n}. Finally, as usual, we set $a^0 = 1$ for every a. We may then deduce the usual laws for calculation with exponents and powers exactly as for real numbers.

Finally, the element $1 + 1$ is sometimes denoted by 2, the element $1 + 1 + 1$ by 3, and in general, the element $1 + 1 + \ldots + 1$, where 1 occurs n times as a summand, by n. The elements 2, 3, 4, ... thus defined need not all be different from 0. In fact, we shall soon be introduced to an example for which this is not the case. Applying the distributive law to the sum $a + a + \ldots + a$, where a occurs as a summand n times, we have

$$(42) \qquad a + a + \cdots + a = (1 + 1 + \cdots + 1) \cdot a = n \cdot a.$$

We have now derived all those rules of calculation which form the basis of the theorems on linear equations and determinants. In fact, all the algebraic results of § 6, § 8, and § 9 hold in our domain F. It is necessary to modify the proofs of these results only very slightly in order to see this. In the derivations, essential use was made of the concept of vector. But in setting up this concept, we made use of rules of calculation which need not hold in our domain—viz. where we made use of the symbols $<$ and $>$. However, the use of these notions may easily be avoided. We simply make the following definitions:

An ordered n-tuple $\{a_1, a_2, \ldots, a_n\}$ of elements of the domain F is called a *vector over* F, or simply a *vector*.[3] The elements $a_1, a_2, \ldots, a_n$ are called the *components* of the vector, and specifically a_1 is called the *first*, a_2 the *second*, ..., a_n the *n-th* component. Two vectors $\{a_1, a_2, a_3, \ldots, a_n\}$ and $\{b_1, b_2, \ldots, b_n\}$ are considered *equal* if and only if $a_1 = b_1$, $a_1 = b_2$, $\ldots$, $a_n = b_n$. As before, we shall denote vectors by lower case German letters.

This definition of the concept of vector is independent of the relations "less than" and "greater than." It only remains to show how to define *addition* of vectors and *multiplication of a vector by an element of* F. As before, we define the *sum* of the two vectors $\mathfrak{a} = \{a_1, a_2, \cdots, a_n\}$ and $\mathfrak{b} = \{b_1, b_2, \cdots, b_n\}$ to be the vector $\{a_1 + b_1, a_2 + b_2, \ldots, a_n + b_n\}$. Thus,

$$\mathfrak{a} + \mathfrak{b} = \{a_1 + b_1, a_2 + b_2, \cdots, a_n + b_n\}.$$

Further, if c is any element of F, we define the *product* $c \cdot \mathfrak{a}$ to be the vector $\{c \cdot a_1, c \cdot a_2, \cdots, c \cdot a_n\}$ so that

$$\mathfrak{a} \cdot c = c \cdot \mathfrak{a} = c \cdot \{a_1, a_2, \cdots, a_n\} = \{c \cdot a_1, c \cdot a_2, \cdots, c \cdot a_n\}.$$

Finally, the *scalar product* $\mathfrak{a} \cdot \mathfrak{b}$ of two vectors is defined as the element $a_1 \cdot b_1 + a_2 \cdot b_2 + \cdots + a_n \cdot b_n$ of F. Thus,

$$\mathfrak{a} \cdot \mathfrak{b} = \sum_{i=1}^{n} a_i \cdot b_i.$$

We may then verify all the rules of calculation for vectors word for word as in § 2. Then, as in § 3, linear dependence and independence of vectors may be defined as follows:

The vectors $\mathfrak{a}_1, \mathfrak{a}_2, \cdots, \mathfrak{a}_n$ are called *linearly dependent* (*with respect to* F) if there exist n elements $\lambda_1, \lambda_2, \cdots, \lambda_n$ of F, not all zero, such that

$$\lambda_1 \mathfrak{a}_1 + \lambda_2 \mathfrak{a}_2 + \cdots + \lambda_n \mathfrak{a}_n = 0.$$

[3] Since we are here concerned only with algebraic results, we could have written vectors with ordinary parentheses, since there is no danger of confusion with points of R_n. Nevertheless we employ braces for the sake of uniformity (and with a view to footnote 5 of this section).

If a set of vectors is not linearly dependent, it is said to be *linearly independent.*

All the results of § 3, § 4, and § 6, and those of determinant theory will then follow just as before.[4] The reader may easily convince himself of this.[5]

Thus we see that every domain F of the sort under consideration displays, in its algebraic structure, a far-reaching similarity to the domain of real numbers. Because of their importance, we shall reserve a special name for such domains. We call them fields. *By a* ***field,*** *we mean a non-empty set of elements in which two operations, called addition and multiplication, are defined satisfying the axioms of* I, II, *and* III. In every field, then, all results which can be derived from the axioms of I, II, and III hold. We have just learned about some of the more elementary of these.

A first example of a field is given by the set of all real numbers, in which the axioms of I, II, and III, the so-called *field axioms*, are certainly satisfied. On the other hand, the totality of all negative real numbers does not form a field under ordinary addition and multiplication. The sum of two negative real numbers, to be sure, is always a negative real number. But the product of two negative real numbers is a positive real number, contrary to the definition of a field, which

---

[4] We consider all of the theorems of sections 8 and 9, with the exception of those which concern volumes of n-dimensional parallelotopes, as belonging to the theory of determinants. In general, it is meaningless to speak of the absolute value of an element in our abstractly defined domain F.

[5] As in the case of vectors over F, we may also speak of points over F. We define

An ordered n-tuple $(a_1, a_2, \cdots, a_n)$ *of elements of* F *is called an (n-dimensional) point over* F. *The totality of all such n-tuples is called n-dimensional space over* F.

Then we must distinguish between two kinds of n-tuples over F, the points $(a_1, a_2, \cdots, a_n)$ and the vectors $\{a_1, a_2, \cdots, a_n\}$. If $P = (x_1, x_2, \cdots, x_n)$, and $Q = (y_1, y_2, \cdots, y_n)$ are two points over F, then we also speak of the vector which *carries P to Q*. We denote it by $\overrightarrow{PQ}$, and define it by the equation

$$\overrightarrow{PQ} = \{y_1 - x_1, y_2 - x_2, \cdots, y_n - x_n\}.$$

For any three points P, Q, R of the n-dimensional space over F we have $\overrightarrow{PQ} + \overrightarrow{QR} = \overrightarrow{PR}$. If $\overrightarrow{PQ} = \mathfrak{a} = \{a_1, a_2, \cdots, a_n\}$, then we say that *the point Q results from P upon the application of the vector* $\mathfrak{a}$. Thus by the application of a vector $\mathfrak{a} = \{a_1, a_2, \cdots, a_n\}$ to the point $P = (x_1, x_2, \cdots, x_n)$, is meant the transformation from the point P to the point $Q = (x_1 + a_1, x_2 + a_2, \cdots, x_n + a_n)$. Now, we may define linear spaces exactly as in § 5 by the following definition:

A p-dimensional linear space results from a point $P = (x_1, x_2, \cdots . x_n)$ *upon applying to it all the vectors of a p-dimensional vector space.*

The theorems stated at the close of § 6 continue to hold for these linear spaces. These include, in particular, Theorem 9, which is but a restatement in another terminology of Theorem 6 of the same section. Of course, the n-dimensional spaces so obtained can not be intuitively interpreted even for $n = 1, 2, 3$.

requires that multiplication can be carried out *in the field itself*. The set of all positive real numbers is also not a field. Here, to be sure, both the sum and the product of two elements of the set are also in the set. But Axiom I, 3 is not satisfied, since for example, there is no positive real number which satisfies the equation $7 + x = 3$.

The totality of all rational numbers constitutes a field. For, the sum and product of two rational numbers are also rational numbers. Moreover, every equation of the form $a + x = b$, with a and b rational, has a rational solution. The same holds for $a \cdot x = b$ if $a \neq 0$. The remaining field axioms are certainly satisfied since they hold for arbitrary real numbers.

Is there a field with only a finite number of elements? Every field certainly must contain at least two elements, the 0 and the 1. There is in fact actually a field which contains only two elements. We shall symbolize the concept "even number" by E and the concept "odd number" by O. We may define an addition and a multiplication of these symbols in a manner consistent with their meaning, as follows:

$$O + O = E, \qquad O + E = O, \qquad E + E = E.$$
$$O \cdot O = O, \qquad O \cdot E = E, \qquad E \cdot E = E.$$

We may easily verify that the set of these two elements does form a field under this addition and multiplication. E is the zero, O the unity. The element $O + O$, i.e. $1 + 1$, which we have agreed to denote by 2, is here equal to E, i.e. 0. Such fields which have only a finite number of elements are called *finite fields*.

Exercises

1. Which of the following domains are fields?
   i. the domain of all numbers of the form $a + b \cdot \sqrt{2}$, where a and b are arbitrary rational numbers,
   ii. the domain of all integers (i.e. positive, negative, and zero),
   iii. the domain of those rational numbers which, when written in lowest terms (i.e. written so that numerator and denominator have no common factor), have a denominator which is divisible by 10.
   iv. the set of all finite decimal fractions in which the second place after the period is 0.

2. Let n be a positive integer. Then by the *residue class* F_a *mod* n, we mean the set of all integers which leave the remainder a upon division by n. There are therefore n residue classes mod n, namely $F_0, F_1, \ldots, F_{n-1}$. We may define an *addition* and a *multiplication* among them as follows: If α is any number in the residue class F_a, and β any number in F_b, and if F_c is the residue class to which $\alpha + \beta$ belongs,

F_d that to which $\alpha \cdot \beta$ belongs, then F_c is called the *sum*, and F_d the *product*, of F_a and F_b. In symbols: $F_c = F_a + F_b$, $F_d = F_a \cdot F_b$. Show that F_c and F_d are uniquely determined by F_a and F_b, i.e. that they are independent of the choice of the numbers α from F_a and β from F_b. Investigate further whether or not the n residue classes mod n form a field, and specifically, 1. in case n is a prime number, and 2. in case n is the product of several primes.

§ 15. Polynomials over a Field

Let there be given an arbitrary field F, which will serve as the basis for the following considerations. In general, we shall denote its elements by lower case italic letters from the beginning of the alphabet: a, b, c, etc. Aside from the elements of the field, we consider another element x as given. We call x a *variable* or better an *indeterminate.* For we have no desire to give this element x any definite meaning; rather we think of it as a pure symbol.[1] In particular, x is not meant to be an element of F. It is rather some new element whose relation to F we must now set up. The elements of F, as contrasted with the variable x, will be referred to as *constants*. The symbols $x^0, x^1 = x, x^2, x^3, x^4, \cdots$ are called *powers of* x and are to be multiplied according to the usual rule $x^m \cdot x^n = x^{m+n}$. We further set $x^0 = 1$, where 1 is the unit of F. Then we form expressions of the following form:

$$(1) \qquad a_0 + a_1 x + a_2 x^2 + \cdots + a_n x^n,$$

where $a_0, a_1, a_2, \cdots, a_n$ are elements of the field F. We call such an expression a ***polynomial*** *in* x and the quantities $a_0, a_1, \ldots, a_n$ its *coefficients.* A polynomial is itself a pure symbol. However, we reserve the right to replace the variable x by some definite quantity, say by an element of F. By such a substitution, the expression (1) yields a calculable value.

We consider two polynomials to be *equal* if and only if one has the same coefficient of x^k as has the other, for every k. By the *degree* of a polynomial, we mean the exponent of the highest power of x whose coefficient $\neq 0$. Thus if $a_n \neq 0$ in (1), then n is the degree of (1). The degree of a polynomial may be arbitrarily large. If in (1),

[1] We have already seen that the validity of mathematical results can be entirely independent of the meaning of the mathematical objects. Thus, if we do not give the symbols any definite meaning, mathematical propositions may be thought of as consisting of *formal* logical relationships. Abstraction from the meaning of the objects under consideration is of definite importance, since it gives a much greater generality to the results.

$a_1 = a_2 = \ldots = a_n = 0$, then the polynomial consists of the constant a_0 alone and no longer contains the variable x. Thus we consider the non-zero constants as polynomials of degree zero. No degree is assigned to the polynomial 0, the *vanishing polynomial.* The totality of all polynomials with coefficients in F is called the ***polynomial domain in one variable*** *over* F, and will be denoted by $F[x]$. We use notations such as $f(x)$, $g(x)$, $h(x)$, etc. for polynomials of $F[x]$.

We define an *addition* and a *multiplication* between polynomials of $F[x]$. Indeed, we shall so define these operations that results will remain valid upon substitution of an element of F for x. Let

$$f(x) = a_0 + a_1 x + \cdots + a_n x^n = \sum_{i=0}^{n} a_i x^i$$

and

$$g(x) = b_0 + b_1 x + \cdots + b_m x^m = \sum_{i=0}^{m} b_i x^i$$

be two polynomials, and let, say, $n \geqq m$. Then the *sum* of $f(x)$ and $g(x)$ is defined by

$$(2) \qquad f(x) + g(x) = (a_0 + b_0) + (a_1 + b_1) x + (a_2 + b_2) x^2 + \cdots + (a_m + b_m) x^m + a_{m+1} x^{m+1} + \cdots + a_n x^n.$$

Thus all the powers of x of the same degree are collected into a single term. We see that equation (2) remains valid upon replacement of x by an element of F. By the *product* of $f(x)$ and $g(x)$ we mean the polynomial

$$(3) \qquad f(x) \cdot g(x) = \sum_{i=1}^{n} \sum_{k=1}^{m} a_i b_k x^{i+k} = a_0 b_0 + (a_1 b_0 + a_0 b_1) x + (a_2 b_0 + a_1 b_1 + a_0 b_2) x^2 + \cdots + a_n b_m x^{n+m}.$$

Thus we multiply out as usual using the distributive law and collecting terms which have the same power of x. (3) also remains valid upon replacing x by an element of F. If a_n and b_m are both $\neq 0$, then also $a_n \cdot b_m \neq 0$, and so by (3), *the degree of a product is equal to the sum of the degrees of the factors.* This result holds for a product of any number of non-vanishing factors.

We may easily verify that addition and multiplication are commutative and associative and are related by the distributive law. Also, addition is always reversible, i.e. we can subtract. In fact, to calculate $f(x) - g(x)$, it is merely necessary to replace b_i by $-b_i$ everywhere in (2). On the other hand, multiplication is not in general reversible in the polynomial domain $F[x]$. From (3) it follows (since b_m and a_n not equal to 0 implies $a_n \cdot b_m$ not equal to 0) that the product of two non-vanishing polynomials is non-vanishing. Or, *if a product of polynomials vanishes, then at least one of the factors is equal to* 0.

If the relation $f(x) = g(x) \cdot h(x)$ subsists between $f(x)$ and $g(x)$ for some polynomial $h(x)$, then $f(x)$ is called a *multiple* of $g(x)$ and is said to be *divisible* by $g(x)$. $g(x)$ is called a *divisor* of $f(x)$. In this case we also write $g(x) = \dfrac{f(x)}{h(x)}$. If $f(x)$ does not vanish then the degree of every divisor of $f(x)$ is at most that of $f(x)$ itself.

Now we shall develop a *division algorithm* which will enable us to divide one polynomial by another obtaining a *remainder*. Again, let $f(x) = \sum_{i=0}^{n} a_i x^i$ and $g(x) = \sum_{i=0}^{m} b_i x^i$, $a_n \neq 0$, $b_m \neq 0$ be two polynomials. Let us form a multiple $h(x) \cdot g(x)$ of $g(x)$ and consider the difference

$$r(x) = f(x) - h(x) \cdot g(x) \tag{4}$$

where $h(x)$ is so chosen that the degree of $r(x)$ is as small as possible. We can show that either $r(x)$ is 0, or its degree is smaller than that of $g(x)$. In order to see this, we first show that if $n \geqq m$, then by subtracting a suitable multiple[2] of $g(x)$ from $f(x)$, the degree will be reduced. This multiple of $g(x)$ is $\dfrac{a_n}{b_m} x^{n-m} g(x)$. For,

$$\begin{aligned} f(x) - \frac{a_n}{b_m} x^{n-m} g(x) &= a_n x^n + a_{n-1} x^{n-1} + \cdots + a_0 \\ &\quad - \left(a_n x^n + \frac{a_n}{b_m} b_{m-1} x^{n-1} + \cdots + \frac{a_n}{b_m} b_0 x^{n-m}\right) \\ &= \left(a_{n-1} - \frac{a_n}{b_m} b_{m-1}\right) x^{n-1} + \cdots, \end{aligned} \tag{5}$$

and this is a polynomial of degree $(n-1)$ at most unless it is identically 0. If the degree of the difference (5) is still $\geqq m$, we iterate the process and reduce the degree further by subtracting a suitable multiple of $g(x)$ from the polynomial (5). We continue in this manner until we finally reach a polynomial which is identically 0 or of degree $< m$. Let us suppose that in carrying out this process we have succes-

[2] If $n < m$, we have only to set $h(x) = 0$ to obtain in $r(x)$ a polynomial of degree less than m.

sively subtracted the multiples $h_1(x) \cdot g(x)$, $h_2(x) \cdot g(x)$, ..., $h_n(x) \cdot g(x)$. Then the final result will be the polynomial

$$r(x) = f(x) - [h_1(x) + h_2(x) + \cdots + h_k(x)]\, g(x),$$

and so a polynomial of the form (4) which is either of degree $< m$, or is identically 0.

This polynomial $r(x)$ of the form (4) is moreover *uniquely determined* by the condition that its degree be $< m$. For let us suppose that $r^*(x)$ is another such polynomial, obtained by subtracting the multiple $h^*(x) \cdot g(x)$ from $f(x)$. Then we would have

$$r^*(x) = f(x) - h^*(x)\, g(x),$$

and, upon subtraction from equation (4), we would obtain

$$r(x) - r^*(x) = [h^*(x) - h(x)]\, g(x).$$

Thus, $r(x) - r^*(x)$ is a multiple of $g(x)$. On the other hand, we know that $r(x)$ and $r^*(x)$ are each either identically 0, or have a smaller degree than $g(x)$, so that the same holds for $r(x) - r^*(x)$. If now $r(x) - r^*(x)$ were $\neq 0$, then its degree would be smaller than that of one of its own divisors $g(x)$. Since this is impossible, we must have $r(x) = r^*(x)$. Thus the uniqueness of the remainder $r(x)$ has been proved. In particular, the remainder must vanish if $f(x)$ is divisible by $g(x)$.

We now shall discuss a very important concept which is similar to that of a vector space, namely the concept of an *ideal*. *By an* ***ideal*** *in the polynomial domain* $\text{F}[x]$, *we shall mean a non-empty set of polynomials which satisfies the following two conditions*:

1. *If $f(x)$ belongs to the set, then so does every multiple $h(x) \cdot f(x)$ (where $h(x)$ is an arbitrary polynomial of* $\text{F}[x]$).
2. *If $f(x)$ and $g(x)$ belong to the set, then so does $f(x) + g(x)$.*

Ideals will ordinarily be denoted by small German letters. As a first example of an ideal, we may take the polynomial domain $\text{F}[x]$ itself. The set whose only element is 0 is also an ideal, the so-called *null ideal*. Another example is the set of all polynomials which are divisible by some fixed polynomial $f(x)$. Such an ideal, which consists of all multiples of a fixed polynomial, is called a **principal ideal.** The following fundamental theorem may now be proved:

THEOREM 1. *Every ideal of the polynomial domain* $F[x]$ *is a principal ideal.*

The theorem is certainly true for the null ideal, which consists of one element only. Furthermore, if $\mathfrak{a}$ is an ideal which contains elements other than 0, then it contains a polynomial of least degree. Let, say, $g(x) \neq 0$ be such a polynomial. (0, of course, has no degree.) We assert that every polynomial of the ideal $\mathfrak{a}$ is a multiple of $g(x)$. For, let $f(x)$ be an arbitrary polynomial of $\mathfrak{a}$, and let us determine the remainder upon division of $f(x)$ by $g(x)$. We thus obtain a polynomial

$$r(x) = f(x) - h(x) \cdot g(x)$$

which is either identically 0 or has a smaller degree than $g(x)$ has. Since $g(x)$ is in $\mathfrak{a}$, so is its multiple $-h(x) \cdot g(x)$ by property 1. Finally, by property 2., the sum $f(x) - h(x)g(x)$, i.e. $r(x)$, is in $\mathfrak{a}$. However since $g(x)$ is a polynomial of least degree in $\mathfrak{a}$, $r(x)$ must of necessity be identically 0. Thus:

$$f(x) = h(x) \cdot g(x).$$

Thus every polynomial of the ideal is a multiple of $g(x)$. By property 1., $\mathfrak{a}$ therefore consists precisely of all the multiples of $g(x)$, i.e. $\mathfrak{a}$ is a principal ideal.

The polynomial $g(x)$ of least degree in $\mathfrak{a}$ is uniquely determined up to a constant factor. For if $g^*(x)$ is another polynomial in $\mathfrak{a}$ of this least degree, then, by what has been proved, $g^*(x)$ is a multiple of $g(x)$:

$$g^*(x) = h(x) \cdot g(x).$$

Since the degree of $g^*(x)$ is equal to the sum of the degrees of $h(x)$ and $g(x)$, and since the degree of $g^*(x)$ is equal to that of $g(x)$, the degree of $h(x)$ must be 0. That is, $h(x)$ is a non-zero constant. If we further require that $g(x)$ be that polynomial of least degree in $\mathfrak{a}$ whose leading coefficient (i.e. the coefficient of the highest power of x that actually occurs in $g(x)$) is equal to 1, then $g(x)$ is uniquely determined. For there can not exist two distinct polynomials which differ only by a constant factor and both of which have leading coefficient 1.

Let $g_1(x), g_2(x), \ldots, g_n(x)$ be any given sequence of polynomials. Every polynomial which is a divisor of each of the $g_i(x)$ is called a *common divisor* of $g_1(x), g_2(x), \ldots, g_n(x)$. Let us examine the set of all such common divisors. If all the $g_i(x)$ are identically 0, then every polynomial is a common divisor, since 0 is divisible by every polynomial (because of $0 \cdot f(x) = 0$). We thus need only discuss the case when not all the $g_i(x)$ vanish identically. Now consider the set of all polynomials of the form

$$h_1(x)\,g_1(x) + h_2(x)\,g_2(x) + \cdots + h_n(x)\,g_n(x), \tag{6}$$

where $h_1(x), h_2(x), \ldots, h_n(x)$ may be any arbitrary polynomials. By analogy with vector algebra, we may call polynomials of the form (6) *linear combinations* of the fixed polynomials $g_1(x), g_2(x), \ldots, g_n(x)$. The set of all polynomials of the form (6), which we will denote by $\mathfrak{a}$, is an ideal. It is clear that this set is non-empty. Moreover, if we multiply (6) by an arbitrary polynomial $f(x)$, we obtain

$$[f(x) \cdot h_1(x)]\,g_1(x) + [f(x) \cdot h_2(x)]\,g_2(x) + \cdots + [f(x) \cdot h_n(x)]\,g_n(x),$$

which is itself a polynomial of the form (6). Finally, if we add two polynomials of $\mathfrak{a}$, say (6) and the polynomial

$$h_1^*(x)\,g_1(x) + h_2^*(x)\,g_2(x) + \cdots + h_n^*(x)\,g_n(x),$$

we once again obtain a polynomial of $\mathfrak{a}$, namely

$$[h_1(x) + h_1^*(x)]\,g_1(x) + [h_2(x) + h_2^*(x)]\,g_2(x) + \cdots + [h_n(x) + h_n^*(x)]\,g_n(x).$$

But every ideal in $F[x]$ is a principal ideal. The ideal $\mathfrak{a}$ therefore consists of all the multiples of some fixed polynomial $d(x)$. This $d(x)$ is $\neq 0$, since $\mathfrak{a}$ contains polynomials $\neq 0$. If we set $h_i(x) = 1$ for some fixed i, and set all other $h_k(x) = 0$, then (6) is none other than $g_i(x)$. Thus each of the polynomials $g_1(x), g_2(x), \ldots, g_n(x)$ belong to $\mathfrak{a}$, and is therefore a multiple of $d(x)$. That is, $d(x)$ is a common divisor of $g_1(x), g_2(x), \ldots, g_n(x)$. On the other hand, $d(x)$ is also a polynomial of $\mathfrak{a}$ and so must have the form (6), say

$$d(x) = f_1(x)\,g_1(x) + f_2(x)\,g_2(x) + \cdots + f_n(x)\,g_n(x). \tag{7}$$

From this, it follows that *every* common divisor of $g_1(x)$, $g_2(x)$, $\ldots$, $g_n(x)$ is also a divisor of $d(x)$. For let $t(x)$ be such a common divisor. Then for every i, an equation of the form $g_i(x) = k_i(x) \cdot t(x)$ must hold. If we substitute this in (7) and factor out $t(x)$, we obtain

$$d(x) = [f_1(x)\,k_1(x) + f_2(x)\,k_2(x) + \cdots + f_n(x)\,k_n(x)]\,t(x).$$

But we then have that $t(x)$ is a divisor of $d(x)$. Because of this property, we call $d(x)$ the *greatest common divisor* of the polynomials $g_1(x), g_2(x), \ldots, g_n(x)$.

The greatest common divisor thus obtained is uniquely determined up to a constant factor. For let, say, $d^*(x)$ be another such greatest common divisor of $g_1(x), g_2(x), \ldots, g_n(x)$. As such $d^*(x)$ must be divisible by every common divisor of the polynomials $g_i(x)$, hence in particular by $d(x)$. Conversely, $d^*(x)$, as a common divisor of the polynomials $g_i(x)$, must be a divisor of $d(x)$. Thus the following two equations hold:

$$(8) \qquad d(x) = m(x)\,d^*(x), \qquad d^*(x) = r(x)\,d(x).$$

If we substitute the value of $d^*(x)$ from the second equation into the first, we have that $m(x)r(x) = 1$.[3] Thus the degree of both $m(x)$ and $r(x)$ must be equal to 0 so that they are both constants. If we require that the leading coefficient of the greatest common divisor $d(x)$ be 1, then $d(x)$ is once again completely determined. We combine these results in the following theorem:

THEOREM 2. *If not all of the polynomials $g_1(x), g_2(x), \ldots, g_n(x)$ vanish identically, then they have a greatest common divisor $d(x)$ with the following characteristic properties: $d(x)$ is a common divisor of the polynomials $g_i(x)$ and a multiple of every other common divisor of these polynomials. $d(x)$ is uniquely determined up to a constant factor, and it may be written in the form* (7) *as a linear combination of the polynomials $g_i(x)$.*

If the greatest common divisor of the polynomials $g_i(x)$ is a constant, the polynomials are said to be *relatively prime*. In this case they have no common factor of a degree higher than 0.

Since for non-zero constants we have $f(x) = c\left[\frac{1}{c}f(x)\right]$, such constants are divisors of every polynomial. Furthermore, the polynomial $f(x)$ is always divisible by $c \cdot f(x)$ where $c \neq 0$. The constants $\neq 0$ and the polynomials $c \cdot f(x)$ are called *improper divisors* of $f(x)$. On the other hand, a divisor of $f(x)$ whose degree is less than that of $f(x)$ but greater than 0, is called a *proper divisor* of $f(x)$. A polynomial whose degree is positive and which has no proper divisor is

[3] For since $d(x) \neq 0$, we infer from $d(x)[1 - m(x)r(x)] = 0$ that

$$1 - m(x)r(x) = 0.$$

called an **irreducible polynomial.** For example, every polynomial of the first degree is irreducible. For, every divisor of such a polynomial must have degree 0 or 1, and so must be improper. Irreducible polynomials play an especially important role in algebra, analogous in fact to that of the prime numbers in the theory of numbers. Polynomials which have proper divisors are called *reducible.*

An immediate consequence of the definition of irreducible polynomials is the following: *Two irreducible polynomials are either relatively prime, or they differ only by a constant factor.* For if $p(x)$ and $q(x)$ are any two irreducible polynomials, then every non-constant common divisor of them must simultaneously be of the forms $c \cdot p(x)$ and $d \cdot q(x)$ where c and d are constants $\neq 0$. Thus $c \cdot p(x) = d \cdot q(x)$; i.e. if they have a non-constant common divisor then $p(x)$ and $q(x)$ differ only by a constant factor.

We now prove

THEOREM 3. *If a product $f(x) \cdot g(x)$ of two polynomials is divisible by an irreducible polynomial $p(x)$, then at least one of the factors $f(x)$, $g(x)$ is divisible by $p(x)$.*

For suppose that $f(x)$ is not divisible by $p(x)$. We must show that $g(x)$ is divisible by $p(x)$. Since $p(x)$ is irreducible, $f(x)$ and $p(x)$ can have only constant factors in common, and so are relatively prime. Their greatest common divisor is thus a constant, and since it is only determined up to a constant factor, we may take it as equal to 1. Thus, by (7), 1 can be represented as a linear combination of $f(x)$ and $p(x)$, say

$$1 = h_1(x) f(x) + h_2(x) p(x).$$

We multiply this equation by $g(x)$:

$$g(x) = h_1(x) f(x) g(x) + h_2(x) g(x) p(x). \tag{9}$$

Now $f(x) g(x)$ was assumed to be divisible by $p(x)$, say $f(x) g(x) = k(x) p(x)$. Substituting this in (9) gives

$$g(x) = [h_1(x) k(x) + h_2(x) g(x)] p(x),$$

i.e. $g(x)$ is divisible by $p(x)$ as was to be proven.

From Theorem 3, using mathematical induction, we easily obtain

THEOREM 4. *If the product of a finite number of polynomials is divisible by some irreducible polynomial, then at least one of the factors must also be divisible by that polynomial.*

For let $p(x)$ denote the irreducible polynomial and let the product which is assumed divisible by $p(x)$ be denoted by

$$f_1(x) \cdot f_2(x) \cdot \ldots \cdot f_n(x).$$

For $n = 2$, Theorem 4 has already been proved. We thus assume that $n > 2$ and suppose the theorem to have been proved for products of $n - 1$ factors. We further suppose that, say, the factors $f_1(x)$, $f_2(x)$, $\ldots, f_{n-1}(x)$ are not divisible by $p(x)$. Then by the induction hypothesis, the product $f_1(x) \cdot f_2(x) \cdot \ldots \cdot f_{n-1}(x)$ is also not divisible by $p(x)$. The product $f_1(x) \cdot f_2(x) \cdot \ldots \cdot f_n(x)$ can be considered as the product of the two factors $f_1(x) \cdot f_2(x) \cdot \ldots \cdot f_{n-1}(x)$ and $f_n(x)$, of which the first is certainly not divisible by $p(x)$. Thus by Theorem 3, $f_n(x)$ must be divisible by $p(x)$, and so Theorem 4 has been proved.

Every polynomial can be decomposed into irreducible factors, i.e. every polynomial may be written as the product of irreducible polynomials. For if a given polynomial $f(x)$ with degree > 0 is not irreducible, then we can write it as the product of two of its proper divisors, each with degree less than that of $f(x)$. If these factors are still not irreducible, we continue the process, decomposing them in turn into proper divisors of their own. This process can not be continued indefinitely since the degrees of the factors decrease at every step. But this process can only come to an end when $f(x)$ has been represented as the product of irreducible polynomials.

Now it is quite conceivable that in carrying out this factorization process in two different ways, we obtain two entirely different decompositions of $f(x)$ into irreducible factors. Actually, however, this cannot happen. No matter how we perform the factorization process, the end result will always be essentially the same. There is essenially only one factorization of $f(x)$ into irreducible factors. The restriction "essentially" is to be interpreted as meaning that the irreducible factors are uniquely determined up to their order and up to constant factors $\neq 0$.

In order to prove this result, we introduce an abbreviation as follows. If two polynomials $f(x)$ and $g(x)$ differ only by a constant factor, so that $f(x) = c \cdot g(x)$ with c in F, then we shall say that $f(x)$ and $g(x)$

are *associated* and write $f(x) \sim g(x)$. We shall now prove the theorem on unique factorization of polynomials into irreducible factors, in the following form:

THEOREM 5. *If a polynomial $f(x)$ whose degree is > 0 is representable as a product of irreducible factors in two ways, say*

$$f(x) = p_1(x) \cdot p_2(x) \cdot \ldots \cdot p_r(x), \tag{10}$$

$$f(x) = q_1(x) \cdot q_2(x) \cdot \ldots \cdot q_s(x), \tag{11}$$

then both these factorizations contain the same number of factors, i.e. $r = s$, and if the numbering of the polynomials $q_i(x)$ (or the $p_i(x)$) is suitably chosen, then we have

$$p_1(x) \sim q_1(x),\ p_2(x) \sim q_2(x),\ \cdots,\ p_r(x) \sim q_r(x).$$

We prove Theorem 5 by induction on the degree of $f(x)$. Polynomials of the first degree are irreducible, and so for them the theorem is trivial since $f(x) = f(x)$ is the only possible decomposition into irreducible factors. The theorem holds for an irreducible polynomial $f(x)$ even if its degree is greater than 1. Thus we may assume that $f(x)$ is reducible and that it has degree $n > 1$. We now take as our induction hypothesis, that the theorem is proved for all polynomials whose degree is less than n.

Then let (10) and (11) be two decompositions of $f(x)$ into irreducible factors. Since $f(x)$ is reducible, there must be at least two factors in each decomposition. Thus both $p_1(x)$ and the product

$$g(x) = p_2(x) \cdot p_3(x) \cdot \ldots \cdot p_r(x) \tag{12}$$

are proper divisors of $f(x)$, that is, the degree of $g(x)$ is less than n but greater than 0. Now $p_1(x)$, as a factor of $f(x)$, is by Theorem 4 a divisor of at least one of the factors $q_i(x)$ in (11). By a change in the numbering (if necessary) we may take this factor to be $q_1(x)$. But since $q_1(x)$ is irreducible this is only possible if $q_1(x) = c \cdot p_1(x)$ where c is a constant $\neq 0$. If we substitute this in (11) and subtract (11) from (10), we have

$$p_1(x)\,[p_2(x)\,p_3(x) \cdots p_r(x) - c \cdot q_2(x)\,q_3(x) \cdots q_s(x)] = 0. \tag{13}$$

Since $p_1(x)$ is certainly $\neq 0$, the second factor in (13) (i.e. the one in brackets) must vanish. Comparing with (12), we have

$$g(x) = q_2^*(x) \cdot q_3(x) \cdot \ldots \cdot q_s(x), \tag{14}$$

where we have set $c \cdot q_2(x) = q_2^*(x)$; $q_2^*(x)$ is also an irreducible polynomial. Now (12) and (14) are two decompositions of $g(x)$ into irreducible factors. Since $g(x)$ is of degree less than n, Theorem 5 holds for $g(x)$ by induction hypothesis. Thus the number of factors must be the same in (12) and (14). This is only possible if $r = s$. Moreover, with suitable numbering of the factors of (12), we must have

$$p_2(x) \sim q_2^*(x),\ p_3(x) \sim q_3(x),\ \cdots,\ p_r(x) \sim q_r(x).$$

If we recall that $q_2^*(x) \sim q_2(x)$, then we have also

$$p_2(x) \sim q_2(x).$$

But we had $q_1(x) = c \cdot p_1(x)$, so that

$$p_1(x) \sim q_1(x).$$

Thus the proof of Theorem 5 is complete.

In the decomposition of a polynomial into irreducible factors, the factors were determined only up to constant factors. This ambiguity may be removed by requiring that all polynomials which occur have leading coefficient 1. This we may always bring about. To this end, we first imagine the given polynomial $f(x)$ normalized[4] so that its leading coefficient is 1. Then let

$$f(x) = p_1(x) \cdot p_2(x) \cdot \ldots \cdot p_r(x) \tag{15}$$

be an arbitrary decomposition of $f(x)$ into irreducible factors. Let a_i be the leading coefficient of $p_i(x)$ $(i = 1, 2, \ldots, r)$. Since $f(x)$ has leading coefficient 1, we have by definition (3) of multiplication that

$$1 = a_1 \cdot a_2 \cdot \ldots \cdot a_r. \tag{16}$$

Now we multiply (15) by $\dfrac{1}{a_1 \cdot a_2 \cdot \ldots \cdot a_r}$, which by (16) is equal to 1. This yields, if we associate each factor $\dfrac{1}{a_i}$ with the corresponding $p_i(x)$,

$$f(x) = \frac{p_1(x)}{a_1} \cdot \frac{p_2(x)}{a_2} \cdot \ldots \cdot \frac{p_r(x)}{a_r}. \tag{17}$$

---

[4] By "normalized," we mean here "multiplied by a suitable constant."

But now $\frac{p_i(x)}{a_i}$ is a polynomial with leading coefficient 1, so that (17) provides the desired decomposition in which each irreducible factor has leading coefficient 1. Since two polynomials with the same leading coefficient which are associated are always identical, this decomposition is completely determined up to the order of the factors. Thus we have the following extension of Theorem 5:

THEOREM 6. *If $f(x)$ is a polynomial with leading coefficient* 1 *and with degree* > 0, *then $f(x)$ may be written as a product of irreducible factors, each with leading coefficient* 1. *This decomposition of $f(x)$ is uniquely determined up to the order of the factors.*

Theorems 5 and 6 are analogous to the representation of an integer as a product of primes. In the decomposition (15), there may of course occur several factors which are associated; these become equal factors in (17). If we combine identical factors, we may also write the decomposition of $f(x)$ into irreducible factors, which for simplicity we may assume to have leading coefficients 1, in the form

$$f(x) = (q_1(x))^{a_1} \cdot (q_2(x))^{a_2} \cdot \ldots \cdot (q_t(x))^{a_t}. \tag{18}$$

Here we require that for $i \neq k$, $q_i(x) \neq q_k(x)$. The exponent a_i indicates the number of times the factor $q_i(x)$ appears in the factorization of $f(x)$.[5]

For every irreducible factor $p(x)$ of $f(x)$, we can (using the factorization algorithm discussed above) obtain a factorization of $f(x)$ into irreducible factors one of which is $p(x)$ itself. By the uniqueness of this decomposition, we see that, up to associated ones, $f(x)$ can have no irreducible factors except those that actually occur in the decomposition of $f(x)$. In an analogous manner we see that every divisor of $f(x)$ (or at least an associated one) may be obtained from the factorization of $f(x)$ by combining several of the irreducible factors. If we assume that $f(x)$ has, say, the factorization (18), then every factor of $f(x)$ has the form (ignoring constant factors)

$$(q_1(x))^{k_1} \cdot (q_2(x))^{k_2} \cdot \ldots \cdot (q_t(x))^{k_t}, \tag{19}$$

where $0 \leq k_i \leq a_i$. Thus, if we let each exponent k_i in (19) run through the values 0, 1, 2, ..., a_i independently of the others, we

[5] Of course, by the symbol $(q(x))^a$ (with positive integral a) we understand the product $q(x) \cdot q(x) \cdot \ldots \cdot q(x)$ in which the factor $q(x)$ occurs a times. We shall also employ the symbol $(q(x))^0$, and we define $(q(x))^0 = 1$ for $q(x) \neq 0$.

obtain all factors of $f(x)$, up to associated ones. In all, there are $(a_1+1)\cdot(a_2+1)\cdot\ldots\cdot(a_t+1)$ divisors.

The greatest common divisor of several polynomials $f_1(x)$, $f_2(x)$, $\ldots, f_n(x)$ is obtained by combining all those irreducible factors which occur simultaneously in the decompositions of all the polynomials $f_i(x)$. The power to which each irreducible factor is to be taken is the highest for which it is a factor of all the $f_i(x)$. If $f(x)$ and $g(x)$ are two relatively prime polynomials, then their factorizations into irreducible components have no factors in common.

We shall next investigate the *common multiples* of two non-vanishing polynomials $f(x)$ and $g(x)$, i.e. polynomials which are divisible by both $f(x)$ and $g(x)$. We denote the set of all common multiples of $f(x)$ and $g(x)$ by $\mathfrak{a}$. Clearly, $\mathfrak{a}$ is an ideal. By Theorem 1 there is a polynomial $m(x)$ in $\mathfrak{a}$ which is a divisor of every polynomial in $\mathfrak{a}$; $m(x)$ is called the *least common multiple* of $f(x)$ and $g(x)$. Since $f(x)\cdot g(x)$ certainly belongs to $\mathfrak{a}$, an equation of the form

$$f(x)\cdot g(x)=m(x)\cdot d(x) \tag{20}$$

must hold.

Since $m(x)$ is a polynomial of $\mathfrak{a}$, it is a common multiple of $f(x)$ and $g(x)$. Thus we have, say,

$$m(x)=f(x)\cdot h_1(x), \quad m(x)=g(x)\cdot h_2(x). \tag{21}$$

By (20) and (21), we have

$$f(x)\cdot g(x)=f(x)\cdot h_1(x)\cdot d(x)$$

or

$$f(x)\,[g(x)-h_1(x)\,d(x)]=0.$$

Since we assumed $f(x)\neq 0$, we obtain

$$g(x)=h_1(x)\cdot d(x). \tag{22}$$

Similarly (20) and (21) yield $f(x)\cdot g(x)=g(x)\cdot h_2(x)\cdot d(x)$, so that

$$f(x)=h_2(x)\cdot d(x). \tag{23}$$

Equations (22) and (23) show that $d(x)$ is a common divisor of $f(x)$ and $g(x)$.

By its definition $m(x)$ is a polynomial of least degree in $\mathfrak{a}$. On the other hand, if $d'(x)$ is the greatest common divisor of $f(x)$ and $g(x)$, then the polynomial

$$\frac{f(x)\cdot g(x)}{d'(x)}=\left(\frac{f(x)}{d'(x)}\right)\cdot g(x)=f(x)\cdot\left(\frac{g(x)}{d'(x)}\right)$$

is a common multiple of $f(x)$ and $g(x)$ and so belongs to $\mathfrak{a}$. Now if $d(x)$ were a proper divisor of $d'(x)$, then the polynomial $\frac{f(x)\cdot g(x)}{d'(x)}$ would have a lower degree than has $m(x)=\frac{f(x)\cdot g(x)}{d(x)}$. This is impossible. Thus $d(x)$ itself is the greatest common divisor of $f(x)$ and $g(x)$. Thus we have proved

THEOREM 7. *If $d(x)$ is the greatest common divisor of $f(x)$ and $g(x)$, then the polynomial $\frac{f(x)\cdot g(x)}{d(x)}$ is the least common multiple of $f(x)$ and $g(x)$.*

Of course the least common multiple is also determined only up to a constant factor. We could also have deduced Theorem 7 from the theorem of unique factorization of a polynomial into irreducible factors.

Exercises

1. If $d(x)$ is the greatest common divisor of the polynomials $f_1(x), f_2(x), \cdots, f_n(x)$, then its coefficients may be calculated from those of the $f_i(x)$ by the rational operations, i.e. by using only the four elementary operations of arithmetic (division algorithm).

2. Let F be the field of real numbers, F$[x]$ the polynomial domain in one variable x with coefficients in F. Determine which of the following sets of polynomials of F$[x]$ are ideals:

   i. the set of all polynomials whose leading coefficients are even numbers;
   ii. the set of of all polynomials whose constant term (i.e. the term a_0 in (1)) vanishes;
   iii. the set of all polynomials whose linear term (i.e. the term a_1x in (1)) vanishes;
   iv. the set of all polynomials whose degree is an even number;
   v. the set of all polynomials with degree $\geqq 10$;
   vi. the set of all common multiples of n fixed polynomials

$$f_1(x),\ f_2(x),\ \cdots,\ f_n(x).$$

3. In polynomial domains of *several* variables with coefficients in some given field, it is by no means true that all ideals are principal ideals. We define a polynomial domain in two variables as follows: We begin with a field F and consider two different variables x and y. We then construct all expressions of the form

$\sum_{i=0}^{n}\sum_{k=0}^{m} a_{ik}x^i y^k$ with coefficients a_{ik} in F. These are the polynomials in the two variables x and y. We consider the set of all linear combinations of the polynomials x and y, that is, all polynomials of the form

$$x \cdot h_1(x, y) + y \cdot h_2(x, y),$$

where $h_1(x, y)$ and $h_2(x, y)$ may be replaced by any polynomials. This set is an ideal. However, as the reader should convince himself, it is not a principal ideal.

4. A polynomial which is reducible in some polynomial domain may well be irreducible in some other polynomial domain. Let R be the field of all rational numbers, F the field of all real numbers, x an indeterminate. We construct the polynomial domains R$[x]$ and F$[x]$. The first of these is contained in the second. The polynomial $x^2 - 3$ is reducible in F$[x]$; in fact, $x^2 - 3 = (x + \sqrt{3})(x - \sqrt{3})$. However, the factors which occur in this expression are not polynomials of R$[x]$. It thus follows, from the uniqueness of such factorizations, that $x^2 - 3$ is irreducible in R$[x]$. Write the following polynomials as products of their irreducible factors, both as polynomials of R$[x]$ and as polynomials of F$[x]$:

$$x^2 - 2x - 3, \quad x^2 + 4x - 1, \quad 3x^2 + 1,$$
$$x^3 - 2x^2 - 2x + 1, \quad x^3 - 19x + 30,$$
$$x^4 - 3x^3 + x^2 - 3x + 1.$$

Construct a polynomial of R$[x]$ of the third degree which is irreducible in R$[x]$.

5. Compute the greatest common divisor and the least common multiple of the polynomials

$$x^3 - 3x^2 - 3x + 1 \quad \text{and} \quad 4x^4 - 21x^3 + 28x^2 - 21x + 4.$$

§ 16. The Field of Complex Numbers

The fact that not every quadratic equation is solvable in the domain of real numbers is, no doubt, familiar. In order to be able to solve all quadratic equations, it is necessary to extend the field of real numbers to obtain the field of complex numbers. We shall now carry out this extension rigorously.

For the sake of clarity in what follows, we introduce a new notation for real numbers. Namely, we shall denote the real number a by the somewhat more complicated symbol $(a, 0)$. Thus the sum of the real numbers $(a, 0)$ and $(b, 0)$ is then written $(a + b, 0)$; the product, $(a \cdot b, 0)$. We now consider all symbols of the form (a, b) where a and b are two arbitrary real numbers; that is, we consider all ordered pairs of real numbers. The totality of all these elements (a, b) will be denoted by F. F thus contains as a subset all elements $(a, 0)$, i.e. the real numbers. We shall define an operation of addition for elements of F. By the *sum* of the elements (a_1, b_1) and (a_2, b_2), we shall mean the element

$(a_1 + a_2,\ b_1 + b_2)$. Thus

$$(a_1, b_1) + (a_2, b_2) = (a_1 + a_2,\ b_1 + b_2). \tag{1}$$

This is ordinary vector addition. However, the *product* of (a_1, b_1) and (a_2, b_2) is defined by

$$(a_1, b_1) \cdot (a_2, b_2) = (a_1 a_2 - b_1 b_2,\ a_1 b_2 + a_2 b_1). \tag{2}$$

For the real numbers in F, these definitions give the usual results. In order to see this, we need only set $b_1 = b_2 = 0$ in (1) and (2).

F *is a field*. The axioms of addition are certainly satisfied by (1) since we know that they hold for vector addition. The element (0, 0), i.e. the zero of the real numbers, plays the role of the 0. Multiplication is commutative, since the right-hand side of (2) remains unchanged upon the interchange of the indices 1 and 2.

If we multiply the right-hand side of (2) by the element (a_3, b_3), then by the definition of multiplication, we obtain

$$\begin{aligned}(a_1 a_2 a_3 - a_1 b_2 b_3 - a_2 b_1 b_3 - a_3 b_1 b_2,\\ a_1 a_2 b_3 + a_1 a_3 b_2 + a_2 a_3 b_1 - b_1 b_2 b_3).\end{aligned} \tag{3}$$

But we obtain the same result if we first form the product

$$(a_2, b_2) \cdot (a_3, b_3)$$

and then multiply it by (a_1, b_1). This is also clear from the fact that (3) remains unchanged under an arbitrary permutation of the digits 1, 2, 3. This proves the associative law. It need hardly be mentioned that there do exist elements $\neq 0$ in F. It remains only to prove that the equation

$$(a_1, b_1) \cdot x = (a_2, b_2) \tag{4}$$

is solvable if $(a_1, b_1) \neq (0, 0)$. But given this last condition, it is clear that $a_1^2 + b_1^2 \neq 0$ and hence

$$x = \left(\frac{a_1 a_2 + b_1 b_2}{a_1^2 + b_1^2},\ \frac{a_1 b_2 - a_2 b_1}{a_1^2 + b_1^2}\right) \tag{5}$$

is a well-determined element of F. If we substitute (5) in (4) and multiply out, we see that (5) satisfies equation (4). Finally, the distributive law may be verified by a simple calculation. Thus all of the field properties are satisfied. We call F the **field of complex numbers.** It contains as a subset (or *subfield*) the field of real numbers.

We wish to convince ourselves that every quadratic equation is solvable in F. As we well know, it suffices to show that the equation $x^2 + 1 = 0$ is solvable. This equation may now be written in the form

$$x^2 + (1, 0) = (0, 0). \tag{6}$$

But we easily see by (2) that $(0, 1)^2 = (-1, 0)$, so that $x = (0, 1)$ is a solution of (6); and $(0, -1)$ is also a solution. The element $(0, 1)$ is called the *imaginary unit*, and is denoted by i. If (a, b) is an arbitrary element of F, then $(a, b) = (a, 0) + (b, 0) \cdot i$, as is easily veri-ed. If we return to our original notation for the real numbers $(a, 0)$, $(b, 0)$ which occur here, writing a and b for them respectively, we have

$$(a, b) = a + bi. \tag{7}$$

Thus we have obtained the usual notation for complex numbers.[1] If we write the elements of F which occur in (1) and (2) in the form (7), then we obtain the usual rules for addition and multiplication of complex numbers:

$$(a_1 + b_1 i) + (a_2 + b_2 i) = (a_1 + a_2) + (b_1 + b_2) \cdot i \tag{8}$$

$$(a_1 + b_1 i) \cdot (a_2 + b_2 i) = (a_1 a_2 - b_1 b_2) + (a_1 b_2 + a_2 b_1) \cdot i. \tag{9}$$

We have seen, in (6), that $i^2 = -1$. Of course, the results on linear equations and determinants, which hold in any field, also hold in the field of complex numbers. Referring to (7), we call a the *real part*, or the *real component*, b the *imaginary part* or the *imaginary component* of the number $a + bi$.

Our introduction of complex numbers suggests a geometric interpretation. We have defined complex numbers as ordered pairs of real numbers. From this it is clear that there is a one-to-one correspondence between the complex numbers and the vectors of the plane. In fact, to the complex number $\alpha = a + ib$, corresponds the vector $\{a, b\}$, and conversely. Addition of complex numbers then corresponds to ordinary vector addition, whose interpretation is familiar from § 2. The length of the vector $\{a, b\}$ is called the *absolute value* (or the *modulus*) of the complex number $\alpha = a + ib$, and is denoted by $|\alpha|$. Thus,

$$|a + ib| = |\alpha| = +\sqrt{a^2 + b^2}. \tag{10}$$

[1] Of course, we could have introduced the field of complex numbers as the totality of symbols $a + bi$ in the first place. The detour by way of number pairs seems preferable, however, for pedagogical reasons.

If $\alpha = a + ib$, $\beta = c + id$ are two complex numbers, and if $\{a, b\}$, $\{c, d\}$ are their corresponding vectors, then we can find three points P, Q, R in the plane such that

$$\overrightarrow{PQ} = \{a, b\}, \quad \overrightarrow{QR} = \{c, d\}$$

Then

$$\overrightarrow{PR} = \{a + c, b + d\}$$

is the vector which corresponds to the complex number $\alpha + \beta$. Now by § 7, we have the triangle inequality

$$\overline{PR} \leqq \overline{PQ} + \overline{QR}. \tag{11}$$

Since, however, $\overline{PR}$, $\overline{PQ}$, and $\overline{QR}$ are nothing but the absolute values of the numbers $\alpha + \beta, \alpha, \beta$ respectively, (11) yields

$$|\alpha + \beta| \leqq |\alpha| + |\beta|. \tag{12}$$

The most intuitive geometric interpretation of complex numbers lies in their relation to points of the plane. We set up a Cartesian coordinate system in the plane and assign to the complex number $a + ib$ the point (a, b) of the plane. This is clearly a one-to-one correspondence. Multiplication of complex numbers then takes on a simple geometric significance. In order to show this we introduce so-called *polar coordinates*, as follows. A point P in the plane is completely determined (Fig. 29) by its distance $r = \overline{OP}$ from the origin and the angle φ which the vector $\overrightarrow{OP}$ makes with the positive x_1-axis. By φ, we mean the angle through which the positive half-ray of the x_1-axis must be turned in the positive (i.e. counterclockwise) sense in order to make it coincide with the vector $\overrightarrow{OP}$. The positive direction.

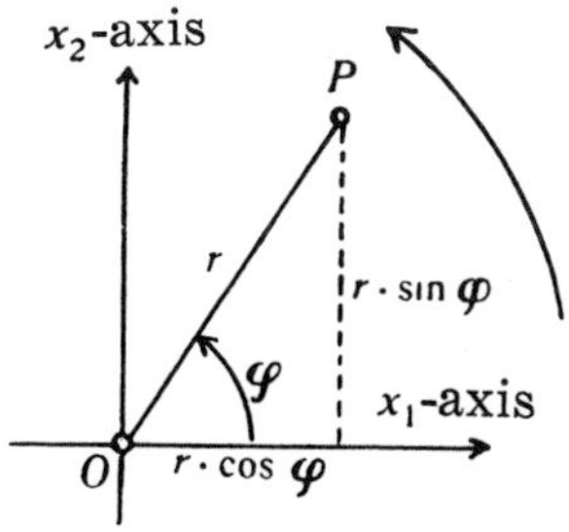

Fig. 29

is indicated by an arrow in the figure. (Cf. § 10, Exercise 4.) The angle φ is determined only up to integral multiples of 2π by these conditions. The "*radius vector*" r and the "*amplitude*" or "*argument*" φ are called the *polar coordinates* of P. The origin has radius vector 0 and a completely arbitrary amplitude.

If a, b are the coordinates of P in the Cartesian coordinate system, then

$$a = r \cdot \cos \varphi, \quad b = r \cdot \sin \varphi. \tag{13}$$

The point P represents the complex number $\alpha = a + ib$. If we observe that $r = |\alpha|$, then by (13), we have

$$\alpha = |\alpha| \cdot (\cos \varphi + i \sin \varphi). \tag{14}$$

Now if $\beta = |\beta| \cdot (\cos \psi + i \sin \psi)$ is another complex number we obtain, for the product $\alpha \cdot \beta$,

$$\begin{aligned} \alpha \cdot \beta &= |\alpha| \cdot |\beta| \cdot [\cos \varphi \cos \psi - \sin \varphi \sin \psi \\ &\qquad + i (\cos \varphi \sin \psi + \sin \varphi \cos \psi)] \\ &= |\alpha| \cdot |\beta| \cdot [\cos(\varphi + \psi) + i \sin(\varphi + \psi)]. \end{aligned} \tag{15}$$

Thus, *to multiply two complex numbers, multiply their absolute values and add their amplitudes*. The same rule then follows for products of any number of factors.

By (15), we also have that

$$|\alpha \cdot \beta| = |\alpha| \cdot |\beta|. \tag{16}$$

The absolute value of a product is equal to the product of the absolute values of the factors. It is clear that this also holds for the product of any finite number of complex numbers $\alpha_1, \alpha_2, \ldots, \alpha_n$, i.e. that we have

$$|\alpha_1 \cdot \alpha_2 \cdot \ldots \cdot \alpha_n| = |\alpha_1| \cdot |\alpha_2| \cdot \ldots \cdot |\alpha_n|.$$

In particular, if we set $\alpha_1 = \alpha_2 = \cdots = \alpha_n = \alpha$, then

$$|\alpha^n| = |\alpha|^n. \tag{17}$$

If $\gamma = \frac{\alpha}{\beta}$, then $\alpha = \beta \cdot \gamma$ so that by (16), $|\alpha| = |\beta| \cdot |\gamma|$, i.e.

$$|\gamma| = \left|\frac{\alpha}{\beta}\right| = \frac{|\alpha|}{|\beta|}. \tag{18}$$

If $\alpha = a + ib$, we call $a - ib$ the *complex conjugate of* α, and we write $\overline{\alpha} = a - ib$. (10) immediately yields

$$\alpha \overline{\alpha} = |\alpha|^2. \tag{19}$$

If furthermore $\beta = c + id$, $\overline{\beta} = c - id$, we have by an easy calculation that

$$\overline{\alpha} + \overline{\beta} = \overline{\alpha + \beta}, \quad \overline{\alpha} \cdot \overline{\beta} = \overline{\alpha \cdot \beta}. \tag{20}$$

Of course, similar results hold for more than two summands or factors. In particular, for integral n we have

$$(21) \qquad (\bar{\alpha})^n = \overline{(\alpha^n)}.$$

The conjugate of $\bar{\alpha}$ is α itself, in symbols: $\bar{\bar{\alpha}} = \alpha$.

We shall prove several theorems concerning limits and convergence of sequences in preparation for the next section. We assume that the reader has a certain familiarity with these concepts as applied to the real number system. We consider infinite sequences of complex numbers

$$(22) \qquad z_1,\ z_2,\ z_3,\ \cdots.$$

If a property is false for at most a finite number of terms of the sequence (22),[2] and true for all others, then we shall say that the property holds for *almost all* terms of (22). We call z_0 a *limit* of the sequence (22) if for every positive real number ε (usually thought of as being "small") the relation

$$(23) \qquad |z_n - z_0| < \varepsilon$$

holds for almost all n.[3] In this case we write

$$(24) \qquad \lim_{n\to\infty} z_n = z_0.$$

Naturally, a sequence need not have a limit. A sequence which has a limit is called *convergent*; one which has no limit, *divergent*.

A sequence of complex numbers cannot have more than one limit. For if z_0 is a limit of the sequence (22) and if $z_0' \neq z_0$, then $|z_0 - z_0'| = d > 0$. Now, $z_0 - z_0' = (z_0 - z_n) + (z_n - z_0')$. Thus by (12), $d \leqq |z_n - z_0| + |z_n - z_0'|$, or

$$(25) \qquad |z_n - z_0'| \geqq d - |z_n - z_0|.$$

If we set $\varepsilon = \frac{d}{2}$ in (23), then we see that for almost all n we must have $|z_n - z_0| < \frac{d}{2}$. Thus by (25), we have that $|z_n - z_0'| > \frac{d}{2}$ for

---

[2] This terminology includes the case in which the relation holds for *all* terms.

[3] Then the relation $|z_n - z_0| \geqq \varepsilon$ holds for at most a finite number of subscripts n. Thus, for $n > N$, we always have $|z_n - z_0| < \varepsilon$. Hence the definition of limit can also be put as follows:

z_0 is called the limit of the sequence (22), if with each $\varepsilon > 0$, there is associated an N such that for all $n > N$, we have $|z_n - z_0| < \varepsilon$.

almost all n. Hence no number z_0' distinct from z_0 can be a limit of the sequence (22).

We now prove

THEOREM 1. *If the sequence* (22) *has the limit* z_0, *then the sequence*

$$|z_1|, |z_2|, |z_3|, \cdots$$

is also convergent, and has in fact the limit $|z_0|$. *In symbols,*

$$\lim_{n\to\infty} |z_n| = |\lim_{n\to\infty} z_n|.$$

We must prove that, given an arbitrary $\varepsilon > 0$, it follows for almost all n that

(26) $$\big||z_n| - |z_0|\big| < \varepsilon.$$

But by (12), the equations

$$z_n = (z_n - z_0) + z_0, \quad z_0 = (z_0 - z_n) + z_n$$

yield

(27) $$|z_n| \leqq |z_n - z_0| + |z_0| \quad |z_0| \leqq |z_n - z_0| + |z_n|,$$

or

(28) $$|z_n| - |z_0| \leqq |z_n - z_0|, \quad |z_0| - |z_n| \leqq |z_n - z_0|.$$

Since $\big||z_n| - |z_0|\big|$ is one of the two numbers $|z_n| - |z_0|$, $|z_0| - |z_n|$, we have by (28) that

(29) $$\big||z_n| - |z_0|\big| \leqq |z_n - z_0|.$$

But since $|z_n - z_0| < \varepsilon$ for almost all n, the inequality (26) must also hold for almost all n. This proves our result.

Now, let there be given a second sequence

(30) $$z_1', z_2', z_3', \cdots.$$

We assume that both (22) and (30) are convergent, so that, say, $\lim_{n\to\infty} z_n = z_0$, $\lim_{n\to\infty} z_n' = z_0'$. Then we have

THEOREM 2. *The sequence*

$$z_1 + z_1', z_2 + z_2', z_3 + z_3', \cdots$$

is convergent, and its limit is $z_0 + z_0'$. *Thus,*

$$\lim_{n\to\infty} (z_n + z_n') = \lim_{n\to\infty} z_n + \lim_{n\to\infty} z_n'.$$

We must prove that for each $\varepsilon > 0$, the relation

$$(31)\qquad |(z_n + z'_n) - (z_0 + z'_0)| < \varepsilon.$$

holds for almost all n. Now by (12), we have

$$(32)\qquad |z_n + z'_n - z_0 - z'_0| \leq |z_n - z_0| + |z'_n - z'_0|.$$

But there are at most a finite number of values of n for which the relation $|z_n - z_0| \geqq \frac{\varepsilon}{2}$ holds, and similarly only a finite number of values of n for which $|z'_n - z'_0| \geqq \frac{\varepsilon}{2}$. Hence, the relation

$$|z_n - z_0| + |z'_n - z'_0| \geqq \varepsilon$$

holds for at most a finite number of values of n, i.e. we have for almost all n that

$$|z_n - z_0| + |z'_n - z'_0| < \varepsilon.$$

Using (32), we see from this that (31) also holds for almost all n.

Under the hypotheses of Theorem 2, we further have

THEOREM 3. *The sequence*

$$z_1 \cdot z'_1,\ z_2 \cdot z'_2,\ z_3 \cdot z_3,\ \cdots$$

is convergent, and its limit is $z_0 \cdot z_0'$. *Thus,*

$$\lim_{n\to\infty} (z_n \cdot z'_n) = (\lim_{n\to\infty} z_n)\ (\lim_{n\to\infty} z'_n).$$

Clearly, by Theorem 1 the sequences $|z_1|, |z_2|, |z_3|, \cdots$ and $|z'_1|, |z'_2|, |z'_3|, \cdots$ are also convergent. Now every convergent sequence of real numbers is *bounded*, i.e. there is some positive real number m which is greater than $|z_i|$ for $i = 0, 1, 2, \ldots$ and a positive real number m' which is greater than $|z_i'|$ for $i = 0, 1, 2, \ldots$.[4]

---

[4] By (23) and (27), for almost all n and a fixed $\varepsilon > 0$, we have

$$|z_n| \leq |z_0| + \varepsilon.$$

Among the finite number of absolute values $|z_n|$ (if any) which do not satisfy this inequality, there is a largest which we call m_0. Then, if n is greater than the larger of the two numbers m_0 and $|z_0| + \varepsilon$, then $m > |z_n|$ for all $n = 0, 1, 2, \ldots$. The existence of m' follows analogously.

Then the larger of m, m', which we shall denote by M is greater than all of the $|z_i|$ and $|z_i'|$. Now

$$z_n z_n' - z_0 z_0' = z_n(z_n' - z_0') + z_0'(z_n - z_0).$$

Hence by (12) and (16),

$$(33) \qquad \begin{aligned} |z_n z_n' - z_0 z_0'| &\leqq |z_n| \cdot |z_n' - z_0'| + |z_0'| \cdot |z_n - z_0| \\ &\leqq M(|z_n' - z_0'| + |z_n - z_0|). \end{aligned}$$

Since $M > 0$, for each $\varepsilon > 0$ the relations $|z_n' - z_0'| < \frac{\varepsilon}{2M}$ and $|z_n - z_0| < \frac{\varepsilon}{2M}$ both hold for almost all n. Thus by (33), we must have for almost all n that

$$|z_n z_n' - z_0 z_0'| < \varepsilon.$$

This proves Theorem 3.

If all the terms of the sequence $z_1', z_2', z_3', \cdots$ are equal to a fixed complex number c, then obviously $\lim_{n \to \infty} z_n' = c$. The sequence $z_1 \cdot z_1', z_2 \cdot z_2', z_3 \cdot z_3', \cdots$ is then the sequence $c \cdot z_1, c \cdot z_2, c \cdot z_3, \cdots$ and its limit, by Theorem 3, is $c \cdot z_0$. We express this result as follows:

THEOREM 4. *If each of the terms of a convergent sequence z_1, z_2, $z_3, \ldots$ is multiplied by some constant c, then the resulting sequence is also convergent and we have*

$$\lim_{n \to \infty} (c \cdot z_n) = c \cdot \lim_{n \to \infty} z_n.$$

The convergence of sequences of complex numbers may be reduced to that of sequences of real numbers. Once again consider the sequence (22). Let $z_n = a_n + ib_n$ for $n = 1, 2, 3, \ldots$. Then we have

THEOREM 5. *The sequence (22) converges if and only if the sequences of the real and imaginary parts, i.e. the sequences $a_1, a_2, a_3, \ldots$ and $b_1, b_2, b_3, \ldots$, converge. Furthermore in the case of convergence, we have*

$$\lim_{n \to \infty} z_n = \lim_{n \to \infty} a_n + i \lim_{n \to \infty} b_n.$$

We first suppose that (22) converges and assume that (24) holds. We show that in this case we must have $\lim_{n \to \infty} a_n = a_0$, $\lim_{n \to \infty} b_n = b_0$ where a_0 is the real part and b_0 the imaginary part of z_0, so that $z_0 = a_0 + ib_0$.

By the definition of absolute value, we have

$$(34)\qquad |z_n - z_0| = +\sqrt{(a_n - a_0)^2 + (b_n - b_0)^2}.$$

Thus,

$$(35)\qquad |a_n - a_0| \leqq |z_n - z_0|, \quad |b_n - b_0| \leqq |z_n - z_0|.$$

By our assumption that the sequence $z_1, z_2, z_3, \ldots$ converges, we have for any $\varepsilon > 0$ that the relation $| z_n - z_0 | < \varepsilon$ holds for almost all n. Thus by (35), we have for almost all n that

$$(36)\qquad |a_n - a_0| < \varepsilon, \quad |b_n - b_0| < \varepsilon,$$

which shows that the sequence $a_1, a_2, a_3, \ldots$ has the limit a_0, and the sequence $b_1, b_2, b_3, \ldots$ has the limit b_0.

The converse remains to be proved. We assume then, that $\lim_{n\to\infty} a_n = a_0$, $\lim_{n\to\infty} b_n = b_0$. We must show that the sequence $z_1, z_2, z_3, \ldots$ has the limit $z_0 = a_0 + ib_0$. However for each fixed ε, and for almost all n, we have $|a_n - a_0| < \frac{\varepsilon}{+\sqrt{2}}$ and similarly $|b_n - b_0| < \frac{\varepsilon}{+\sqrt{2}}$.

Thus for almost all n,

$$(37)\qquad |a_n - a_0|^2 + |b_n - b_0|^2 < \varepsilon^2.$$

Comparison of (37) and (34) yields immediately that $| z_n - z_0 | < \varepsilon$ for almost all n, i.e. that

$$\lim_{n\to\infty} z_n = z_0.$$

Thus Theorem 5 is completely proved.

By a *subsequence* of (22) we shall mean a sequence $z_{\nu_1}, z_{\nu_2}, z_{\nu_3}, \cdots$, where the subscripts $\nu_1 < \nu_2 < \nu_3 < \cdots$ form a monotonically increasing sequence of positive integers. The sequence (22) is said to be *bounded* if there is a positive real number m which is greater than all of the absolute values $| z_n |$ for $n = 1, 2, 3, \ldots$. We shall also need the following Bolzano-Weierstrass Theorem:

THEOREM 6. *Every bounded sequence of complex numbers has a convergent subsequence.*

We assume that the reader is familiar with this theorem for sequences of real numbers.[5] Once again, let $z_n = a_n + ib_n$ for $n = 1, 2, 3, \ldots$. Since $|a_n| \leqq |z_n|$ and $|b_n| \leqq |z_n|$, the sequences of real numbers

$$a_1, a_2, a_3, \cdots, \tag{38}$$

$$b_1, b_2, b_3, \cdots \tag{39}$$

must be bounded along with (22). Thus the sequence (38), as a bounded sequence of real numbers, has a convergent subsequence, say $a_{\nu_1}, a_{\nu_2}, a_{\nu_3}, \cdots$. We consider the corresponding subsequence, $z_{\nu_1}, z_{\nu_2}, z_{\nu_3}, \cdots$ of (22). In order to simplify our notation, we set

$$z_{\nu_k} = z'_k, \ a_{\nu_k} = a'_k, \ b_{\nu_k} = b'_k.$$

Thus $z'_k = a'_k + ib'_k$, and the subsequence

$$z'_1, z'_2, z'_3, \cdots \tag{40}$$

is such, by construction, that the sequence $a'_1, a'_2, a'_3, \cdots$ of its real parts converges. The sequence

$$b'_1, b'_2, b'_3, \cdots \tag{41}$$

of imaginary parts of (40) is a subsequence of (39), and as such is bounded. Therefore, by the Bolzano-Weierstrass Theorem, it has a convergent subsequence, say

---

[5] Cf. any text on the theory of functions of a real variable or on the advanced calculus, or, Hardy's *Pure Mathematics*, p. 32. Theorem 6 is equivalent to the following theorem:

Every bounded sequence has a limit point. By a *limit point* of the sequence (22) we mean a number α which has the property that for every real number $\varepsilon > 0$, the relation $|z_n - \alpha| < \varepsilon$ is satisfied for infinitely many n. If we assume that the existence of a limit point α of the sequence (22) has been demonstrated, then we can easily construct a convergent subsequence of (22). To this end, we choose a sequence $\varepsilon_1, \varepsilon_2, \varepsilon_3, \cdots$ of positive numbers which converges to 0 as a limit (say $1, \frac{1}{2}, \frac{1}{3}, \cdots$). Since α is a limit point, there correspond to each ε_k infinitely many numbers z_n of the sequence (22) for which $|z_n - \alpha| < \varepsilon_k$. We now associate with $\varepsilon_1, \varepsilon_2, \varepsilon_3$, etc., numbers $z_{\nu_1}, z_{\nu_2}, z_{\nu_3}, \cdots$ from the sequence (22) such that

$$|z_{\nu_k} - \alpha| < \varepsilon_k$$

and such that $\nu_1 < \nu_2 < \nu_3 < \cdots$ is a monotonically increasing sequence. We now may choose ν_k larger than any of the preceding subscripts $\nu_1, \nu_2, \cdots, \nu_{k-1}$, since there are infinitely many terms of (22) which satisfy the relation $|z_n - \alpha| < \varepsilon_k$. The sequence $z_{\nu_1}, z_{\nu_2}, z_{\nu_3}, \cdots$ converges and has the limit α. For if ε is an arbitrary positive number, then for almost all k, we have $|\varepsilon_k - 0| = \varepsilon_k < \varepsilon$, so that for almost all k, $|z_{\nu_k} - \alpha| < \varepsilon_k < \varepsilon$.

$$b'_{\mu_1}, b'_{\mu_2}, b'_{\mu_3}, \cdots.$$

The corresponding subsequence of (40) is

$$(42) \qquad z'_{\mu_1}, z'_{\mu_2}, z'_{\mu_3}, \cdots.$$

Naturally, this is also a subsequence of (22). The sequence of real parts of (42), namely

$$a'_{\mu_1}, a'_{\mu_2}, a'_{\mu_3}, \cdots,$$

is convergent since it is a subsequence of the convergent sequence $a'_1, a'_2, a'_3, \cdots$.[6] Thus both the sequences of the real and of the imaginary parts of (42) converge, so that, by Theorem 5, the sequence (42) converges. Thus the existence of a convergent subsequence of (22) is proved.

Exercises

1. Let $\mathfrak{M}$ be the set of all ordered pairs (a, b) of real numbers a and b. Let addition be taken in the sense of vector addition,

$$(a_1, b_1) + (a_2, b_2) = (a_1 + a_2, b_1 + b_2).$$

Let multiplication be defined by the equation

$$(a_1, b_1) \cdot (a_2, b_2) = (a_1 a_2, b_1 b_2).$$

Is $\mathfrak{M}$ then a field?

2. Let F be the set of all ordered triples of *rational* numbers. Let addition be defined in F as vector addition,

$$(a_1, b_1, c_1) + (a_2, b_2, c_2) = (a_1 + a_2, b_1 + b_2, c_1 + c_2).$$

Let multiplication be defined by

$$(a_1, b_1, c_1) \cdot (a_2, b_2, c_2) = (a_1 c_2 + b_1 b_2 + c_1 a_2, 2 a_1 a_2 + b_1 c_2 + b_2 c_1, 2 b_1 a_2 + 2 a_1 b_2 + c_1 c_2).$$

Is F a field?

Moreover, is F a field if multiplication is defined by

---

[6] Let $w_1, w_2, w_3, \cdots$ be a convergent sequence with limit w_0, and let

$$w_{\nu_1}, w_{\nu_2}, w_{\nu_3}, \cdots$$

be an arbitrary subsequence. For any choice of ε we have for almost all n that $|w_n - w_0| < \varepsilon$, so that we certainly have for almost all k that $|w_{\nu_k} - w_0| < \varepsilon$, i.e., the subsequence $w_{\nu_1}, w_{\nu_2}, w_{\nu_3}, \cdots$ is also convergent to w_0.

$(a_1, b_1, c_1) \cdot (a_2, b_2, c_2) = (a_1 c_2 + b_1 b_2 + c_1 a_2,\ a_1 a_2 + b_1 c_2 + b_2 c_1,\ b_1 a_2 + a_1 b_2 + c_1 c_2)$?

3. Let the complex numbers α, β be represented by the points P, Q of the complex plane. Express in terms of α and β those complex numbers which are represented by points of the segment PQ. Do the same for those complex numbers which are represented by point of the line through P and Q.

§ 17. The Fundamental Theorem of Algebra

We have extended the real number system to the field of complex numbers in order to be able to solve arbitrary quadratic equations with real coefficients. In this section, we shall see that with this step we have actually achieved a good deal more. In fact, we are going to show that *every* algebraic equation in one unknown is solvable in the field of complex numbers. Such an equation has the form

$$(1) \qquad x^n + a_1 x^{n-1} + a_2 x^{n-2} + \cdots + a_{n-1} x + a_n = 0.$$

The coefficients $a_1, a_2, \ldots, a_n$ may be arbitrary real or complex numbers. The left-hand side of equation (1) is a polynomial in the variable x, which we will denote by $f(x)$. A root of equation (1) is also called a *zero of the polynomial* $f(x)$. Before we prove the existence of such a zero, we must first derive some lemmas concerning polynomials.

We shall concern ourselves only with polynomials of the form

$$(2) \qquad f(x) = x^n + a_1 x^{n-1} + \cdots + a_{n-1} x + a_n,$$

whose leading coefficient is 1. As a matter of fact any polynomial may be reduced to this form without changing its zeros, by multiplication with a suitable constant. Let

$$(3) \qquad z_1, z_2, z_3, \cdots,$$

be a convergent sequence of complex numbers, and suppose that

$$(4) \qquad \lim_{i \to \infty} z_i = z_0.$$

We substitute the successive terms of the sequence (3) for the variable x in the polynomial $f(x)$ obtaining a new sequence of complex numbers,

$$(5) \qquad f(z_1),\ f(z_2),\ f(z_3), \cdots.$$

We wish to determine whether (5) is also convergent.

Consider the individual term $a_k x^{n-k}$ of the polynomial (2). By Theorems 3 and 4 of § 16, we see that the sequence

$$a_k z_1^{n-k}, a_k z_2^{n-k}, a_k z_3^{n-k}, \cdots,$$

converges, and that

$$\lim_{i\to\infty} (a_k z_i^{n-k}) = a_k (\lim_{i\to\infty} z_i)^{n-k}. \tag{6}$$

Since $f(z_i) = z_i^n + a_1 z_i^{n-1} + \cdots + a_{n-1} z_i + a_n$, we have by Theorem 2 of § 16 that (5) converges, and by comparing with (4) and (6) we see that[1]

$$\begin{aligned}\lim_{i\to\infty} f(z_i) &= \lim_{i\to\infty} (z_i^n) + \lim_{i\to\infty} (a_1 z_i^{n-1}) + \cdots + \lim_{i\to\infty} (a_{n-1} z_i) + \lim_{i\to\infty} a_n \\ &= (\lim_{i\to\infty} z_i)^n + a_1 (\lim_{i\to\infty} z_i)^{n-1} + \cdots + a_{n-1} (\lim_{i\to\infty} z_i) + a_n \\ &= z_0^n + a_1 z_0^{n-1} + \cdots + a_{n-1} z_0 + a_n \\ &= f(z_0).\end{aligned}$$

Thus we have

THEOREM 1. *If we replace x by the terms of a convergent sequence $z_1, z_2, z_3, \ldots$ in the polynomial $f(x)$, then the resulting sequence $f(z_1), f(z_2), f(z_3), \ldots$ is also convergent, and we have*

$$\lim_{i\to\infty} f(z_i) = f(\lim_{i\to\infty} z_i).$$

The property expressed in Theorem 1 is called the *continuity* of the polynomial $f(x)$.

We next consider a polynomial $g(x)$ of the form

$$g(x) = b_1 x + b_2 x^2 + \cdots + b_n x^n,$$

whose constant term vanishes. Substituting 0 for x, yields $g(0) = 0$. We can also prove something about the behavior of $g(x)$ in the neighborhood of the origin; namely, we assert that

THEOREM 2. *To every preassigned real number $\varepsilon > 0$, there corresponds a real number $\delta > 0$ such that for every complex number z for which $|z| < \delta$, we have $|g(z)| < \varepsilon$.*

To prove this, let $M > 0$ be a real number which is greater than

---

[1] By $\lim_{i\to\infty} a_n$ is meant the limit of the sequence $a_n, a_n, a_n, \cdots$. Thus,

$$\lim_{i\to\infty} a_n = a_n.$$

any of the values $|b_1|, |b_2|, \cdots, |b_n|$, so that for $i = 1, 2, \ldots, n$, we have

$$|b_i| < M. \tag{7}$$

Now for any preassigned $\varepsilon > 0$, we determine a corresponding $\delta > 0$ which is less than both 1 and $\frac{\varepsilon}{n \cdot M}$. Then we have

$$\delta \cdot n \cdot M < \varepsilon. \tag{8}$$

Furthermore, since $\delta < 1$ we have

$$\delta > \delta^2 > \delta^3 > \cdots. \tag{9}$$

Now by (12), (16), and (17) of § 16, we have for any complex number z that

$$|g(z)| \leqq |b_1| \cdot |z| + |b_2| \cdot |z|^2 + \cdots + |b_n| \cdot |z|^n.$$

If we further assume that $|z| < \delta$, then by (7) and (9),

$$|b_k| \cdot |z|^k < M \cdot \delta,$$

so that by (8), we obtain

$$|g(z)| \leqq n \cdot M \cdot \delta < \varepsilon.$$

Therefore δ is a number which satisfies the requirements of Theorem 2.[2]

We now return to our consideration of polynomials $f(x)$ of the form (2). We assume that the degree of $f(x)$ is greater than 0. For such polynomials, Theorem 2 yields a result which is important for our purposes, namely

THEOREM 3. *To every preassigned real number $M > 0$, there corresponds a real number $m > 0$ such that for every complex number z for which $|z| > m$, we have $|f(z)| > M$.*

If we substitute a complex number $z \neq 0$ for x in $f(x)$, we may write, since $n > 0$,

$$f(z) = z^n \left(1 + a_1 \frac{1}{z} + a_2 \frac{1}{z^2} + \cdots + a_n \frac{1}{z^n}\right). \tag{10}$$

We set

[2] Theorem 2 could also easily have been proved indirectly from Theorem 1.

$$g(x) = a_1 x + a_2 x^2 + \cdots + a_n x^n. \tag{11}$$

Then by (10),

$$f(z) = z^n\left(1 + g\left(\frac{1}{z}\right)\right). \tag{12}$$

The polynomial $g(x)$ satisfies the hypotheses of Theorem 2. We apply this theorem to $g(x)$ setting $\varepsilon = \frac{1}{2}$. Thus there is then a $\delta > 0$ such that for every complex number u for which $|u| < \delta$, we have

$$|g(u)| < \tfrac{1}{2}.$$

Now let $M > 0$ be any given real number. We choose a real number m which is greater than 1, $2M$, and $\dfrac{1}{\delta}$. We assert that this number m has the property stated in Theorem 3.

For if z is a complex number for which $|z| > m$, then by (18) of § 16, and since $m > \dfrac{1}{\delta}$, we have

$$\left|\frac{1}{z}\right| = \frac{1}{|z|} < \frac{1}{m} < \delta.$$

Thus by our choice of δ, this implies

$$g\left(\frac{1}{z}\right) < \frac{1}{2}. \tag{13}$$

Now clearly, $1 = \left[1 + g\left(\dfrac{1}{z}\right)\right] - g\left(\dfrac{1}{z}\right)$. Applying (12) of § 16, we obtain

$$1 \leqq \left|1 + g\left(\frac{1}{z}\right)\right| + \left|g\left(\frac{1}{z}\right)\right|,$$

$$\left|1 + g\left(\frac{1}{z}\right)\right| \geqq 1 - \left|g\left(\frac{1}{z}\right)\right|. \tag{14}$$

Comparison of (13) and (14) yields

$$\left|1 + g\left(\frac{1}{z}\right)\right| \geqq \frac{1}{2}. \tag{15}$$

If we substitute this in (12), we have

$$|f(z)| \geqq |z|^n \cdot \frac{1}{2}. \tag{16}$$

We chose $m > 1$, so that $m < m^2 < m^3 < \cdots$. Moreover, we had

$|z| > m$ and $m > 2M$, so that $|z|^n > m^n \geqq m > 2M$ (since $n \geqq 1$). Thus by (16),

$$|f(z)| > M,$$

as was to be proved.

Now let us consider the set of all absolute values $|f(z)|$ which are obtained by inserting any and all complex numbers for x in (2). Since $|f(z)| \geqq 0$ holds for all z, the set is bounded from below. We assume as known that every non-empty set of real numbers which is bounded from below has a greatest lower bound.[3] This greatest lower bound of our set of all absolute values $|f(z)|$ is a real number g with the following property: g is the *greatest* real number for which the relation $g \leqq |f(z)|$ holds for all z. Thus there is no number $|f(z)|$ which is less than g. But if we chose an arbitrarily small real number $\delta > 0$, then $g + \delta$ is no longer $\leqq f(z)$ for *all* z, but there is a complex number z for which $|f(z)| < g + \delta$. In other words, to every real number $\delta > 0$ there corresponds a complex z such that $\left| |f(z)| - g \right| < \delta$.[4]

But the existence of g does not suffice for our purposes. Indeed, we do have $g \leqq |f(z)|$ for all z, but it might even be that $g < |f(z)|$ for all z. We shall soon see that this cannot happen. There exist complex numbers z_0 for which $g = |f(z_0)|$. In the proof we again assume that the degree of $f(x)$ is > 0. We then assert:

THEOREM 4. *If g is the greatest lower bound of all absolute values $|f(z)|$, then there is at least one complex number z_0 for which $g = |f(z_0)|$.*

In proof, let us consider a sequence $\delta_1, \delta_2, \delta_3, \cdots$ of positive numbers which converges to 0. As we have just seen, for each δ_i there is a z_i for which

$$(17) \qquad \left| |f(z_i)| - g \right| < \delta_i, \qquad i = 1, 2, 3, \cdots.$$

Since the sequence $\delta_1, \delta_2, \delta_3, \cdots$ converges to 0, then for any preassigned positive ε the relation $|\delta_i| < \varepsilon$ holds for almost all i. Thus by (17), we have for almost all i that

$$\left| |f(z_i)| - g \right| < \varepsilon.$$

But this means that the sequence

$$(18) \qquad |f(z_1)|, \quad |f(z_2)|, \quad |f(z_3)|, \quad \cdots$$

[3] Cf., for example, Hardy's *Pure Mathematics*, p. 32.

[4] Since $|f(z)| \geqq g$, we have $\left| |f(z)| - g \right| = |f(z)| - g$.

converges to g. Every convergent sequence is bounded (cf. footnote 4, § 16); i.e. there is a real number $M > 0$ which is greater than each of the $|f(z_i)|$:

$$|f(z_i)| < M, \qquad i = 1, 2, 3, \cdots. \tag{19}$$

By Theorem 3, there is, corresponding to this M, a real number $m > 0$ such that for all z for which $|z| > m$, we have $|f(z)| > M$. Since this last condition does not hold for $z_1, z_2, z_3, \ldots$, by (19), we must have for all $i = 1, 2, 3, \ldots$ that

$$|z_i| \leq m.$$

That is, the sequence $z_1, z_2, z_3, \ldots$ is bounded. By Theorem 6 of § 16, it must contain a convergent subsequence, say

$$z_{\nu_1}, z_{\nu_2}, z_{\nu_3}, \cdots. \tag{20}$$

Let, say,

$$\lim_{k\to\infty} z_{\nu_k} = z_0. \tag{21}$$

The sequence $|f(z_{\nu_k})|$ which corresponds to (20) i.e. the sequence

$$|f(z_{\nu_1})|, |f(z_{\nu_2})|, |f(z_{\nu_3})|, \cdots \tag{22}$$

is a subsequence of (18), and as such it also converges to g (cf. footnote 6, § 16). Thus

$$\lim_{k\to\infty} |f(z_{\nu_k})| = g. \tag{23}$$

By Theorem 1 of this section, it follows from (21) that the sequence

$$f(z_{\nu_1}), f(z_{\nu_2}), f(z_{\nu_3}), \cdots$$

converges to $f(z_0)$. By Theorem 1 of § 16, the sequence (22) therefore converges to the limit $|f(z_0)|$, so that

$$\lim_{k\to\infty} |f(z_{\nu_k})| = |f(z_0)|. \tag{24}$$

The limit of a convergent sequence is, however, uniquely determined. Thus by (23) and (24), we have

$$g = |f(z_0)|,$$

which completes the proof of Theorem 4.

We require one final result on polynomials of the form (2) whose degree is > 0. Namely, we assert

THEOREM 5. *If* $|f(z_0)| \neq 0$ *for some complex number* z_0, *then there is some other complex number* z *for which* $|f(z)| < |f(z_0)|$.

Let z be the required number; we shall determine its value in the course of the proof. Let $z - z_0 = u$, i.e. $z = u + z_0$. If we substitute this in $f(z)$, then by (2) we have

$$(25)\quad f(z) = (u + z_0)^n + a_1(u + z_0)^{n-1} + \cdots + a_{n-1}(u + z_0) + a_n.$$

Let the powers $(u + z_0)^k$ be evaluated by the binomial theorem,[5] and let us write the result arranged according to descending powers of u. The coefficient of u^n is equal to 1, and thus we may write

$$(26)\qquad f(z) = u^n + \alpha_1 u^{n-1} + \cdots + \alpha_{n-1} u + \alpha_n,$$

where $\alpha_1, \alpha_2, \cdots, \alpha_n$ are certain complex numbers. By an easy calculation we find that

$$(27)\quad \alpha_n = z_0^n + a_1 z_0^{n-1} + a_2 z_0^{n-2} + \cdots + a_{n-1} z_0 + a_n = f(z_0).$$

Since we have assumed $|f(z_0)| \neq 0$, we can factor out $f(z_0)$ on the right-hand side of (26). This gives

$$(28)\qquad f(z) = f(z_0)\cdot(1 + \gamma_1 u + \gamma_2 u^2 + \cdots + \gamma_n u^n),$$

where $\gamma_1, \gamma_2, \cdots, \gamma_n$ are certain complex numbers; by (26),

$$(29)\qquad \gamma_n = \frac{1}{f(z_0)} \neq 0$$

where $n \geqq 1$, since we have assumed that the degree of $f(x)$ is > 0. Several, or even all, of the numbers $\gamma_1, \gamma_2, \cdots, \gamma_{n-1}$ may be equal to 0. Let the first non-vanishing term of the sequence $\gamma_1, \gamma_2, \cdots, \gamma_{n-1}, \gamma_n$, be γ_k. k is at most equal to n. We consider the polynomial

$$(30)\qquad \gamma_{k+1} x^{k+1} + \gamma_{k+2} x^{k+2} + \cdots + \gamma_n x^n.$$

If $k < n$, then by (29) this is a polynomial which not identically 0.

---

[5] The following will be familiar:

$$(u + z_0)^k = u^k + \binom{k}{1} u^{k-1} z_0 + \binom{k}{2} u^{k-2} z_0^2 + \cdots + \binom{k}{k-1} u z_0^{k-1} + z_0^k.$$

On the other hand if $k = n$, it is identically 0. In either case, since we have assumed $\gamma_k \neq 0$, the polynomial (30) may be written in the form

(31) $$\gamma_k \cdot x^k \cdot g(x),$$

where

(32) $$g(x) = \frac{\gamma_{k+1}}{\gamma_k} \cdot x + \frac{\gamma_{k+2}}{\gamma_k} x^2 + \cdots + \frac{\gamma_n}{\gamma_k} x^{n-k}.$$

For $k = n$, $g(x) = 0$ identically. Since $\gamma_i = 0$ for $i < k$, (28) takes on the form

(33) $$f(z) = f(z_0) \cdot (1 + \gamma_k u^k + \gamma_k u^k g(u)).$$

$g(x)$ is a polynomial which satisfies the hypotheses of Theorem 2. We apply that theorem, setting $\varepsilon = \frac{1}{2}$. Thus there is a real number $\delta > 0$ such that for any complex number u for which $|u| < \delta$, we have $|g(u)| < \frac{1}{2}$.

Now if c is the absolute value of γ_k, φ the amplitude, then, by (14) of § 16,

(34) $$\gamma_k = c(\cos\varphi + i \sin\varphi).$$

Since $\gamma_k \neq 0$, we certainly have $c > 0$. We shall now define the complex number u, by setting $u = t(\cos\psi + i\sin\psi)$, where $\psi = \dfrac{\pi - \varphi}{k}$, so that

(35) $$k \cdot \psi + \varphi = \pi.$$

$t > 0$ is to be chosen small enough to satisfy

(36) $$c \cdot t^k < 1.$$

It suffices to take $t < {}_{+}\sqrt[k]{\dfrac{1}{c}}$.[6] Finally t is also to be less than the number δ mentioned above

(37) $$t < \delta.$$

Now we contend that $z = u + z_0$ is a number satisfying Theorem 5, i.e. a number for which $|f(z)| < |f(z_0)|$. First, applying equation (15) of § 16,

[6] If $A > 0$, then by ${}_{+}\sqrt[k]{A}$ is meant that uniquely determined positive real number whose k-th power is A.

$$\gamma_k \cdot u^k = c t^k \cdot (\cos(\varphi + k\psi) + i \sin(\varphi + k\psi)).$$

Thus by (35),

$$\gamma_k \cdot u^k = -c t^k. \tag{38}$$

Furthermore, by (12) and (16) of § 16,

$$|1 + \gamma_k \cdot u^k + \gamma_k \cdot u^k \cdot g(u)| \leqq |1 + \gamma_k \cdot u^k| + |\gamma_k \cdot u^k| \cdot |g(u)|. \tag{39}$$

By the choice of δ, it follows from (37) that $|g(u)| < \frac{1}{2}$, so that by (38) and (39),

$$|1 + \gamma_k u^k + \gamma_k u^k g(u)| \leqq |1 - c t^k| + \frac{1}{2} c t^k. \tag{40}$$

Now however, by (36), $ct^k < 1$, so that $|1 - c t^k| = 1 - c t^k$. Taking note of this fact, and substituting (40) into (33), we obtain

$$|f(z)| \leqq |f(z_0)| \left(1 - \frac{1}{2} c t^k\right). \tag{41}$$

But $c \neq 0$ and $t \neq 0$. Hence $1 - \frac{1}{2} c t^k < 1$, so that by (41), we have

$$|f(z)| < |f(z_0)|,$$

as was to be proved.

We are now in a position to prove the result mentioned at the beginning of this section. Namely, we shall prove the so-called **fundamental theorem of algebra:**

THEOREM 6. *Every polynomial*

$$f(x) = x^n + a_1 x^{n-1} + a_2 x^{n-2} + \cdots + a_{n-1} x + a_n$$

with complex coefficients $a_1, a_2, \ldots, a_n$ and of degree $n \geqq 1$ has at least one zero in the field of complex numbers.

In other words, every equation of the form (1) has at least one root in the field of complex numbers.

To prove this result, we first recall Theorem 4, to the effect that there is a complex number z_0 for which $g = |f(z_0)|$, where g is the greatest lower bound of all the absolute values $|f(z)|$. Now if g were different from 0, then by Theorem 5, there would be a complex number z for which $|f(z)| < g$, which contradicts the definition of g as the greatest lower bound of all $|f(z)|$. Hence $g = 0$. Therefore $f(z_0) = 0$, and Theorem 6 has been proved.

We shall now derive some corollaries of Theorem 6. If a polynomial

$f(x)$ is divisible by a polynomial of the first degree of the form $x - \alpha$, that is if

$$f(x) = (x - \alpha) f_1(x) \tag{42}$$

then α is a zero of $f(x)$; for we have defined multiplication of polynomials in such a manner that products were to be calculated as though x were a quantity of the coefficient field. Thus equation (42) remains correct if we substitute a complex number for the variable x. In particular, if we substitute the number α for x, this yields $f(\alpha) = 0$, i.e. α is a zero of $f(x)$.

Conversely, if we know that α is a zero of $f(x)$, then it follows that $f(x)$ is divisible by the polynomial $x - \alpha$. By the division algorithm discussed in § 14, we may determine a suitable multiple $f_1(x) \cdot (x - \alpha)$ of the polynomial $x - \alpha$, such that the remainder

$$r = f(x) - f_1(x) \cdot (x - \alpha) \tag{43}$$

is a polynomial of lower degree than $x - \alpha$. Thus r must be a constant. We may easily determine the value of this constant; for, if we replace x by a quantity of the coefficient field in (43), the equation continues to hold. In particular, if we replace x by α, we deduce that $r = 0$. Thus

$$f(x) = f_1(x)\ (x - \alpha), \tag{44}$$

i.e. $x - \alpha$ is a divisor of $f(x)$. Thus we have proved

THEOREM 7. *The polynomial $f(x)$ is divisible by the linear*[7] *polynomial $x - \alpha$ if and only if α is a zero of $f(x)$.*

By Theorem 6, a polynomial $f(x)$ of the form (2), and of degree > 0, certainly has a zero α in the field of complex numbers. Thus by Theorem 7, in the domain of polynomials with complex coefficients[8] every polynomial $f(x)$ of degree > 0 is divisible by a polynomial $x - \alpha$ of the first degree. Hence in this polynomial domain, every polynomial of degree $\geqq 2$ certainly has at least one proper divisor (namely a linear one), and so is reducible. *The only irreducible polynomials over the field of complex numbers are those of the first degree.*

Now if we factorize a polynomial $f(x)$ of the form (2) into irreducible factors, then the polynomials so obtained must be of the first degree. Since the leading coefficient of $f(x)$ is 1, we may, by Theorem 6

---

[7] A polynomial of the first degree is also called *linear*.

[8] I.e. in the polynomial domain $F[x]$, where F is the field of complex numbers.

of § 15, carry out the factorization in such a way that each of the irreducible factors has leading coefficient 1. But since these factors are linear, we may assume them to be of the form $x - \alpha$.[9] The factorization of $f(x)$ will then have the following form:

$$f(x) = (x - \alpha_1) \cdot (x - \alpha_2) \cdot \ldots \cdot (x - \alpha_n). \tag{45}$$

We have thus proved

THEOREM 8. *In the domain of polynomials $f(x)$ with complex coefficients, every polynomial of degree > 0 may be factored into a product of linear polynomials. If $f(x)$ has leading coefficient* 1, *then the factorization may be written in the form* (45).

By Theorem 7, the numbers $\alpha_1, \alpha_2, \cdots, \alpha_n$ in (45) are zeros of $f(x)$. By Theorem 6 of § 15, the linear factors of (45) are uniquely determined up to their order, and therefore so are zeros $\alpha_1, \alpha_2, \cdots, \alpha_n$ of $f(x)$. Thus $f(x)$ can have no additional zeros.[10]

Of course the α_i in (45) need not all differ. Let there be r distinct ones among them. We imagine the roots so numbered that the r distinct ones are $\alpha_1, \alpha_2, \cdots, \alpha_r$. Moreover, let α_i occur as a root n_i times $(1 \leqq i \leqq r)$, so that we may rewrite (45) in the form

$$f(x) = (x - \alpha_1)^{n_1} \cdot (x - \alpha_2)^{n_2} \cdot \ldots \cdot (x - \alpha_r)^{n_r}. \tag{46}$$

n_i is the largest exponent for which $(x - \alpha_i)^{n_i}$ is still a divisor of $f(x)$.

We count the zero α_i precisely as often as the linear factor $x - \alpha_i$ occurs in (45), i.e. n_i times $(1 \leqq i \leqq r)$. The number n_i is called the **multiplicity** of the zero α_i. By (46) it is clear that

$$n = n_1 + n_2 + \ldots + n_r.$$

Thus for a polynomial $f(x)$ of the n-th degree, we have

THEOREM 9. *$f(x)$ has precisely n roots where each root is counted according to its multiplicity.*

In connection with Theorem 8, we wish to investigate the form of the factorization of polynomials into irreducible factors if we restrict ourselves to the domain of polynomials with *real* coefficients. For this

---

[9] If a linear polynomial is of the form $x + a$, then it goes over into the form $x - \alpha$ under the substitution $\alpha = -a$.

[10] We may also see this by substituting an arbitrary zero α for x in (45). Then the left-hand side becomes 0, so that at least one factor on the right must vanish, i.e. $\alpha = \alpha_i$ for a suitable i.

purpose, we first investigate a preliminary question. Combining (45) and (2), we have

$$(47) \quad x^n + a_1 x^{n-1} + \cdots + a_{n-1} x + a_n = (x - \alpha_1)(x - \alpha_2) \cdots (x - \alpha_n).$$

Let $\bar{a}_i$ be the complex conjugate of a_i. We consider the polynomial $x^n + \bar{a}_1 x^{n-1} + \cdots + \bar{a}_{n-1} x + \bar{a}_n$, which we shall call the *complex conjugate of the polynomial* $f(x)$. What is the form of the factorization of this polynomial into linear factors? We assert that if $\bar{a}_i$ is the complex conjugate of a_i, then

$$(48) \quad x^n + \bar{a}_1 x^{n-1} + \cdots + \bar{a}_{n-1} x + \bar{a}_n = (x - \bar{\alpha}_1)(x - \bar{\alpha}_2) \cdots (x - \bar{\alpha}_n).$$

This follows easily, say by mathematical induction on the degree of $f(x)$. Our assertion is trivial in the case of polynomials of the first degree. We suppose the result proven for polynomials of degree less than n, and proceed to derive it for those of degree n. We multiply the first $n - 1$ factors of (47) and of (48), forming the products

$$(x - \alpha_1)(x - \alpha_2) \cdots (x - \alpha_{n-1}) \quad \text{and} \quad (x - \bar{\alpha}_1)(x - \bar{\alpha}_2) \cdots (x - \bar{\alpha}_{n-1}).$$

By induction hypothesis, these two polynomials are complex conjugates of each other, say

$$(49) \quad x^{n-1} + b_1 x^{n-2} + \cdots + b_{n-2} x + b_{n-1} = (x - \alpha_1)(x - \alpha_2) \cdots (x - \alpha_{n-1}),$$

$$(50) \quad x^{n-1} + \bar{b}_1 x^{n-2} + \cdots + \bar{b}_{n-2} x + \bar{b}_{n-1} = (x - \bar{\alpha}_1)(x - \bar{\alpha}_2) \cdots (x - \bar{\alpha}_{n-1}).$$

If we now multiply (49) by $(x - \alpha_n)$ and (50) by $(x - \bar{\alpha}_n)$ then the left-hand sides become

$$(51) \quad x^n + (b_1 - \alpha_n) x^{n-1} + (b_2 - \alpha_n b_1) x^{n-2} + \cdots + (b_{n-2} - \alpha_n b_{n-3}) x^2 + (b_{n-1} - \alpha_n b_{n-2}) x - \alpha_n b_{n-1},$$

$$(52) \quad x^n + (\bar{b}_1 - \bar{\alpha}_n) x^{n-1} + (\bar{b}_2 - \bar{\alpha}_n \bar{b}_1) x^{n-2} + \cdots + (\bar{b}_{n-2} - \bar{\alpha}_n \bar{b}_{n-3}) x^2 + (\bar{b}_{n-1} - \bar{\alpha}_n \bar{b}_{n-2}) x - \bar{\alpha}_n \bar{b}_{n-1}.$$

But the polynomial (51) is the same as the polynomial (47). Furthermore, (52) is equal to the right-hand side of equation (48), i.e. of the equation we wish to prove. But, by formulas (20) of § 16, we see that the corresponding coefficients in (51) and (52) are conjugates. Hence (52) is the complex conjugate polynomial of (47), and so is also equal to the left-hand side of (48). This proves (48).

Now let $f(x)$ be a polynomial with real coefficients $a_1, a_2, \ldots, a_n$. Then $\bar{a}_i = a_i$; employing (47) and (48) and combining equal factors (as we did in (46)), we have

$$f(x) = (x - \alpha_1)^{n_1} \cdot (x - \alpha_2)^{n_2} \cdot \ldots \cdot (x - \alpha_r)^{n_r} = (x - \bar{\alpha}_1)^{n_1} \cdot (x - \bar{\alpha}_2)^{n_2} \cdot \ldots \cdot (x - \bar{\alpha}_r)^{n_r}. \tag{53}$$

Since the numbers $\alpha_1, \alpha_2, \cdots, \alpha_r$ are all distinct, the same also holds for $\bar{\alpha}_1, \bar{\alpha}_2, \cdots, \bar{\alpha}_r$. Thus we have the following: *If α_i is a zero of $f(x)$ of multiplicity n_i, then $\bar{\alpha}_i$ is also a zero, and with the same multiplicity n_i.* Of course by the uniqueness of factorization, each factor $(x - \bar{\alpha}_k)^{n_k}$ must be one of the original factors $(x - \alpha_i)^{n_i}$.

Clearly not all of the zeros α_i of $f(x)$ need be real even if all the coefficients of $f(x)$ are real. If the α_i are not all real, then the decomposition (46) is not a factorization in the domain of polynomials with real coefficients. For, a factor $x - \alpha_i$ with complex α_i is not a polynomial of this domain. However we may easily derive from (46) a decomposition of $f(x)$ into irreducible factors in the domain of real polynomials.[11] In fact, let α_i be a complex zero of $f(x)$. Then $\alpha_i \neq \bar{\alpha}_i$ and both the factors $(x - \alpha_i)^{n_i}$ and $(x - \bar{\alpha}_i)^{n_i}$ must occur in (46). Now consider the quadratic polynomial

$$(x - \alpha_i)(x - \bar{\alpha}_i) = x^2 - (\alpha_i + \bar{\alpha}_i)x + \alpha_i \bar{\alpha}_i. \tag{54}$$

By the definition of complex conjugate, and by equation (19) of § 16, the coefficients of (54) are real. But (54) is certainly irreducible in the domain of real polynomials. For, every proper divisor of $(x - \alpha_i)(x - \bar{\alpha}_i)$ in the real domain would certainly also be a proper divisor in the domain of complex polynomials. But by the uniqueness of factorization, $(x - \alpha_i)$ and $(x - \bar{\alpha}_i)$ are the only proper divisors in the latter domain. Thus the quadratic polynomial (54) has no real proper divisors. Hence the two complex conjugate factors $(x - \alpha_i)^{n_i}$ and $(x - \bar{\alpha}_i)^{n_i}$ in (47) may be combined as follows:

$$(x - \alpha_i)^{n_i} \cdot (x - \bar{\alpha}_i)^{n_i} = [x^2 - (\alpha_i + \bar{\alpha}_i)x + \alpha_i \bar{\alpha}_i]^{n_i}. \tag{55}$$

On the right-hand side is a product of real irreducible polynomials of

---

[11] I.e. polynomials with real coefficients.

the second degree. We do this with each of the complex factors. Combining, we obtain, with somewhat different notation,

THEOREM 10. *Let $f(x)$ be a polynomial of the form* (2) *with real coefficients and of degree* > 0. *Let the real zeros of $f(x)$ be $\alpha_1, \alpha_2, \cdots, \alpha_s$; the pairs of complex conjugate zeros, $\beta_1, \overline{\beta}_1$; $\beta_2, \overline{\beta}_2$; $\cdots$; $\beta_t, \overline{\beta}_t$. Let n_i be the multiplicity of α_i, m_i that of β_i. Then*

$$f(x) = (x-\alpha_1)^{n_1}(x-\alpha_2)^{n_2}\cdots(x-\alpha_s)^{n_s}\cdot$$
$$[x^2-(\beta_1+\overline{\beta}_1)x+\beta_1\overline{\beta}_1]^{m_1}[x^2-(\beta_2+\overline{\beta}_2)x+\beta_2\overline{\beta}_2]^{m_2}\cdots$$
$$\cdots[x^2-(\beta_t+\overline{\beta}_t)x+\beta_t\overline{\beta}_t]^{m_t}$$

is the factorization of $f(x)$ into its irreducible real factors.

Hence it is clear that real polynomials of higher than the second degree are reducible even in the domain of real polynomials.

Exercises

1. As in (47), let

$$x^n + a_1x^{n-1} + \cdots + a_{n-1}x + a_n = (x-\alpha_1)(x-\alpha_2)\cdots(x-\alpha_n).$$

Prove that

$$a_k = (-1)^k \cdot \sum_{\substack{i_1, i_2, \cdots, i_k = 1 \\ i_1 < i_2 < \cdots < i_k}}^{n} \alpha_{i_1}\cdot\alpha_{i_2}\cdot\cdots\cdot\alpha_{i_k}.$$

2. If $f(x) = (x-\alpha_1)(x-\alpha_2)\cdots(x-\alpha_n)$, then $g_i(x) = \dfrac{f(x)}{x-\alpha_i}$ is also a polynomial. The sum of all of these $g_i(x)$, i.e. $\sum_{i=1}^{n} g_i(x)$, is a polynomial of degree $n-1$, and is called the *derivative* of $f(x)$. We write $f'(x) = \sum_{i=1}^{n} g_i(x)$. Show, using Exercise 1, that

$$f'(x) = nx^{n-1} + (n-1)a_1x^{n-2} + \cdots + 2a_{n-2}x + a_{n-1}.$$

3. α is a multiple zero of $f(x)$ if and only if α is a zero of both $f(x)$ and $f'(x)$.
4. If $f(x)$ and its derivative $f'(x)$ are relatively prime, then all zeros of $f(x)$ are of multiplicity 1.
5. Let R be the field of rational numbers, R$[x]$ the domain of polynomials with coefficients in R. Prove that an irreducible polynomial of R$[x]$ has only simple zeros (i.e. zeros of multiplicity 1) in the field of complex numbers.
6. A quadratic polynomial ax^2+bx+c with real coefficients a, b, c is irreducible in the domain of real polynomials if and only if $b^2-4ac<0$.

7. Let F be an arbitrary field, F$[x]$ the polynomial domain in one variable with coefficients in F. Prove that

a) Every polynomial of F$[x]$ of degree n has at most n roots in F.

b) Let F contain infinitely many elements. Let $f(x)$ and $g(x)$ be two polynomials such that $f(a)=g(a)$ for *every* element a of F. Then we also have $f(x)=g(x)$.

c) Let F contain only a *finite* number of elements. Then there exist two polynomials $f(x)$ and $g(x)$ of F$[x]$ such that $f(x) \neq g(x)$, but that nevertheless $f(a)=g(a)$ for *every* a of F.

CHAPTER IV

ELEMENTS OF GROUP THEORY

§ 18. The Concept of a Group

In Chapter III we made an abstract study of certain systems of elements called fields, for which two operations were defined satisfying certain laws (the field axioms). Now there also exist certain systems of elements for which not all of the field axioms are satisfied. It often happens that only *one* operation is given, satisfying certain laws from which consequences are to be drawn. This last case has been developed in modern mathematics as an independent discipline called *group theory*. We shall now give a brief introduction to this branch of mathematics.

Let G be a non-empty set of elements $A, B, C, \ldots$, in which a *binary operation* is defined; that is, to every *ordered pair* A, B of G, the binary operation assigns a third element $F(A, B)$, where for the moment we leave open the question of whether or not $F(A, B)$ belongs to G. In other words, a mapping is given which sends the ordered pairs of elements of G into certain image elements $F(A, B)$. We must note that it is the *ordered* pairs which are mapped, i.e. it may well be that $F(A, B)$ and $F(B, A)$ are different.

We call this operation *multiplication* and call $F(A, B)$ the *product* of A and B. We write $F(A, B) = A \cdot B$.[1]

The set G is called a **group** *with respect to the given multiplication* if the following conditions—the so-called *group axioms*—are satisfied.

I. *Closure: Multiplication may be carried out in* G, *i.e. the product of any two elements A, B of* G *is itself in* G.[2]

II. *The Associative Law: For any three elements A, B, C of* G, *we always have* $(A \cdot B) \cdot C = A \cdot (B \cdot C)$.

---

[1] This agrees with the general usage. Of course we could just as well have written $A + B$, $A \circ B$, or any other symbol.

[2] Of course, we could have taken this requirement as part of the concept "operation," as we did earlier in connection with addition and multiplication in a field (cf., for example, footnote 1 in § 14). We have listed it separately here, since it often needs verification which should not be forgotten.

III. *The Possibility of Division: For any two elements A, B of* G *there is always at least one X in* G *such that $A \cdot X = B$, and always at least one Y in* G, *such that $Y \cdot A = B$.*

As usual (cf. p. 189), a product $A \cdot B \cdot \ldots \cdot D$ of a finite number of elements of G is understood to stand for that element of G which is obtained by the step-by-step replacement of pairs of neighboring elements by their products until but one element remains. By I, this element is itself in G. The ambiguity of this rule is removed by means of the Associative Law. For it follows by mathematical induction exactly as on p. 189, that the value of $A \cdot B \cdot \ldots \cdot D$ is independent of the manner of "parenthesization."

However the value of a product is, in general, dependent on the order of its elements. In fact the Commutative Law $A \cdot B = B \cdot A$ is not required to hold, and indeed is often not fulfilled. If the Commutative Law is also satisfied, then one calls the group *commutative* or *abelian.*

Let us compare the group axioms with the field axioms. We see immediately that the "Laws of Addition" on p. 188 say that the totality of elements of a field form a commutative group with respect to field addition as the operation.[3] Similarly it follows from the "Laws of Multiplication" on p. 194 that all the elements of a field which are $\neq 0$, form a commutative group with respect to field multiplication. This statement is however not fully equivalent to the Laws of Multiplication. For it does not include the rules for multiplication of the element 0 with the other elements.[4]

We mention a few other simple examples and counter-examples, as follows:

Examples of groups:

The set of all rational integers under the operation of ordinary addition.

The set of all rational integers which are divisible by a *fixed* integer n, under the operation of ordinary addition.

The set of all vectors of a linear vector space of R_n under the operation of vector addition.

---

[3] As regards Axiom I, cf. footnote 1.

[4] On the other hand, Rule 4 of multiplication on p. 194 follows from the statement, "The totality of all elements of a field which are not equal to 0 form a group under multiplication." For we have explicitly assumed that a group is non-empty which here implies the existence of an element unequal to 0.

The set of all complex numbers of absolute value 1, under the operation of multiplication (cf. § 16).

Counter-examples:

The set of all rational integers under the operation of ordinary multiplication. Group Axiom III is not satisfied.

The set of all rational integers under the operation of ordinary subtraction. Group Axiom II is not satisfied.

The set of all positive real numbers under the operation of ordinary addition. Axiom III is not satisfied.

The set of all negative real numbers under the operation of ordinary multiplication. Axioms I and III are not satisfied.

We now wish to derive a few consequences from the group axioms which will correspond to our discussion of the field axioms on p. 195 (also on p. 192 ff.). First we will prove the existence of an "identity" or "unit element." We have to proceed somewhat more carefully than in the above-mentioned places, since we do not assume the Commutative Law.

We first prove the following: *There is at least one right identity in the group* G, *i.e. an element* E_r, *which satisfies the equation* $A \cdot E_r = A$ *for every* A *of* G.

To prove this, let A_0 be a fixed element of G. Then the equation $A_0 \cdot X = A_0$ has at least one solution $X = X_0$, so that

(1) $$A_0 \cdot X_0 = A_0.$$

Multiplying (1) *on the left*[5] by any element Y of the group, we have by use of the Associative Law II that

(2) $$(Y \cdot A_0) \cdot X_0 = (Y \cdot A_0).$$

Because of the solvability of the equation $Y \cdot A_0 = A$ for Y, we have that the product $Y \cdot A_0$ can be made equal to any given element A of the group, by proper choice of the element Y. Thus we see from (2) that for every A in G we have

(3) $$A \cdot X_0 = A.$$

But this means that our X_0 is a right identity.

In the same way, we prove the existence of at least one *left identity*, i.e. of an element E_l such that $E_l \cdot A = A$ for any A of G.

Next we shall prove

[5] To "multiply an equation *on the left* by Y" of course means to "place Y at the *left* of both sides of the equation as a factor."

THEOREM 1. *For any two elements A, B of* G, *the equation*

$$X \cdot A = B \tag{4}$$

has only one solution X in G.

Proof: Let E_r be a definite right identity of G and Y a definite solution of the equation

$$A \cdot Y = E_r. \tag{5}$$

Multiply (4) on the right by Y. We then have

$$(XA)Y = BY,$$
$$X(AY) = BY,$$
$$X \cdot E_r = BY, \qquad \text{(by (5))},$$
$$X = BY \quad \text{(since } E_r \text{ is a right identity)}. \tag{6}$$

If X' is another solution of (4), it follows similarly that $X' = BY$ *with the same* Y. Thus we must have $X' = X$, i.e. there is but one solution of (4).

Analogously, using a fixed left identity, we obtain

THEOREM 1a. *For any two elements A, B of* G, *the equation $AX = B$ has precisely one solution X in* G.

Applying Theorems 1 and 1a to the equations $AX = A$, $YB = B$, it follows that there is only one left identity E_l and only one right identity E_r in G. Furthermore we have for these identities E_l, E_r that

$$E_l \cdot E_r = E_l,$$

because E_r is a right identity, and

$$E_l \cdot E_r = E_r,$$

because E_l is a left identity. Therefore we must have $E_l = E_r$. This proves

THEOREM 2. *There is one (and only one) identity in* G, *i.e. an element E such that $EA = AE = A$ holds for all A of* G.

In what follows we always use the letter E for the identity of G.

It follows from Theorems 1 and 1a that for any fixed A, the elements X and Y satisfying the equations

$$AX = E, \quad YA = E \tag{7}$$

are also uniquely determined. For these elements X and Y we can deduce from (7) that

$$YAX = Y(AX) = YE = Y,$$
$$YAX = (YA)X = EX = X.$$

Therefore $X = Y$. This element $X = Y$ is called the *inverse* (or *reciprocal*) of A and is denoted by A^{-1}. Thus we have

THEOREM 3. *To every element A, there is a uniquely determined inverse, i.e. an element A^{-1} satisfying the equation $A^{-1}A = AA^{-1} = E$.*

A trivial consequence of this theorem is the "*cancellation law*," i.e. $A \cdot X = A \cdot Y$ implies $X = Y$. This can be seen by simply multiplying on the left by A^{-1}. Of course we similarly have that $XA = YA$ implies $X = Y$.

A further rule is that

$$(A^{-1})^{-1} = A \tag{8}$$

for each A. For, $(A^{-1})^{-1}$ is, by Theorem 1a, the uniquely determined solution of $A^{-1} \cdot X = E$. But this last equation is satisfied by $X = A$. The inverse of an arbitrary product $B = A_1 A_2 \ldots A_r$ is given by $B^{-1} = A_r^{-1} A_{r-1}^{-1} \cdots A_2^{-1} A_1^{-1}$. (Note the change in order.) This follows from the fact that in the product $B \cdot B^{-1}$ we may first combine and cancel A_r and A_r^{-1} in the center, then A_{r-1} and A_{r-1}^{-1}, etc.

We now explain what is meant by a *power with integral exponent* of an element of a group. By A^n, with n a positive integer, we mean, as usual, the product $A \cdot A \cdot \ldots \cdot A$, in which the element A appears n times as a factor. By A^{-n} we shall mean simply the n-th power of A^{-1}. Finally we set $A^0 = E$ (the identity). With this understanding we have the usual[6] rules of exponents, namely

$$A^k \cdot A^l = A^{k+l}, \tag{9}$$

$$(A^k)^l = A^{kl}. \tag{10}$$

For many applications it is useful to know that Axiom III for groups may be replaced by one which is apparently weaker, namely by

III*. *There is (at least) one element E in G with the following two properties:*

(*i*) *for every A in G we have $AE = A$,*

(*ii*) *for every A in G the equation $AX = E$ has a solution.*

---

[6] In order to see why equations (9) and (10) hold, we need only count the number of factors A and A^{-1} on both sides of the equations. In (10) (in case l is negative) we must use the fact that $(A^k)^{-1} = A^{-k}$ for every integer k.

III* states the existence of a right identity and of a "right inverse" with respect to this identity, and so is certainly satisfied in any group. We shall now show that Axiom III is a consequence of Axioms I, II, and III*, i.e. that if G satisfies Axioms I, II, and III*, then it is a group.

To this end, let A be an arbitrary element of G. By III* (*ii*) there is an element $\bar{A}$ satisfying $A\bar{A} = E$ and an element $\bar{\bar{A}}$ satisfying $\bar{A} \cdot \bar{\bar{A}} = E$. We now consider the product $\bar{A}A\bar{A}\bar{\bar{A}}$. By breaking it up in two different ways and using III* (*i*), we have

$$\bar{A}(A\bar{A})\bar{\bar{A}} = \bar{A}E\bar{\bar{A}} = (\bar{A}E)\bar{\bar{A}} = \bar{A}\bar{\bar{A}} = E,$$
$$(\bar{A}A)(\bar{A}\bar{\bar{A}}) = (\bar{A}A)E = \bar{A}A.$$

Thus by the Associative Law, $\bar{A}A = E$. That is, *if $\bar{A}$ is a right inverse of A, then it is also a left inverse.*

Furthermore,

$$EA = (A\bar{A})A = A(\bar{A}A) = AE = A.$$

Therefore, *E is also a left identity.*

Now we can easily deduce III. The element $X = \bar{A}B$ is a solution of the equation $AX = B$, since

$$A(\bar{A}B) = (A\bar{A})B = E \cdot B = B.$$

Furthermore, a solution of the equation $Y \cdot A = B$ is given by $Y = B\bar{A}$, since

$$(B\bar{A})A = B(\bar{A}A) = B \cdot E = B.$$

Analogous results could, of course, have been obtained if we had postulated, instead of III*, the existence of a left identity and of a left inverse.

Exercises

1. Show directly from I, II, III*, that

a) An element J which satisfies $J^2 = J$ is necessarily the right identity.
b) If $A\bar{A} = E$, then the element $J = \bar{A}A$ satisfies the equation $J^2 = J$.

2. Let G be a *finite* set of elements. Let an operation be defined in G, satisfying Axioms I and II, as well as the cancellation rules; i.e.

$$AX = AY \text{ implies } X = Y,$$
$$XA = YA \text{ implies } X = Y.$$

Show that G is a group.

Hint: Compare the products $AA_1, AA_2, \cdots, AA_n$, where $A_1, A_2, \cdots, A_n$ ($A_i \neq A_k$ for $i \neq k$) are all the different elements of G and A is a fixed one of them.

§ 19. Subgroups; Examples

If a subset H of a group G is also a group under the binary operation defined for G, then H is called a *subgroup* of G. In order to decide whether or not a subset H is a subgroup it is not necessary to verify all of the group axioms. For example, the Associative Law is automatically satisfied for every subset, since the equation $(AB)C = A(BC)$ holds for *any* three elements of G. We shall now show that a non-empty subset H of G is a subgroup if both of the following conditions are fulfilled:

(*i*) *Closure for* H.

(*ii*) *If H belongs to* H, *then so does H^{-1}.*

For by (*ii*), if H belongs to H, so does H^{-1}, and so, by (*i*), does $H \cdot H^{-1} = E$. Thus, Axiom III* is seen to be satisfied, and H is indeed a group.

If we know that H consists of only a *finite number* of elements (as, for example, is the case if G is finite), then property (*ii*) need not be verified. It is, in this case, actually a consequence of (*i*). We see this as follows:

If H is any element of H, then all the elements of the infinite sequence $H, H^2, H^3, \ldots$ belong to H by (*i*). But then, since H is finite, the elements in this infinite sequence cannot all be distinct. Thus there must be two different exponents m and n for which $H^m = H^n$. We then have that $H \cdot H^{m-n-1} = E$. Since we may take $m > n$ and so have $m - n - 1 \geqq 0$, we have shown that the inverse of H can be represented as a power of H with exponent $k \geqq 0$. If k is positive, then H^k is an element of H. If k is zero, then the inverse of H is E, and so H itself is E, and the inverse of H is in H. Thus (*ii*) follows from (*i*).[1]

It should be stressed that for infinite H, statement (*ii*) is by no means a consequence of (*i*).[2]

Our further discussion of subgroups will be simplified by the following notation. If H and K are any two *complexes* in G, i.e. non-empty subsets of G (not necessarily subgroups), then by H • K we mean the

---

[1] The fact that H is a subgroup if H is finite and (*i*) holds, also follows from exercise 2 of § 1, for the cancellation rules certainly hold in H since they hold in G.

[2] *Example*: Let G be the group of integers under the operation of addition; H the class of all positive integers. Then (*i*) is satisfied, while (*ii*) is not.

set of all elements of the form $H \cdot K$ with H in H and K in K. By this definition, *multiplication of complexes* is obviously associative.[3]

Now, let H be a fixed subgroup. Let us form all complexes of the form $\mathrm{H} \cdot X$ with X an arbitrary element of G. Such a complex $\mathrm{H} \cdot X$ is called a *right coset* of H. As we shall soon see, a right coset is *not* in general a group. Similarly, the complexes $X \cdot \mathrm{H}$ are called *left cosets* of H.

Every element X in G belongs to at least one right coset and to at least one left coset, namely to $\mathrm{H} \cdot X$ and to $X \cdot \mathrm{H}$. For, H contains the identity E, and thus $\mathrm{H} \cdot X$ contains $E \cdot X = X$, and similarly $X \cdot \mathrm{H}$ contains $X \cdot E = X$.

If X is in H, then $\mathrm{H} \cdot X = X \cdot \mathrm{H} = \mathrm{H}$. For, by the closure of H, $\mathrm{H} \cdot X$ and $X \cdot \mathrm{H}$ are then both contained in H. But every element of H is an element of both $\mathrm{H} \cdot X$ and $X \cdot \mathrm{H}$, since every element of H is representable in the form $H \cdot X$ as well as in the form $X \cdot H$ with H in H.[4]

Furthermore, we have the following: If two right cosets $\mathrm{H} \cdot X_1$ and $\mathrm{H} \cdot X_2$ have an element in common, then they consist of exactly the same elements. In other words, *two right cosets are either disjoint or identical.*

Proof: Let K be an element common to $\mathrm{H} \cdot X_1$ and $\mathrm{H} \cdot X_2$. Then there is an element H of H for which $H \cdot X_1 = K$ and an element H' of H for which $K = H' \cdot X_2$. However, since $\mathrm{H} = \mathrm{H} \cdot H = \mathrm{H} \cdot H'$, we have

$$\mathrm{H} \cdot X_1 = (\mathrm{H} \cdot H) \cdot X_1 = \mathrm{H}(H \cdot X_1) = \mathrm{H} \cdot K,$$
$$\mathrm{H} \cdot X_2 = (\mathrm{H} \cdot H') \cdot X_2 = \mathrm{H} \cdot (H' \cdot X_2) = \mathrm{H} \cdot K,$$

from which we deduce that $\mathrm{H}X_1 = \mathrm{H}X_2$.

Naturally, the same statement holds for two left cosets.

We next choose any one element from each right coset as a *representative* of this coset. Let R be the set of all representatives. The entire group G is the union of all $\mathrm{H} \cdot X$ with X in R. This is usually written:

---

[3] For if $\mathrm{H}_1, \mathrm{H}_2, \mathrm{H}_3$ are any three complexes, then $\mathrm{H}_1 \cdot (\mathrm{H}_2 \cdot \mathrm{H}_3)$ consists of all elements of the form $H_1 \cdot (H_2 \cdot H_3)$ with H_i in H_i; on the other hand $(\mathrm{H}_1 \cdot \mathrm{H}_2) \cdot \mathrm{H}_3$ consists of all elements of the form $(H_1 \cdot H_2) \cdot H_3$, which are the same as the others because the associative law holds for group elements.

[4] Indeed, this representation merely means that each of the equations $H \cdot X = K$ and $X \cdot H = K$, where H is the unknown and X and K are given elements of H, has a solution in H.

$$G = \sum_{X \subset R} H \cdot X, \tag{1}$$

Here, any two summands $H \cdot X$ and $H \cdot X'$ ($X \neq X'$) are disjoint. Naturally, analogous statements hold for any system L of representatives consisting of one and only one element of every left coset. Thus

$$G = \sum_{Y \subset L} Y \cdot H, \tag{2}$$

where any two summands $Y \cdot H$ and $Y' \cdot H$ ($Y \neq Y'$) are disjoint.

What is the relation between the numbers of elements of two different cosets? We assert that *if* H *is infinite, then so is every right coset and every left coset. If* H *is finite and has r elements, then every right coset and every left coset also has exactly r elements.*

Both of these statements are contained in the following theorem: *There may be set up a one-to-one correspondence between the elements of* H *and those of any coset.* Let us compare H with, say, the coset $H \cdot X$. With the element H of H we associate the element $H \cdot X$ of $H \cdot X$. That this correspondence is one-to-one follows from the fact that if $H \neq H'$ then $H \cdot X \neq H'X$ (the cancellation law).

What is the relation between the number of right cosets of H and the number of left cosets? We have that *the number of right cosets and the number of left cosets are either both infinite, or both finite and equal.*

In fact, we can set up a one-to-one correspondence between the right cosets and the left cosets. Let R be a system of representatives for the right cosets (which thus contains exactly one element from each right coset). We map each element X of R onto its inverse X^{-1}. The set of these inverses X^{-1} will then be seen to form a system of representatives for the left cosets. This will be proved by showing that

1) Every element A of G belongs to at least one left coset $X^{-1} \cdot H$ with X in R.

2) $X^{-1} \cdot H$ and $X'^{-1} \cdot H$ are different if $H \cdot X$ and $H \cdot X'$ are different.

1) is deduced as follows: A^{-1} is certainly a member of some right coset $H \cdot X$ with X in R, i.e. there is an H in H such that $A^{-1} = H \cdot X$. It follows that $A = X^{-1} \cdot H^{-1}$, i.e. that A belongs to $X^{-1} \cdot H$.

2) is obtained as follows: If $X^{-1} \cdot H = X'^{-1} \cdot H$, then $H = X \cdot X'^{-1} \cdot H$ and thus $X \cdot X'^{-1}$ is an element of H. Hence $H \cdot X \cdot X'^{-1} = H$, i.e. $H \cdot X = H \cdot X'$.

The number of elements of a group is called its *order*. The number of right cosets (or equally well, of left cosets) of a subgroup H of G is called the *index of* H *in* G. Both order and index can be finite or infinite.

If the order of a group G is finite, say n, then the order of any subgroup H will certainly also be finite, say r. Every coset of H has then also r elements. If there are i right cosets, then

$$n = r \cdot i. \tag{3}$$

It thus follows that *in a finite group, the order and the index of a subgroup are divisors of the order of the entire group.*

As we shall soon see, by means of examples, a right coset of H need not in general be a left coset of H. But there are certain subgroups in which every right coset is also a left coset, and vice versa.[5] Subgroups having this property are called *normal subgroups*, or *normal divisors*, or *invariant subgroups*, of G.[6] A normal subgroup N of a group G is, according to our definition, characterized by the following property: For every X in G, the relation

$$X \cdot \mathrm{N} = \mathrm{N} \cdot X \tag{4}$$

holds. Multiplying the equation on the right by X^{-1}, we see that the condition states that for every X in G, the relation

$$X \cdot \mathrm{N} \cdot X^{-1} = \mathrm{N} \tag{5}$$

holds.

If one multiplies two cosets of a normal subgroup N *(in the sense of multiplication of complexes), the result is itself a coset.* For, from (4) and from the fact that N, being a subgroup, satisfies $\mathrm{N} \cdot \mathrm{N} = \mathrm{N}$, we have

$$(\mathrm{N} \cdot X_1) \cdot (\mathrm{N} \cdot X_2) = \mathrm{N} \cdot (X_1 \cdot \mathrm{N}) X_2 = \mathrm{N} \cdot (\mathrm{N} \cdot X_1) X_2 = (\mathrm{N} \cdot \mathrm{N}) \cdot (X_1 \cdot X_2) = \mathrm{N}(X_1 \cdot X_2). \tag{6}$$

But what is more, *the cosets of a normal subgroup form a group under multiplication of complexes.* We have already verified closure above. The Associative Law, as we know, holds generally for the multiplication of complexes in G and so is certainly verified here. Finally,

[5] For example the trivial subgroup consisting of the identity element alone, is of this type.

[6] The condition "of G" is essential. A group which is at the same time a subgroup of two different groups may well be a normal subgroup of one but not of the other.

there exists a right identity, namely N itself, and $N \cdot X^{-1}$ is a right inverse of $N \cdot X$, since by (6),

$$(N \cdot X) \cdot N = (N \cdot X) \cdot (N \cdot E) = N(X \cdot E) = N \cdot X,$$
$$(N \cdot X) \cdot (N \cdot X^{-1}) = N(X \cdot X^{-1}) = N.$$

The group of cosets of a normal subgroup N of G is called the *quotient group of* G *with respect to* N and is written G/N. Its order is precisely the index of N in G.

We shall now clarify the foregoing ideas and theorems by a few examples. First we consider the group of rational integers under addition (cf. p. 246), which we denote by G. If n is any integer, then all the integral multiples of n form a subgroup H_n of G.[7] H_n is even a normal subgroup of G. For, G is an *abelian* or *commutative*[8] group, and in such a group every subgroup is normal, since in this case condition (4) is always satisfied. The coset of H_n in which the integer a lies, consists of the elements $xn + a$, where x runs through all the integers. In number theory, such a coset is called a *residue class modulo n*. There are n different cosets of H_n, and so H_n has index n in G. The quotient group of G with respect to H_n is called the *additive group of residue classes modulo n*.

We now give an *example* of a group in which it is easy to construct various subgroups. Let M be any set (M may be finite or infinite). Let the elements of M be called points and denote them by $\alpha, \beta, \gamma \ldots$. Consider the set P of all one-to-one mappings of M onto itself. For these mappings, we define a rule of composition as follows: If s and t are two mappings of P, then by the product of s and t, which we write $s \cdot t$, we mean the mapping whose effect is that of first applying t to an element of M and then applying s to the result. In other words, if $\beta = t(\alpha)$ is the image of α under the mapping t, and $\gamma = s(\beta)$ is the image of β under s, then $\gamma = s \cdot t(\alpha) = s[t(\alpha)]$ is defined to be the image of α under the mapping $s \cdot t$.[9] It is clear that the product of two one-to-one mappings of M onto itself is a one-to-one mapping of M onto itself. The Associative Law is satisfied in P. For, let

$$u(\alpha) = \beta, \qquad t(\beta) = \gamma, \qquad s(\gamma) = \delta.$$

[7] The sum of two multiples of n is also a multiple of n, since $xn + yn = (x + y)n$. And the "inverse" of xn is $-xn = (-x)n$.

[8] Cf. p. 246.

[9] Observe the order! We apply the factors in a product from right to left.

Then, by the above definition of multiplication,

$$s[(t \cdot u)(\alpha)] = s(\gamma) = \delta \text{ and } (s \cdot t)[u(\alpha)] = (s \cdot t)(\beta) = \delta.$$

The identity of P is the identity mapping, i.e. the mapping e which sends each point of M into itself. For, we have $(s \cdot e)(\alpha) = s(\alpha)$, so that $s \cdot e = s$ and similarly $e \cdot s = s$. Furthermore, for every mapping t which sends, say, α into β, there is a left inverse in P, namely the mapping x of M onto itself which sends β into α, so that we have for every α that $x[t(\alpha)] = \alpha$, i.e. $xt = e$. We have thus shown that P is a group under this method of composition. This group P is called the *complete permutation group of the set* M.

Now let M be finite. M then consists of, say, n points, which for simplicity we designate by $1, 2, \ldots, n$. Then the one-to-one mappings of M onto itself are the permutations of $1, 2, \ldots, n$. There are $n!$ of these. The complete permutation group of M has order $n!$ in this case and is called the *symmetric group of degree n.*

We can easily determine various subgroups of the symmetric group (as well as of the complete permutation group of any set) by certain requirements of *invariance*. For example, the set of elements of the symmetric group of degree n which leave a fixed point, say 1, invariant (i.e. map it onto itself) constitutes a subgroup. For, if two of these mappings (i.e. elements of the group) leave the point 1 fixed, then so does their product. This subgroup consists of all elements which permute the points $2, 3, \ldots, n$ among themselves and therefore has order $(n-1)!$ and hence has index n in the whole group.

It is easy to find the right and left cosets of this subgroup, which we call H. Let σ be an element of the subgroup and τ any group element. If τ sends the point k into the point 1, then so does $\sigma \cdot \tau$, since σ keeps 1 fixed. If we hold τ fixed, then this applies with any σ of the subgroup. Thus, we see that if two elements belong to the same right coset, they always send the same point k into 1. Conversely, if τ_1, τ_2 are two mappings sending a fixed point k into 1, then τ_2^{-1} sends 1 into k, and thus the product $\tau_1 \cdot \tau_2^{-1}$ keeps 1 fixed, and hence is some element σ of H. However, if $\tau_1 \cdot \tau_2^{-1} = \sigma$, then $\tau_1 = \sigma\tau_2$, i.e. τ_1 and τ_2 belong to the same right coset. Thus two elements τ_1, τ_2 belong to the same right coset of H *if and only if* there is a point k for which $\tau_1(k) = \tau_2(k) = 1$.

Similarly, we see that two elements τ_1, τ_2 belong to the same left coset of H if and only if $\tau_1(1) = \tau_2(1)$, i.e. if τ_1 and τ_2 send the point 1 into the same image.

If the degree n of the symmetric group is greater than 2, then we can always find elements which satisfy only one of the above conditions.[10] Thus H is not a normal subgroup of the symmetric group if the degree is greater than 2.

From now on, let M be the set of all points in euclidean R_n. We shall obtain some subgroups of its complete permutation group, again by means of invariance requirements. As a first such requirement, we take the defining property of an affine transformation (p. 180). In other words, we wish to show that those affine transformations which belong to the complete permutation group of M, form a subgroup of that permutation group. What kind of affine transformations are these? Precisely those which represent one-to-one mappings of M onto itself, i.e. the non-singular ones (cf. p. 184).

We have first to show that if σ and τ are non-singular affine transformations, then so is their product $\sigma \cdot \tau$. This, however, is trivial. For if all the relations of the form (1) of p. 180 are invariant under τ and under σ, then they are also invariant under successive application of both τ and σ in either order.

In order to see that the same holds for the inverse of σ, let P, Q, R, S be four points and let $P^* = \sigma(P)$, $Q^* = \sigma(Q)$, $R^* = \sigma(R)$, $S^* = \sigma(S)$ be their image points. We must show that if a relation $\overrightarrow{R^*S^*} = \lambda \cdot \overrightarrow{P^*Q^*}$ holds, then the relation $\overrightarrow{RS} = \lambda \cdot \overrightarrow{PQ}$ must also hold. We can certainly find a point T such that $\overrightarrow{RT} = \lambda \cdot \overrightarrow{PQ}$. Let $T^* = \sigma(T)$ be its image point. Then (since σ is an affine transformation) $\overrightarrow{R^*T^*} = \lambda \cdot \overrightarrow{P^*Q^*}$. Therefore $\overrightarrow{R^*T^*} = \overrightarrow{R^*S^*}$ so that $T^* = S^*$. And, since σ is a one-to-one mapping, we have $T = S$, from which the relation $\overrightarrow{RS} = \lambda \cdot \overrightarrow{PQ}$ follows.

The group of all non-singular affine transformations is called the *affine group of R_n*.

We know from p. 183 that every affine transformation can be represented, relative to a fixed linear coordinate system, by a system of linear equations (p. 183, (15)). Let there be given two affine trans-

---

[10] For $n = 3$, two such transformations τ_1, τ_2, may be defined by

$$\begin{aligned} \tau_1(1) &= 2, & \tau_2(1) &= 3, \\ \tau_1(2) &= 1, & \tau_2(2) &= 1, \\ \tau_1(3) &= 3, & \tau_2(3) &= 2. \end{aligned}$$

Both take the point 2 into 1, but $\tau_1(1) \neq \tau_2(1)$.

formations σ and τ relative to a fixed coordinate system, as follows:[11]

$$(7) \qquad \sigma: \quad y_i = t_i + \sum_{k=1}^{n} a_{ik} x_k, \qquad i = 1, 2, \cdots, n,$$

$$(8) \qquad \tau: \quad z_i = s_i + \sum_{k=1}^{n} b_{ik} x_k, \qquad i = 1, 2, \cdots, n.$$

The coordinates of $\sigma \cdot \tau(P)$ are obtained when we substitute the coordinates of $\tau(P)$ in (7), i.e. replace the x_k in (7) by the z_k of (8). Thus, *the equations for the product* $\sigma \cdot \tau$ *are given by*

$$(9) \quad y_i = \left(t_i + \sum_{k=1}^{n} a_{ik} s_k\right) + \sum_{k=1}^{n} \left(\sum_{\nu=1}^{n} a_{i\nu} b_{\nu k}\right) \cdot x_k, \qquad i = 1, 2, \cdots, n.$$

Evidently, the *equations for the inverse mapping* σ^{-1} are obtained from (7) by solving[12] for the x_k.

The set of all rigid motions of euclidean R_n is a subgroup of the affine group. For, these are precisely those one-to-one transformations which leave all distances invariant. Moreover, if σ, τ are two such transformations, then it is clear that σ^{-1} and $\sigma \cdot \tau$ also preserve distance.

The rigid motions are divided into two classes—the proper and improper motions (p. 184). The proper motions are characterized by the following property (cf. p. 184): The value of a determinant $|u_{ik}|$ whose rows are the components of n linearly independent vectors with respect to a cartesian coordinate system, is unchanged if we replace the u_{ik} by the components of the image vectors.[13] This invariance property shows that the proper motions form a subgroup of the group of all motions.

Let B be the group of all motions, and E the group of all proper motions. What is the index of E in B? Since the above determinant $|u_{ik}|$ changes its sign under application of an improper motion, it remains invariant upon the successive application of two improper motions.

---

[11] These equations are to be understood as follows: If P has coordinates

$$x_1, x_2, \cdots, x_n,$$

then $\sigma(P)$ has the coordinates y_i given by (7) and $\tau(P)$ has the coordinates z_i given by (8).

[12] This solution is possible because σ is non-singular, and so (by p. 184) the determinant $|a_{ik}|$ is non-vanishing.

[13] The sign of this determinant is changed if the rigid motion is improper.

This shows that the product of two improper motions is a proper motion. Let σ be a fixed improper motion, and τ any other one. Then $\tau \cdot \sigma = \chi$ is a proper motion. Since $\tau = \chi \cdot \sigma^{-1}$, we see that any improper motion τ is in the right coset $\mathrm{E} \cdot \sigma^{-1}$. This shows that there are exactly two right cosets of E in B, namely E itself and the totality of all improper motions. *Thus the index of* E *in* B *is equal to* 2.

The totality of improper motions is also the only left coset other than E.[14] Therefore the left and right cosets of E are identical. E *is a normal subgroup of* B.

As our last example, we shall consider some subgroups of the group of proper motions in three-dimensional space, whose geometric significance is evident. Let O be a fixed point of this space. The set of all proper motions which leave this point fixed clearly forms such a subgroup. Since any such motion maps every sphere with center O onto itself as a whole, we can look upon this subgroup as the (proper) motions of a sphere onto itself.

What sort of motions are these? This is easily clarified by consulting the table on p. 178. Since our motions are proper, they must appear in rows I and II of this table. Furthermore, since they have a fixed point, any such motion is seen to be a rotation of R_3 about some line. This line, or axis, evidently passes through the point O. We can state this result as follows: *The set of all rotations of R_3 about axes passing through some fixed point O, form a group.*

Instead of requiring the invariance of a sphere, we might investigate all proper motions of R_3 which map a regular polyhedron onto itself. Such motions are also rotations, because they keep the midpoint of the polyhedron fixed. The subgroups which we thus obtain are finite. For, every such rotation results in a permutation of the vertices of the polyhedron, and conversely is determined by this permutation.[15] Since the number of vertices is finite, there can only be a finite number of rotations mapping the polyhedron onto itself. One obtains a group of order 12 for the tetrahedron, groups of order 24 for the cube and for the octahedron, and groups of order 60 for the dodecahedron and for the icosahedron. We leave the easy verification of these results to the reader.

---

[14] Since the index of E in B is 2, there is only one left coset different from E, and it must therefore consist of all elements not in E. This all follows from the fact that the index is 2, and the argument shows that *every subgroup of index* 2 *is a normal subgroup.*

[15] Of course, not every permutation of the vertices gives rise to such a rotation.

Exercises

1. Let $O = (0, 0, \ldots, 0)$ be the origin of R_n, and furthermore let $\mathfrak{e}_1, \mathfrak{e}_2, \cdots, \mathfrak{e}_n$ be the unit vectors. Let an affine transformation be given in the coordinate system $[O; \mathfrak{e}_1, \mathfrak{e}_2, \cdots, \mathfrak{e}_n]$ (cf. p. 117ff.) by

$$y_i = t_i + \sum_{k=1}^{n} a_{ik} x_k, \qquad i = 1, 2, \cdots, n.$$

Show that the determinant $|a_{ik}| = A$ has the following significance (independent of the coordinate system): For any n vectors $\mathfrak{u}_i = \{u_{i1}, u_{i2}, \cdots, u_{in}\}$, $i = 1, 2, \cdots, n$, and their images $\mathfrak{u}_i^* = \{u_{i1}^*, u_{i2}^*, \cdots, u_{in}^*\}$, we have $|u_{ik}^*| = A \cdot |u_{ik}|$. The quantity A is called the determinant of the affine transformation. We can easily form subgroups of the affine group by imposing conditions on A; e.g. the following are subgroups:

The totality of affine transformations with rational $A \neq 0$;
the totality of affine transformations with $A = \pm 1$ (or only with $A = +1$).

2. Is the affine group a normal subgroup of the complete permutation group of R_n? Is the group of all rigid motions a normal subgroup of the affine group?

3. A *translation* (cf. p. 164) is a one-to-one mapping of R_n onto itself which keeps every *vector* invariant (i.e. $\overrightarrow{P^* Q^*} = \overrightarrow{PQ}$). The set of translations is a subgroup of the group of proper motions. Is it a normal subgroup?

4. Which of the groups occurring in exercises 1 to 3 are abelian, and which are not?

§ 20. The Basis Theorem for Abelian Groups

Abelian groups, i.e. those in which the Commutative law for group multiplication always holds, are the simplest of all groups. The so-called *basis theorem* for abelian groups, whose proof is the principal task of this section, gives us an especially thorough knowledge of such groups.

We begin by defining certain terms as follows:

A *power-product* of r group elements $A_1, A_2, \ldots, A_r$ is an expression of the form $A_1^{x_1} \cdot A_2^{x_2} \cdot \cdots \cdot A_r^{x_r}$, where the exponents may be any integers.

Multiplication of two power-products of the same element A_i may be carried out in an especially simple way in an abelian group. For since (by the Commutative law) the order of factors in a product does not matter, we have the following rule:

$$(A_1^{x_1} \cdot A_2^{x_2} \cdot \cdots \cdot A_r^{x_r}) \cdot (A_1^{y_1} \cdot A_2^{y_2} \cdot \cdots \cdot A_r^{y_r}) = A_1^{x_1+y_1} \cdot A_2^{x_2+y_2} \cdot \cdots \cdot A_r^{x_r+y_r}.$$

A *finite system of generators* of an *abelian* group G is a finite set $A_1, A_2, \ldots, A_r$ of elements of G having the following property: Every element X of G can be represented as a power-product of the A_i, i.e.

in the form $X = A_1^{x_1} \cdot A_2^{x_2} \cdot \cdots \cdot A_r^{x_r}$. For example, the set of all the elements of a finite abelian group is such a system of generators for the group. An infinite abelian group need not necessarily have a finite system of generators.

Two representations of an element X as a power-product of $A_1, A_2, \ldots, A_r$, say $X = A_1^{x_1} \cdot A_2^{x_2} \cdot \cdots \cdot A_r^{x_r} = A_1^{y_1} \cdot A_2^{y_2} \cdot \cdots \cdot A_r^{y_r}$ are said to be *equivalent* if $A_i^{x_i} = A_i^{y_i}$ for $i = 1, 2, \ldots, r$. (Note that we do *not* require that $x_i = y_i$.)

We say that *the element X has only one representation as a power-product of the A_i up to equivalence* if any two representations of X as a power-product are equivalent, i.e. if

$$X = A_1^{x_1} \cdot A_2^{x_2} \cdot \cdots \cdot A_r^{x_r} = A_1^{y_1} \cdot A_2^{y_2} \cdot \cdots \cdot A_r^{y_r}$$

always implies $A_i^{x_i} = A_i^{y_i}$, $i = 1, 2, \cdots, r$.

A **basis** of an abelian group is a finite system of generators such that every element in the group has exactly one representation up to equivalence as a power-product of these generators.

In order to determine whether a system of generators is a basis, one need not go to the trouble of proving that every element of the group is uniquely representable up to equivalence. It suffices to verify this for the identity E. Namely, the uniqueness of representation for the identity means that any relation $A_1^{x_1} \cdot A_2^{x_2} \cdot \cdots \cdot A_r^{x_r} = E$ implies $A_i^{x_i} = E$ for $i = 1, 2, \ldots, r$. For, $E = A_1^0 \cdot A_2^0 \cdot \cdots \cdot A_r^0$ is surely a representation of E, and if $E = A_1^{x_1} \cdot A_2^{x_2} \cdot \cdots \cdot A_r^{x_r}$ is an equivalent representation, then necessarily $A_i^{x_i} = A_i^0 = E$ for $i = 1, 2, \ldots, r$.

Let us now compare two representations of a group element X:

$$X = A_1^{x_1} \cdot A_2^{x_2} \cdot \cdots \cdot A_r^{x_r} = A_1^{y_1} \cdot A_2^{y_2} \cdot \cdots \cdot A_r^{y_r}.$$

It follows that

$$A_1^{x_1 - y_1} \cdot A_2^{x_2 - y_2} \cdot \cdots \cdot A_r^{x_r - y_r} = E.$$

If we assume the unique representability of E, this last equation yields

$$A_i^{x_i - y_i} = E, \qquad A_i^{x_i} = A_i^{y_i}, \qquad i = 1, 2, \cdots, r.$$

But this implies that X has only one representation as a power-product of the A_i up to equivalence.

Thus a basis of an abelian group could also have been defined as follows: *A finite system of generators $A_1, A_2, \ldots, A_r$ is a basis if every relation $A_1^{x_1} \cdot A_2^{x_2} \cdot \ldots \cdot A_r^{x_r} = E$ implies $A_i^{x_i} = E$ for $i = 1, 2, \ldots, r$.*

We shall now illustrate these concepts by an *example.* Let us consider the n-th roots of unity, i.e. the solutions of the equation $x^n = 1$ in the field of complex numbers. As we know, these are the n numbers

$$\varepsilon^k = \cos\left(\frac{2\pi \cdot k}{n}\right) + i \sin\left(\frac{2\pi \cdot k}{n}\right), \quad k = 1, 2, \cdots, n.$$

If ε^h and ε^k are n-th roots of unity, then so is $\varepsilon^h \cdot \varepsilon^k = \varepsilon^{h+k}$. Thus the n-th roots of unity clearly form a commutative group under ordinary multiplication in the field of complex numbers. This group has order n (i.e. contains n elements). The element ε forms a generating system, and in fact a basis, of this group. On the other hand, if we adjoin any other element $\varepsilon^k (k \neq n)$ then $\varepsilon, \varepsilon^k$ do not form a basis. A less trivial example of a generating system that is not a basis is obtained by letting $n = 12$ and considering the elements $A_1 = \varepsilon^2, A_2 = \varepsilon^3$. These form a system of generators, since, say, $\varepsilon^k = A_1^{-k} \cdot A_2^k$ for every k. Although $A_1^3 \cdot A_2^2 = 1 = E$, nevertheless $A_1^3 \neq 1$, $A_2^2 \neq 1$ so that A_1, A_2 do not form a basis. On the other hand, the elements ε^4 and ε^3, taken together, do form a basis.

Returning to our general considerations, we shall now formulate the *fundamental theorem* or ***Basis Theorem*** *for abelian groups,* as follows:

A (finite or infinite) abelian group which has a finite system of generators, has at least one basis.

To prove this, we choose a definite system of generators $A_1, A_2, \ldots, A_r$ whose order we keep fixed for the time being. We then consider all relations of the form

$$A_1^{a_1} \cdot A_2^{a_2} \cdot \ldots \cdot A_r^{a_r} = E. \tag{1}$$

Such a relation is uniquely determined by the exponents in their proper order, i.e. by the vector $\{a_1, a_2, \ldots, a_r\}$. Instead of speaking of "a relation (1) with the exponent vector $\{a_1, a_2, \ldots, a_r\}$," we shall often just speak of "a relation $\{a_1, a_2, \ldots, a_r\}$," for short.

If we take the n-th power of the relation (1) for some integer n, or if we multiply two equations of the form (1), we see that if $\{a_1, a_2, \ldots, a_r\}$ is an exponent vector of a relation (1), then so is any integral multiple $\{na_1, na_2, \ldots, na_r\}$, and if $\{a_1, a_2, \ldots, a_r\}$, $\{b_1, b_2, \ldots, b_r\}$ are exponent vectors, then so is their sum $\{a_1 + b_1, a_2 + b_2, \ldots, a_r + b_r\}$. Thus if the vectors $\mathfrak{a}_i = \{a_{i1}, a_{i2}, \cdots, a_{ir}\}$, $i = 1, 2, \ldots, s$, are relations, then so is every integral linear combination

$$n_1\mathfrak{a}_1 + n_2\mathfrak{a}_2 + \cdots + n_s\mathfrak{a}_s$$

(n_i integral). We call the relation

$$n_1\mathfrak{a}_1 + n_2\mathfrak{a}_2 + \cdots + n_s\mathfrak{a}_s$$

a *derived relation* of the relations $\mathfrak{a}_1, \mathfrak{a}_2, \ldots, \mathfrak{a}_s$.

A system of relations[1] in terms of which every relation which holds in the group G is representable as a derived relation, is called a *fundamental system* (with respect to the system $A_1, A_2, \ldots, A_r$ of generators).[2] A fundamental system may consist of a finite or of an infinite number of relations. For example, the system of *all* relations of a group is a fundamental system.

Let there be given a fixed fundamental system and let the exponent vectors of all its relations be written down in some definite order, say in such a way that these vectors form the rows of a matrix

$$(2) \qquad \begin{pmatrix} a_{11} & a_{12} & \cdots & a_{1r} \\ a_{21} & a_{22} & \cdots & a_{2r} \\ \cdot & \cdot & \cdot & \cdot \end{pmatrix}.$$

A fundamental system is completely determined by its associated matrix (2). We call (2) the *matrix of the fundamental system.*[3]

First note that we may transform our matrix in certain ways without losing the property that it is a matrix of a fundamental system with respect to our fixed system $A_1, A_2, \ldots, A_r$ of generators.

Such a permissible transformation is, for example, an arbitrary change in the order of the rows. It is also clear that we may add an additional row consisting of an integral linear combination of a finite number of its rows to the matrix (2). Conversely, if a row is an integral linear combination of some others (different from itself), then this row may be eliminated.

[1] In what follows, by relations we always mean relations of the form (1).

[2] Thus, if S is a fundamental system, then any relation $\mathfrak{a}$ of G may be represented as an integral linear combination of a finite number of relations $\mathfrak{a}_1, \mathfrak{a}_2, \cdots, \mathfrak{a}_s$ of S.

[3] Observe that we do not ask for linear independence of the rows of (2); we can even, for example, have some rows repeated.

From these transformations, we easily obtain other permissible transformations. If $\mathfrak{a}_i$ is a fixed row of (2) we may insert $-\mathfrak{a}_i$ as a new row, and then strike out $\mathfrak{a}_i$. But this means that we may replace $\mathfrak{a}_i$ by $-\mathfrak{a}_i$ or, in other words, we may multiply a row of (2) by (-1). Furthermore, we see that if $\mathfrak{a}_i, \mathfrak{a}_k$ $(i \neq k)$ are two different rows, and n is any integer, we may take $\mathfrak{a}_i + n\mathfrak{a}_k$ as a new row, and then strike out $\mathfrak{a}_i$. Thus we may add an integral multiple of the k-th row to the i-th row. This process may be performed simultaneously for a fixed k on arbitrarily many (possibly infinitely many) rows $\mathfrak{a}_{i_1}, \mathfrak{a}_{i_2}, \cdots$ $(k \neq i_1, i_2, \cdots)$.[4]

We set down the permissible transformations which we will need, namely:

I. Changing the order of the rows (in particular, interchanging two rows).

II. Multiplication of any number of rows by ± 1.

III. Addition of any integral multiple of some fixed row to any number of other rows.

The question arises as to whether we may perform similar transformations on the columns of our matrix. This cannot be done without further justification. The result of applying the corresponding transformations to the columns of our matrix will not in general be a matrix of a fundamental system with respect to $A_1, A_2, \ldots, A_r$. But we shall show that for any such column transformation, we may find a new generating system with respect to which the transformed matrix is a matrix of a fundamental system. Let us set down the column transformations that we shall be considering.

I*. Interchanging two columns.[5]

II*. Multiplication of a column by ± 1.

III*. Addition of an integral multiple of one column to another column.[6]

We have to show that for any transformation I*, II*, III*, we obtain a new generating system with respect to which the resulting matrix is a matrix of a fundamental system of relations. This is easy

---

[4] Thus if $n_1, n_2, \cdots$ are arbitrary integers, we may add $n_1 \cdot \mathfrak{a}_k$ to $\mathfrak{a}_{i_1}$, $n_2 \cdot \mathfrak{a}_k$ to $\mathfrak{a}_{i_2}$, etc.

[5] Since there are but a finite number of columns, any rearrangement may be obtained by a finite number of successive interchanges.

[6] As in I*, we need only consider two columns, since there are only a finite number of columns.

for I*. If we interchange the i-th column and the k-th column, the new generating system is obtained by interchanging A_i and A_k in the original generating system.

For II* we have to consider the multiplication of a column, say the i-th, by (-1). The new generating system will then be obtained if we replace A_i by A_i^{-1}. For, certainly every row in the transformed matrix is a relation with respect to the new generating system $A_1, \cdots, A_{i-1}, A_i^{-1}, A_{i+1}, \cdots, A_r$, since (1) implies

$$A_1^{a_1} \cdot \cdots \cdot A_{i-1}^{a_{i-1}} \cdot (A_i^{-1})^{-a_i} A_{i+1}^{a_{i+1}} \cdot \cdots \cdot A_r^{a_r} = E.$$

Furthermore, if $\mathfrak{b} = \{b_1, \cdots, b_{i-1}, b_i, b_{i+1}, \cdots, b_r\}$ is an integral linear combination of the vectors

$$\mathfrak{a}_k = \{a_{k1}, \cdots, a_{k,i-1}, a_{ki}, a_{k,i+1}, \cdots, a_{kr}\}$$

$(k = 1, 2, \ldots, s)$, then $\mathfrak{b}^* = \{b_1, \cdots, b_{i-1}, -b_i, b_{i+1}, \cdots, b_r\}$ is a linear combination of the vectors

$$\mathfrak{a}_k^* = \{a_{k1}, \cdots, a_{k,i-1}, -a_{ki}, a_{k,i+1}, \cdots, a_{kr}\}$$

$(k = 1, 2, \ldots, s)$, with the same integral coefficients. Thus it follows that the new matrix also represents a fundamental system with respect to $A_1, \cdots, A_{i-1}, A_i^{-1}, A_{i+1}, \cdots, A_r$.

Only III* remains to be checked. Let, say, n times the k-th column be added to the i-th $(i \neq k)$ column. We obtain a generating system of the desired kind by replacing A_k by $A_k \cdot A_i^{-n}$. For, from (1) it follows that[7]

$$A_1^{a_1} \cdot \cdots \cdot A_i^{a_i + n a_k} \cdot \cdots \cdot (A_k \cdot A_i^{-n})^{a_k} \cdot \cdots \cdot A_r^{a_r} = E.$$

This means that every row of the new matrix is a relation with respect to $A_1, \cdots, A_{k-1}, A_k A_i^{-n}, A_{k+1}, \cdots, A_r$. That the transformed matrix also represents a fundamental system follows immediately from the following considerations: If $\mathfrak{b} = \{b_1, \cdots, b_i, \cdots, b_r\}$ is an integral linear combination of

$$\mathfrak{a}_\nu = \{a_{\nu 1}, \cdots, a_{\nu i}, \cdots, a_{\nu r}\},\ \nu = 1, 2, \cdots, s,$$

say

$$\mathfrak{b} = \sum_{\nu=1}^{s} n_\nu \mathfrak{a}_\nu,$$

[7] The factors not written out are to be taken over unchanged from (1).

then the vectors $\mathfrak{b}^* = \{b_1, \cdots, b_{i-1}, b_i + n b_k, b_{i+1}, \cdots, b_r\}$,

$$\mathfrak{a}_\nu^* = \{a_{\nu 1}, \cdots, a_{\nu, i-1}, a_{\nu i} + n a_{\nu k}, a_{\nu, i+1}, \cdots, a_{\nu r}\},\ \nu = 1, 2, \cdots, s,$$

will satisfy the equation

$$\mathfrak{b}^* = \sum_{\nu=1}^{s} n_\nu \mathfrak{a}_\nu^*.$$

Thus we have proved our assertion.

The operations I, II, III, I*, II*, and III*, are called *elementary transformations* of (2).

By means of these elementary transformations, we shall proceed to bring (2) into a simple form. If (2) contains only zeros, we cannot simplify it further. If it contains non-zero entries, we proceed as follows: Let e_1 be the smallest positive integer which occurs in any of the matrices obtainable from (2) by a finite succession of elementary transformations. By means of operations I and I*, we bring e_1 into the upper left-hand corner. The matrix (2) will then take on the form

$$\begin{pmatrix} e_1 & b_{12} & \cdots & b_{1r} \\ b_{21} & b_{22} & \cdots & b_{2r} \\ \cdot & \cdot & \cdot & \cdot \end{pmatrix}. \tag{3}$$

We shall show that every element in the first row and column of (3) is divisible by e_1. For, we may find integers x, r, satisfying $b_{1i} = x \cdot e_1 + r$, $0 \leqq r < e_1$. If we then add $(-x)$ times the first column to the i-th column, the element r is obtained in the first row and i-th column. r is non-negative and less than e_1, and hence we must have $r = 0$, by our choice of e_1. Thus $b_{1i} = x \cdot e_1$, as was to be proved. In the same way we show that every element in the first column is an integral multiple of e_1. Knowing this, we may add a suitable multiple of the first column (row) to the i-th column (row) to make all of the elements of the first row and column with the exception of e_1 vanish. Our matrix then takes on the form

$$\begin{pmatrix} e_1 & 0 & \cdots & 0 \\ 0 & c_{22} & \cdots & c_{2r} \\ \cdot & \cdot & \cdot & \cdot \end{pmatrix}. \tag{4}$$

In the same way, we show that e_1 is a divisor of every element c_{ik} of the "*residual matrix*." For, let $c_{ik} = x \cdot e_1 + r$, $0 \leqq r < e_1$. By adding $(-x)$ times the first row to the i-th row, and then adding the first column to the k-th column, we reduce the matrix to one having the element r in the i-th row and k-th column. But $0 \leqq r < e_1$. Thus, as above, $r = 0$ and $c_{ik} = x \cdot e_1$.

If it is not the case that all $c_{ik} = 0$, the process is continued as before. First we find the smallest positive e_2 which occurs in any of the matrices obtainable from the residual matrix by a finite succession of elementary transformations.[8] We then bring e_2 into the second row and second column and by the above method we may make the remaining elements of the second row and second column vanish. All elements of the new residual matrix will then be divisible by e_2. We continue this process as long as possible, i.e. r times at most. And in this way, by a finite succession of elementary transformations, we can put the matrix (2) into the form

$$(5) \qquad \begin{pmatrix} e_1 & 0 & & & & & 0 \\ 0 & e_2 & & & & & \\ & & \ddots & & & & \\ & & & e_s & & & \\ & & & & 0 & & \\ & & & & & \ddots & \\ 0 & & & & & & 0 \end{pmatrix}$$

where (5) consists only of zeros with the exception of the principal diagonal[9] which itself consists of $e_1, e_2, \ldots, e_s$ and zeros. Furthermore, e_1 divides e_2, e_2 divides e_3, etc.

Now, the matrix (5) is still the matrix of a fundamental system with respect to some system of generators. For, it was obtained by operating on the matrix (2) by a finite succession of the six elementary transformations. Let the system of generators associated with (5) be, say, $B_1, B_2, \ldots, B_r$. What will be the corresponding fundamental system given by (5)? First we may eliminate all the rows in (5) from the $(s+1)$-st on, for they are obviously integral linear

[8] Elementary operations on the residual matrix can be considered as elementary operations on the whole matrix since under such operations the first row and column are unchanged.

[9] Of course by the principal (or main) diagonal we mean that diagonal which begins at the upper left-hand corner of the matrix. Its end need by no means coincide with the end of the matrix. The rows may extend below the end of this diagonal.

combinations of the first s rows. Our fundamental system of relations will then simply consist of the s equations

$$(6) \qquad B_1^{e_1} = E,\ B_2^{e_2} = E,\ \cdots,\ B_s^{e_s} = E.$$

If

$$(7) \qquad B_1^{x_1} \cdot B_2^{x_2} \cdot \cdots \cdot B_r^{x_r} = E$$

is any other relation, it must be a derived relation of the relations (6). Thus we must have $x_{s+1} = x_{s+2} = \cdots = x_r = 0$, and moreover there must be s integers $n_1, n_2, \ldots, n_s$ for which

$$(8) \qquad x_i = n_i e_i$$

for $i = 1, 2, \ldots, s$. This implies

$$(9) \qquad \begin{aligned} B_i^{x_i} &= (B_i^{e_i})^{n_i} = E \quad \text{for} \quad i = 1, 2, \cdots, s; \\ B_i^{x_i} &= B_i^0 \qquad = E \quad \text{for} \quad i = s+1,\ s+2, \cdots, r. \end{aligned}$$

We have shown that, given any relation (7), it follows that $B_i^{x_i} = E$ for $i = 1, 2, \ldots, r$. Thus the B_i form a basis. This proves the Basis Theorem.

It may happen that some of the numbers e_i of the principal diagonal of (5) are equal to 1. Since e_i divides e_{i+1}, the 1's among the e_i must come first. Suppose $e_1 = e_2 = \ldots = e_h = 1$, and $e_{h+1} \neq 1\ (h \leqq s)$. It then follows from the first h relations of (6) that $B_1 = B_2 = \ldots = B_h = E$. If we eliminate $B_1, B_2, \ldots, B_h$, then the remainder, i.e. $B_{h+1}, \cdots, B_s, B_{s+1}, \cdots, B_r$, still form a system of generators, and even a basis. None of these elements $B_{h+1}, \ldots, B_r$ equals the identity; for if $B_k = E$, it would follow from (8) that 1 is an integral multiple of e_k, which is impossible for $k \geqq h+1$. A basis among whose elements the identity does not occur is called a *proper* basis.

In what follows, we shall always assume that we are dealing with a proper basis. To simplify notation, we make the assumption that in (5), we have $e_1 \neq 1$. Thus either $e_1 = 0$ or $e_1 > 1$. With these assumptions we will continue the discussion of our result.

First consider the case in which our matrix (5) has but one column. The basis then consists of only one element $B_1 = B$. Suppose $e_1 = 0$. Then we know that $B^x = E$ only when $x = 0$. It follows that if $B^x = B^y$, then $B^{x-y} = E$, and hence that $x = y$. Thus $B^x \neq B^y$ for $x \neq y$. In this case our group is infinite and consists of the infinity of distinct elements

$$E,\ B,\quad B^2,\ B^3,\ \cdots,$$
$$B^{-1},\ B^{-2},\ B^{-3},\ \cdots.$$

Such a group is called an *infinite cyclic group*. For example, the group of integers under ordinary addition is an infinite cyclic group. Each of 1 and — 1 is a generating element.

If however (still assuming (5) to have only one column) $e_1 > 1$, then $B^0\ B^{\pm e_1},\ B^{\pm 2e_1},\ B^{\pm 3e_1}, \cdots$ are precisely the powers of B which are equal to E. It then follows that for two integers $x \neq y$ satisfying $1 \leqq x \leqq e_1$, $1 \leqq y \leqq e_1$ we must have[10] $B^x \neq B^y$. We thus see that

$$B,\ B^2,\ B^3, \cdots, B^{e_1} = E$$

are e_1 distinct elements of the group. What is more, they constitute *all* the elements of the group, since

$$\begin{array}{l} B = B^{1\pm e_1} = B^{1\pm 2e_1} = \cdots, \\ B^2 = B^{2\pm e_1} = B^{2\pm 2e_1} = \cdots, \\ \cdot\ \cdot\ \cdot\ \cdot\ \cdot\ \cdot\ \cdot\ \cdot\ \cdot\ \cdot\ \cdot\ \cdot\ \cdot \\ B^{e_1} = B^{e_1\pm e_1} = B^{e_1\pm 2e_1} = \cdots \end{array}$$

and since this array contains every power of B. In this case the group G is called a *finite cyclic group*. An example of a finite cyclic group of order e_1 is the group of e_1-th roots of unity (cf. p. 262).

We now turn to the case where the matrix (5) has more than one column. First, there is the possibility that (5) consists of zeros alone. Then $B_1^{x_1} \cdot B_2^{x_2} \cdot \cdots \cdot B_r^{x_r} = E$ implies $x_1 = x_2 = \ldots = x_r = 0$. Thus two power products

$$B_1^{x_1} \cdot B_2^{x_2} \cdot \cdots \cdot B_r^{x_r}, \qquad B_1^{y_1} \cdot B_2^{y_2} \cdot \cdots \cdot B_r^{y_r}$$

are equal if and only if $x_i = y_i$ for $i = 1, 2, \ldots, r$. For reasons which will appear later, such an abelian group is called the direct product of infinite cyclic groups.[11] As an example, the r-dimensional vectors $\{x_1, x_2, \ldots, x_r\}$ with integral components x_i form such a group under vector addition.

At the opposite extreme is the case $r = s$, i.e. the case in which the number of $e_i > 1$ is the same as the number of columns in the matrix (5). Here, two power products

$$B_1^{x_1} \cdot B_2^{x_2} \cdot \cdots \cdot B_r^{x_r}, \qquad B_1^{y_1} \cdot B_2^{y_2} \cdot \cdots \cdot B_r^{y_r}$$

[10] For otherwise $B^{x-y} = E$, while $0 < |x - y| < e_1$, which is impossible.

[11] Infinite cyclic groups are included in this category.

are equal if and only if $x_i - y_i$ is a multiple of e_i for $i = 1, 2, \ldots, r$. If we let every x_i in $B_1^{x_1} \cdot B_2^{x_2} \cdot \ldots \cdot B_r^{x_r}$ run independently through the e_i numbers $1, 2, \ldots, e_i$, then we obtain all the elements of the group, and each one once.[12] Thus our group contains exactly $e_1 \cdot e_2 \cdot \ldots \cdot e_r$ elements; it is of *finite order*. E.g., the group of all vectors $\{x_1, x_2, \ldots, x_r\}$, where x_i is an e_i-th root of unity ($i = 1, 2, \ldots, r$), and the product of two such vectors $\{x_1, x_2, \ldots, x_r\}$, $\{y_1, y_2, \ldots, y_r\}$ is defined to be $\{x_1y_1, x_2y_2, \ldots, x_ry_r\}$.

The intermediate case, where $0 < s < r$ in (5), yet remains. This case may be described as a combination of the two preceding cases.

Using the concept of a cyclic group we may state the Basis Theorem in another form. Let us consider any system of generators $A_1, A_2, \ldots, A_r$ of the abelian group G. The powers A_i^k of a fixed A_i form a cyclic subgroup of G. Let the subgroup thus generated by A_i be denoted by Z_i. The statement that the A_i form a system of generators of G is equivalent to the statement that $G = Z_1 \cdot Z_2 \cdot \ldots \cdot Z_r$ in the sense of multiplication of complexes (§ 19). And moreover to say that $A_1, A_2, \ldots, A_r$ form a basis of G means that every element of C of G can be represented in only one way as a product $C = C_1 \cdot C_2 \cdot \ldots \cdot C_r$ with C_i in Z_i. If this is the case we say that G is the *direct product* of the Z_i.

In this terminology, the Basis Theorem reads as follows:

Every abelian group with a finite system of generators can be represented as a direct product of a finite number of its cyclic subgroups.[13]

The number e_i, if it is > 0, is called the *order* of the basis element B_i. In general, by the *order of an element A* of an arbitrary (thus possibly non-commutative) group we mean the order of the cyclic subgroup generated by A. We easily see that this order is, in the finite case, the smallest positive integer e such that $A^e = E$.

Finally we remark that we have actually proven more. For we have obtained a very special basis; if we consider the orders $e_1, e_2, \ldots, e_r$ of the basis elements, we have that e_i always divides e_{i+1}. This condi-

[12] For to any power product $B_1^{y_1} \cdot B_2^{y_2} \cdot \ldots \cdot B_r^{y_r}$ there correspond numbers x_i satisfying $1 \leq x_i \leq e_i$, $y_i - x_i$ a multiple of e_i.

[13] Analogously, the existence of a basis $\mathfrak{a}_1, \mathfrak{a}_2, \cdots, \mathfrak{a}_r$ in a linear vector space L can be expressed as follows: L can be represented as a "direct sum" (cf. p. 312) of a finite number of its one-dimensional subspaces, namely those generated by the individual elements $\mathfrak{a}_i$.

tion need not hold for an arbitrary basis. For example, there are finite abelian groups whose order is not a power of a prime and for which there exists a basis the orders of whose elements are relatively prime. (See exercise 4 of this section.)

The Basis Theorem is important because it makes possible, in any abelian group with a finite number of generators, a very simple procedure of performing the calculations with the elements of the group,[14] leading to a more thorough knowledge of the properties of such groups. Aside from these considerations, however, an important reason for our discussion was that it enabled us to introduce ideas and methods whose generalization will be very important for our development of the theory of matrices in the next chapter.

Exercises

1. Every group of prime order is cyclic.

2. Let $H_1, H_2, \ldots, H_r$ be subgroups of an abelian group G where $G = H_1 \cdot H_2 \cdot \ldots \cdot H_r$. Prove that G is the direct product of the H_i if and only if for every $i = 1, 2, \ldots, r$ the subgroup H_i has only the identity element in common with the product $H_1 \cdot \ldots \cdot H_{i-1} \cdot H_{i+1} \cdot \ldots \cdot H_r$. The proof is easy by induction on r.

Using this, prove the following: If every H_i is of finite order n_i and if n_i and n_k are relatively prime for $i \neq k$, then G is the direct product of the H_i and the order of G is equal to $n_1 n_2 \ldots n_r$. Prove this by mathematical induction, applying the induction hypothesis to the above product.

3. Let G be a finite cyclic group, A a generator of G, n the order of A and of G. Let the factorization of n into primes be $n = p_1^{e_1} p_2^{e_2} \cdots p_r^{e_r}$ $(p_i \neq p_k$ for $i \neq k)$. Let $n_i = np_i^{-e_i}$ and let H_i be the cyclic subgroup which is generated by A^{n_i} of order $p_i^{e_i}$. From exercise 2 it follows that $H_1 \cdot H_2 \cdot \ldots \cdot H_r$ is a direct product. Because the orders are the same we have $G = H_1 H_2 \ldots H_r$.

This result has the following consequence: In an (arbitrary) abelian group, every element of finite order can be represented as a product of elements whose orders are prime powers.

4. Let G be a finite abelian group of order n, and let p be a prime dividing n. Then there is an element in G of order p. The set of all elements other than the identity whose order is a power of p is a subgroup H of G. The order of H must be a power of p.

Let $p_1, p_2, \ldots, p_r$ be the distinct primes which divide n. Let H_i be the subgroup consisting of all elements whose order is of the form p_i^k. It then easily follows from the second paragraph of exercise 3 that $G = H_1 H_2 \ldots H_r$. By the second paragraph of exercise 2, G is then the direct product of the H_i.

---

[14] The advantage of a basis, as compared to an arbitrary system of generators, lies in the fact that the equality of two power products formed with elements of the basis can be decided in a very simple way.

If we choose a basis for each H_i, then the set of all these basis elements will form a basis of G. Thus, for every finite abelian group there is a basis such that the order of every basis element is a prime power.

5. If G is an abelian group, k a fixed positive integer, then all powers A^k, with A in G form a subgroup $G^{(k)}$ of G. Show that if $B_1, B_2, \ldots, B_r$ is a basis of G, then $B_1^k, B_2^k, \cdots, B_r^k$ is a basis of $G^{(k)}$.

6. Let G be a finite abelian group, $B_1, B_2, \ldots, B_r$ a basis of G, e_i the order of B_i, and e_i a divisor of e_{i+1}. Choose two consecutive terms e_i, e_{i+1} from the sequence $e_1, e_2, \ldots, e_r$. Let k be a divisor of e_{i+1}. Show that the order of the subgroup $G^{(k)}$ (notation as in exercise 5) is always $\geqq \frac{e_{i+1}}{k} \frac{e_{i+2}}{k} \cdots \frac{e_r}{k}$. The equality sign holds if and only if k is a multiple of e_i. The number e_i itself is thus characterized as the smallest divisor of e_{i+1} for which the equality sign holds.

7. Let G, B_i, e_i be as in exercise 6. Moreover, let $B_1', B_2', \cdots, B_s'$ be a second basis of G, e_i' the order of B_i' and let e_i' divide e_{i+1}'. First we see that $e_r = e_s'$, since both are the largest possible order of any element in G. By exercise 6 it follows that $e_{r-1} = e_{s-1}'$, $e_{r-2} = e_{s-2}'$, etc. If, moreover, both bases are proper (p. 268), then $r = s$.

CHAPTER V

LINEAR TRANSFORMATIONS AND MATRICES

§ 21. The Algebra of Linear Transformations

We have already been introduced to the concept of linear transformations in connection with our study of affine transformations in § 13. We there observed (pp. 181-183) that the investigation of affine transformations is essentially the investigation of linear transformations. It is the object of this chapter to study linear transformations.

We begin, somewhat more generally than in § 13, with an arbitrary field F. We have already said, in § 14, what is to be meant by vectors over F: *An n-dimensional vector over* F is nothing but an ordered n-tuple $\{a_1, a_2, \ldots, a_n\}$ of elements of F. The totality of n-dimensional vectors over F (for a fixed n) is called the ***n*-dimensional vector space** over F and is denoted by V_n.[1]

In § 14 we have already given the rules for calculating with vectors of V_n. These rules enable us to add two vectors of V_n, and to multiply any vector of V_n by an element of F. Having these operations, we then may establish all the derived concepts, such as linear dependence, linear independence, linear combination, etc. By a *vector space* in V_n we accordingly mean a non-empty collection M of vectors of V_n having the following properties:

1. Any multiple $\lambda \cdot \mathfrak{a}$ of an element $\mathfrak{a}$ in M by an element λ of F is also in M.

2. The sum $\mathfrak{a} + \mathfrak{b}$ of two vectors $\mathfrak{a}$ and $\mathfrak{b}$ of M is also in M.

The *dimension* of a vector space L in V_n is the maximal number of linearly independent vectors of L. If p is the dimension of L, then any system of p linearly independent vectors of L is called a *basis* of L.

In the sense of these definitions all of the results of § 4 are valid for an n-dimensional vector space V_n over F. In particular we mention the following results, which are important for later applications:

[1] Actually the dependence of V_n on the field F should be indicated in the symbolism. But since we shall always deal with a fixed field F, we retain the simple symbol V_n.

1. *The maximal number of linearly independent vectors of* V_n *is* n. *The dimension of a vector space in* V_n *is therefore always* $\leqq n$.
2. *If* $\mathfrak{a}_1, \mathfrak{a}_2, \ldots, \mathfrak{a}_n$ *is a basis of a p-dimensional vector space* L, *then every vector of* L *can be written in one and only one way as a linear combination of the basis* $\mathfrak{a}_1, \mathfrak{a}_2, \ldots, \mathfrak{a}_p$.
3. *Any k linearly independent vectors* $\mathfrak{a}_1, \mathfrak{a}_2, \ldots, \mathfrak{a}_k$ *of a p-dimensional vector space* L *can be extended to form a basis of* L *by adjoining to them* $p - k$ *suitably chosen vectors* $\mathfrak{a}_{k+1}, \mathfrak{a}_{k+2}, \ldots, \mathfrak{a}_p$.

Now let L be an arbitrary vector space in V_n. *By* **linear transformation** *on* L *is meant a single-valued mapping*[2] *of* L *into itself satisfying the following two properties* (cf. p. 181):

i) *If* $\mathfrak{a}^*$ *is the image of* $\mathfrak{a}$, *then* $\lambda\mathfrak{a}^*$ *is the image of* $\lambda\mathfrak{a}$ *for any* λ *of* F.
ii) *If* $\mathfrak{a}^*, \mathfrak{b}^*$ *are the images of* $\mathfrak{a}, \mathfrak{b}$ *respectively, then* $\mathfrak{a}^* + \mathfrak{b}^*$ *is the image of* $\mathfrak{a} + \mathfrak{b}$.

We shall henceforth denote linear transformations by small Greek letters. We shall denote by $\sigma(\mathfrak{a})$ the image of a vector $\mathfrak{a}$ of L under the linear transformation σ. We will sometimes express this by saying that $\sigma(\mathfrak{a})$ is obtained from $\mathfrak{a}$ by applying σ, or that σ transforms (or carries) $\mathfrak{a}$ into $\sigma(\mathfrak{a})$. The defining properties *i* and *ii* of a linear transformation may then be expressed by the formulas:

$$\sigma(\lambda\mathfrak{a}) = \lambda \cdot \sigma(\mathfrak{a}), \tag{1}$$
$$\sigma(\mathfrak{a} + \mathfrak{b}) = \sigma(\mathfrak{a}) + \sigma(\mathfrak{b}). \tag{2}$$

Two linear transformations σ and τ on L are called "*equal*," if they represent the same mapping of L into itself. Thus $\sigma = \tau$ if and only if $\sigma(\mathfrak{a}) = \tau(\mathfrak{a})$ for every vector $\mathfrak{a}$ of L.

From (1) we see that *the image of the null vector under any linear transformation is the null vector*. For, by (1), the multiple of any vector by 0 (i.e. the null vector) is carried into the null vector.

A simple example of a linear transformation is the mapping which carries every vector $\mathfrak{a}$ of L into $c \cdot \mathfrak{a}$, where c is a fixed element of F. If σ is this transformation, we have

$$\sigma(\mathfrak{a}) = c \cdot \mathfrak{a}. \tag{3}$$

That this is a single-valued mapping of L into itself is clear. If $\mathfrak{a}$ and $\mathfrak{b}$ are any two vectors of L, and λ any element of F, then by (3),

[2] That is, a mapping which assigns to every vector of L a uniquely determined vector of L as its "image."

$$\sigma(\mathfrak{a}) = c \cdot \mathfrak{a}, \quad \sigma(\mathfrak{b}) = c \cdot \mathfrak{b}, \quad \sigma(\lambda \mathfrak{a}) = c \cdot \lambda \cdot \mathfrak{a}, \quad \sigma(\mathfrak{a}+\mathfrak{b}) = c \cdot (\mathfrak{a}+\mathfrak{b}).$$

Equations (1) and (2) follow from these equations, so that σ is a linear transformation.

We shall now define some operations on linear transformations which are basic in all that follows. Let σ and τ be two arbitrary linear transformations on L. We now define a new mapping φ by the definition

A. *φ carries any vector $\mathfrak{a}$ of* L *into the vector $\sigma(\mathfrak{a}) + \tau(\mathfrak{a})$, so that*

$$\varphi(\mathfrak{a}) = \sigma(\mathfrak{a}) + \tau(\mathfrak{a}). \tag{4}$$

First, this is a single-valued mapping of L into itself. Furthermore, by A,

$$\varphi(\lambda \mathfrak{a}) = \sigma(\lambda \mathfrak{a}) + \tau(\lambda \mathfrak{a}).$$

for any λ of F. It follows from (1) applied to σ and τ, and by (4) that

$$\varphi(\lambda \mathfrak{a}) = \lambda \cdot [\sigma(\mathfrak{a}) + \tau(\mathfrak{a})] = \lambda \cdot \varphi(\mathfrak{a}).$$

If $\mathfrak{b}$ is another vector of L, we see again from A that

$$\varphi(\mathfrak{a}+\mathfrak{b}) = \sigma(\mathfrak{a}+\mathfrak{b}) + \tau(\mathfrak{a}+\mathfrak{b}).$$

Applying formula (2) to σ and τ we obtain:

$$\varphi(\mathfrak{a}+\mathfrak{b}) = [\sigma(\mathfrak{a}) + \tau(\mathfrak{a})] + [\sigma(\mathfrak{b}) + \tau(\mathfrak{b})] = \varphi(\mathfrak{a}) + \varphi(\mathfrak{b}).$$

The mapping defined by A is thus another linear transformation. It is called the *sum of the linear transformations σ and τ* and is denoted by the symbol $\sigma + \tau$. The image of $\mathfrak{a}$ under this transformation is denoted by $(\sigma + \tau)(\mathfrak{a})$.

We may form another linear transformation from the linear transformations σ and τ as follows: Define a mapping ψ by the stipulation

B. *ψ carries any vector $\mathfrak{a}$ of* L *into the vector $\sigma(\tau(\mathfrak{a}))$, so that*

$$\psi(\mathfrak{a}) = \sigma(\tau(\mathfrak{a})).$$

This means that we are to apply τ and σ in succession. We first find the image $\tau(\mathfrak{a})$ of any vector $\mathfrak{a}$ of L under τ. $\tau(\mathfrak{a})$ is in L and is uniquely determined by $\mathfrak{a}$. We then find the image of the vector $\tau(\mathfrak{a})$ under the transformation σ, namely $\sigma(\tau(\mathfrak{a}))$. This is uniquely determined by $\tau(\mathfrak{a})$ and so by $\mathfrak{a}$, and lies in L. Thus B defines a single-valued mapping of L into itself.

By applying (1) and (2) to σ and τ, we obtain

$$\psi(\lambda\mathfrak{a}) = \sigma[\tau(\lambda\mathfrak{a})] = \sigma[\lambda\cdot\tau(\mathfrak{a})] = \lambda\cdot\sigma[\tau(\mathfrak{a})] = \lambda\cdot\psi(\mathfrak{a}),$$
$$\psi(\mathfrak{a}+\mathfrak{b}) = \sigma[\tau(\mathfrak{a}+\mathfrak{b})] = \sigma[\tau(\mathfrak{a})+\tau(\mathfrak{b})] = \sigma[\tau(\mathfrak{a})]+\sigma[\tau(\mathfrak{b})]$$
$$= \psi(\mathfrak{a})+\psi(\mathfrak{b}).$$

Thus ψ is also a linear transformation.

The linear transformation defined by B is denoted by the symbol $\sigma\cdot\tau$ and is called *the product of the linear transformations σ and τ.* It is important to notice that this product depends upon the order of its factors. *In applying $\sigma\cdot\tau$, one must first apply τ and then σ. The product $\tau\cdot\sigma$, however, means: First apply σ, and then τ.* In general, $\tau\cdot\sigma$ is not the same linear transformation as $\sigma\cdot\tau$.[3] Thus, multiplication of two linear transformations is *not commutative.* The image of the vector $\mathfrak{a}$ under $\sigma\cdot\tau$ is accordingly denoted by $(\sigma\cdot\tau)(\mathfrak{a})$.

We also introduce multiplication of a linear transformation τ by an element c of the field F; this is a special case of B. Indeed, for a given c of F we form the linear transformation σ defined by (3), and we then set $c\cdot\tau=\sigma\cdot\tau$. The linear transformation $c\cdot\tau$ thus carries every vector $\mathfrak{a}$ into $c\cdot\tau(\mathfrak{a})$. The same is true of the transformation $\tau\cdot\sigma=\tau\cdot c$, so that the commutative law

$$c\cdot\tau=\tau\cdot c \tag{5}$$

holds in this special case.

We have now defined sums and products of linear transformations. We now ask which of the fundamental rules of calculation, which we called the field axioms,[4] are valid for the addition and multiplication of linear transformations. Let us investigate each of the field axioms as to its validity here.

---

[3] Consider, for example, the following two mappings on V_2 (i.e. on the two-dimensional vector space over any field F):

$$\sigma\{x_1, x_2\} = \{x_1, 0\},$$
$$\tau\{x_1, x_2\} = \{x_1, x_1\}.$$

It is easily verified that σ and τ are linear transformations. Now

$$\tau(\sigma\{x_1, x_2\}) = \tau\{x_1, 0\} = \{x_1, x_1\},$$
$$\sigma(\tau\{x_1, x_2\}) = \sigma\{x_1, x_1\} = \{x_1, 0\}.$$

Thus

$$\tau\cdot\sigma = \tau, \qquad \sigma\cdot\tau = \sigma,$$

so that $\tau\cdot\sigma \neq \sigma\cdot\tau$, since $\sigma\neq\tau$.

[4] Cf. § 14.

We have seen that multiplication is not in general commutative. However the *commutative law for addition* always holds, i.e. we have, for any two linear transformations σ and τ of L:

$$\sigma + \tau = \tau + \sigma. \tag{6}$$

For by the definition of $\sigma + \tau$ and $\tau + \sigma$, we see that

$$(\sigma + \tau)(\mathfrak{a}) = \sigma(\mathfrak{a}) + \tau(\mathfrak{a}) = \tau(\mathfrak{a}) + \sigma(\mathfrak{a}) = (\tau + \sigma)(\mathfrak{a})$$

for any vector $\mathfrak{a}$ of L.

The *associative law* is fulfilled for both of these operations. For if $\sigma_1, \sigma_2, \sigma_3$, are three linear transformations, then

$$\sigma_1 + (\sigma_2 + \sigma_3) = (\sigma_1 + \sigma_2) + \sigma_3, \tag{7}$$

$$\sigma_1 \cdot (\sigma_2 \cdot \sigma_3) = (\sigma_1 \cdot \sigma_2) \cdot \sigma_3. \tag{8}$$

These formulas are seen to be true, by comparing both sides of these equations as to their effect on any vector. To prove (7), for example, let $\mathfrak{a}$ be any vector of L. Then

$$\begin{aligned} [\sigma_1 + (\sigma_2 + \sigma_3)](\mathfrak{a}) &= \sigma_1(\mathfrak{a}) + (\sigma_2 + \sigma_3)(\mathfrak{a}) = \sigma_1(\mathfrak{a}) + \sigma_2(\mathfrak{a}) + \sigma_3(\mathfrak{a}), \\ [(\sigma_1 + \sigma_2) + \sigma_3](\mathfrak{a}) &= (\sigma_1 + \sigma_2)(\mathfrak{a}) + \sigma_3(\mathfrak{a}) = \sigma_1(\mathfrak{a}) + \sigma_2(\mathfrak{a}) + \sigma_3(\mathfrak{a}), \end{aligned} \tag{7 a}$$

so that both sides of (7) send the vector $\mathfrak{a}$ of L into the same image vector $\sigma_1(\mathfrak{a}) + \sigma_2(\mathfrak{a}) + \sigma_3(\mathfrak{a})$, and so are identical. Formula (8) follows from the equations

$$\begin{aligned} [\sigma_1 \cdot (\sigma_2 \cdot \sigma_3)](\mathfrak{a}) &= \sigma_1[(\sigma_2 \cdot \sigma_3)(\mathfrak{a})] = \sigma_1[\sigma_2(\sigma_3(\mathfrak{a}))], \\ [(\sigma_1 \cdot \sigma_2) \cdot \sigma_3](\mathfrak{a}) &= (\sigma_1 \cdot \sigma_2) \cdot (\sigma_3(\mathfrak{a})) = \sigma_1[\sigma_2(\sigma_3(\mathfrak{a}))]. \end{aligned} \tag{8a}$$

Since multiplication of a linear transformation by an element of F was introduced as a special case of multiplication, the formula (8) remains valid if one or two of the factors are replaced by field elements. Thus, with the help of (5) we obtain

$$c \cdot (\sigma_1 \cdot \sigma_2) = (c \cdot \sigma_1) \cdot \sigma_2 = \sigma_1 \cdot (c \cdot \sigma_2), \tag{9}$$

$$(c \cdot d) \cdot \sigma_1 = c \cdot (d \cdot \sigma_1) = d \cdot (c \cdot \sigma_1). \tag{10}$$

Furthermore addition and multiplication are connected by the *distributive law*:[5]

---

[5] There are now two of these laws since multiplication of linear transformations is not commutative.

$$\sigma \cdot (\sigma_1 + \sigma_2) = \sigma \cdot \sigma_1 + \sigma \cdot \sigma_2, \tag{11}$$

$$(\sigma_1 + \sigma_2) \cdot \sigma = \sigma_1 \cdot \sigma + \sigma_2 \cdot \sigma. \tag{12}$$

Again the validity of these formulas is verified by investigating the meaning of the two sides in each of these equations.

We may substitute field elements for σ or σ_1, σ_2 in (11) or (12) and by using the commutative law (5) we then obtain the following special cases of the distributive laws:

$$c \cdot (\sigma_1 + \sigma_2) = (\sigma_1 + \sigma_2) \cdot c = c \cdot \sigma_1 + c \cdot \sigma_2, \tag{13}$$

$$\sigma \cdot (c + d) = (c + d) \cdot \sigma = c \cdot \sigma + d \cdot \sigma. \tag{14}$$

We now ask, *are there two linear transformations playing roles similar to zero and unity in a field?* This question is answered in the affirmative. For, if we set $c = 0$ (i.e. the zero element of the base field) in the transformation defined by (3), or set $c = 1$ (i.e. the unity of F) we obtain two linear transformations which we denote by the symbols 0 and 1 respectively,[6] and which are as required.

The transformation 0 maps every vector into the null vector, while 1 keeps every vector fixed. We then may easily verify the following equations, from the meaning of each sum and product occurring in them:

$$\tau + 0 = \tau, \tag{15}$$

$$0 \cdot \tau = \tau \cdot 0 = 0, \tag{16}$$

$$1 \cdot \tau = \tau \cdot 1 = \tau. \tag{17}$$

The transformations 0 and 1 are also called the *null* and *the identity transformation* (of L). These transformations are distinct if L contains at least one vector $\mathfrak{x} \neq 0$. For, the image of this vector under the null transformation is 0 and is $\mathfrak{x}$ under the identity transformation. If the dimension n of L is equal to 0, the null and identity transformations are identical. But this trivial case is so uninteresting and so unimportant that we assume that $n > 0$ from now on.

---

[6] We here follow general usage. Thus the symbol 0 represents three different things (the zero of the field F, the null vector of V_n, and the "*null transformation*" just defined) while the symbol 1 stands for two different things (the unity of F and the "*identity transformation*"). A little experience shows that despite the many possible meanings, there is no danger of confusion since in any context only one interpretation is meaningful.

We finally ask about the *possibility of subtraction and division.* We first consider the special equation

$$\sigma + \xi = 0, \tag{18}$$

whose right-hand side is the null transformation. This equation always has a solution. For, $\xi = (-1) \cdot \sigma$ is clearly a solution. We denote it by $-\sigma$. We further see that the general equation

$$\sigma + \xi = \tau \tag{19}$$

has the solution $\xi = \tau + (-\sigma)$, which we write as $\tau - \sigma$.

We thus see that the totality of linear transformations of L into itself forms a group under addition. It follows, in particular, that the solutions of equations (18) and (19) are uniquely determined.

But it is different in the case of multiplication. Division is not in general possible. We are going to characterize the important special case for which division is possible. To this end we investigate the solvability of the two special equations

$$\xi \cdot \sigma = 1, \quad \sigma \cdot \xi = 1 \tag{20}$$

with the identity transformation on the right-hand side. Let $\mathfrak{a}_1, \mathfrak{a}_2, \ldots, \mathfrak{a}_k$ form a basis of L, and let $\sigma(\mathfrak{a}_1), \sigma(\mathfrak{a}_2), \ldots, \sigma(\mathfrak{a}_k)$ be their images. Then we have

THEOREM 1. *Each of the equations* (20) *is solvable if and only if the vectors* $\sigma(\mathfrak{a}_1), \sigma(\mathfrak{a}_2), \ldots, \sigma(\mathfrak{a}_k)$ *are linearly independent. The solutions are, if they exist, uniquely determined by these equations and are equal to one another.*

Proof: We first consider the first of the equations (20). In order to see how a linear transformation σ acts, we write some arbitrary vector $\mathfrak{x}$ of L in the form

$$\mathfrak{x} = \lambda_1 \mathfrak{a}_1 + \lambda_2 \mathfrak{a}_2 + \cdots + \lambda_k \mathfrak{a}_k. \tag{21}$$

By the defining properties (1) and (2) of a linear transformation it then follows that

$$\sigma(\mathfrak{x}) = \lambda_1 \sigma(\mathfrak{a}_1) + \lambda_2 \sigma(\mathfrak{a}_2) + \cdots + \lambda_k \sigma(\mathfrak{a}_k). \tag{22}$$

A linear transformation ξ such that $\xi \cdot \sigma$ leaves every vector fixed must then send every vector (22) into the vector (21).

This is certainly impossible if σ maps some vector $\mathfrak{x} \neq 0$ into the null vector. For, the null vector must be mapped onto itself by ξ, and thus cannot be mapped back onto $\mathfrak{x}$ by this transformation.

But it is possible if the vectors $\sigma(\mathfrak{a}_1), \sigma(\mathfrak{a}_2), \ldots, \sigma(\mathfrak{a}_k)$ are linearly dependent. For in this case we have only to choose the λ_i in (22) in such a way that they do not all vanish, but that $\sigma(\mathfrak{x}) = 0$. But $\mathfrak{x} \neq 0$ in (21) because of the linear independence of the $\mathfrak{a}_i$.

On the other hand, if the $\sigma(\mathfrak{a}_i)$ are linearly independent, then by the above the only possibility for the definition of the required transformation ξ is the following: ξ sends every vector

$$\lambda_1 \sigma(\mathfrak{a}_1) + \lambda_2 \sigma(\mathfrak{a}_2) + \cdots + \lambda_k \sigma(\mathfrak{a}_k) \tag{23}$$

into

$$\lambda_1 \mathfrak{a}_1 + \lambda_2 \mathfrak{a}_2 + \cdots + \lambda_k \mathfrak{a}_k. \tag{24}$$

If in (23) we let the λ_i assume all values in the field independently, then every vector of L will be represented exactly once by (23) (because of the linear independence of the $\sigma(\mathfrak{a}_i)$). Thus the mapping sending (23) into (24) is a single-valued mapping of L onto itself. It may be immediately verified that this mapping satisfies the two defining properties of a linear transformation. The mapping ξ thus defined will then satisfy the equation $\xi \cdot \sigma = 1$.

Let us now turn to the second of the equations (20). From the above proof we see that if the equation $\xi \cdot \sigma = 1$ is solvable for ξ then the mapping $\sigma \cdot \xi$ is also equal to the identity transformation. For, ξ carries any vector (23) into (24), and σ transforms (24) back into (23).

Conversely, we may now easily see that the solvability of the second equation of (20) implies the solvability of the first equation, and that in fact any solution of the second is a solution of the first. For if ξ satisfies the second equation of (20), we may apply the above considerations to the equation $\eta \cdot \xi = 1$, taking η as the unknown. Now $\eta = \sigma$ is a solution of this equation. By what we have just proved σ is therefore also a solution of $\xi \cdot \eta = 1$, as was to be proved.

The above results immediately show that the equations (20) are either both solvable or both unsolvable, and that if they are solvable, they have the same solution. Thus the condition that we have derived for the solvability of the first equation is valid for the second, and Theorem 1 is proved. We say that a linear transformation σ of L is *singular* if for some basis $\mathfrak{a}_1, \mathfrak{a}_2, \ldots, \mathfrak{a}_k$ of L, the image vectors

$\sigma(\mathfrak{a}_1), \sigma(\mathfrak{a}_2), \ldots, \sigma(\mathfrak{a}_k)$ are linearly dependent. Otherwise we call the transformation *non-singular*. Theorem 1 implies that these definitions are independent of the choice of basis.

We may now apply our results to say that *the non-singular linear transformations on* L *form a group under multiplication of transformations*. Thus for any non-singular σ, the solution of $\sigma \cdot \xi = 1$ is non-singular and is called the *inverse* of σ, denoted by σ^{-1}.

The distinction between singular and non-singular linear transformations may be formulated in other ways. In the singular case, as seen in the proof of Theorem 1, there are always two distinct vectors of L each of which has the null vector as its image. *A singular linear transformation is not a one-to-one transformation of* L *into itself*. On the other hand *the non-singular linear transformations are one-to-one transformations of* L *onto itself*. This is seen in the proof of Theorem 1. For, the correspondence between (23) and (24) is one-to-one in this case.

It follows immediately from Theorem 1 that the general equation $\sigma \cdot \xi = \tau$ always has a unique solution if σ is non-singular. This solution is given by $\sigma^{-1} \cdot \tau$. Similarly $\tau \cdot \sigma^{-1}$ is the solution of the equation $\xi \cdot \sigma = \tau$. But these two equations are by no means always solvable if σ is singular. (Construct an example. Cf. also § 22, exercise 6.)

Although the totality of all linear transformations does not form a group under multiplication, the Associative Law, as we have seen, always holds. This has as a consequence that a product of arbitrarily many linear transformations depends only on the order of the factors, but not on the method of parenthesization or grouping, so that a product need not be written with parentheses. In particular the powers σ_k for integral $k > 0$ can be defined for arbitrary linear transformations σ and can also be defined for negative k in the case of non-singular linear transformations. If we define $\sigma^0 = 1$ then the formulas[7]

$$\sigma^k \cdot \sigma^l = \sigma^l \cdot \sigma^k = \sigma^{k+l}, \tag{25}$$

$$(\sigma^k)^l = \sigma^{k \cdot l} \tag{26}$$

hold for arbitrary non-negative k and l. For non-singular σ, the ex-

[7] One proves these formulas by counting the number of times the factor appears on each side of the equations.

ponents in these equations may also be negative. Equation (25) shows that multiplication of the powers of a fixed linear transformation σ is commutative.

We often have to consider expressions of the form

$$a_k \sigma^k + a_{k-1} \sigma^{k-1} + \cdots + a_1 \sigma + a_0 \sigma^0, \tag{27}$$

where σ is an arbitrary linear transformation and the a_i are elements of F. Such an expression is called a *polynomial in* σ. We say that (27) is obtained from the ordinary polynomial

$$f(u) = a_k u^k + a_{k-1} u^{k-1} + \cdots + a_1 u + a_0$$

(u an indeterminate) by the "*substitution*" of the linear transformation σ for u. It is to be understood that before the substitution, the term a_0 is to be replaced by $a_0 u^0$, so that all the terms in the resulting expression represent linear transformations.

If we calculate the sum and product of two such polynomials $f(\sigma)$ and $g(\sigma)$, we see that addition and multiplication of polynomials in σ may be carried out as if these were ordinary polynomials in an unknown. Thus, *if the equations*

$$p(u) = f(u) + g(u), \qquad q(u) = f(u) \cdot g(u),$$

are true for polynomials in an indeterminate u, then they remain true if u is replaced by a linear transformation σ.[8]

The following simple fact is of importance. If $f(\sigma)$ and $g(\sigma)$ are two polynomials in the same linear transformation σ, then

$$f(\sigma) \cdot g(\sigma) = g(\sigma) \cdot f(\sigma). \tag{28}$$

This may be verified by a simple calculation, or by substituting σ in the valid polynomial equation $f(u) \cdot g(u) = g(u) \cdot f(u)$.

Exercises

1. Let F be the field of real numbers, V_3 the three-dimensional vector space over F. (V_3 is thus the totality of vectors of affine R_3.) Let the vector $\mathfrak{x} = \{x_1, x_2, x_3\}$ run through all V_3. Consider the following mappings of V_3 into itself:

a) $\sigma_1(\mathfrak{x}) = \mathfrak{x} + \mathfrak{a}$, where $\mathfrak{a}$ is a fixed vector;
b) $\sigma_2(\mathfrak{x}) = \mathfrak{e}_1$;
c) $\sigma_3(\mathfrak{x}) = \{\lambda_1 x_1, \lambda_2 x_2, \lambda_3 x_3\}$, where $\lambda_1, \lambda_2, \lambda_3$ are fixed real numbers;

[8] The converse is not true. The reader should supply a counter-example.

d) $\sigma_4(\mathfrak{x}) = (\mathfrak{a}\cdot\mathfrak{x})\cdot\mathfrak{x}$, where $\mathfrak{a}$ is a fixed vector;
e) $\sigma_5(\mathfrak{x}) = \{x_1^2, x_2+x_3, x_3^3\}$;
f) $\sigma_6(\mathfrak{x}) = \{\sin x_2, \cos x_1, 0\}$;
g) $\sigma_7(\mathfrak{x}) = \{2x_1 - x_3, x_2+x_3, x_1\}$.

Which of these transformations are linear transformations?

2. Let $\mathfrak{a}_1, \mathfrak{a}_2, \cdots, \mathfrak{a}_k$ be a basis of a vector space L, $\mathfrak{b}_1, \mathfrak{b}_2, \cdots, \mathfrak{b}_k$ any k vectors of L (which need not be linearly independent). Then there is one and only one linear transformation σ on L such that $\sigma(\mathfrak{a}_i) = \mathfrak{b}_i$ for $i = 1, 2, \ldots, k$.

3. Let V_4 be the four-dimensional vector space over the field of complex numbers. By exercise 2 there is a linear transformation σ under which

$$\begin{array}{lll} \mathfrak{e}_1 & \text{goes into} & \{2, -1, 1, -2\}, \\ \mathfrak{e}_2 & \text{"} \quad \text{"} & \{1, 0, 0, -1\}, \\ \mathfrak{e}_3 & \text{"} \quad \text{"} & \{0, 2, 0, -1\}, \\ \mathfrak{e}_4 & \text{"} \quad \text{"} & \{2, 0, 1, -2\}. \end{array}$$

Furthermore there is a linear transformation τ, such that

$$\begin{array}{lll} \mathfrak{e}_1 & \text{goes into} & \{0, 0, 0, 0\}, \\ \mathfrak{e}_2 & \text{"} \quad \text{"} & \{1, 1, -1, 1\}, \\ \mathfrak{e}_3 & \text{"} \quad \text{"} & \{0, 0, 1, 0\}, \\ \mathfrak{e}_4 & \text{"} \quad \text{"} & \{1, 0, 1, 0\}. \end{array}$$

What are the images of the unit vectors under the linear transformations $\sigma\cdot\tau$ and $\tau\cdot\sigma$? Under the linear transformations σ^2+1 and $\tau^3-\tau^2$?

§ 22. Calculation with Matrices

We shall now consider the problem of representing linear transformations analytically. The hypotheses are the same as in § 21, but we shall change some notation. Let F again be any given field. Let V_q be the q-dimensional vector space over F, and L any n-dimensional vector space of V_q. Then $n \leqq q$. We also assume $n > 0$.

Let a linear transformation σ on L be given. We take a basis $\mathfrak{a}_1, \mathfrak{a}_2, \cdots, \mathfrak{a}_n$ of L. The image $\sigma(\mathfrak{a}_k)$ of the k-th basis vector is a vector of L and so is uniquely representable as a linear combination of the basis $\mathfrak{a}_1, \mathfrak{a}_2, \cdots, \mathfrak{a}_n$. Thus

$$(1) \qquad \sigma(\mathfrak{a}_k) = a_{1k}\mathfrak{a}_1 + a_{2k}\mathfrak{a}_2 + \cdots + a_{nk}\mathfrak{a}_n,$$

where the a_{ik} are definite elements of F. We have such an equation for $k = 1, 2, \ldots, n$. Now let

$$(2) \qquad \mathfrak{x} = x_1\mathfrak{a}_1 + x_2\mathfrak{a}_2 + \cdots + x_n\mathfrak{a}_n$$

be any vector of L. We shall call the elements $x_1, x_2, \ldots, x_n$ of F *the components of the vector* $\mathfrak{x}$ *with respect to the basis* $\mathfrak{a}_1, \mathfrak{a}_2, \ldots, \mathfrak{a}_n$ or *the components of* $\mathfrak{x}$ *in the coordinate system* $[\mathfrak{a}_1, \mathfrak{a}_2, \ldots, \mathfrak{a}_n]$. The elements $x_1, x_2, \ldots, x_n$ are uniquely determined by $\mathfrak{x}$. Conversely the vector $\mathfrak{x}$ is, by (2), uniquely determined by the components $x_1, x_2, \ldots, x_n$.[1]

The linear transformation σ sends the vector $\mathfrak{x}$ into its image $\sigma(\mathfrak{x})$. Let $y_1, y_2, \ldots, y_n$ be the components of $\sigma(\mathfrak{x})$ in the coordinate system $[\mathfrak{a}_1, \mathfrak{a}_2, \ldots, \mathfrak{a}_n]$, so that

$$\sigma(\mathfrak{x}) = y_1\mathfrak{a}_1 + y_2\mathfrak{a}_2 + \ldots + y_n\mathfrak{a}_n. \tag{3}$$

The components $y_1, y_2, \ldots, y_n$ of the vector $\sigma(\mathfrak{x})$ can be calculated from the components $x_1, x_2, \ldots, x_n$ of the vector $\mathfrak{x}$, since they are uniquely determined by them. This calculation can be carried out easily. First we have

$$\sigma(\mathfrak{x}) = \sigma\left(\sum_{k=1}^{n} x_k \mathfrak{a}_k\right) = \sum_{k=1}^{n} x_k \sigma(\mathfrak{a}_k).$$

Substituting the expression (1) for $\sigma(\mathfrak{a}_k)$ (for $k = 1, 2, \ldots, n$), we have

$$\sigma(\mathfrak{x}) = \sum_{k=1}^{n}\left(x_k \sum_{i=1}^{n} a_{ik}\, \mathfrak{a}_i\right) = \sum_{k=1}^{n}\sum_{i=1}^{n} a_{ik}\, x_k\, \mathfrak{a}_i.$$

Comparing this equation with (3) we obtain, after an easy calculation,

$$\sum_{i=1}^{n}\left(y_i - \sum_{k=1}^{n} a_{ik}\, x_k\right) \mathfrak{a}_i = 0.$$

But since the vectors $\mathfrak{a}_1, \mathfrak{a}_2, \ldots, \mathfrak{a}_n$, as a basis of L, are linearly independent, all of the coefficients of the last equation must vanish, so that for $i = 1, 2, \ldots, n$,

$$y_i = \sum_{k=1}^{n} a_{ik}\, x_k. \tag{4}$$

This is our required expression. The system of equations (4) indicates how the components $y_1, y_2, \ldots, y_n$ of the vector $\sigma(\mathfrak{x})$ may be calculated from the components $x_1, x_2, \ldots, x_n$ of the vector $\mathfrak{x}$ of L. We say that *the linear transformation* σ *is represented by the system of equations* (4) *in the coordinate system* $[\mathfrak{a}_1, \mathfrak{a}_2, \ldots, \mathfrak{a}_n]$.[2]

We now start, conversely, with an arbitrary system of linear equations (4). A linear transformation is always determined by such a

[1] Cf. § 10, p. 117.
[2] Cf. p. 184.

system of equations in every coordinate system $[\mathfrak{a}_1, \mathfrak{a}_2, \ldots, \mathfrak{a}_n]$. We interpret these equations as saying that the image of the vector $\sum_{i=1}^{n} x_i \mathfrak{a}_i$ is the vector $\sum_{i=1}^{n} y_i \mathfrak{a}_i$. The defining properties of a linear transformation are satisfied by this mapping, as can immediately be verified. We have thus obtained

THEOREM 1. *Every linear transformation on* L *can be represented in any coordinate system by a system of linear equations* (4), *and conversely any such system of equations represents some linear transformation on* L *in any coordinate system.*

Let a second system of linear equations be given in addition to (4), by

$$y_i = \sum_{k=1}^{n} b_{ik} x_k, \qquad i = 1, 2, \cdots, n. \tag{5}$$

If we again interpret the elements $x_1, x_2, \ldots, x_n$, and $y_1, y_2, \ldots, y_n$, as vector components in our coordinate system $[\mathfrak{a}_1, \mathfrak{a}_2, \ldots, \mathfrak{a}_n]$, then this system of equations also defines a linear transformation, say τ. We shall show that *the linear transformations* σ *and* τ *defined by* (4) *and* (5) *cannot be identical unless* (4) *and* (5) *are identical* (*but both taken with respect to the same basis* $\mathfrak{a}_1, \mathfrak{a}_2, \ldots, \mathfrak{a}_n$). The two systems (4) and (5) are called identical if, for every pair of indices i, k ($1 \leqq i \leqq n$, $1 \leqq k \leqq n$), we have $a_{ik} = b_{ik}$.

For suppose that (4) and (5) represent the same linear transformation. Then in particular, $\sigma(\mathfrak{a}_\nu) = \tau(\mathfrak{a}_\nu)$ for $\nu = 1, 2, \ldots, n$. Since the components of $\mathfrak{a}_\nu$ in $[\mathfrak{a}_1, \mathfrak{a}_2, \cdots, \mathfrak{a}_n]$ are all 0, except for the ν-th which is 1, the components of $\sigma(\mathfrak{a}_\nu)$ and of $\tau(\mathfrak{a}_\nu)$ are, by (4) and (5), $a_{1\nu}, a_{2\nu}, \cdots, a_{n\nu}$ and $b_{1\nu}, b_{2\nu}, \cdots, b_{n\nu}$ respectively. Thus for every ν we must have

$$a_{1\nu} = b_{1\nu}, \quad a_{2\nu} = b_{2\nu}, \quad \cdots, \quad a_{n\nu} = b_{n\nu}.$$

We thus see that our assumption implies the identity of the systems (4) and (5).

The system of equations (4) is known if its *coefficient matrix*, i.e.

$$\begin{pmatrix} a_{11} & a_{12} & \cdots & a_{1n} \\ a_{21} & a_{22} & \cdots & a_{2n} \\ \cdot & \cdot & \cdot & \cdot \\ a_{n1} & a_{n2} & \cdots & a_{nn} \end{pmatrix}, \tag{6}$$

is given.

We shall call two n-by-n square matrices

$$\begin{pmatrix} a_{11} & a_{12} & \cdots & a_{1n} \\ a_{21} & a_{22} & \cdots & a_{2n} \\ \cdot & \cdot & \cdot & \cdot \\ a_{n1} & a_{n2} & \cdots & a_{nn} \end{pmatrix}, \qquad \begin{pmatrix} b_{11} & b_{12} & \cdots & b_{1n} \\ b_{21} & b_{22} & \cdots & b_{2n} \\ \cdot & \cdot & \cdot & \cdot \\ b_{n1} & b_{n2} & \cdots & b_{nn} \end{pmatrix}$$

equal if and only if their corresponding systems of equations (4) and (5) both represent the same linear transformation, i.e. if for every pair of indices i, k we have $a_{ik} = b_{ik}$.

If a linear transformation σ is given in the coordinate system $[\mathfrak{a}_1, \mathfrak{a}_2, \ldots, \mathfrak{a}_n]$ by the system of equations (4), we shall call the coefficient matrix (6) *the matrix of* σ *in the coordinate system* $[\mathfrak{a}_1, \mathfrak{a}_2, \ldots, \mathfrak{a}_n]$, and we shall say that (6) belongs to σ in the coordinate system $[\mathfrak{a}_1, \mathfrak{a}_2, \ldots, \mathfrak{a}_n]$. In this way, to every coordinate system and to every linear transformation, there corresponds one and only one matrix. Conversely, every matrix corresponds to but one linear transformation, for any coordinate system. We thus have

THEOREM 2. *The correspondence which associates each linear transformation* σ *on* L *with the matrix of the system of equations representing* σ *in some fixed coordinate system* $[\mathfrak{a}_1, \mathfrak{a}_2, \ldots, \mathfrak{a}_n]$, *is a one-to-one correspondence*[3] *between all linear transformations on* L *and the n-by-n square matrices whose entries belong to* F.

The matrix corresponding to a given linear transformation σ in a fixed coordinate system $[\mathfrak{a}_1, \mathfrak{a}_2, \ldots, \mathfrak{a}_n]$ is easily determined. Let us recall that the coefficients of (4) are given by the equations (1). Comparing (1), (4), and (6), we see that the k-th column of the matrix belonging to σ in the coordinate system $[\mathfrak{a}_1, \mathfrak{a}_2, \ldots, \mathfrak{a}_n]$ consists of the components of $\sigma(\mathfrak{a}_k)$ with respect to the basis $\mathfrak{a}_1, \mathfrak{a}_2, \ldots, \mathfrak{a}_n$.[4] The reader should remember this statement since it is often applied in what follows.

We denote matrices by large capital italic letters A, B, etc.

Let σ, τ be two linear transformations on L. Let the matrices

---

[3] It is important that the basis $\mathfrak{a}_1, \mathfrak{a}_2, \cdots, \mathfrak{a}_n$ be kept fixed. One linear transformation will, in general, be given by two different systems of equations in two different coordinate systems. Conversely one system of equations in general represents two different linear transformations with respect to two different bases.

[4] It should be stressed that the order of the basis vectors is kept fixed. A linear transformation will be represented, in general, by two different matrices in the different coordinate systems $[\mathfrak{a}_1, \mathfrak{a}_2, \mathfrak{a}_3, \cdots, \mathfrak{a}_n]$ and $[\mathfrak{a}_2, \mathfrak{a}_1, \mathfrak{a}_3, \cdots, \mathfrak{a}_n]$.

corresponding to these in the coordinate system $[\mathfrak{a}_1, \mathfrak{a}_2, \ldots, \mathfrak{a}_n]$ be, respectively,

$$(7) \qquad A = \begin{pmatrix} a_{11} & a_{12} & \cdots & a_{1n} \\ a_{21} & a_{22} & \cdots & a_{2n} \\ \cdot & \cdot & \cdot & \cdot \\ a_{n1} & a_{n2} & \cdots & a_{nn} \end{pmatrix}, \quad B = \begin{pmatrix} b_{11} & b_{12} & \cdots & b_{1n} \\ b_{21} & b_{22} & \cdots & b_{2n} \\ \cdot & \cdot & \cdot & \cdot \\ b_{n1} & b_{n2} & \cdots & b_{nn} \end{pmatrix}.$$

Let us determine the matrix which corresponds to the linear transformation $\sigma + \tau$ in the same coordinate system. Since A belong to σ, the k-th column of this matrix consists of the components of $\sigma(\mathfrak{a}_k)$ with respect to the basis $\mathfrak{a}_1, \mathfrak{a}_2, \ldots, \mathfrak{a}_n$, so that

$$(8) \qquad \sigma(\mathfrak{a}_k) = \sum_{i=1}^{n} a_{ik}\, \mathfrak{a}_i, \qquad k = 1, 2, \cdots, n.$$

Analogously, since B corresponds to τ, we have

$$(9) \qquad \tau(\mathfrak{a}_k) = \sum_{i=1}^{n} b_{ik}\, \mathfrak{a}_i, \qquad k = 1, 2, \cdots, n.$$

It then follows that

$$(\sigma + \tau)(\mathfrak{a}_k) = \sigma(\mathfrak{a}_k) + \tau(\mathfrak{a}_k) = \sum_{i=1}^{n} (a_{ik} + b_{ik})\, \mathfrak{a}_i,$$

so that the vector $(\sigma + \tau)(\mathfrak{a}_k)$ has the components

$$a_{1k} + b_{1k}, \quad a_{2k} + b_{2k}, \quad \cdots, \quad a_{nk} + b_{nk}.$$

But these must be the entries of the k-th column of the matrix corresponding to $\sigma + \tau$ in the coordinate system $[\mathfrak{a}_1, \mathfrak{a}_2, \ldots, \mathfrak{a}_n]$. This matrix therefore is of the form

$$(10) \qquad \begin{pmatrix} a_{11} + b_{11}, & a_{12} + b_{12}, & \cdots, & a_{1n} + b_{1n} \\ a_{21} + b_{21}, & a_{22} + b_{22}, & \cdots, & a_{2n} + b_{2n} \\ \cdot & \cdot & \cdot & \cdot \\ a_{n1} + b_{n1}, & a_{n2} + b_{n2}, & \cdots, & a_{nn} + b_{nn} \end{pmatrix}.$$

Because of this relation, the matrix (10) is called the *sum of the matrices* (7) and is denoted by $A + B$. Thus in order to add two n-by-n square matrices, we simply add their corresponding entries.

We next determine the matrix which corresponds to $\sigma \cdot \tau$. It follows from (9) that

$$(\sigma \cdot \tau)(\mathfrak{a}_k) = \sigma[\tau(\mathfrak{a}_k)] = \sigma\left(\sum_{\nu=1}^{n} b_{\nu k}\, \mathfrak{a}_\nu\right) = \sum_{\nu=1}^{n} b_{\nu k}\, \sigma(\mathfrak{a}_\nu).$$

Substituting (8) in this equation, we obtain

$$(\sigma \cdot \tau)(\mathfrak{a}_k) = \sum_{\nu=1}^{n} b_{\nu k} \sum_{i=1}^{n} a_{i\nu}\, \mathfrak{a}_i = \sum_{i=1}^{n} \left(\sum_{\nu=1}^{n} a_{i\nu}\, b_{\nu k} \right) \mathfrak{a}_i .$$

But the components of $(\sigma \cdot \tau)(\mathfrak{a}_k)$ form the k-th column of the matrix corresponding to $\sigma \cdot \tau$ in the coordinate system $[\mathfrak{a}_1, \mathfrak{a}_2, \ldots, \mathfrak{a}_n]$. Hence this matrix is of the form

$$(11) \qquad \begin{pmatrix} \sum_{\nu=1}^{n} a_{1\nu}\, b_{\nu 1}, & \sum_{\nu=1}^{n} a_{1\nu}\, b_{\nu 2}, & \cdots, & \sum_{\nu=1}^{n} a_{1\nu}\, b_{\nu n} \\ \sum_{\nu=1}^{n} a_{2\nu}\, b_{\nu 1}, & \sum_{\nu=1}^{n} a_{2\nu}\, b_{\nu 2}, & \cdots, & \sum_{\nu=1}^{n} a_{2\nu}\, b_{\nu n} \\ \cdot & \cdot & \cdot & \cdot \\ \sum_{\nu=1}^{n} a_{n\nu}\, b_{\nu 1}, & \sum_{\nu=1}^{n} a_{n\nu}\, b_{\nu 2}, & \cdots, & \sum_{\nu=1}^{n} a_{n\nu}\, b_{\nu n} \end{pmatrix}.$$

The matrix (11) is called the *product of the matrices A and B* and is denoted by $A \cdot B$. We have thus defined multiplication of n-by-n square matrices.

The element in the i-th row and k-th column of the product matrix (11) is the scalar product of the i-th *row vector* $\{a_{i1}, a_{i2}, \cdots, a_{in}\}$ of A and the k-th *column vector* $\{b_{1k}, b_{2k}, \cdots, b_{nk}\}$ of B. This suggests multiplication of determinants. But there is an important difference. In multiplying determinants, it is irrelevant whether we combine the rows of the first factor with the rows of the second, or the columns of the first with the columns of the second, or the rows of one factor with the column of the other.[5] Multiplication of matrices, however, is defined in only one way. The entry occuping the i-th row and k-th column of the matrix $A \cdot B$ is the scalar product

$$\{a_{i1}, a_{i2}, \cdots, a_{in}\} \cdot \{b_{1k}, b_{2k}, \cdots, b_{nk}\}.$$

As a special case of the product just defined, we shall determine the matrix of the linear transformation $c \cdot \tau$ $(= \tau \cdot c)$ where c is any element of F. By the definition of $c \cdot \tau$ we have to replace the first factor in the product $A \cdot B$ by the matrix of that linear transformation which maps every vector of L into its product by c. But the matrix of this linear transformation is

[5] Cf. § 9, p. 96.

$$\begin{pmatrix} c & & & 0 \\ & c & & \\ & & \ddots & \\ 0 & & & c \end{pmatrix},$$

since, in particular, each basis vector is mapped into its product by c. Replacing the a_{ik} in (11) by the entries of this matrix, we see that the matrix of $c \cdot \tau$ is

$$\begin{pmatrix} cb_{11} & cb_{12} & \cdots & cb_{1n} \\ cb_{21} & cb_{22} & \cdots & cb_{2n} \\ \cdot & \cdot & \cdot & \cdot \\ cb_{n1} & cb_{n2} & \cdots & cb_{nn} \end{pmatrix}. \tag{12}$$

This matrix is called *the product of B by c* and is denoted by $c \cdot B$ or by $B \cdot c$. A matrix is multiplied by c if each of its entries is multiplied by c.

We have thus defined several operations on n-by-n square matrices. But more than this, we have so defined these operations that under the one-to-one correspondence between linear transformations and matrices in a fixed coordinate system, the corresponding operations will be preserved. Writing $\sigma \longleftrightarrow A$ to mean that the matrix A corresponds to σ with respect to some fixed coordinate system $[\alpha_1, \alpha_2, \ldots, \alpha_n]$, we have that

$$\sigma \longleftrightarrow A, \qquad \tau \longleftrightarrow B$$

implies

$$\sigma + \tau \longleftrightarrow A + B, \qquad \sigma \cdot \tau \longleftrightarrow A \cdot B, \qquad c \cdot \tau \longleftrightarrow c \cdot B.$$

Furthermore, since the correspondence is one-to-one we have that $\sigma = \tau$ implies $A = B$ and conversely. A correspondence such as that which we have here between the totality of linear transformations and their matrices is called an *isomorphism*. This isomorphism has as a consequence that all equations connecting linear transformations by addition and multiplication also hold for the corresponding matrices, and conversely. As an example we consider (7) of § 21, stating the Associative Law of Addition. Let $\sigma_1 \longleftrightarrow A$, $\sigma_2 \longleftrightarrow B$, $\sigma_3 \longleftrightarrow C$. It then follows that

$$(\sigma_2 + \sigma_3) \longleftrightarrow (B + C),$$
$$\sigma_1 + (\sigma_2 + \sigma_3) \longleftrightarrow A + (B + C),$$

and similarly

$$(\sigma_1 + \sigma_2) \longleftrightarrow (A + B),$$
$$(\sigma_1 + \sigma_2) + \sigma_3 \longleftrightarrow (A + B) + C.$$

Thus equation (7) of § 21 implies *the Associative Law of Addition for Matrices*:

$$A+(B+C) = (A+B)+C. \tag{13}$$

In the same way we obtain the following rules, in analogy to those of the preceding section:

The Commutative Law of Addition:

$$A+B = B+A; \tag{14}$$

The Associative Laws of Multiplication:

$$A\cdot(B\cdot C) = (A\cdot B)\cdot C, \tag{15}$$

$$c\cdot(A\cdot B) = (c\cdot A)\cdot B = A\cdot(c\cdot B), \tag{16}$$

$$(c\cdot d)\cdot A = c\cdot(d\cdot A) = d\cdot(c\cdot A), \tag{17}$$

The Distributive Laws:

$$A\cdot(A_1+A_2) = A\cdot A_1+A\cdot A_2, \tag{18}$$

$$(A_1+A_2)\cdot A = A_1\cdot A+A_2\cdot A, \tag{19}$$

$$c\cdot(A_1+A_2) = c\cdot A_1+c\cdot A_2, \tag{20}$$

$$(c+d)\cdot A = c\cdot A+d\cdot A. \tag{21}$$

It is important to make clear which matrices correspond to the null and identify transformations in some definite coordinate system $[\mathfrak{a}_1, \mathfrak{a}_2, \ldots, \mathfrak{a}_n]$. Since the null transformation maps every basis vector onto the null vector, all of the entries in the corresponding matrix are 0. This matrix is called the *null matrix* or the *zero matrix* and is denoted by O.

The identity transformation maps every basis vector $\mathfrak{a}_i$ onto itself. The corresponding matrix will thus be of the form

$$\begin{pmatrix} 1 & 0 & \cdots & 0 \\ 0 & 1 & \cdots & 0 \\ \cdot & \cdot & \cdot & \cdot \\ 0 & 0 & \cdots & 1 \end{pmatrix}.$$

It is called the *unit matrix*, and is denoted by E.

Thus the matrices O and E correspond to the null and identity transformations respectively in *any* coordinate system $[\mathfrak{a}_1, \mathfrak{a}_2, \ldots, \mathfrak{a}_n]$ of L.

Equations (15) through (17) of § 21 yield as corresponding matrix equations, for any A,

$$A + O = A, \tag{22}$$

$$O \cdot A = A \cdot O = O, \tag{23}$$

$$E \cdot A = A \cdot E = A. \tag{24}$$

Of course all of these rules of calculation with matrices (equations (13)—(24)) could have been proved by direct appeal to the definition of addition and multiplication of matrices and an easy calculation. It is suggested that the student work out the details.

Now, what can be said about the *possibility of subtraction and division of matrices?* Equations of the form $A + X = B$, $A \cdot Y = B$ and $Z \cdot A = B$ hold if and only if they hold for the corresponding linear transformations. Thus the first is always uniquely solvable, the second and third are in general not solvable, but are always uniquely solvable if A corresponds to a non-singular linear transformation.

How can one determine whether a matrix $A = (a_{ik})$ represents a non-singular linear transformation σ in a given coordinate system $[\mathfrak{a}_1, \mathfrak{a}_2, \ldots, \mathfrak{a}_n]$? We know that the k-th column of A consists of the components of the vector $\sigma(\mathfrak{a}_k)$ for $k = 1, 2, \ldots, n$, i.e.

$$\sigma(\mathfrak{a}_k) = \sum_{i=1}^{n} a_{ik}\, \mathfrak{a}_i .$$

The linear transformation σ was called singular (§ 21) if the $\sigma(\mathfrak{a}_k)$ were linearly dependent, non-singular otherwise. By Theorem 1 of § 10 we see that σ is non-singular if the rank of A equals n while σ is singular if this rank is less than n. In other words,[6]

THEOREM 3. *If the matrix* (a_{ik}) *represents a non-singular linear transformation, then the determinant* $|a_{ik}| \neq 0$. *If it represents a singular one, then* $|a_{ik}| = 0$.

The criterion of Theorem 3 makes no reference to a particular coordinate system. Thus a matrix is called *non-singular* or *singular* according to whether its determinant $\neq 0$ or $= 0$.

If the equation $A \cdot X = E$ (= unit matrix) is solvable we denote its solution by A^{-1} and call it the *inverse matrix* of A. If A corresponds to σ, then A^{-1} corresponds to σ^{-1} in the same coordinate system.

A^{-1} can easily be calculated if $A = (a_{ik})$ is given. For let the determinant $|a_{ik}| \neq 0$ and let us write the matrix X in the form (x_{ik})

[6] Cf. the similar concept for affine transformations on p. 184.

where the n^2 unknowns x_{ik} are to be determined. By calculating the product on the left-hand side of $A \cdot X = E$, we obtain

$$\left(\sum_{\nu=1}^{n} a_{i\nu}\, x_{\nu k}\right) = (\delta_{ik}).^{7}$$

The equality of these matrices is equivalent to the equality of their corresponding elements. Thus for a fixed k we must have the n equations

$$\begin{aligned} a_{11}\, x_{1k} + a_{12}\, x_{2k} + \cdots + a_{1n}\, x_{nk} &= \delta_{1k}, \\ \cdots\cdots\cdots&\cdots \\ a_{k1}\, x_{1k} + a_{k2}\, x_{2k} + \cdots + a_{kn}\, x_{nk} &= \delta_{kk}, \\ \cdots\cdots\cdots&\cdots \\ a_{n1}\, x_{1k} + a_{n2}\, x_{2k} + \cdots + a_{nn}\, x_{nk} &= \delta_{nk}. \end{aligned} \tag{25}$$

We may now determine the n unknowns $x_{1k}, x_{2k}, \cdots, x_{nk}$ from these equations. By Cramer's rule we obtain

$$x_{ik} = \frac{\sum_{\nu=1}^{n} \delta_{\nu k}\, A_{\nu i}}{|\, a_{ik}\,|} = \frac{A_{ki}}{|\, a_{ik}\,|}, \qquad i = 1, 2, \cdots, n, \tag{26}$$

where A_{ik} is the cofactor of a_{ik} in the determinant $|\, a_{ik}\,|$. Since we may do this for each k, the matrix X is determined. It is given by

$$X = \frac{1}{|\, a_{ik}\,|} \begin{pmatrix} A_{11} & A_{21} & \cdots & A_{n1} \\ A_{12} & A_{22} & \cdots & A_{n2} \\ \cdot & \cdot & \cdot & \cdot \\ A_{1n} & A_{2n} & \cdots & A_{nn} \end{pmatrix}. \tag{27}$$

Calculations with powers of a matrix A can be performed with any integral exponents for non-singular matrices, and with any non-negative exponents for singular ones. The same rules hold for matrices as for linear transformations. Thus equations (25) and (26) of § 21 are true if σ and τ are matrices.

Moreover, we may form polynomials by using the powers of some matrix. Calculations are performed exactly as with polynomials in an indeterminate. In particular, equations of the form $f(u) + g(u) = p(u)$, $f(u) \cdot g(u) = q(u)$ remain valid if the indeterminate u is replaced by some matrix A.

---

[7] By using the Kronecker delta (cf. p. 100) we can write the identity matrix in the form (δ_{ik}).

Let A be the matrix of a linear transformation σ in $[\mathfrak{a}_1, \mathfrak{a}_2, \ldots, \mathfrak{a}_n]$. Then $f(A) \longleftrightarrow f(\sigma)$ in the same coordinate system for any polynomial $f(u) = a_0 + a_1 u + a_2 u^2 + \cdots + a_r u^r$. For, $a_k A^k$ corresponds to $a_k \sigma^k$ so that $\sum_{k=0}^{r} a_k A^k$ corresponds to $\sum_{k=0}^{r} a_k \sigma^k$.

Linear Transformations Under a Change of Coordinate System

The transition from a basis $\mathfrak{a}_1, \mathfrak{a}_2, \ldots, \mathfrak{a}_n$ to another basis $\mathfrak{b}_1, \mathfrak{b}_2, \ldots, \mathfrak{b}_n$ is called a *coordinate transformation.*[8] Let $\mathfrak{x}$ be a vector of L whose components are $x_1, x_2, \ldots, x_n$ in the coordinate system $[\mathfrak{a}_1, \mathfrak{a}_2, \ldots, \mathfrak{a}_n]$ and are $x_1^*, x_2^*, \ldots, x_n^*$ in the coordinate system $[\mathfrak{b}_1, \mathfrak{b}_2, \ldots, \mathfrak{b}_n]$, so that

$$\mathfrak{x} = \sum_{k=1}^{n} x_k \mathfrak{a}_k = \sum_{k=1}^{n} x_k^* \mathfrak{b}_k. \tag{28}$$

Each of the vectors $\mathfrak{a}_1, \mathfrak{a}_2, \ldots, \mathfrak{a}_n$ may be written as a linear combination of the basis $[\mathfrak{b}_1, \mathfrak{b}_2, \ldots, \mathfrak{b}_n]$, say by the equations

$$\mathfrak{a}_k = \sum_{i=1}^{n} t_{ik} \mathfrak{b}_i, \qquad k = 1, 2, \cdots, n. \tag{29}$$

If we then calculate the components x_i^* exactly as in § 10, p. 121 by substituting (29) into (28), we obtain

$$x_i^* = \sum_{k=1}^{n} t_{ik} x_k, \qquad i = 1, 2, \cdots, n. \tag{30}$$

These equations are called the *equations of transformation* of the transition from the coordinate system $[\mathfrak{a}_1, \mathfrak{a}_2, \ldots, \mathfrak{a}_n]$ to the coordinate system $[\mathfrak{b}_1, \mathfrak{b}_2, \ldots, \mathfrak{b}_n]$.

We may combine equations (30) into a single matrix equation. For this purpose we define the following n-by-n matrices:

$$(x) = \begin{pmatrix} x_1 & 0 & 0 & \cdots & 0 \\ x_2 & 0 & 0 & \cdots & 0 \\ \cdot & \cdot & \cdot & \cdot & \cdot \\ x_n & 0 & 0 & \cdots & 0 \end{pmatrix}, \qquad (x^*) = \begin{pmatrix} x_1^* & 0 & 0 & \cdots & 0 \\ x_2^* & 0 & 0 & \cdots & 0 \\ \cdot & \cdot & \cdot & \cdot & \cdot \\ x_n^* & 0 & 0 & \cdots & 0 \end{pmatrix}. \tag{31}$$

In the first columns of these matrices we write the components x_i and

[8] Cf. § 10.

x_i^* respectively of the vector $\mathfrak{x}$ in their natural order, and we put zeros in the remaining columns. If we now form the matrix $T=(t_{ik})$ from the coefficients of the right-hand side of (30), we obtain

$$T \cdot (x) = \begin{pmatrix} \sum_{k=1}^{n} t_{1k} x_k & 0 & 0 & \cdots & 0 \\ \sum_{k=1}^{n} t_{2k} x_k & 0 & 0 & \cdots & 0 \\ \cdot & \cdot & \cdot & \cdot & \cdot \\ \sum_{k=1}^{n} t_{nk} x_k & 0 & 0 & \cdots & 0 \end{pmatrix}. \tag{32}$$

Comparing (30) and (31), we obtain

$$(x^*) = T \cdot (x). \tag{33}$$

This matrix equation is completely equivalent to the system (30).

It follows from (29) that the maximal number of linearly independent vectors among $\mathfrak{a}_1, \mathfrak{a}_2, \ldots, \mathfrak{a}_n$ is equal to the rank of the matrix T. (Cf. § 10, Theorem 1.) But the vectors $\mathfrak{a}_1, \mathfrak{a}_2, \ldots, \mathfrak{a}_n$ are a basis of L and so are linearly independent. Hence the rank of T is n, and therefore $| t_{ik} | \neq 0$.

Thus the inverse matrix T^{-1} exists. Multiplying (33) on the left by T^{-1}, we obtain

$$(x) = T^{-1} \cdot (x^*). \tag{34}$$

This equation shows how to calculate the x_i from the x_i^*. (34) is equivalent to n linear equations, namely the equations of transformation for the transition from the coordinate system $[\mathfrak{b}_1, \mathfrak{b}_2, \ldots, \mathfrak{b}_n]$ to the system $[\mathfrak{a}_1, \mathfrak{a}_2, \ldots, \mathfrak{a}_n]$.

Now let σ be a linear transformation, $A = (a_{ik})$ its matrix in the coordinate system $[\mathfrak{a}_1, \mathfrak{a}_2, \ldots, \mathfrak{a}_n]$, and $B = (b_{ik})$ its matrix in the coordinate system $[\mathfrak{b}_1, \mathfrak{b}_2, \ldots, \mathfrak{b}_n]$. A and B are not in general equal. However they are connected by a simple equation which we shall now derive.

The linear transformation σ is represented in the coordinate system $[\mathfrak{a}_1, \mathfrak{a}_2, \ldots, \mathfrak{a}_n]$ by the system of linear equations:

$$y_i = \sum_{k=1}^{n} a_{ik} x_k, \qquad i = 1, 2, \cdots, n \tag{35}$$

and in $[\mathfrak{b}_1, \mathfrak{b}_2, \ldots, \mathfrak{b}_n]$ by

$$(36) \qquad y_i^* = \sum_{k=1}^{n} b_{ik} x_k^* ;^{9} \qquad i = 1, 2, \cdots, n.$$

If we define, as before, the matrices

$$(37) \quad (y) = \begin{pmatrix} y_1 & 0 & 0 & \cdots & 0 \\ y_2 & 0 & 0 & \cdots & 0 \\ . & . & . & . & . \\ y_n & 0 & 0 & \cdots & 0 \end{pmatrix}, \qquad (y^*) = \begin{pmatrix} y_1^* & 0 & 0 & \cdots & 0 \\ y_2^* & 0 & 0 & \cdots & 0 \\ . & . & . & . & . \\ y_n^* & 0 & 0 & \cdots & 0 \end{pmatrix},$$

then we shall have, as above, the equations

$$(38) \qquad (y) = A \cdot (x),$$

$$(39) \qquad (y^*) = B \cdot (x^*)$$

which are equivalent to the systems (35) and (36). We must also bring in the equations of transformation representing the transition from the x_i^* to the x_i and from the y_i^* to the y_i. By (34), these equations are the following:

$$(x) = T^{-1} \cdot (x^*), \qquad (y) = T^{-1} \cdot (y^*).$$

If we substitute these in equation (38) it follows that

$$T^{-1} \cdot (y^*) = A \cdot T^{-1} \cdot (x^*),$$

or upon multiplication by T on the left, that

$$(40) \qquad (y^*) = T \cdot A \cdot T^{-1} \cdot (x^*).$$

Equation (40) gives the components y_i^* of $\sigma(\mathfrak{x})$ in $[\mathfrak{b}_1, \mathfrak{b}_2, \ldots, \mathfrak{b}_n]$ in terms of the components x_i^* of $\mathfrak{x}$ in the *same* coordinate system. But the system of equations representing σ in the coordinate system $[\mathfrak{b}_1, \mathfrak{b}_2, \ldots, \mathfrak{b}_n]$ is uniquely determined, so that equation (40) must be identical with (39). Thus we must have

$$T^{-1} \cdot (y^*) = A \cdot T^{-1} \cdot (x^*),$$

[9] x_i or y_i denote the components of the vectors in the coordinate system

$$[\mathfrak{a}_1, \mathfrak{a}_2, \cdots, \mathfrak{a}_n]$$

and x_i^* or y_i^* denote the components of the same vectors in the coordinate system

$$[\mathfrak{b}_1, \mathfrak{b}_2, \cdots, \mathfrak{b}_n]$$

We have thus obtained the relation connecting A and B. We say that *the non-singular matrix T transforms A into B* and that *A is similar to B*. We thus have the following theorem:

THEOREM 4. *If the linear transformation σ is represented by the matrix A in the coordinate system $[\mathfrak{a}_1, \mathfrak{a}_2, \ldots, \mathfrak{a}_n]$ and by the matrix B in the coordinate system $[\mathfrak{b}_1, \mathfrak{b}_2, \ldots, \mathfrak{b}_n]$ then there exists a non-singular T which transforms A into B. T is the coefficient matrix of the equations of transformation from the coordinate system $[\mathfrak{a}_1, \mathfrak{a}_2, \ldots, \mathfrak{a}_n]$ into the system $[\mathfrak{b}_1, \mathfrak{b}_2, \ldots, \mathfrak{b}_n]$.*

We point out once more how the matrix T in equation (41) was obtained. Its elements are given by (29). The k-th column of T thus consists of the components of $\mathfrak{a}_k$ in the coordinate system $[\mathfrak{b}_1, \mathfrak{b}_2, \ldots, \mathfrak{b}_n]$. We shall use this fact later.

Of course, T^{-1} transforms B into A. We may see this algebraically by multiplying equation (41) on the left by T^{-1} and on the right by T. This yields

$$B = T \cdot A \cdot T^{-1}. \tag{41}$$

With an eye to later applications we shall now prove the following converse of Theorem 4:

THEOREM 5. *Let A be the matrix of the linear transformation σ in the coordinate system $[\mathfrak{a}_1, \mathfrak{a}_2, \ldots, \mathfrak{a}_n]$ and let $B = T \cdot A \cdot T^{-1}$ be any matrix similar to A. Then there is a coordinate system $[\mathfrak{b}_1, \mathfrak{b}_2, \ldots, \mathfrak{b}_n]$ in which σ has the matrix B.*

Proof: The theorem amounts to determining vectors $\mathfrak{b}_i$ which satisfy equation (29). In other words, for the given $\mathfrak{a}_i$ and t_{ik} we must solve (29) for the $\mathfrak{b}_i$. But this is always possible if the determinant $|t_{ik}| \neq 0$, and may be accomplished by Cramer's rule.

The Determinant of a Linear Transformation

In connection with Theorem 3, we considered, along with the matrix $A = (a_{ik})$, the determinant formed with the elements of this matrix. We denote this determinant $|a_{ik}|$ by $|A|$ and call it the *determinant of A*.

The rule for the multiplication of matrices corresponds to one of the methods by which determinants may be multiplied. Thus, $A \cdot B = C$ implies $|A| \cdot |B| = |C|$.[10]

[10] But not conversely. The reader should supply a counter-example.

THEOREM 6. *If A and B are any two matrices, then*

$$|A \cdot B| = |A| \cdot |B|.$$

If A is non-singular, we may substitute $B = A^{-1}$ in the above equality. We then obtain

$$|A| \cdot |A^{-1}| = |A \cdot A^{-1}| = |E| = 1.$$

The determinants $|A|$ *and* $|A^{-1}|$ *are therefore reciprocal elements of* F.

By the *determinant of a linear transformation* we mean, of course, the determinant of its matrix in some definite coordinate system. Although the matrix corresponding to a given linear transformation depends on the coordinate system, this is not true of its determinant, for we have

THEOREM 7. *If A and B are the matrices of some linear transformation* σ *in two coordinate systems, then* $|A| = |B|$.

We also say that *the determinant of a linear transformation is invariant under coordinate transformations.*

Proof: The relation between A and B is, by Theorem 4, given by the equation

$$B = T \cdot A \cdot T^{-1}.$$

Applying Theorem 6, we obtain

$$|B| = |T| \cdot |A| \cdot |T^{-1}|.$$

But since the elements of F are commutative under multiplication and since $|T| \cdot |T^{-1}| = 1$, we have $|B| = |A|$.

Linear Dependence of Matrices

An n-by-n square matrix is nothing but an ordered n^2-tuple of elements of F. It is irrelevant for our present purposes that the entries are written not in a row but in n rows of n elements each. We may thus consider an n-by-n square matrix as an n^2-dimensional vector over F. Addition of matrices is then the usual vector addition, for it requires that corresponding entries (components) be added. And similarly the multiplication of a matrix by an element λ of F corresponds to the multiplication of a vector by λ, since in both cases it is effected by multiplying each entry (component) by λ. Because of this, the concepts of linear dependence and independence carry over word for word to matrices, as follows:

The n-by-n square matrices $A_1, A_2, \ldots, A_r$ are called *linearly dependent* if there are r elements $\lambda_1, \lambda_2, \ldots, \lambda_r$ of F which are not all 0 and which are such that

$$\lambda_1 A_1 + \lambda_2 A_2 + \cdots + \lambda_r A_r = O.$$

Otherwise the matrices are called *linearly independent.*

All of the theorems of vector algebra concerning linear dependence or independence of vectors will then hold for n-by-n square matrices. This is so because such matrices are nothing but n^2-dimensional vectors. It thus follows that any $r + 1$ (or more) linear combinations[11] of r matrices $A_1, A_2, \ldots, A_r$ are linearly dependent. Furthermore every n-by-n square matrix is a linear combination of the n^2 matrices E_{ik} which correspond to the unit vectors and are defined as follows: For each fixed pair of indices i, k $(1 \leqq i, k \leqq n)$ the matrix E_{ik} is that matrix all of whose entries are 0 except that in the i-th row and k-th column, which is 1. It then follows that any $n^2 + 1$ (or more) matrices are linearly dependent. We state this as a theorem.

THEOREM 8. *Let $A_1, A_2, \ldots, A_r$ be any n-by-n square matrices and let their number r be $> n^2$. Then there are r elements λ_i of* F *which are not all* 0 *such that*

$$\lambda_1 A_1 + \lambda_2 A_2 + \cdots + \lambda_r A_r = O.$$

We shall soon make use of this theorem.

Calculation With Matric Polynomials

We shall later have to operate with matrices and determinants whose elements are polynomials. Now, we have derived the theorems of matrix and determinant theory on the sole assumption that their entries were elements of a field. However the domain F$[u]$ of all polynomials in one indeterminate over a field K is not itself a field. For, the axiom of reversibility of multiplication (i.e. possibility of division) is not satisfied in K$[u]$. *Despite this, all of the rules and theorems concerning determinants and matrices will be true in this case also, if*

[11] A *linear combination* of the matrices $A_1, A_2, \cdots, A_r$ is an expression of the form $\lambda_1 A_1 + \lambda_2 A_2 + \cdots + \lambda_r A_r$ where the coefficients λ_i are elements of F.

suitably interpreted. To establish this, it is only necessary to show that F[u] can be imbedded in a field,[12] which we proceed to do.

To this end we consider all symbols of the form $\frac{f}{g}$ where f and g are polynomials of F[u],[13] with $g \neq 0$. Two such elements $\frac{f}{g}$ and $\frac{f^*}{g^*}$ are called *equal,* if

$$f \cdot g^* = f^* \cdot g. \tag{42}$$

This definition of equality is 1. *reflexive,* i.e. every element is equal to itself, 2. *symmetric,* i.e. the two sides of an equation may be interchanged, and 3. *transitive,* i.e. if $\frac{f}{g} = \frac{f^*}{g^*}$ and $\frac{f^*}{g^*} = \frac{f^{**}}{g^{**}}$, then $\frac{f}{g} = \frac{f^{**}}{g^{**}}$. 1. and 2. are trivial. 3. states that (42) and $f^*g^{**} = f^{**}g^*$ imply $fg^{**} = f^{**}g$. This may easily be verified.

We identify the element $\frac{f}{1}$ with the polynomial f itself (i.e. the symbols $\frac{f \cdot d}{d}$ are to be considered merely as new symbols for the polynomial f).

We now define an *addition* and a *multiplication* for our symbols by the formulas

$$\frac{f_1}{g_1} + \frac{f_2}{g_2} = \frac{f_1 g_2 + f_2 g_1}{g_1 g_2}, \tag{43}$$

$$\frac{f_1}{g_1} \cdot \frac{f_2}{g_2} = \frac{f_1 \cdot f_2}{g_1 \cdot g_2}. \tag{44}$$

Since by our definition of equality, the same element may be denoted by various symbols, we must show that if we substitute equal elements for the above summands and factors we still obtain equal results. Thus let, say, $\frac{f_1}{g_1} = \frac{f_1^*}{g_1^*}$, $\frac{f_2}{g_2} = \frac{f_2^*}{g_2^*}$ i.e.

$$f_1 g_1^* = f_1^* g_1, \qquad f_2 g_2^* = f_2^* g_2. \tag{45}$$

---

[12] The construction which follows is a special case of the construction of the quotient field of an integral domain. Cf. H. Hasse, *Höhere Algebra I,* Sammlung Göschen 1926, p. 27; O. Haupt, *Einf. in d. Algebra I,* Leipzig 1929, p. 43; B. L. van der Waerden, *Moderne Algebra I,* Berlin 1930, p. 46; C. C. MacDuffee, *Introduction to Abstract Algebra,* New York, 1940, p. 153; B. L. van der Waerden, *Modern Algebra,* New York, 1949, p. 40.

[13] The polynomials of F[u] will be denoted for short by f, g, h, k instead of $f(u)$ etc. This is done because the following arguments remain valid even if f, g, h, k are not polynomials but elements of an arbitrary integral domain. Cf. footnote 12.

Adding $\frac{f_1^*}{g_1^*}$ and $\frac{f_2^*}{g_2^*}$ we obtain

$$\frac{f_1^*}{g_1^*}+\frac{f_2^*}{g_2^*}=\frac{f_1^* g_2^* + f_2^* g_1^*}{g_1^* g_2^*}.$$

This element is equal to the element in (43) if

$$g_1 g_2 (f_1^* g_2^* + f_2^* g_1^*) = g_1^* g_2^* (f_1 g_2 + f_2 g_1)$$

holds. But this is seen to be true on the basis of (45). The proof is similar for multiplication.

We shall now show that *for those of our symbols which represent polynomials, these definitions coincide with ordinary addition and multiplication.* The polynomials f and g can be represented by the symbols $\frac{f}{1}$ and $\frac{g}{1}$ respectively. Adding and multiplying these symbols by using (43) and (44), we obtain $\frac{f+g}{1}$ and $\frac{f\cdot g}{1}$, which in turn represent the polynomials $f + g$ and $f \cdot g$, respectively.

However this is precisely what we sought. *For, the totality of elements* $\frac{f}{g}$ *forms a field under the above rules for addition and multiplication.* We leave the easy verification of the Commutative and Associative laws, and of the Distributive law, to the reader. As for subtraction and division, the equation $\frac{f_1}{g_1}+X=\frac{f_2}{g_2}$ has the solution $\frac{f_2 g_1 - f_1 g_2}{g_1 g_2}$, as may be verified by substitution. Finally, the equation $\frac{f_1}{g_1}\cdot X=\frac{f_2}{g_2}$ has the solution $\frac{f_2 g_1}{f_1 g_2}$.

This field of elements $\frac{f}{g}$ thus obtained is called the **field of rational functions in one indeterminate** over F and is denoted by F(u).[14]

We have thus imbedded the polynomial domain F$[u]$ in a field F(u) in such a way that addition and multiplication of polynomials of F(u) is the same as in F$[u]$.[15] The above discussion enables us to state the

[14] We use parentheses here to distinguish this field from the polynomial domain F$[u]$.

[15] This is of importance for further applications. Consider, for example, the addition of matrices. This is defined by the addition of corresponding elements. Now if the addition of elements of the polynomial domain F$[u]$ were defined differently from the addition of polynomials in the field F(u), then addition of polynomial matrices could be defined in two different ways, according to which of the two methods of addition we use for the polynomials. The rules of matrix addition would then apply only in the second case, and for matrices with elements from the polynomial domain F$[u]$ we would have to make new definitions.

following: Since the theorems on determinants and matrices hold for determinants and matrices whose entries belong to an arbitrary field, *they also hold for determinants and matrices whose entries belong to* F(u), *and hence in particular if the entries are polynomials.* Such a matrix (or determinant) whose entries are polynomials is called a *polynomial matrix* (or *polynomial determinant*). However, it must be emphasized that calculations involving polynomial matrices (or determinants) may lead outside the domain of such matrices (or determinants). Thus, for example, it is easy to see that the inverse of a polynomial matrix may well have entries which are elements of F(u) but are not polynomials. However, addition, subtraction, and multiplication of polynomial matrices (or determinants) always yield polynomial matrices (or determinants).

The Transpose of a Matrix

The *transpose* of a matrix A is, by p. 43, that matrix whose rows are the columns of A and whose columns are the rows of A, i.e. the reflection of the matrix A about its principal diagonal. The transpose of the matrix A will always be denoted by A'. Of course $(A')' = A$.

We now state a few rules concerning the transposes of n-by-n square matrices.

I. The transpose of a sum is the sum of the transposes. That is,

$$(A + B)' = A' + B'. \tag{46}$$

II. The transpose of a product may be determined by the rule

$$(A \cdot B)' = B' \cdot A'. \tag{47}$$

III. The operations of forming the transpose of a matrix and of taking its inverse commute, as follows:

$$(A^{-1})' = (A')^{-1}. \tag{48}$$

Easy calculations suffice to prove these statements.

Exercises

1. Let A, B, C be the following three matrices with real (as a matter of fact, rational) entries:

$$A = \begin{pmatrix} 1 & 0 & 1 & -1 \\ 2 & -1 & 0 & -2 \\ -3 & 1 & -2 & 4 \\ 1 & -1 & 0 & -1 \end{pmatrix}, \quad B = \begin{pmatrix} 7 & -2 & 4 & -8 \\ 4 & -3 & 0 & -4 \\ -2 & 2 & 1 & 2 \\ 4 & 0 & 4 & -5 \end{pmatrix},$$

$$C = \begin{pmatrix} 2 & 1 & 1 & 0 \\ 0 & 1 & 0 & -2 \\ 1 & -1 & 0 & 1 \\ 2 & 0 & 1 & 1 \end{pmatrix}.$$

Evaluate the products $A \cdot C$; $A \cdot B$; $B \cdot C$; $A \cdot (B \cdot C)$; $(A \cdot B) \cdot C$.

2. Evaluate A^{-1} and B^{-1}, if

$$A = \begin{pmatrix} 1 & 1+i & -i \\ 0 & i & 1-2i \\ 1 & 1 & i \end{pmatrix}, \quad B = \begin{pmatrix} -4 & -1 & -4 & 1 \\ 2 & 1 & 2 & 0 \\ 8 & 3 & 7 & -1 \\ -3 & -1 & -3 & 1 \end{pmatrix}$$

and verify that $A \cdot A^{-1} = B \cdot B^{-1} = E$.

3. Let F be the totality of all 3-by-3 matrices of the form

$$\begin{pmatrix} a & b & c \\ 3c & a-3c & b \\ 3b & -3b+3c & a-3c \end{pmatrix},$$

where a, b, c are arbitrary rational numbers. Show that F is a field under the operations of matrix addition and multiplication. Is F a field if a, b, c are permitted to be real or complex numbers?

4. Let V_n be the n-dimensional vector space over some field F and let

$$\mathfrak{a}_1, \mathfrak{a}_2, \cdots, \mathfrak{a}_n$$

and $\mathfrak{b}_1, \mathfrak{b}_2, \cdots, \mathfrak{b}_n$ be two bases of V_n. Let an arbitrary vector $\mathfrak{x}$ of V_n have the components $x_1, x_2, \cdots, x_n$ in the coordinate system

$$[\mathfrak{a}_1, \mathfrak{a}_2, \cdots, \mathfrak{a}_n]$$

and the components $x_1^*, x_2^*, \cdots, x_n^*$ in the coordinate system $[\mathfrak{b}_1, \mathfrak{b}_2, \cdots, \mathfrak{b}_n]$. Let

$$\mathfrak{a}_i = \{a_{1i}, a_{2i}, \cdots, a_{ni}\} = \sum_{k=1}^{n} a_{ki}\, \mathfrak{e}_k, \quad \mathfrak{b}_i = \{b_{1i}, b_{2i}, \cdots, b_{ni}\} = \sum_{k=1}^{n} b_{ki}\, \mathfrak{e}_k \qquad i = 1, 2, \cdots, n.$$

Set $A = (a_{ik})$, $B = (b_{ik})$ and define (x) and (x^*) as in equations (31) of this section. Show that the equations for the coordinate transformation under the transition from the basis $\mathfrak{a}_1, \mathfrak{a}_2, \cdots, \mathfrak{a}_n$ to the basis $\mathfrak{b}_1, \mathfrak{b}_2, \cdots, \mathfrak{b}_n$ are given by

$$(x^*) = B^{-1} \cdot A \cdot (x).$$

5. A linear transformation is completely determined by the image vectors of one basis; for one can then form its matrix corresponding to this basis. Let V_3 be the three-dimensional vector space over the field of complex numbers. The vectors

$$\mathfrak{a}_1 = \{1, 0, 1\}, \quad \mathfrak{a}_2 = \{1+i, i, 1\}, \quad \mathfrak{a}_3 = \{-i, 1-2i, i\}$$

form a basis of V_3. Let σ be that linear transformation on V_3 for which

$$\sigma(\mathfrak{a}_1) = \mathfrak{a}_1, \quad \sigma(\mathfrak{a}_2) = 0, \quad \sigma(\mathfrak{a}_3) = i\, \mathfrak{a}_3.$$

What is the matrix of σ in the coordinate system $[\mathfrak{e}_1, \mathfrak{e}_2, \mathfrak{e}_3]$?

Determine the vectors $\sigma(\mathfrak{a}_1)$, $\sigma(\mathfrak{a}_2)$, $\sigma(\mathfrak{a}_3)$ by means of the system of equations for σ in the coordinate system $[\mathfrak{e}_1, \mathfrak{e}_2, \mathfrak{e}_3]$.

6. Let $A = (a_{ik})$, $B = (b_{ik})$ be any two n-by-n matrices (singular or non-singular). For $k = 1, 2, \ldots, n$, let $A^{(k)}$ be the matrix

$$A^{(k)} = \begin{pmatrix} a_{11} & a_{12} & \cdots & a_{1n} & b_{1k} \\ a_{21} & a_{22} & \cdots & a_{2n} & b_{2k} \\ \cdot & \cdot & \cdot & \cdot & \cdot \\ a_{n1} & a_{n2} & \cdots & a_{nn} & b_{nk} \end{pmatrix}.$$

Thus $A^{(k)}$ is a matrix having n rows and $n + 1$ columns. Prove that the equation $A \cdot X = B$ is solvable for the n-by-n matrix X if and only if the $n + 1$ matrices $A, A^{(1)}, A^{(2)}, \cdots, A^{(n)}$ all have the same rank.

7. Let

$$A = \begin{pmatrix} 1 & 3 \\ -2 & 2 \end{pmatrix}.$$

Investigate the question of whether the matrices E, A, A^2 are linearly dependent. Do the same for

$$A = \begin{pmatrix} 2 & -6 & 6 \\ 3 & -7 & 6 \\ 3 & -6 & 5 \end{pmatrix}.$$

§ 23. The Minimal Polynomial; Invariant Subspaces

Having accomplished the necessary preliminaries in the last two sections, we proceed with our investigation of linear transformations. For the time being, we retain the general assumptions we have been using. Let F be any field, V_q the q-dimensional vector space over F, L an arbitrary vector space of V_q whose dimension is $n > 0$, and σ a linear transformation on L. We also consider the polynomial domain F$[u]$ in an indeterminate u over F. These conventions will be adopted for this entire section.

The Minimal Polynomial

The first question that we ask is the following: Is there a *non-vanishing* polynomial $f(u)$ in F$[u]$ such that $f(\sigma) = 0$ (= the null transformation on L)? Let $\mathfrak{a}_1, \mathfrak{a}_2, \ldots, \mathfrak{a}_n$ be a basis of L and let A be the matrix of σ in the coordinate system $[\mathfrak{a}_1, \mathfrak{a}_2, \ldots, \mathfrak{a}_n]$. Consider the matrices $A^0 = E, A, A^2, A^3, \ldots, A^k$. In all, there are $n^2 + 1$ of these n-by-n matrices. By Theorem 8 of § 22 there are $n^2 + 1$ elements $\lambda_0, \lambda_1, \cdots, \lambda_{n^2}$ of F which do not all vanish, such that

(1) $$\lambda_{n^2} A^{n^2} + \lambda_{n^2-1} A^{n^2-1} + \cdots + \lambda_1 A + \lambda_0 A^0 = O.$$

If we set
$$f(u) = \lambda_{n^2} u^{n^2} + \lambda_{n^2-1} u^{n^2-1} + \cdots + \lambda_1 u + \lambda_0,$$

then the left-hand side of (1) is precisely the matrix $f(A)$. By § 22 the matrix of the linear transformation $f(\sigma)$ is precisely $f(A)$, in the coordinate system $[\mathfrak{a}_1, \mathfrak{a}_2, \ldots, \mathfrak{a}_n]$. Since $f(A)$ is, by (1), the null matrix, we must have

(2) $$f(\sigma) = 0.$$

We say that σ *is a zero of* $f(u)$. Since not all of the elements λ_i vanish, the polynomial $f(u)$ does not vanish identically. We have thus shown the existence of a polynomial $f(u) \neq 0$ which has σ as a zero.

Consider the set of all polynomials of $\mathrm{F}[u]$ having σ as a zero. Let this set be denoted by $\mathfrak{a}$. Then $\mathfrak{a}$ is a non-empty set and indeed contains non-vanishing polynomials. We further see that $\mathfrak{a}$ *is an ideal* (cf. p. 207). For if $f(u)$ and $g(u)$ belong to $\mathfrak{a}$, so that $f(\sigma) = g(\sigma) = 0$, then $f(\sigma) + g(\sigma) = 0$ and $h(\sigma) \cdot f(\sigma) = 0$ for any $h(u)$ of $\mathrm{F}[u]$.

But by § 15, Theorem 1, every ideal in the polynomial domain $\mathrm{F}[u]$ is a principal ideal. Thus there is a polynomial $m(u)$ in $\mathfrak{a}$ with the property that $\mathfrak{a}$ consists of all the multiples $h(u) \cdot m(u)$ of this polynomial. $m(u)$ is a polynomial of least degree in $\mathfrak{a}$ and is uniquely determined if we require its leading coefficient to be 1. We have thus proved

THEOREM 1. *To every linear transformation σ on* L *there corresponds one and only one polynomial $m(u)$ in* $\mathrm{F}[u]$ *with the following properties: $m(u)$ is not identically* 0, *and has its leading coefficient equal to* 1; *it is the polynomial of least degree having σ as a zero, and is a divisor of any such polynomial.*

$m(u)$ is called the ***minimal polynomial*** *of the linear transformation σ.*

Finally, the degree of the minimal polynomial is > 0. For otherwise $m(u) = 1$ and $m(\sigma)$ would be the identity transformation.

Consider the polynomials $f(u)$ for which $f(A) = O$. This equation is satisfied if and only if $f(\sigma) = 0$. Thus $m(u)$ is the polynomial of least degree having A as a zero. $m(u)$ is thus also referred to as the *minimal polynomial of the matrix A*. We thus have

THEOREM 2. *A linear transformation σ on* L *and its matrix in any coordinate system have the same minimal polynomial.*

Invariant Subspaces

We shall now concern ourselves with certain subspaces of L, namely those which are mapped into themselves by σ. It will be shown that there is a close connection between certain of these subspaces and the minimal polynomial.

Let M be a vector space of V_q which is contained in L, so that it is a *subspace* of L. We consider the set of all image vectors of M under σ; we denote this set by $\sigma(\text{M})$ and refer to $\sigma(\text{M})$ as the image of M under the linear transformation σ. We assert the following:

$\sigma(\text{M})$ *is also a vector space.*

First, it is clear that $\sigma(\text{M})$ is not empty since M is not empty. Furthermore, if $\mathfrak{c}$ and $\mathfrak{d}$ are any two vectors of $\sigma(\text{M})$, then by the definition of $\sigma(\text{M})$ they are the images of certain vectors of M, say of $\mathfrak{a}$ and $\mathfrak{b}$. We then have

$$\lambda \cdot \mathfrak{c} = \lambda \cdot \sigma(\mathfrak{a}) = \sigma(\lambda \cdot \mathfrak{a}), \tag{3}$$
$$\mathfrak{c} + \mathfrak{d} = \sigma(\mathfrak{a}) + \sigma(\mathfrak{b}) = \sigma(\mathfrak{a} + \mathfrak{b}). \tag{4}$$

Thus $\lambda\mathfrak{c}$ and $\mathfrak{c} + \mathfrak{d}$ are themselves images of vectors of M (namely of $\lambda\mathfrak{a}$ and $\mathfrak{a} + \mathfrak{b}$) and so belong to $\sigma(\text{M})$. We have thus shown that $\sigma(\text{M})$ satisfies the two defining properties of a vector space.

In particular, it may happen that $\sigma(\text{M})$ is contained entirely within M, i.e. that every image of a vector of M is in M. If this occurs, we call M an **invariant subspace** of L with respect to σ.

If M is invariant with respect to σ, we define the mapping σ' of M into itself by the condition $\sigma'(\mathfrak{x}) = \sigma(\mathfrak{x})$ for any $\mathfrak{x}$ in M. σ' is defined only on M, and agrees with σ on M. We call σ' the mapping *induced* on M by σ. Of course, σ' is itself a linear transformation.

We observe that σ and σ' are two distinct linear transformations according to this definition. In general, they will have different minimal polynomials. As an example, let σ be that linear transformation on a two-dimensional vector space which is given by the system of equations

$$y_1 = x_1, \quad y_2 = -x_2$$

with respect to the basis $\mathfrak{a}_1, \mathfrak{a}_2$. Then the space spanned by $\mathfrak{a}_1$ is a one-dimensional subspace, and is invariant with respect to σ. The induced transformation σ' is represented by the equation $y_1 = x_1$ with respect to the basis $\mathfrak{a}_1$. In this case the minimal polynomial of σ is[1] $u^2 - 1$, and that of σ' is $u - 1$.

Let us return to our general considerations. The equation $\sigma'(\mathfrak{x}) = \sigma(\mathfrak{x})$ is satisfied for every $\mathfrak{x}$ in M. It then follows that

$$\sigma'^2(\mathfrak{x}) = \sigma'[\sigma'(\mathfrak{x})] = \sigma'[\sigma(\mathfrak{x})] = \sigma[\sigma(\mathfrak{x})] = \sigma^2(\mathfrak{x}),$$

and that $\sigma'^3(\mathfrak{x}) = \sigma^3(\mathfrak{x})$, and in general $\sigma'^k(\mathfrak{x}) = \sigma^k(\mathfrak{x})$. Observing that these equations may be multiplied by constants of F and added, we see the validity of

THEOREM 3. *Let* M *be invariant with respect to* σ, *and let* σ' *be induced by* σ *on* M. *Let* $f(u)$ *be any polynomial of* $F[u]$. *Then for every* $\mathfrak{x}$ *of* M *we have*

$$f(\sigma')(\mathfrak{x}) = f(\sigma)(\mathfrak{x}).$$

Since $f(\sigma')$ is a linear transformation on M, the vector $f(\sigma')(\mathfrak{x})$ belongs to M for every $\mathfrak{x}$ of M; by Theorem 3, so does $f(\sigma)(\mathfrak{x})$. But this means that M is invariant with respect to the linear transformation $f(\sigma)$. We thus have the following theorem:

THEOREM 4. *If a subspace* M *of* L *is invariant with respect to the linear transformation* σ, *then* M *is also invariant with respect to every linear transformation* $f(\sigma)$, *where* $f(u)$ *is any polynomial of* $F[u]$.

The Null Space of a Linear Transformation $f(\sigma)$

We now consider a special class of invariant subspaces. We take a polynomial $f(u)$ of $F[u]$, substitute for u the linear transformation σ on L, and consider the set of all vectors which are mapped on the null vector by $f(\sigma)$. These are the vector solutions of the equation

$$f(\sigma)(\mathfrak{x}) = 0. \qquad (5)$$

The set of all vectors of L which satisfy this equation is a vector space. For, there do exist vectors which are solutions of this equation, for instance the null vector. And if $\mathfrak{x}$ and $\mathfrak{y}$ are two solutions of (5), then

$$f(\sigma)(\mathfrak{x} + \mathfrak{y}) = f(\sigma)(\mathfrak{x}) + f(\sigma)(\mathfrak{y}) = 0$$

and $f(\sigma)(\lambda\mathfrak{x}) = \lambda \cdot f(\sigma)(\mathfrak{x}) = 0$ for any λ of F.

---

[1] The minimal polynomial must be at least of the second degree since there is no linear relation between $A^0 = E$ and $A = \begin{pmatrix} 1 & 0 \\ 0 & -1 \end{pmatrix}$. On the other hand the polynomial $u^2 - 1$ does have the matrix A as a zero, and so it must be the minimal polynomial (Theorem 1).

The vector space of all the solutions of (5) is called the ***null space of the linear transformation*** $f(\sigma)$, and is denoted by L_f. It is of importance that *every such null space* L_f *is invariant with respect to* σ.

For considering formula (28) of § 21, which in particular yields $f(\sigma)\cdot\sigma = \sigma\cdot f(\sigma)$, we have for any vector $\mathfrak{x}$ of L_f that

$$f(\sigma)[\sigma(\mathfrak{x})] = [f(\sigma)\cdot\sigma](\mathfrak{x}) = [\sigma\cdot f(\sigma)](\mathfrak{x}) = \sigma[f(\sigma)(\mathfrak{x})] = 0,$$

which implies that $\sigma(\mathfrak{x})$ is in L_f. This proves the invariance of L_f.

As has just been stated, L_f contains at least the null vector. However we do not know whether it contains any non-vanishing vectors. Of course this depends on the choice of the polynomial $f(u)$. By way of investigation of this question, which, incidentally, will be answered by Theorem 10, we now investigate the connection between the null spaces of different polynomials. We first prove

THEOREM 5. *If* $f(u)$ *is a polynomial of* $F[u]$, $g(u)$ *a divisor of* $f(u)$, *then the null space* L_g *of the linear transformation* $g(\sigma)$ *is contained in the null space* L_f *of the linear transformation* $f(\sigma)$.

Proof: Since $g(u)$ divides $f(u)$, there is an equation of the form $f(u) = r(u)\cdot g(u)$ for some definite polynomial $r(u)$ of $F[u]$. By § 21 we then have $f(\sigma) = r(\sigma)\cdot g(\sigma)$. Now letting $\mathfrak{x}$ be any vector of L_g, we see that $f(\sigma)(\mathfrak{x}) = r(\sigma)(g(\sigma)(\mathfrak{x})) = 0$ so that $\mathfrak{x}$ is also in L_f as was to be proved.

Next, we have

THEOREM 6. *Let* $f(u)$ *and* $g(u)$ *be two arbitrary polynomials of* $F[u]$ *and let* $d(u)$ *be their greatest common divisor. Then the null space* L_d *of the linear transformation* $d(\sigma)$ *is identical with the intersection of the null spaces* L_f *and* L_g *of* $f(\sigma)$ *and* $g(\sigma)$ *respectively.*

Proof: Let D be the intersection of L_f and L_g. Since $d(u)$ is a divisor of $f(u)$ and $g(u)$, the space L_d is, by Theorem 5, contained in both L_f and L_g and so in their intersection D. We shall now show that D is contained in L_d, which will prove our assertion.

Since $d(u)$ is the greatest common divisor of $f(u)$ and $g(u)$, there exist, by Theorem 2 of § 15, two polynomials $h_1(u)$ and $h_2(u)$ such that

$$d(u) = h_1(u)f(u) + h_2(u)g(u).$$

This equation remains valid if we substitute σ for u, so that

$$d(\sigma) = h_1(\sigma)f(\sigma) + h_2(\sigma)g(\sigma).$$

Now if $\mathfrak{x}$ is any vector of D, so that

$$f(\sigma)(\mathfrak{x}) = 0, \quad g(\sigma)(\mathfrak{x}) = 0$$

then $\mathfrak{x}$ also belongs to L_d, since

$$d(\sigma)(\mathfrak{x}) = h_1(\sigma)(f(\sigma)(\mathfrak{x})) + h_2(\sigma)(g(\sigma)(\mathfrak{x})) = 0.$$

Thus Theorem 6 is proved.

If $f(u)$ and $g(u)$ are relatively prime, so that their greatest common divisor $d(u) = 1$, then L_d is the null space of the identity transformation. But this consists of the null vector alone. Thus from Theorem 6, we derive

THEOREM 7. *If $f(u)$ and $g(u)$ are two relatively prime polynomials of $F[u]$, then the null spaces L_f and L_g of the linear transformations $f(\sigma)$ and $g(\sigma)$ have a 0-dimensional intersection.*

We now apply Theorem 6 in the special case in which one of the two polynomials, say $g(u)$, is the minimal polynomial $m(u)$ of σ. In this case $L_g = L_m = L$, since $m(\sigma)$ maps every vector of L on the null vector. The intersection of L_f and L_g is in this case L_f itself, for L_f is by definition a subspace of L. Thus Theorem 6 states the following, in the present special case:

THEOREM 8. *Let $m(u)$ be the minimal polynomial of the linear transformation σ, $f(u)$ any polynomial of $F[u]$, and $d(u)$ the greatest common divisor of $f(u)$ and $m(u)$. Then the null space L_d of the linear transformation $d(\sigma)$ is identical with the null space L_f of the linear transformation $f(\sigma)$.*

This result has as a consequence that we may from now on restrict our considerations to the *divisors of the minimal polynomial,* since the general case can be reduced to this case. We further show

THEOREM 9. *If $f(u)$ is a divisor of the minimal polynomial $m(u)$ of σ, and $g(u)$ is a divisor of $f(u)$ of lower degree than $f(u)$, then the null space L_g is a proper subspace of the null space L_f, that is, L_g has a smaller dimension than L_f.*

By Theorem 5, L_g is a subspace of L_f. We must thus show that L_g is not the whole of L_f. Let $m(u) = f(u) \cdot h(u)$. Form the polynomial $k(u) = g(u) \cdot h(u)$, so that $k(u)$ is a proper divisor of $m(u)$. Thus $k(\sigma) = g(\sigma) \cdot h(\sigma)$ is not the null transformation, since $m(u)$ is the polynomial of the least degree with this property. It then follows that there is a vector $\mathfrak{x}$ in L such that

$$k(\sigma)(\mathfrak{x}) = g(\sigma)[h(\sigma)(\mathfrak{x})] \neq 0.$$

But this means that the vector $h(\sigma)(\mathfrak{x})$ does not belong to L_g. On the other hand, we have

$$f(\sigma) \cdot [h(\sigma)(\mathfrak{x})] = m(\sigma)(\mathfrak{x}) = 0,$$

so that $h(\sigma)(\mathfrak{x})$ belongs to L_f. Thus $h(\sigma)(\mathfrak{x})$ is a vector which belongs to L_f, but not to L_g. This proves that L_g is a proper subspace of L_f.

Let us now drop the hypothesis that $f(u)$ divides the minimal polynomial $m(u)$. Let $d(u)$ be the greatest common divisor of $f(u)$ and $m(u)$. If $d(u) = 1$, then L_d consists of the null vector alone. If however the degree of $d(u)$ is greater than 0, then the constant 1 is a divisor of $d(u)$ of lesser degree than $d(u)$. Hence by Theorem 9, L_1 is a proper subspace of L_d, so that the dimension of L_d is greater than 0. Since, by Theorem 8, we have $L_f = L_d$, we have proved

THEOREM 10. *Let $d(u)$ be the greatest common divisor of the minimal polynomial $m(u)$ of σ and the (arbitrary) polynomial $f(u)$ of $F[u]$. Then the dimension of the null space L_f (of the linear transformation $f(\sigma)$) is greater than 0 if and only if the degree of $d(u)$ is greater than 0.*

As an easy application of Theorem 9, we may derive the following result concerning the linear transformation σ' induced by σ on L_f.

THEOREM 11. *Let $f(u)$ be a divisor of the minimal polynomial $m(u)$ of σ whose leading coefficient is 1 and whose degree is > 0. Then $f(u)$ is the minimal polynomial of the linear transformation σ' which is induced by σ on the null space L_f.*

Proof: By Theorem 3, we have for all vectors $\mathfrak{x}$ of L_f that

$$f(\sigma')(\mathfrak{x}) = f(\sigma)(\mathfrak{x}) = 0.$$

Thus $f(\sigma')$ is the null transformation on L_f. Let $h(u)$ be the minimal polynomial of σ'. Theorem 1, applied to the linear transformation σ', shows that $h(u)$ is a divisor of $f(u)$. But

$$h(\sigma)(\mathfrak{x}) = h(\sigma')(\mathfrak{x}) = 0$$

for every $\mathfrak{x}$ of L_f, by the definition of the minimal polynomial. Thus L_h is not a proper subspace of L_f. Hence by Theorem 9, $h(u)$ cannot have a smaller degree than $f(u)$. Since $f(u)$ and $h(u)$ both have highest coefficient 1, we see that $h(u)=f(u)$. Thus Theorem 11 is proved.

Decomposition of L Into Invariant Subspaces

We now need a theorem which is a partial converse of Theorem 6, namely:

THEOREM 12. *Let* $f_1(u), f_2(u), \ldots, f_r(u)$ *be arbitrary polynomials of* $F[u]$ *and let* $h(u)$ *be the least common multiple*[2] *of these* r *polynomials. Let* $L_{f_1}, L_{f_2}, \ldots, L_{f_r}, L_h$ *be the null spaces of the linear transformations* $f_1(\sigma), f_2(\sigma), \cdots, f_r(\sigma), h(\sigma)$. *Then* L_h *is the sum*[3] *of the vector spaces* $L_{f_1}, L_{f_2}, \ldots, L_{f_r}$, *i.e.* L_h *consists of all vectors* $\mathfrak{x}$ *of* L *of the form*

$$\mathfrak{x} = \mathfrak{x}_1 + \mathfrak{x}_2 + \ldots + \mathfrak{x}_r \tag{6}$$

with $\mathfrak{x}_1$ *in* L_{f_1}, $\mathfrak{x}_2$ *in* L_{f_2}, $\ldots$, $\mathfrak{x}_r$ *in* L_{f_r}.

Proof: Let S be the sum of the vector spaces $L_{f_1}, L_{f_2}, \ldots, L_{f_r}$. Because of the possibility of the representation of every vector $\mathfrak{x}$ in the form (6), it easily follows that S is contained in L_h. For, each polynomial $f_i(u)$ divides $h(u)$, so that each L_{f_i} is a subspace of L_h, by Theorem 5. Thus each of the vectors $\mathfrak{x}_1, \mathfrak{x}_2, \ldots, \mathfrak{x}_r$ belongs to L_h and consequently so does their sum.

It remains to be shown that, conversely, every vector of L_h belongs to S. Since $h(u)$ is a common multiple of the polynomials $f_i(u)$, we must have r equations of the form

$$h(u) = f_i(u) \cdot h_i(u), \qquad i = 1, 2, \cdots, r. \tag{7}$$

The polynomials $h_1(u), h_2(u), \ldots, h_r(u)$ are relatively prime. For if not they would have a common divisor $d(u)$ whose degree is greater than 0. Then $\frac{h(u)}{d(u)}, \frac{h_1(u)}{d(u)}, \cdots, \frac{h_r(u)}{d(u)}$ would be polynomials of $F[u]$

---

[2] The least common multiple of r polynomials is obtained in the same way as for two polynomials in § 15, p. 216. For we immediately see that the totality of common multiples of the r polynomials $f_1(u), f_2(u), \cdots, f_r(u)$ is an ideal $\mathfrak{a}$. Since every ideal of $F[u]$ is a principal ideal, there is a polynomial $h(u)$ in $\mathfrak{a}$ which divides all polynomials in $\mathfrak{a}$, $h(u)$ is the least common multiple of the polynomials

$$f_1(u), f_2(u), \cdots, f_r(u).$$

[3] Cf. § 4, p. 25.

for which the equations

$$\frac{h(u)}{d(u)} = \left(\frac{h_i(u)}{d(u)}\right) \cdot f_i(u), \qquad i = 1, 2, \cdots, r$$

would hold. Thus the polynomial $\frac{h(u)}{d(u)}$ would have a smaller degree than $h(u)$ and would be a common multiple of the polynomials $f_1(u), f_2(u), \ldots, f_r(u)$, which would contradict the definition of $h(u)$.

Because the polynomials $h_1(u)$, $h_2(u)$, ..., $h_r(u)$ are relatively prime, there exist (by § 15, Theorem 2) r polynomials $s_1(u)$, $s_2(u)$, ..., $s_r(u)$, such that

$$1 = s_1(u) \cdot h_1(u) + s_2(u) \cdot h_2(u) + \cdots + s_r(u) \cdot h_r(u).$$

By § 21, the transformation

$$s_1(\sigma) \cdot h_1(\sigma) + s_2(\sigma) \cdot h_2(\sigma) + \cdots + s_r(\sigma) \cdot h_r(\sigma)$$

must then be the identity transformation on L. Thus for any vector $\mathfrak{x}$ of L we have

$$(8) \quad \mathfrak{x} = s_1(\sigma)(h_1(\sigma)(\mathfrak{x})) + s_2(\sigma)(h_2(\sigma)(\mathfrak{x})) + \cdots + s_r(\sigma)(h_r(\sigma)(\mathfrak{x})).$$

In particular if we choose $\mathfrak{x}$ from L_h, then (8) is a representation of $\mathfrak{x}$ of the form (6). For,

$$h(\sigma)(\mathfrak{x}) = 0$$

for every vector $\mathfrak{x}$ of L_h. Hence by (7), $f_i(\sigma)(h_i(\sigma)(\mathfrak{x})) = 0$ for every i. But this means that each of the vectors $h_i(\sigma)(\mathfrak{x})$ is in L_{f_i}. But each of the spaces L_{f_i} is invariant with respect to σ, and so by Theorem 4, they are invariant with respect to the linear transformation $s_i(\sigma)$. Thus the vector $s_i(\sigma)(h_i(\sigma)(\mathfrak{x}))$ is itself in L_{f_i}. Thus by (8), every vector $\mathfrak{x}$ of L_h has a representation of the form (6) and so is in S. This completes the proof of Theorem 12.

Now consider the case in which the polynomials $f_1(u)$, $f_2(u)$, ..., $f_r(u)$ are relatively prime in pairs. In this case their least common multiple $h(u)$ is

$$h(u) = f_1(u) \cdot f_2(u) \cdot \ldots \cdot f_r(u).^4$$

---

[4] That the product $f_1(u) \cdot f_2(u) \cdot \cdots \cdot f_r(u)$ is in this case the least common multiple of $f_1(u), f_2(u), \cdots, f_r(u)$ follows from the fact that each $f_i(u)$ is uniquely factorable into irreducible factors in $F[u]$. Since $f_i(u)$ and $f_k(u)$, for $i \neq k$ are relatively prime, they have no irreducible factors in common, which easily yields our result.

We assert that in this case, every vector $\mathfrak{x}$ has only one representation of the form (6). In order to prove this we first prove that an equation of the form

$$\mathfrak{x}_1 + \mathfrak{x}_2 + \ldots + \mathfrak{x}_r = 0 \tag{9}$$

where $\mathfrak{x}_i$ is in L_{f_i}, implies that $\mathfrak{x}_i = 0$ for $i = 1, 2, \ldots, r$.

(9) is equivalent to

$$\mathfrak{x}_i = -\mathfrak{x}_1 - \cdots - \mathfrak{x}_{i-1} - \mathfrak{x}_{i+1} - \cdots - \mathfrak{x}_r. \tag{10}$$

Setting

$$p_i(u) = \frac{h(u)}{f_i(u)} = f_1(u) \cdot \ldots \cdot f_{i-1}(u) \cdot f_{i+1}(u) \cdot \ldots \cdot f_r(u),$$

we see that $p_i(u)$ is the least common multiple of the polynomials $f_1(u), \ldots, f_{i-1}(u), f_{i+1}(u), \ldots, f_r(u)$. By Theorem 12, the vector on the right-hand side of (10) is therefore in the null space L_{p_i}. But $\mathfrak{x}_i$ is in L_{f_i}, so that, by (10), $\mathfrak{x}_i$ is in the intersection of L_{f_i} and L_{p_i}. But since the polynomials $f_i(u)$ were relatively prime in pairs, the two polynomials $f_i(u)$ and $p_i(u)$ are also relatively prime. By Theorem 7, the intersection of L_{f_i} and L_{p_i} consists therefore of the null vector alone. Thus $\mathfrak{x}_i = 0$, which was to be proved.

Now suppose that some arbitrary vector $\mathfrak{x}$ of L_h has, besides (6), a second representation of the form

$$\mathfrak{x} = \mathfrak{x}_1' + \mathfrak{x}_2' + \ldots + \mathfrak{x}_r' \tag{11}$$

with $\mathfrak{x}_i'$ in L_{f_i} (for $i = 1, 2, \ldots, r$). Subtracting (11) from (6), we obtain

$$(\mathfrak{x}_1 - \mathfrak{x}_1') + (\mathfrak{x}_2 - \mathfrak{x}_2') + \ldots + (\mathfrak{x}_r - \mathfrak{x}_r') = 0.$$

But $\mathfrak{x}_i - \mathfrak{x}_i'$ is in L_{f_i} for $i = 1, 2, \ldots, r$. This is an equation of the form (9), and by what has just been proved we must have $\mathfrak{x}_i - \mathfrak{x}_i' = 0$, i.e. $\mathfrak{x}_i = \mathfrak{x}_i'$ for all i. This proves that the representation (6) is unique.

If every vector of L_h is representable in the form (6) in one and only one way, we call L_h the *direct* sum of $L_{f_1}, L_{f_2}, \ldots, L_{f_r}$. We have thus obtained

THEOREM 12a. *If, in addition to the hypotheses of Theorem 12, we have that the polynomials $f_i(u)$ are relatively prime in pairs, then L_h is the direct sum of the spaces $L_{f_1}, L_{f_2}, \ldots, L_{f_r}$.*

Using this theorem we may *decompose* the vector space L into *in-*

variant subspaces in the following manner. Let $m(u)$ be the minimal polynomial of σ. Let us factor $m(u)$ into its irreducible factors. By combining equal irreducible factors (if any), we may write the factorization in the form

$$(12) \qquad m(u) = (q_1(u))^{a_1} \cdot (q_2(u))^{a_2} \cdot \cdots \cdot (q_r(u))^{a_r}.$$

Here we have $a_i \geqq 1$ and $q_i(u) \neq q_k(u)$ for $i \neq k$. We may also assume that the leading coefficient of each polynomial $q_i(u)$ is 1.[5]

Now let $L^{(1)}, L^{(2)}, \ldots, L^{(r)}$ be the null spaces of the linear transformations $(q_1(\sigma))^{a_1}, (q_2(\sigma))^{a_2}, \cdots, (q_r(\sigma))^{a_r}$, respectively. The null space L_m of $m(\sigma)$ is L itself. By Theorem 12a, L is the direct sum of the vector spaces $L^{(1)}, L^{(2)}, \ldots, L^{(r)}$.

Let e_i be the dimension of $L^{(i)}$ $(i = 1, 2, \ldots, r)$. Choose a basis $\mathfrak{a}_{i1}, \mathfrak{a}_{i2}, \cdots, \mathfrak{a}_{ie_i}$ of each $L^{(i)}$. The totality of these basis vectors is

$$(13) \qquad \mathfrak{a}_{11}, \mathfrak{a}_{12}, \cdots, \mathfrak{a}_{1e_1};\quad \mathfrak{a}_{21}, \mathfrak{a}_{22}, \cdots, \mathfrak{a}_{2e_2};\quad \cdots;\quad \mathfrak{a}_{r1}, \mathfrak{a}_{r2}, \cdots, \mathfrak{a}_{re_r}.$$

We shall prove that *the vectors* (13) *form a basis of* L.

We first note that these vectors span L. For by Theorem 12, any vector $\mathfrak{x}$ of L is of the form (6), and each vector $\mathfrak{x}_i$ of $L^{(i)}$ is in turn a linear combination of the basis vectors $\mathfrak{a}_{i1}, \mathfrak{a}_{i2}, \cdots, \mathfrak{a}_{ie_i}$ of $L^{(i)}$.

The vectors (13) are also linearly independent. For suppose we had some linear relation among them, say

$$(14) \qquad \sum_{k=1}^{e_1} \lambda_{1k}\, \mathfrak{a}_{1k} + \sum_{k=1}^{e_2} \lambda_{2k}\, \mathfrak{a}_{2k} + \cdots + \sum_{k=1}^{e_r} \lambda_{rk}\, \mathfrak{a}_{rk} = 0.$$

Let $\mathfrak{x}_i = \sum_{k=1}^{e_i} \lambda_{ik}\, \mathfrak{a}_{ik}$ for $i = 1, 2, \ldots, r$. Then $\mathfrak{x}_i$ is in $L^{(i)}$ and we have a relation of the form (9). It then follows, in the same way as after (9), that $\mathfrak{x}_i = 0$ for each i, so that

$$\sum_{k=1}^{e_i} \lambda_{ik}\, \mathfrak{a}_{ik} = 0, \qquad i = 1, 2, \cdots, r.$$

But this implies that the coefficients $\lambda_{i1}, \lambda_{i2}, \cdots, \lambda_{ie_i}$ must all vanish for each i, since $\mathfrak{a}_{i1}, \mathfrak{a}_{i2}, \cdots, \mathfrak{a}_{ie_i}$ is a basis of $L^{(i)}$. Hence the vectors (13) are linearly independent and so form a basis of L. The dimension of L is equal to the number of the vectors (13), so that

$$n = e_1 + e_2 + \ldots + e_r.$$

[5] Cf. § 15, Theorem 6.

We say that L *is decomposed into the invariant subspaces* $L^{(1)}$, $L^{(2)}$, ..., $L^{(r)}$.

For easier reference, we summarize this result in a theorem, as follows:

THEOREM 13.   *Let σ be a linear transformation on the n-dimensional vector space* L, *and let $m(u)$ be the minimal polynomial of σ. Let equation* (12) *be the factorization of $m(u)$ into irreducible factors. Let* $L^{(i)}$ *be the null space of the linear transformation* $(q_i(\sigma))^{a_i}$ *(for $i = 1, 2, \ldots, r$). Then the dimension of* L *is equal to the sum of the dimensions of* $L^{(1)}$, $L^{(2)}$, ..., $L^{(r)}$. *If we choose a basis of* $L^{(i)}$ *for each i, then the totality of these basis vectors forms a basis of* L.

We now wish to determine the matrix of the linear transformation σ with respect to the basis (13). For this purpose we have to determine, by § 22, the components of the vectors $\sigma(\mathfrak{a}_{ik})$ with respect to (13). Let us do this for a fixed i ($1 \leq i \leq r$). Each of the vectors

$$\sigma(\mathfrak{a}_{i1}), \ \sigma(\mathfrak{a}_{i2}), \ \cdots, \ \sigma(\mathfrak{a}_{ie_i})$$

belongs to $L^{(i)}$, since $L^{(i)}$ is invariant with respect to σ. Thus each of the vectors $\sigma(\mathfrak{a}_{i1})$, $\sigma(\mathfrak{a}_{i2})$, $\cdots$, $\sigma(\mathfrak{a}_{ie_i})$ is a linear combination of the basis $\mathfrak{a}_{i1}, \mathfrak{a}_{i2}, \cdots, \mathfrak{a}_{ie_i}$ of $L^{(i)}$, say

$$(15) \qquad \sigma(\mathfrak{a}_{ik}) = x_{1k}^{(i)} \mathfrak{a}_{i1} + x_{2k}^{(i)} \mathfrak{a}_{i2} + \cdots + x_{e_i k}^{(i)} \mathfrak{a}_{ie_i}, \qquad k = 1, 2, \cdots, e_i.$$

From (15) it is easy to see that for the components of $\sigma(\mathfrak{a}_{ik})$ with respect to the basis (13), we have the following: the first $e_1 + e_2 + \ldots + e_{i-1}$ components of $\sigma(\mathfrak{a}_{ik})$ are 0; they are followed by $x_{1k}^{(i)}$, $x_{2k}^{(i)}$, $\cdots$, $x_{e_i k}^{(i)}$, while the last $e_{i+1} + e_{i+2} + \cdots + e_r$ components vanish. Thus the vectors $\sigma(\mathfrak{a}_{i1})$, $\sigma(\mathfrak{a}_{i2})$, $\cdots$, $\sigma(\mathfrak{a}_{ie_i})$ contribute to the matrix of σ a square box of the form

$$(16) \qquad \begin{vmatrix} x_{11}^{(i)} & x_{12}^{(i)} & \cdots & x_{1e_i}^{(i)} \\ x_{21}^{(i)} & x_{22}^{(i)} & \cdots & x_{2e_i}^{(i)} \\ \cdot & \cdot & \cdots & \cdot \\ x_{e_i 1}^{(i)} & x_{e_i 2}^{(i)} & \cdots & x_{e_i e_i}^{(i)} \end{vmatrix} .$$

Moreover this box extends from the $(e_1 + e_2 + \ldots + e_{i-1} + 1)$-st row and column to the $(e_1 + e_2 + \ldots + e_i)$-th row and column. Thus the principal diagonal of this box is on the principal diagonal of the matrix of σ.

Therefore the *matrix of* σ *with respect to the basis* (13) is of the following form: Along the main diagonal appear the square boxes of the form (16) one after the other. Outside these boxes we have nothing but zeros. Denoting the box (16) by $A^{(i)}$, we see that the scheme

$$(17) \qquad \begin{pmatrix} A^{(1)} & & & 0 \\ & A^{(2)} & & \\ & & \ddots & \\ 0 & & & A^{(r)} \end{pmatrix}$$

represents the matrix of σ.

We now consider *the linear transformation* $\sigma^{(i)}$ *which is induced by* σ *on* $\mathrm{L}^{(i)}$. The *matrix of* $\sigma^{(i)}$ *with respect to the basis* $\mathfrak{a}_{i1}, \mathfrak{a}_{i2}, \cdots, \mathfrak{a}_{ie_i}$ of $\mathrm{L}^{(i)}$ is determined by the components of the vectors

$$\sigma(\mathfrak{a}_{i1}), \quad \sigma(\mathfrak{a}_{i2}), \quad \cdots, \quad \sigma(\mathfrak{a}_{ie_i})$$

with respect to this basis. The matrix of $\sigma^{(i)}$ is thus, by equation (15), precisely the box (16). The component parts $A^{(i)}$ of the matrix (17) are thus precisely the matrices of $\sigma^{(1)}, \sigma^{(2)}, \ldots, \sigma^{(r)}$.

But the *minimal polynomial of* $\sigma^{(i)}$ is, by Theorem 11, equal to $(q_i(u))^{a_i}$. Thus it follows from Theorem 2 that *the individual box* $A^{(i)}$ *in* (17), *considered as a matrix, has the minimal polynomial* $(q_i(u))^{a_i}$.

Geometric Interpretation

If we take the field F to be the real numbers, we can give the theorems of this section a geometric meaning by using what we learned in earlier parts of this book about affine transformations in affine R_n.

By p. 183, an affine transformation is represented by a system of equations of the form

$$(18) \qquad y_i = t_i + \sum_{k=1}^{n} a_{ik} x_k, \qquad i = 1, 2, \cdots, n,$$

in a linear coordinate system of R_n. This affine transformation induces the linear transformation

$$(19) \qquad y_i = \sum_{k=1}^{n} a_{ik} x_k, \qquad i = 1, 2, \cdots, n,$$

in real n-dimensional vector space.

We obtain a particularly simple situation if in (18) we choose all the $t_i = 0$,[6] i.e. if we consider equations (19) themselves as the system of equations of an affine transformation. All the theorems on invariant subspaces of linear transformations will then carry over immediately to affine transformations. To such an invariant (vector) subspace will then correspond a linear space containing the origin. Note that the origin of the space must be mapped on itself.

In particular, we may carry out the analogue for affine transformations of the decomposition of a vector space into invariant subspaces. For if we choose a linear coordinate system $[P_0; \mathfrak{b}_1, \mathfrak{b}_2, \ldots, \mathfrak{b}_n]$ in such a way that the basis $\mathfrak{b}_i$ is composed of the bases of the invariant subspaces, then the matrix (a_{ik}) of the system of equations (19) or (18) takes on the form (17). This simplification of the equations for an affine transformation is very useful for many investigations.

As an *example*,[7] let us consider the affine transformation

$$(20)\qquad \begin{aligned} y_1 &= 3x_1 - 2x_2 + x_3, \\ y_2 &= 2x_1 - x_2 + x_3, \\ y_3 &= -2x_1 + 2x_2 \end{aligned}$$

in R_3. Suppose the linear coordinate system used is $[P_0; \mathfrak{a}_1, \mathfrak{a}_2, \mathfrak{a}_3]$. We can immediately verify that the matrix

$$(21)\qquad A = \begin{pmatrix} 3 & -2 & 1 \\ 2 & -1 & 1 \\ -2 & 2 & 0 \end{pmatrix}$$

of the system of equations (20) satisfies

$$(22)\qquad A^2 = A.$$

Thus the polynomial $u^2 - u$ has the matrix A as a zero. The minimal polynomial $m(u)$ of A must therefore be a divisor of $u^2 - u = u(u-1)$.

---

[6] Every affine transformation may be decomposed into the two mappings

$$\begin{aligned} y_i' &= \sum_{k=1}^{n} a_{ik} x_k, & i &= 1, 2, \cdots, n, \\ y_i &= t_i + y_i', & i &= 1, 2, \cdots, n, \end{aligned}$$

applied successively. This "factorization" is to be understood in the same manner as the product mappings for linear transformations. The first of these equations has the desired form, and the second represents a very simple mapping, namely a translation. Cf. p. 163.

[7] Cf. also exercises 7 and 8.

But since neither u nor $u-1$ has the matrix A as a zero, we see that $m(u) = u(u-1)$.

We now proceed to find the invariant (point-) subspaces corresponding to the divisors $u-1$ and u. Denoting the linear transformation corresponding to (20) by σ, the invariant (vector-) subspaces $L^{(1)}$ and $L^{(2)}$ are given by the equations $\sigma(\mathfrak{x}) = \mathfrak{x}$ and $\sigma(\mathfrak{x}) = 0$ respectively, i.e. the vectors $\{x_1, x_2, x_3\}$ of $L^{(1)}$ satisfy $y_1 = x_1$, $y_2 = x_2$, $y_3 = x_3$ in (20) and those of $L^{(2)}$ satisfy $y_1 = y_2 = y_3 = 0$. Of these systems of homogeneous equations defining $L^{(1)}$ and $L^{(2)}$ as well as the invariant linear (i.e. point-) subspaces that we set out to find, the first has rank 1 and the second rank 2, as can easily be seen. Thus $L^{(1)}$ has dimension 2, $L^{(2)}$ dimension 1. Let $\mathfrak{b}_1, \mathfrak{b}_2$ be a basis of $L^{(1)}$ and $\mathfrak{b}_3$ a basis of $L^{(2)}$. By Theorem 13, the vectors $\mathfrak{b}_1, \mathfrak{b}_2, \mathfrak{b}_3$ are linearly independent and so $[P_0; \mathfrak{b}_1, \mathfrak{b}_2, \mathfrak{b}_3]$ is a linear coordinate system of R_3.

We now write the matrix of σ with respect to the basis $\mathfrak{b}_i$. We have $\sigma(\mathfrak{b}_1) = \mathfrak{b}_1$, $\sigma(\mathfrak{b}_2) = \mathfrak{b}_2$, $\sigma(\mathfrak{b}_3) = 0$, so that our matrix is of the form

$$\begin{pmatrix} 1 & 0 & 0 \\ 0 & 1 & 0 \\ 0 & 0 & 0 \end{pmatrix}.$$

Hence our affine transformation (20) is represented by the equations

$$y_1 = x_1,\ y_2 = x_2,\ y_3 = 0 \tag{23}$$

in the coordinate system $[P_0; \mathfrak{b}_1, \mathfrak{b}_2, \mathfrak{b}_3]$.

What does the system (23) mean geometrically? Let P be a point with the coordinates x_1, x_2, x_3 in $[P_0; \mathfrak{b}_1, \mathfrak{b}_2, \mathfrak{b}_3]$. Its image point P^* has by (23) the coordinates $x_1, x_2, 0$. By the definition of linear coordinates we therefore have

$$\overrightarrow{P_0 P^*} = x_1\mathfrak{b}_1 + x_2\mathfrak{b}_2. \tag{24}$$

Thus *the vector* $\overrightarrow{P_0 P^*}$, *and so also its endpoint* P^*, *lies in the plane* E *which passes through* P_0 *and is parallel to the vectors* $\mathfrak{b}_1, \mathfrak{b}_2$. We also have

$$\overrightarrow{P_0 P} = x_1\mathfrak{b}_1 + x_2\mathfrak{b}_2 + x_3\mathfrak{b}_3.$$

Thus by (24),

$$\overrightarrow{P^* P} = \overrightarrow{P_0 P} - \overrightarrow{P_0 P^*} = x_3\mathfrak{b}_3.$$

This means that *the vector* $\overrightarrow{P^* P}$ *is parallel to* $\mathfrak{b}_3$. *The point* P^* *is thus the intersection of the plane* E *and the line through* P *parallel to the vector* $\mathfrak{b}_3$.

Our mapping is thus simply a *projection* of the space onto the plane E. The *direction of the projection* is the direction of $\mathfrak{b}_3$.

Exercises

1. Let σ be a linear transformation on the vector space L. Let $m(u)$ be the minimal polynomial of σ, and let the degree of $m(u)$ be r. Prove that if the vectors

$$\mathfrak{a}, \sigma(\mathfrak{a}), \sigma^2(\mathfrak{a}), \cdots, \sigma^{r-1}(\mathfrak{a})$$

are linearly dependent, then there is a divisor $f(u)$ of $m(u)$ such that the null space L_f of the linear transformation $f(\sigma)$ is a proper subspace of L (i.e. $f(u)$ has a smaller degree than $m(u)$), and contains $\mathfrak{a}$.

2. As an additional hypothesis to exercise 1, let $m(u)$ be a power of an irreducible polynomial $p(u)$, say $m(u) = (p(u))^k$. Let L′ be the null space of the linear transformation $(p(\sigma))^{k-1}$. Prove the following:

   i) If the vectors $\mathfrak{a}, \sigma(\mathfrak{a}), \sigma^2(\mathfrak{a}), \cdots, \sigma^{r-1}(\mathfrak{a})$ are linearly dependent, then $\mathfrak{a}$ belongs to L′.

   ii) The dimension of L is $\geqq r$.

3. The dimension of L is also $\geqq r$ under the more general hypotheses of exercise 1. *Hint*: Use exercise 2, and Theorems 11 and 13 of this section.

4. Determine the minimal polynomial of the matrix

$$A = \begin{pmatrix} -1 & 1 & -1 \\ 1 & 0 & 1 \\ 3 & 2 & 3 \end{pmatrix}.$$

Hint: Compare exercise 7 of § 22.

5. In affine R_4, let the linear transformation σ have, in the coordinate system $\lfloor \mathfrak{e}_1, \mathfrak{e}_2, \mathfrak{e}_3, \mathfrak{e}_4 \rfloor$, the matrix

$$\begin{pmatrix} -1 & 0 & -1 & -2 \\ -2 & 3 & -1 & -6 \\ 4 & -2 & 3 & 8 \\ 0 & 2 & 0 & -3 \end{pmatrix}.$$

Furthermore, let

$$\begin{aligned} f_1(u) &= u^2 - 1, \\ f_2(u) &= u + 1, \\ f_3(u) &= u^2 + 1, \\ f_4(u) &= u^3 - u^2 + u - 1. \end{aligned}$$

Determine the null spaces $L_{f_1}, L_{f_2}, L_{f_3}, L_{f_4}$ of the linear transformations

$$f_1(\sigma), f_2(\sigma), f_3(\sigma), f_4(\sigma).$$

What is the minimal polynomial of σ?

6. Let the vector space L be the sum of the subspaces $L_1, L_2, \ldots, L_h$. Let σ be a linear transformation on L, and suppose that each L_i is invariant with respect to σ. Let σ induce σ_i on L_i. Then the minimal polynomial of σ is the least common multiple of the minimal polynomials of $\sigma_1, \sigma_2, \cdots, \sigma_h$.

7. Describe the geometric meaning of the affine transformation

$$\begin{aligned} y_1 &= -3x_1+6x_2-3x_3, \\ y_2 &= -\ x_1+2x_2-\ x_3, \\ y_3 &= \ 2x_1-4x_2+2x_3? \end{aligned}$$

Generalize this example (and that of p. 316) to the affine transformation $y_i = \sum_{k=1}^{n} a_{ik}x_k \quad (i = 1, 2, \cdots, n)$ of R_n, whose matrix $A = (a_{ik})$ satisfies the condition $A^2 = A$.

8. Describe the geometric meaning of the affine transformation

$$\begin{aligned} y_1 &= -\ x_1+2x_2-2x_3, \\ y_2 &= \ 4x_1-3x_2+4x_3, \\ y_3 &= \ 4x_1-4x_2+5x_3. \end{aligned}$$

In general: What is the geometric meaning of an affine transformation

$$y_i = \sum_{k=1}^{n} a_{ik}x_k$$

$(i = 1, 2, \ldots, n)$ of R_n whose matrix satisfies the equation $A^2 = E$?

The following examples assume that the reader has some knowledge of infinite series.[8]

9. Let $A_1 = (a_{ik}^{(1)}),\ A_2 = (a_{ik}^{(2)}),\ \cdots,$ be an infinite sequence of n-by-n square matrices whose elements are complex numbers. Let the series $\sum_{\nu=1}^{\infty} a_{ik}^{(\nu)}$ converge for every pair of subscripts i, k. Define the sum $\sum_{\nu=1}^{\infty} A_\nu$ as the matrix $\left(\sum_{\nu=1}^{\infty} a_{ik}^{(\nu)}\right)$. We call the series $\sum_{\nu=1}^{\infty} A_\nu$ absolutely convergent if each of the series $\sum_{\nu=1}^{\infty} a_{ik}^{(\nu)}$ is absolutely convergent. The order of the terms of an absolutely convergent series of matrices may be arbitrarily changed. Show that if $\sum_{\nu=1}^{\infty} A_\nu$ and $\sum_{\nu=1}^{\infty} B_\nu$ are two absolutely convergent series of matrices, then

$$\left(\sum_{\nu=1}^{\infty} A_\nu\right)\left(\sum_{\nu=1}^{\infty} B_\nu\right) = \sum_{\nu,\mu=1}^{\infty} A_\nu B_\mu.$$

Let $A = (a_{ik})$ be an arbitrary square matrix with complex elements. Prove that the series

$$\sum_{n=0}^{\infty} \frac{A^n}{n!} = E + A + \frac{A^2}{2!} + \cdots$$

is absolutely convergent. We denote the sum of this series by e^A. Prove that if A, B are two matrices such that $A \cdot B = B \cdot A$, then

$$e^A \cdot e^B = e^B \cdot e^A = e^{A+B}.$$

10. Let $y_1, y_2, \cdots, y_n$ be any n fixed complex numbers. Let (y) be the matrix

---

[8] I wish to thank Professor E. Artin for exercises 9 and 10. They contain, in a very elegant form, the application of matrix theory (and in particular of the theorems of § 23) to systems of linear differential equations with constant coefficients.

(37) on p. 295, formed with these y_i, and let $A = (a_{ik})$ be a matrix with complex elements. If x is a variable, then the matrix $e^{Ax} \cdot (y)$ contains n everywhere convergent power series in its first columns, and zeros elsewhere.[9] We say that the matrix $e^{Ax} \cdot (y)$ *represents n power series.*

a) For which complex numbers α and which matrices (y) do almost all terms of the power series represented by $e^{(A-\alpha E)x}(y)$ vanish; i.e. when does this matrix represent n polynomials?

b) We have $e^{\alpha Ex} B = e^{\alpha x} B$ for any matrix B.

c) To any two given matrices A and (y), there correspond a finite number of complex numbers $\alpha_1, \alpha_2, \cdots, \alpha_r$ and matrices $(y^{(1)}), (y^{(2)}), \cdots, (y^{(r)})$ of the form

$$(y^{(i)}) = \begin{pmatrix} y_1^{(i)} & 0 & \cdots & 0 \\ y_2^{(i)} & 0 & \cdots & 0 \\ \cdot & \cdot & \cdot & \cdot \\ y_n^{(i)} & 0 & \cdots & 0 \end{pmatrix}$$

with the following property: For every i, $e^{(A-\alpha_i E)x}(y^{(i)})$ represents n polynomials, and moreover

$$e^{Ax}(y) = \sum_{i=1}^{r} (e^{\alpha_i x} \cdot e^{(A-\alpha_i E)x}(y^{(i)})).$$

Thus each of the power series represented by $e^{Ax}(y)$ can be written as a sum $\sum_{i=1}^{r} e^{\alpha_i x} f_i(x)$ where $f_1(x), f_2(x), \cdots, f_r(x)$ are polynomials.

§ 24. The Diagonal Form and its Applications

If we wish to investigate a given linear transformation, it is expedient to use a coordinate system with respect to which the system of equations, and the matrix of the transformation, are of the simplest possible form. The question arises as to how such a coordinate system can be found. Some light has been thrown on this problem at the end of the preceding section. But the simplified form obtained there for

---

[9] The symbol $\frac{d}{dx}(e^{Ax}(y))$ means that each of the power series

$$P_1(x), P_2(x), \cdots, P_n(x)$$

which are represented by the matrix $e^{Ax}(y)$ is to be differentiated. It then follows that

$$\frac{d}{dx}(e^{Ax}(y)) = A \cdot e^{Ax}(y).$$

But this means that

$$(*) \qquad \frac{d P_i(x)}{dx} = \sum_{k=1}^{n} a_{ik} P_k(x), \qquad i = 1, 2, \cdots, n.$$

Thus the functions $P_i(x)$ are solutions of the differential equations (*). $P_i(x) = y_i$ for $x = 0$. The y_i are the "initial values" of the solution.

the matrix of a linear transformation does not suffice for many investigations. We will therefore be concerned, in what follows, with methods for obtaining still simpler forms for matrices.

In this section we shall consider this problem first for a special class of linear transformations which are of particular importance for the applications of matrix theory. These are the linear transformations whose matrices have, in a suitable coordinate system, the so-called *diagonal form,* i.e. contain only zeros except on the principal diagonal.

As before let the field F be arbitrary, and let L be an n-dimensional vector space ($n \geqq 1$) of V_q over F.

We shall first derive a necessary condition for a linear transformation to be representable by a matrix in diagonal form. Suppose a linear transformation σ, on L, has the diagonal form in a suitable coordinate system $[\alpha_1, \alpha_2, \ldots, \alpha_n]$, say

$$\begin{pmatrix} \beta_1 & & & 0 \\ & \beta_2 & & \\ & & \ddots & \\ 0 & & & \beta_n \end{pmatrix}. \tag{1}$$

The k-th row of (1) consists of the components of $\sigma(\alpha_k)$ in our coordinate system, so that

$$\sigma(\alpha_k) = \beta_k \alpha_k, \qquad k = 1, 2, \cdots, n. \tag{2}$$

Let $m(u)$ be the minimal polynomial of σ. We first prove that $\beta_1, \beta_2, \ldots, \beta_n$ *are zeros of* $m(u)$ or, what is the same, that the polynomials $u - \beta_1$, $u - \beta_2$, $\ldots$, $u - \beta_n$ are divisors of $m(u)$. Setting $f_k(u) = u - \beta_k$, we see that (2) is equivalent to $f_k(\sigma)(\alpha_k) = 0$. Thus in the terminology of the preceding section, the vector $\alpha_k \neq 0$ belongs to L_{f_k}. It thus follows from § 23, Theorem 10, that $u - \beta_k$ is a divisor of $m(u)$.

Let there be r different elements among the elements $\beta_1, \beta_2, \ldots, \beta_n$ of the principal diagonal of (1). Let these distinct elements be, say, $\beta_{\nu_1}, \beta_{\nu_2}, \ldots, \beta_{\nu_r}$. Thus the polynomial

$$g(u) = (u - \beta_{\nu_1}) \cdot (u - \beta_{\nu_2}) \cdot \ldots \cdot (u - \beta_{\nu_r}) \tag{3}$$

is a divisor of the minimal polynomial $m(u)$. On the other hand, we shall show presently that σ is a zero of $g(u)$, which will imply $g(u) = m(u)$.

If we show that $g(\sigma)$ maps all the basis vectors $\mathfrak{a}_1, \mathfrak{a}_2, \ldots, \mathfrak{a}_n$ on the null vector, then every linear combination of them, and hence every vector of L, is also mapped on the null vector. Thus, let $\mathfrak{a}_i$ be any basis vector. One of the equations (2) holds for this vector, where β_i is also among the β_{ν_i}. Thus $\mathfrak{a}_i$ is mapped on the null vector by that factor of $g(\sigma)$ in which β_{ν_i} occurs, and hence also by $g(\sigma)$ itself.

We have thus found the following condition: *If the matrix of σ has diagonal form in some coordinate system, then the minimal polynomial of σ is necessarily of the form* (3), *where $\beta_{\nu_i} \neq \beta_{\nu_k}$ for $i \neq k$.*

The converse of this result is also true. Let σ be a linear transformation on L with a minimal polynomial $m(u)$ *all of whose distinct factors in* F$[u]$ *are of the first degree,* say

(4) $$m(u) = (u - \alpha_1)(u - \alpha_2) \cdots (u - \alpha_r), \quad \alpha_i \neq \alpha_k \text{ for } i \neq k.$$

Here r is the degree of $m(u)$.

We decompose L into invariant subspaces as in the preceding section. The null space $L^{(i)}$ of $\sigma - \alpha_i\sigma^0$ (i.e. of the linear transformation arising from $u - \alpha_i$ by the substitution of σ for u) consists of all vectors $\mathfrak{x}$ of L which satisfy the equation $(\sigma - \alpha_i\sigma^0)(\mathfrak{x}) = 0$ or

(5) $$\sigma(\mathfrak{x}) = \alpha_i \mathfrak{x}.$$

Let $\mathfrak{a}_{i1}, \mathfrak{a}_{i2}, \cdots, \mathfrak{a}_{ie_i}$ be a basis of $L^{(i)}$. Then by Theorem 13 of the preceding section, the totality of vectors

(6) $$\mathfrak{a}_{11}, \mathfrak{a}_{12}, \cdots, \mathfrak{a}_{1e_1}; \mathfrak{a}_{21}, \mathfrak{a}_{22}, \cdots, \mathfrak{a}_{2e_2}; \cdots; \mathfrak{a}_{r1}, \mathfrak{a}_{r2}, \cdots, \mathfrak{a}_{re_r}$$

is a basis of L. We now find the matrix of σ with respect to this basis. For this purpose we consider the image of an arbitrary vector $\mathfrak{a}_{\nu k}$ of the sequence (6). $\mathfrak{a}_{\nu k}$ belongs to $L^{(\nu)}$, so that, by (5),

(7) $$\sigma(\mathfrak{a}_{\nu k}) = \alpha_\nu \mathfrak{a}_{\nu k}, \qquad \begin{cases} k = 1, 2, \cdots, e_\nu; \\ \nu = 1, 2, \cdots, r. \end{cases}$$

If the vector $\mathfrak{a}_{\nu k}$ is, say, the h-th vector of the sequence (6), then the h-th column of the matrix of σ with respect to the basis (6) consists of the components of $\sigma(\mathfrak{a}_{\nu k})$, so that by (7) it contains only zeros except for its h-th place, in which α_ν appears. Thus our matrix has the diagonal form

$$(8)\qquad \begin{pmatrix} \alpha_1 & & & & & & & & & \cdots 0 \\ & \alpha_1 & & & & & & & & \vdots \\ & & \ddots & & & & & & & \\ & & & \alpha_1 & & & & & & \\ & & & & \alpha_2 & & & & & \\ & & & & & \ddots & & & & \\ & & & & & & \alpha_2 & & & \\ & & & & & & & \alpha_r & & \\ \vdots & & & & & & & & \ddots & \\ 0 \cdots & & & & & & & & & \alpha_r \end{pmatrix}.$$

(α_1 repeated e_1-times, α_2 repeated e_2-times, …, α_r repeated e_r-times.)

We have thus proved

Theorem 1. *The matrix of a linear transformation σ on the vector space* L *can be brought into diagonal form if and only if the minimal polynomial of σ in* F$[u]$ *can be factored into distinct factors all of the first degree.*

We observe that the second part of the proof of Theorem 1 *contains a method of finding a basis with respect to which σ has diagonal form.* This method will often be used in what follows.

Along with the matrix, the system of equations for σ takes on a very simple form. The i-th equation has the form $y_i = c \cdot x_i$, where $c = \alpha_1$ for $i = 1, 2, \ldots, e_1$; $c = \alpha_2$ for $i = e_1 + 1,\ e_1 + 2, \ldots, e_2$; etc.

Now consider an n-by-n square matrix A with entries from F. We shall say that A can be *transformed into diagonal form in the field* F if there is a non-singular matrix T with elements in F such that TAT^{-1} is in diagonal form. Using the linear transformation σ whose matrix is A with respect to a definite coordinate system of L, we see by § 22, Theorems 4 and 5, that the statement "A can be transformed into diagonal form in F" is equivalent to the statement "There is a coordinate system in L in which the matrix of σ has diagonal form." If we observe that the minimal polynomial of A is also the minimal polynomial of σ, then Theorem 1 implies

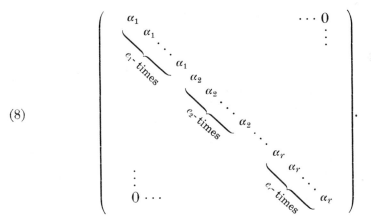

Theorem 1a. *A square matrix A with elements in* F *can be transformed into diagonal form in the field* F *if and only if the minimal*

polynomial of A can be factored in F$[u]$ *into distinct factors all of the first degree.*[1]

For the remainder of this section the field F shall be the *field of complex numbers*. The vector space L is then called a *complex* vector space. We shall first indicate how the results just obtained are to be interpreted for this special case. By § 17 *every* polynomial of F$[u]$ now can be factored into linear factors in F$[u]$, so that in particular we have for the minimal polynomial $m(u)$ of a linear transformation σ that

$$m(u) = (u-\alpha_1)^{a_1} \cdot (u-\alpha_2)^{a_2} \cdot \cdots \cdot (u-\alpha_r)^{a_r}. \tag{9}$$

Of course we take $a_i \neq a_k$ for $i \neq k$, and all multiplicities $a_i \geqq 1$. Theorem 1 gives for this case

THEOREM 2. *The matrix of a linear transformation σ on a complex vector space* L *can be brought into diagonal form in the field of complex numbers if and only if the minimal polynomial of σ has only simple zeros.*

Similarly for a matrix A, we have

THEOREM 2a. *A matrix A can be transformed into diagonal form in the field of complex numbers if and only if the minimal polynomial of A has only simple zeros.*

It is convenient for many applications to further transform the criterion of Theorem 2. Let α be a zero, i.e. $f_1(u) = u - \alpha$ a divisor, of $m(u)$. The criterion of Theorem 2 requires that $f_2(u) = (u-\alpha)^2$ not be a divisor of $m(u)$, so that $u - \alpha$ is the greatest common divisor of $m(u)$ and $f_2(u)$. But then, by § 23, Theorem 8, the null spaces L_{f_1} and L_{f_2} of the linear transformations $f_1(\sigma)$ and $f_2(\sigma)$ are identical. And conversely it follows by § 23, Theorem 9, that $L_{f_1} = L_{f_2}$ implies that $f_2(u)$ is not a divisor of $m(u)$. Thus we obtain

THEOREM 3. *A zero α of the minimal polynomial $m(u)$ is a simple zero of $m(u)$ if and only if the null spaces of the linear transformations $(\sigma - \alpha\sigma^0)$ and $(\sigma - \alpha\sigma^0)^2$ are identical.*

---

[1] The restriction "in the field F" is essential. It is possible that one and the same matrix can be transformed into diagonal form in one field, but not in another. (Cf. exercise 3.)

But we may obtain not only the multiplicities of these zeros, but also the values of the zeros themselves, without knowing the minimal polynomial in advance. Consider the polynomial $u - \lambda$ where λ is any complex number. By § 23, Theorem 10, we have

THEOREM 4. *The equation*

$$(\sigma - \lambda\sigma^0)(\mathfrak{x}) = 0 \tag{10}$$

has a solution $\mathfrak{x} \neq 0$ *in* L *if and only if* $u - \lambda$ *is a divisor* (*i.e.* λ *is a zero of*) *the minimal polynomial of* σ.

We shall now transform (10). For this purpose let $A = (a_{ik})$ be the matrix of σ in some definite coordinate system $[\mathfrak{a}_1, \mathfrak{a}_2, \ldots, \mathfrak{a}_n]$. The transformation $\sigma - \lambda\sigma^0$ has the matrix

$$A - \lambda E = (a_{ik} - \lambda\delta_{ik}). \tag{11}$$

Thus the linear transformation $(\sigma - \lambda\sigma^0)$ is represented by the system of equations

$$y_i = \sum_{k=1}^{n} (a_{ik} - \lambda\,\delta_{ik})\, x_k, \qquad i = 1, 2, \cdots, n \tag{12}$$

in the coordinate system $[\mathfrak{a}_1, \mathfrak{a}_2, \ldots, \mathfrak{a}_n]$.

If $\mathfrak{x}$ is any vector satisfying equation (10), and if $x_1, x_2, \ldots, x_n$ are its components in the coordinate system $[\mathfrak{a}_1, \mathfrak{a}_2, \ldots, \mathfrak{a}_n]$ then by (12) we have

$$\sum_{k=1}^{n} (a_{ik} - \lambda\,\delta_{ik})\, x_k = 0, \qquad i = 1, 2, \cdots, n.$$

This is a system of homogeneous linear equations in the components $x_1, x_2, \ldots, x_n$. It has a non-trivial solution if and only if the determinant $|\, a_{ik} - \lambda\delta_{ik} \,|$ vanishes. Thus we have

THEOREM 5. *The equation* (10) *has a solution* $\mathfrak{x} \neq 0$ *if and only if* λ *satisfies the equation*

$$|\, A - \lambda \cdot E \,| = 0. \tag{13}$$

Substituting the variable u for λ in (13), we obtain

$$|A - uE| = \begin{vmatrix} a_{11} - u, & a_{12}\;, & \cdots, & a_{1n} \\ a_{21}\;, & a_{22} - u, & \cdots, & a_{2n} \\ \cdot & \cdot & \cdot & \cdot \\ a_{n1}\;, & a_{n2}\;, & \cdots, & a_{nn} - u \end{vmatrix} \tag{14}$$

as a polynomial of $\mathrm{F}[u]$. The degree of this polynomial is n, as can be seen by evaluating the determinant.[2] The polynomial (14) is called the ***characteristic polynomial*** *of the matrix A.*

A was the matrix of σ in the coordinate system $[\mathfrak{a}_1, \mathfrak{a}_2, \ldots, \mathfrak{a}_n]$. Let $B = (b_{ik})$ be the matrix of σ in any other coordinate system $[\mathfrak{b}_1, \mathfrak{b}_2, \ldots, \mathfrak{b}_n]$. Then *the characteristic polynomial of the matrix B equals the characteristic polynomial of the matrix A.* Thus

$$|A - uE| = |B - uE|. \tag{15}$$

In order to prove this, we recall from § 22, Theorem 4 that some non-singular matrix T transforms A into B so that

$$B = TAT^{-1}. \tag{16}$$

Then

$$B - u \cdot E = T \cdot A \cdot T^{-1} - u \cdot T \cdot E \cdot T^{-1} = T \cdot (A - u \cdot E) \cdot T^{-1}.$$

We then obtain (15) as in the proof of Theorem 7 of § 22.

The characteristic polynomial of the matrix of a linear transformation σ is thus *independent of the choice of the coordinate system.* It depends only on σ and is therefore also called the *characteristic polynomial of the linear transformation* σ.

Theorems 4 and 5 may be combined in the following

THEOREM 6. *The minimal polynomial and the characteristic polynomial of a linear transformation have the same zeros.*

Of course, this does not mean that the multiplicity of these zeros is also the same. For example the minimal polynomial of the

---

[2] We have (cf. p. 89)

$$|A - uE| = \sum_{(\nu_1, \nu_2, \cdots, \nu_n)} \operatorname{sgn}(\nu_1, \nu_2, \cdots, \nu_n) \cdot (a_{1\nu_1} - u\delta_{1\nu_1}) \cdot (a_{2\nu_2} - u\delta_{2\nu_2}) \cdot \ldots \cdot (a_{n\nu_n} - u\delta_{n\nu_n}).$$

The sum on the right has only one term of the n-th degree, namely the term in which $\nu_1 = 1, \nu_2 = 2, \cdots, \nu_n = n$. For this term we have

$$(a_{11} - u) \cdot (a_{22} - u) \cdot \cdots \cdot (a_{nn} - u) = (-u)^n + r(u),$$

where $r(u)$ is a polynomial of degree $n - 1$ at most. Thus

$$|A - uE| = (-u)^n + R(u),$$

where $R(u)$ is also a polynomial of degree at most $n - 1$. Naturally these statements and their proofs hold in the general case for any matrix A whose elements are in any field.

identity transformation is $u - 1$, but its characteristic polynomial is $|E - uE| = (1 - u)^n$. Thus in this case, 1 is a simple zero of the minimal polynomial, but is a zero of multiplicity n of the characteristic polynomial.

We also call the zeros of the characteristic polynomial of σ *characteristic roots of* σ.

Applying Theorems 2, 3, and 6, we immediately have

THEOREM 7. *The matrix of a linear transformation σ on a complex vector space* L *can be brought into diagonal form if and only if the null space of $(\sigma - a\sigma^0)$ is the same as the null space of $(\sigma - a\sigma^0)^2$ for any zero a of the characteristic polynomial of σ.*

We can easily see that if a matrix is in diagonal form, say

$$A = \begin{pmatrix} \alpha_1 & & & 0 \\ & \alpha_2 & & \\ & & \ddots & \\ 0 & & & \alpha_n \end{pmatrix},$$

then the characteristic polynomial of A is

$$|A - uE| = (\alpha_1 - u) \cdot (\alpha_2 - u) \cdot \ldots \cdot (\alpha_n - u).$$

Thus the principal diagonal of A contains every zero of the characteristic polynomial and each as often as its multiplicity indicates.

Conversely, if we know that a matrix B can be transformed into diagonal form, and if we know the characteristic polynomial of B, then we know its diagonal form. For we simply have to put all of the roots of the characteristic polynomial in the principal diagonal, each as often as is indicated by its multiplicity.

Unitary Transformations

We shall now apply these general results to a few special classes of linear transformations. We first investigate certain linear transformations on a complex vector space[3] which are generalizations of rigid motions of affine R_n (or of the corresponding linear transformations).

First we shall introduce a concept of length in complex V_n. As a generalization of euclidean length in affine R_n, we define it as follows: The ***length*** (or the *absolute value*, or the *norm*) *of a complex vector* $\mathfrak{x} = \{x_1, x_2, \ldots, x_n\}$ is given by the formula[4]

[3] This is, of course, the vector space over the field of complex numbers.

[4] The symbols $|x_i|$ and $\bar{x}_i$ are used as in § 16, pp. 220 and 222.

(17) $$|\mathfrak{x}| = +\sqrt{\sum_{i=1.}^{n} |x_i|^2} = +\sqrt{\sum_{i=1}^{n} x_i \bar{x}_i}\,.$$

By its definition, $|\mathfrak{x}|$ is a non-negative real number. Moreover, $|\mathfrak{x}|$ equals 0 if and only if $\mathfrak{x}$ is the null vector.

We shall call the vector $\{\bar{x}_1, \bar{x}_2, \ldots, \bar{x}_n\}$ the *complex conjugate vector* of $\mathfrak{x}$, or simply the *conjugate* of $\mathfrak{x}$, and denote it by the symbol $\bar{\mathfrak{x}}$. Using the scalar product, we can write (17) in the form

(18) $$|\mathfrak{x}|^2 = \mathfrak{x} \cdot \bar{\mathfrak{x}}.$$

For real vectors, $\mathfrak{x} = \bar{\mathfrak{x}}$ and definition (18) or (17) coincides in this case with the previous definition of euclidean length.

Two complex vectors $\mathfrak{x} = \{x_1, x_2, \ldots, x_n\}$, $\mathfrak{y} = \{y_1, y_2, \ldots, y_n\}$ are called **orthogonal** if

(19) $$\mathfrak{x} \cdot \bar{\mathfrak{y}} = 0.$$

This definition is symmetric in $\mathfrak{x}$ and $\mathfrak{y}$, for from (19) it follows that $\overline{\mathfrak{x} \cdot \bar{\mathfrak{y}}} = 0$, so that[5]

(20) $$\overline{\mathfrak{x} \cdot \bar{\mathfrak{y}}} = \bar{\mathfrak{x}} \cdot \bar{\bar{\mathfrak{y}}} = \bar{\mathfrak{x}} \cdot \mathfrak{y} = 0.$$

This concept of orthogonality coincides, in the case of two real vectors $\mathfrak{x}$, $\mathfrak{y}$, with our earlier concept of orthogonality.

Finally a system $\mathfrak{v}_1, \mathfrak{v}_2, \ldots, \mathfrak{v}_r$ of vectors is called *orthonormal* if for every pair of subscripts i, k $(1 \leqq i \leqq r,\ 1 \leqq k \leqq r)$ we have

(21) $$\mathfrak{v}_i \cdot \bar{\mathfrak{v}}_k = \delta_{ik}.$$

By (20) we must then also have $\bar{\mathfrak{v}}_i \cdot \mathfrak{v}_k = \delta_{ik}$. If an orthonormal system consists of real vectors only, then it is a *normal orthogonal system* (in the sense of p. 127), since $\bar{\mathfrak{v}}_k = \mathfrak{v}_k$ in this case.

We shall now prove some simple theorems on orthonormal systems. We first note that

Every orthonormal system $\mathfrak{v}_1, \mathfrak{v}_2, \ldots, \mathfrak{v}_r$ *consists of linearly independent vectors.* For exactly as for normal orthogonal systems (p. 127) a relation $\lambda_1 \mathfrak{v}_1 + \lambda_2 \mathfrak{v}_2 + \cdots + \lambda_r \mathfrak{v}_r = 0$ implies $\lambda_k = 0$ upon

[5] For complex vectors we have the rules

$$\overline{\mathfrak{x}+\mathfrak{y}} = \bar{\mathfrak{x}} + \bar{\mathfrak{y}}, \quad \overline{\mathfrak{x} \cdot \mathfrak{y}} = \bar{\mathfrak{x}} \cdot \bar{\mathfrak{y}}, \quad \bar{\bar{\mathfrak{x}}} = \mathfrak{x}.$$

They follow immediately from p. 222, formula (20).

multiplication by $\bar{\mathfrak{v}}_k$, for $k = 1, 2, \ldots, r$.

We next prove

Any vector space L *of* V_n *of dimension* $\geqq 1$ *has an orthonormal basis.*

We prove this theorem (as we did for a normal orthogonal basis; p. 140) by mathematical induction on the dimension of L. If L is one-dimensional and if $\mathfrak{a} \neq 0$ is any vector in L, then the vector $\frac{\mathfrak{a}}{|\mathfrak{a}|}$ is an orthonormal basis of L.

Now let the dimension p of L be greater than 1, and let $\mathfrak{a}_1, \mathfrak{a}_2, \ldots, \mathfrak{a}_p$ be a basis of L. The vector space L′ spanned by the vectors $\mathfrak{a}_1, \mathfrak{a}_2, \ldots, \mathfrak{a}_{p-1}$ has, by induction hypothesis, an orthonormal basis, say $\mathfrak{v}_1, \mathfrak{v}_2, \ldots, \mathfrak{v}_{p-1}$. The vectors $\mathfrak{v}_1, \mathfrak{v}_2, \ldots, \mathfrak{v}_{p-1}, \mathfrak{a}_p$ are linearly independent, for otherwise $\mathfrak{a}_p$ would be in L′. Thus the vector

$$\mathfrak{b} = \mathfrak{a}_p - \sum_{i=1}^{p-1} (\mathfrak{a}_p \cdot \bar{\mathfrak{v}}_i) \cdot \mathfrak{v}_i$$

is not 0. With the aid of (21) we calculate that $\mathfrak{b} \cdot \bar{\mathfrak{v}}_k = 0$ for $k = 1, 2, \ldots, p - 1$. Setting $\mathfrak{v}_p = \frac{\mathfrak{b}}{|\mathfrak{b}|}$, the vectors $\mathfrak{v}_1, \mathfrak{v}_2, \ldots, \mathfrak{v}_p$ are seen to form an orthonormal basis of L.

Finally we wish to see how the length of a vector $\mathfrak{x}$ can be calculated from its components with respect to an arbitrary orthonormal basis $\mathfrak{v}_1, \mathfrak{v}_2, \ldots, \mathfrak{v}_n$ of V_n. Let

$$\mathfrak{x} = \lambda_1 \mathfrak{v}_1 + \lambda_2 \mathfrak{v}_2 + \cdots + \lambda_n \mathfrak{v}_n.$$

Using (21) we calculate

$$\mathfrak{x} \cdot \bar{\mathfrak{x}} = \sum_{i=1}^{n} \lambda_i \bar{\lambda}_i. \tag{22}$$

This is the desired formula.

We now consider those linear transformations on V_n which leave the lengths of all vectors invariant. Let τ be such a transformation, so that for every vector $\mathfrak{x}$ of V_n we have

$$|\tau(\mathfrak{x})| = |\mathfrak{x}|, \tag{23}$$

or, by (18),

$$\tau(\mathfrak{x}) \cdot \overline{\tau(\mathfrak{x})} = \mathfrak{x} \cdot \bar{\mathfrak{x}}. \tag{24}$$

We call any linear transformation with this property a **unitary transformation.**

Our goal is to show that *the matrix of every unitary transformation can be brought into diagonal form.* We first prove that for any unitary transformation τ and any $\mathfrak{x}$, $\mathfrak{y}$ of V_n we have.

(25) $$\tau(\mathfrak{x}) \cdot \overline{\tau(\mathfrak{y})} = \mathfrak{x} \cdot \overline{\mathfrak{y}}.$$

Formula (25) is a generalization of (24). In fact, let us apply (24) to the vector $\mathfrak{x} + a\mathfrak{y}$ where a is an arbitrary complex number. This yields

$$\tau(\mathfrak{x} + a\mathfrak{y}) \cdot \overline{\tau(\mathfrak{x} + a\mathfrak{y})} = (\mathfrak{x} + a\mathfrak{y}) \cdot \overline{(\mathfrak{x} + a\mathfrak{y})}.$$

Since τ is a linear transformation we obtain

$$\begin{aligned}\tau(\mathfrak{x}) \cdot \overline{\tau(\mathfrak{x})} + a \cdot \tau(\mathfrak{y}) \cdot \overline{\tau(\mathfrak{x})} + \overline{a} \cdot \tau(\mathfrak{x}) \cdot \overline{\tau(\mathfrak{y})} + a \cdot \overline{a} \cdot \tau(\mathfrak{y}) \cdot \overline{\tau(\mathfrak{y})} \\ = \mathfrak{x} \cdot \overline{\mathfrak{x}} + a \cdot \mathfrak{y} \cdot \overline{\mathfrak{x}} + \overline{a} \cdot \mathfrak{x} \cdot \overline{\mathfrak{y}} + a \cdot \overline{a} \cdot \mathfrak{y} \cdot \overline{\mathfrak{y}}.\end{aligned}$$

Using (24), we can simplify this to

$$a \cdot \tau(\mathfrak{y}) \cdot \overline{\tau(\mathfrak{x})} + \overline{a} \cdot \tau(\mathfrak{x}) \cdot \overline{\tau(\mathfrak{y})} = a \cdot \mathfrak{y} \cdot \overline{\mathfrak{x}} + \overline{a} \cdot \mathfrak{x} \cdot \overline{\mathfrak{y}}.$$

This is true for all a. If, in particular, we put $a = 1$ and $a = i$, we obtain

(26) $$\tau(\mathfrak{y}) \cdot \overline{\tau(\mathfrak{x})} + \tau(\mathfrak{x}) \cdot \overline{\tau(\mathfrak{y})} = \mathfrak{y} \cdot \overline{\mathfrak{x}} + \mathfrak{x} \cdot \overline{\mathfrak{y}},$$

(27) $$i \cdot \tau(\mathfrak{y}) \cdot \overline{\tau(\mathfrak{x})} - i \cdot \tau(\mathfrak{x}) \cdot \overline{\tau(\mathfrak{y})} = i \cdot \mathfrak{y} \cdot \overline{\mathfrak{x}} - i \cdot \mathfrak{x} \cdot \overline{\mathfrak{y}}.$$

By multiplying (27) by i and adding the result to (26), we obtain equation (25) which we wanted to prove.

We shall next prove the following: *The zeros of the characteristic polynomial of a unitary transformation* τ *all have absolute value* 1. For let a be such a zero. By Theorem 5 there is a *non-vanishing* vector $\mathfrak{x}$ such that $\tau(\mathfrak{x}) = a \cdot \mathfrak{x}$. Thus

$$\tau(\mathfrak{x}) \cdot \overline{\tau(\mathfrak{x})} = a \cdot \overline{a} \cdot \mathfrak{x} \cdot \overline{\mathfrak{x}}.$$

By cancelling the factor $\tau(\mathfrak{x}) \cdot \overline{\tau(\mathfrak{x})} = \mathfrak{x} \cdot \overline{\mathfrak{x}} \neq 0$, we obtain the desired equation

(28) $$a \cdot \overline{a} = 1.$$

Now by means of the criterion of Theorem 7, we can easily prove our assertion concerning the possibility of diagonalization for a unitary transformation. For let a be any characteristic root of τ. Let $\mathfrak{x}$ be any vector of the null space of the linear transformation $(\tau - \alpha\tau^0)^2$, so that

(29) $$(\tau - \alpha\tau^0)^2(\mathfrak{x}) = 0.$$

We must now show that $\mathfrak{x}$ also belongs to the null space of $(\tau - \alpha\tau^0)$, i.e. that

(30) $$\mathfrak{y} = (\tau - \alpha\tau^0)(\mathfrak{x})$$

is the null vector.

To prove this, we use equation (25). From (29) and (30) we obtain $\tau(\mathfrak{x}) = \alpha\mathfrak{x} + \mathfrak{y}$ and $\tau(\mathfrak{y}) = \alpha\mathfrak{y}$, which we substitute in (25) to obtain

$$\mathfrak{x} \cdot \bar{\mathfrak{y}} = \alpha\,\bar{\alpha}\,\mathfrak{x}\bar{\mathfrak{y}} + \bar{\alpha}\,\mathfrak{y}\,\bar{\mathfrak{y}}.$$

Since $\alpha\,\bar{\alpha} = 1$ so that $\bar{\alpha} \neq 0$, we obtain $\mathfrak{y}\,\bar{\mathfrak{y}} = 0$ and so $\mathfrak{y} = 0$, and thus the criterion of Theorem 7 is fulfilled.

Having thus shown the possibility of diagonalizing the matrix of τ we shall now prove even more, namely the following: *There is an orthonormal basis of V_n with respect to which the matrix of τ has diagonal form.*

In order to find any coordinate system with respect to which the matrix of τ is in diagonal form, we may proceed as on p. 322 (cf. also Theorem 6). First find all of the characteristic roots $\alpha_1, \alpha_2, \cdots, \alpha_r$ ($\alpha_i \neq \alpha_k$ for $i \neq k$) of τ. Then determine the null space $\mathrm{L}^{(i)}$ of $\tau - \alpha_i\tau^0$, for $i = 1, 2, \ldots, r$. Then by finding a basis for each $\mathrm{L}^{(1)}, \mathrm{L}^{(2)}, \ldots, \mathrm{L}^{(r)}$, we have that the totality of these basis vectors form a basis of V_n with respect to which the matrix of τ has diagonal form.

We now prove the following theorem: *For $i \neq k$, $\mathrm{L}^{(i)}$ is orthogonal to $\mathrm{L}^{(k)}$.* This means that if $\mathfrak{x}$ is any vector of $\mathrm{L}^{(i)}$ and $\mathfrak{y}$ any vector of $\mathrm{L}^{(k)}$, then $\mathfrak{x}$ and $\mathfrak{y}$ are orthogonal. For from $\tau(\mathfrak{x}) = \alpha_i\mathfrak{x}$ and $\tau(\mathfrak{x}) = \alpha_k\mathfrak{y}$, we have by (25) that

(31) $$\mathfrak{x} \cdot \bar{\mathfrak{y}} = \alpha_i \cdot \bar{\alpha}_k \cdot \mathfrak{x} \cdot \bar{\mathfrak{y}}.$$

But since $\alpha_i \neq \alpha_k$, so that $\alpha_i\bar{\alpha}_k \neq 1$,[6] we deduce from (31) that $\mathfrak{x} \cdot \bar{\mathfrak{y}} = 0$, as was to be proved.

The result just obtained implies that orthonormal bases of the L_i, when combined, form an orthonormal basis of V_n. In this way, an orthonormal basis of V_n is obtained with respect to which τ is in diagonal form.

[6] For from $\alpha_i\bar{\alpha}_k = 1$ we obtain $(\alpha_i - \alpha_k)\bar{\alpha}_k = 0$ by (28), so that $\alpha_i = \alpha_k$ contrary to our hypothesis.

We now wish to determine how to characterize the matrix of a unitary transformation τ with respect to an orthonormal basis $\mathfrak{v}_1, \mathfrak{v}_2, \ldots, \mathfrak{v}_n$. For this purpose we must first represent each of the vectors $\tau(\mathfrak{v}_i)$ as a linear combination of the $\mathfrak{v}_i$. Let, say,

$$\tau(\mathfrak{v}_i) = \sum_{\nu=1}^{n} b_{\nu i}\mathfrak{v}_\nu, \qquad i = 1, 2, \cdots, n. \tag{32}$$

Then the matrix of τ is

$$B = \begin{pmatrix} b_{11} & b_{12} & \cdots & b_{1n} \\ b_{21} & b_{22} & \cdots & b_{2n} \\ \cdot & \cdot & \cdot & \cdot \\ b_{n1} & b_{n2} & \cdots & b_{nn} \end{pmatrix}. \tag{33}$$

Letting $\mathfrak{x} = \mathfrak{v}_i$ and $\mathfrak{y} = \mathfrak{v}_k$ in (25) and using the equations

$$\mathfrak{v}_\nu \cdot \overline{\mathfrak{v}_\mu} = \delta_{\nu\mu},$$

we easily obtain

$$\sum_{\nu=1}^{n} b_{\nu i}\overline{b_{\nu k}} = \delta_{ik}, \qquad i, k = 1, 2, \cdots, n. \tag{34}$$

The left-hand side of this equation is the scalar product of the vectors $\{b_{1i}, b_{2i}, \cdots, b_{ni}\}$ and $\{\overline{b_{1k}}, \overline{b_{2k}}, \cdots, \overline{b_{nk}}\}$. Thus the equations (34) state that the column vectors of the matrix (33) form an orthonormal system.

Conversely, let $B = (b_{ik})$ be a matrix whose elements satisfy (34). Then the system of equations

$$y_i = \sum_{k=1}^{n} b_{ik}x_k, \qquad i = 1, 2, \cdots, n$$

represents a unitary transformation with respect to an orthonormal basis $\mathfrak{v}_1, \mathfrak{v}_2, \ldots, \mathfrak{v}_n$. For, from (34) it follows that

$$\sum_{i=1}^{n} y_i\overline{y_i} = \sum_{i=1}^{n}\sum_{k,j=1}^{n} b_{ik}x_k\overline{b_{ij}}\,\overline{x_j} = \sum_{k,j=1}^{n}\left(\sum_{i=1}^{n} b_{ik}\overline{b_{ij}}\right)x_k\overline{x_j} =$$
$$= \sum_{k,j=1}^{n}\delta_{kj}x_k\overline{x_j} = \sum_{k=1}^{n} x_k\overline{x_k}.$$

But this, by (22), means that $\tau(\mathfrak{x}) \cdot \overline{\tau(\mathfrak{x})} = \mathfrak{x} \cdot \overline{\mathfrak{x}}$.

Thus matrices which represent unitary transformations with respect to an orthonormal basis $\mathfrak{v}_1, \mathfrak{v}_2, \ldots, \mathfrak{v}_n$, are characterized by equations (34). A matrix with this property is called a **unitary matrix.**

The matrix which is obtained from (33) by replacing each b_{ik} by $\overline{b}_{ik}$ is denoted by $\overline{B}$. Also, let B' denote the transpose of the matrix B (§ 22). The equations (34) may then be combined into the single matrix equation

$$B' \cdot \overline{B} = E. \tag{35}$$

This means that $\overline{B}$ is the inverse matrix of B'. (35) implies

$$\overline{B} \cdot B' = E. \tag{36}$$

This equation means that $\sum_{\nu=1}^{n} \overline{b_{i\nu}}\, b_{k\nu} = \delta_{ik}$ for $i, k = 1, 2, \ldots, n$. And this in turn means that the *row* vectors of B also form an orthonormal system. A unitary matrix is characterized by either of the equations (35) and (36).

If B is a unitary matrix, then so are B', $\overline{B}$, $\overline{B}'$. By taking the transpose of (35), we obtain $\overline{B}' \cdot B = E$, i.e. $\overline{B}' = B^{-1}$, so that B^{-1} *is also a unitary matrix.*

Finally, we shall state our results entirely in terms of matrices. We first observe that the unit vectors e_i of V_n form an orthonormal basis of V_n. Thus a given unitary matrix B represents a unitary transformation τ in the coordinate system $[\mathfrak{e}_1, \mathfrak{e}_2, \ldots, \mathfrak{e}_n]$. Now we already know that the matrix of τ has diagonal form with respect to some orthonormal basis $\mathfrak{v}_1, \mathfrak{v}_2, \ldots, \mathfrak{v}_n$. Let C be the matrix of τ with respect to $\mathfrak{v}_1, \mathfrak{v}_2, \ldots, \mathfrak{v}_n$. Then by § 22, Theorem 4, we have

$$B = T \cdot C \cdot T^{-1}, \tag{37}$$

where T is the matrix of the coordinate transformation from the basis $\mathfrak{v}_1, \mathfrak{v}_2, \ldots, \mathfrak{v}_n$ to the basis $\mathfrak{e}_1, \mathfrak{e}_2, \ldots, \mathfrak{e}_n$. In order to evaluate this matrix T, we must represent each of the vectors $\mathfrak{v}_i$ as a linear combination of the $\mathfrak{e}_i$.[7] Let, say,

$$\mathfrak{v}_k = \{v_{1k}, v_{2k}, \ldots, v_{nk}\} = \sum_{i=1}^{n} v_{ik}\, \mathfrak{e}_i.$$

The matrix T is then

$$T = \begin{pmatrix} v_{11} & v_{12} & \cdots & v_{1n} \\ v_{21} & v_{22} & \cdots & v_{2n} \\ \cdot & \cdot & \cdot & \cdot \\ v_{n1} & v_{n2} & \cdots & v_{nn} \end{pmatrix}.$$

[7] Cf. the remark at the end of Theorem 4 of § 22.

This matrix is unitary, for its column vectors are $\mathfrak{v}_1, \mathfrak{v}_2, \ldots, \mathfrak{v}_n$. Thus T^{-1} is also unitary. By (37) we have $C = T^{-1} \cdot B \cdot T$, so that

THEOREM 8. *Every unitary matrix may be transformed into diagonal form by another unitary matrix.*

Orthogonal Transformations

Let an orthonormal basis $\mathfrak{v}_1, \mathfrak{v}_2, \ldots, \mathfrak{v}_n$ which consists of *real* vectors only,[8] be chosen in V_n. This basis therefore forms a normal orthogonal system in the sense of p. 127. A unitary transformation is represented in this system $[\mathfrak{v}_1, \mathfrak{v}_2, \ldots, \mathfrak{v}_n]$ (just as in any other orthonormal system) by a unitary matrix. Let us consider those unitary matrices whose elements are all real. Such matrices are then *orthogonal* in the sense of p. 128. Unitary transformations whose matrices with respect to some orthonormal system consisting of real vectors only are real orthogonal, are called **orthogonal transformations.**

It is easy to show that this definition is independent of the particular choice of the real, normal orthogonal system $\mathfrak{v}_1, \mathfrak{v}_2, \ldots, \mathfrak{v}_n$. In fact, the following holds:

The orthogonal transformations are those unitary transformations which map real vectors on real vectors.

It is clear that an orthogonal transformation has this property, since its system of equations with respect to a real, orthonormal basis has only real coefficients. Conversely, if for every real vector $\mathfrak{x}$ the vector $\tau(\mathfrak{x})$ is real, then this is true in particular of the images $\tau(\mathfrak{v}_i)$ of the vectors of a real orthonormal system $\mathfrak{v}_i$. Then each $\tau(\mathfrak{v}_i)$ may be written as a linear combination of the $\mathfrak{v}_i$ with real coefficients only.[9] But these coefficients constitute the elements of the matrix of τ. Thus our characterization is established.

We shall now derive *real normal forms* (i.e. normal forms in the real domain) for the matrices of orthogonal transformations. We already know (cf. p. 331) that every orthogonal transformation (as a unitary transformation) can be brought into diagonal form in complex V_n. But this diagonal form will have all its entries in the real domain only if the characteristic roots of τ are all real. (Cf., say, Theorems 1a and 6 of this section.) But a real characteristic root α

---

[8] I.e. the components of each $\mathfrak{v}_i$ are real.

[9] For, these coefficients are the solutions of a system of equations with real coefficients.

satisfies $\alpha^2 = 1$ by (28) so that it must equal ± 1. Thus if the diagonal form is possible in the real domain, it must have the form

$$\begin{pmatrix} +1 & & & & & & & 0 \\ & +1 & & & & & & \\ & & \ddots & & & & & \\ & & & +1 & & & & \\ & & & & -1 & & & \\ & & & & & -1 & & \\ & & & & & & \ddots & \\ 0 & & & & & & & -1 \end{pmatrix}$$

($+1$ repeated a times, -1 repeated b times)

where $(-1)^n (u-1)^a \cdot (u+1)^b$ is the characteristic polynomial of the orthogonal transformation (cf. p. 327).

Now consider the case where the characteristic polynomial $\chi(u)$ of the orthogonal transformation τ may have non-real roots. Let α be one such root. Since the matrix of τ with respect to a real basis is real, the characteristic polynomial $\chi(u)$ has real coefficients only. It then follows[10] that α is also a zero of $\chi(u)$, (and with the same multiplicity as α).

As we did above in discussing the diagonal form, we now consider the invariant subspaces corresponding to the roots α, $\overline{\alpha}$ of the characteristic polynomial of τ. Let L_α and $L_{\overline{\alpha}}$ be the null spaces of the linear transformations $\tau - \alpha\tau^0$ and $\tau - \overline{\alpha}\tau^0$ respectively. It is easy to give a system of equations for L_α (and likewise for $L_{\overline{\alpha}}$). For let us take the unit vectors $e_1, e_2, \ldots, e_n$ as a coordinate system in V_n. If $B = (b_{ik})$ is the matrix of τ in this system, then $B - \alpha E$ is the matrix of $\tau - \alpha\tau^0$. The transformation $\tau - \alpha\tau^0$ is then represented by the equation[11] $(y) = (B - \alpha E)(x)$. Thus, all vectors which are mapped on the zero vector satisfy $(B - \alpha E)(x) = 0$. Thus L_α *is represented by the system of equations*

$$(38) \qquad \sum_{k=1}^{n} (b_{ik} - \alpha\delta_{ik}) x_k = 0, \qquad i = 1, 2, \cdots, n.$$

B, as the matrix of an orthogonal transformation with respect to a real coordinate system has real elements only. Thus we have

$$\sum_{k=1}^{n} (b_{ik} - \overline{\alpha}\delta_{ik}) \overline{x_k} = 0$$

---

[10] Cf. § 17.

[11] Cf. § 22, equation (38).

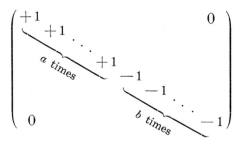

by taking the conjugates of both sides of equation (38). We have thus shown that *if* $\mathfrak{x}$ *is a vector of* L_α, *then* $\overline{\mathfrak{x}}$ *is a vector of* $L_{\overline{\alpha}}$.

Now let r be the dimension of L_α and let $\mathfrak{v}_1, \mathfrak{v}_2, \ldots, \mathfrak{v}_r$ be an orthonormal basis of L_α. Then the vectors $\overline{\mathfrak{v}}_1, \overline{\mathfrak{v}}_2, \ldots, \overline{\mathfrak{v}}_r$ also form an orthonormal system. Thus they are linearly independent. Since they all belong to $L_{\overline{\alpha}}$, the dimension of $L_{\overline{\alpha}}$ is at least r, i.e. at least as great as the dimension of $L_{\overline{\alpha}}$. However the converse is also true since α is the conjugate of $\overline{\alpha}$. Thus the two dimensions are equal, and the vectors $\overline{\mathfrak{v}}_1, \overline{\mathfrak{v}}_2, \ldots, \overline{\mathfrak{v}}_r$ form an orthonormal basis of $L_{\overline{\alpha}}$.

Now we set

$$(39) \qquad \mathfrak{f}_\nu = \frac{\mathfrak{v}_\nu + \overline{\mathfrak{v}}_\nu}{+\sqrt{2}}, \qquad \mathfrak{g}_\nu = \frac{\mathfrak{v}_\nu - \overline{\mathfrak{v}}_\nu}{+\sqrt{2}\, i}.$$

The vectors $\mathfrak{f}_\nu, \mathfrak{g}_\nu$ are real. We shall now prove that *the vectors* $\mathfrak{f}_1, \mathfrak{g}_1, \mathfrak{f}_2, \mathfrak{g}_2, \cdots, \mathfrak{f}_r, \mathfrak{g}_r$ *form a normal orthogonal system.* Since α is not real, $\alpha \neq \overline{\alpha}$. It thus follows, as before, that L_α is orthogonal to $L_{\overline{\alpha}}$. Thus if $\mathfrak{x}$ is any vector of L_α, $\mathfrak{y}$ any vector of $L_{\overline{\alpha}}$, we have $\mathfrak{x} \cdot \overline{\mathfrak{y}} = 0$. Setting $\mathfrak{x} = \mathfrak{v}_\nu, \mathfrak{y} = \overline{\mathfrak{v}}_\mu$, we obtain $\mathfrak{v}_\nu \cdot \overline{\overline{\mathfrak{v}}}_\mu = \mathfrak{v}_\nu \cdot \mathfrak{v}_\mu = 0$. We then also have $\overline{\mathfrak{v}}_\nu \cdot \overline{\mathfrak{v}}_\mu = 0$. Also using the relations $\mathfrak{v}_\nu \cdot \overline{\mathfrak{v}}_\mu = \delta_{\nu\mu}$, we obtain from (39) that

$$\begin{aligned} \mathfrak{f}_\nu \cdot \mathfrak{f}_\mu &= \frac{\mathfrak{v}_\nu \cdot \overline{\mathfrak{v}}_\mu + \overline{\mathfrak{v}}_\nu \cdot \mathfrak{v}_\mu}{2} = \delta_{\nu\mu}, \\ \mathfrak{f}_\nu \cdot \mathfrak{g}_\mu &= 0, \\ \mathfrak{g}_\nu \cdot \mathfrak{g}_\mu &= \frac{\mathfrak{v}_\nu \cdot \overline{\mathfrak{v}}_\mu + \overline{\mathfrak{v}}_\nu \cdot \mathfrak{v}_\mu}{2} = \delta_{\nu\mu}. \end{aligned}$$

These equations prove that the vectors $\mathfrak{f}_1, \mathfrak{g}_1, \mathfrak{f}_2, \mathfrak{g}_2, \cdots, \mathfrak{f}_r, \mathfrak{g}_r$ form a normal orthogonal system.

Now let $L_{\alpha,\overline{\alpha}}$ be the sum of the vector spaces L_α and $L_{\overline{\alpha}}$. The dimension of $L_{\alpha,\overline{\alpha}}$ is $\leqq 2r$. Since the vectors $\mathfrak{f}_\nu, \mathfrak{g}_\nu$ are in $L_{\alpha,\overline{\alpha}}$ and are linearly independent (as a normal orthogonal system), the dimension of $L_{\alpha,\overline{\alpha}}$ equals $2r$ and the vectors $\mathfrak{f}_1, \mathfrak{g}_1, \mathfrak{f}_2, \mathfrak{g}_2, \ldots, \mathfrak{f}_r, \mathfrak{g}_r$ form a basis of $L_{\alpha,\overline{\alpha}}$.

If the characteristic polynomial $\chi(u)$ has other non-real roots $\alpha', \overline{\alpha'}, \alpha'', \overline{\alpha''}, \cdots,$ different from α and $\overline{\alpha}$ we proceed with each pair of roots as we just did with α and $\overline{\alpha}$. In this way we obtain other vector spaces $L_{\alpha',\overline{\alpha'}}, L_{\alpha'',\overline{\alpha''}}, \ldots$ and corresponding bases $\mathfrak{f}_1', \mathfrak{g}_1', \mathfrak{f}_2', \mathfrak{g}_2', \cdots, \mathfrak{f}_{r'}', \mathfrak{g}_{r'}'$; $\mathfrak{f}_1'', \mathfrak{g}_1'', \mathfrak{f}_2'', \mathfrak{g}_2'', \cdots, \mathfrak{f}_{r''}'', \mathfrak{g}_{r''}''$; etc.

Besides these complex roots we may also obtain the real roots ± 1. In this case, let L_{+1} and L_{-1} be their null spaces, which are given by (38) on setting $\alpha = \pm 1$. Let p and q be the dimensions of L_{+1} and L_{-1}

respectively. Since all the coefficients of (38) are in this case real, we can find p (or q) *real* linearly independent solutions of (38) for $\alpha = +1$ (or -1). Thus the bases of L_{+1} and L_{-1} can be chosen real, and can therefore be made normal orthogonal. Let $\mathfrak{c}_1, \mathfrak{c}_2, \ldots, \mathfrak{c}_p$ and $\mathfrak{d}_1, \mathfrak{d}_2, \ldots, \mathfrak{d}_q$ be normal orthogonal bases for L_{+1} and L_{-1} respectively.

We now write down the basis systems for L_{+1}, L_{-1}, $L_{\alpha,\bar{\alpha}}$, $L_{\alpha',\bar{\alpha}'}$, $L_{\alpha'',\bar{\alpha}''}, \ldots$, one after another, as follows:

(40) $$\mathfrak{c}_1, \cdots, \mathfrak{c}_p;\ \mathfrak{d}_1, \cdots, \mathfrak{d}_q;\ \mathfrak{f}_1, \mathfrak{g}_1, \cdots, \mathfrak{f}_r, \mathfrak{g}_r;\ \mathfrak{f}_1', \mathfrak{g}_1', \cdots, \mathfrak{f}_{r'}', \mathfrak{g}_{r'}'; \cdots.$$

The number of these vectors is equal to the sum of the dimensions of L_{+1}, L_{-1}, $L_{\alpha,\bar{\alpha}}$, $L_{\alpha',\alpha'}, \ldots$, and hence is equal to n.[12]

Furthermore *the vectors* (40) *form a normal orthogonal system.* For, since the bases of L_{+1}, L_{-1}, $L_{\alpha,\bar{\alpha}}$, $L_{\alpha',\bar{\alpha}'}, \ldots$ were chosen to be normal orthogonal, we need only show that any two distinct spaces in this list are orthogonal to each other. But this follows from the fact that the spaces $L_{+1}, L_{-1}, L_{\alpha}, L_{\bar{\alpha}}, L_{\alpha'}, L_{\bar{\alpha}'}, \ldots$ are orthogonal to each other.

Being a normal orthogonal system, the n vectors (40) are linearly independent and therefore form a real basis of V_n. We now calculate the matrix of τ with respect to (40). For the basis vectors $\mathfrak{c}_i$ and $\mathfrak{d}_i$ we have the equations

(41) $$\tau(\mathfrak{c}_i) = \mathfrak{c}_i, \qquad \tau(\mathfrak{d}_i) = -\mathfrak{d}_i.$$

By the definition of $\mathfrak{f}_\nu$ and $\mathfrak{g}_\nu$, we further have that

$$\mathfrak{v}_\nu = \frac{+\sqrt{2}}{2}(\mathfrak{f}_\nu + i\,\mathfrak{g}_\nu).$$

Hence it follows from $\tau(\mathfrak{v}_\nu) = \alpha\mathfrak{v}_\nu$ that

(42) $$\tau(\mathfrak{f}_\nu) + i\,\tau(\mathfrak{g}_\nu) = \alpha(\mathfrak{f}_\nu + i\,\mathfrak{g}_\nu).$$

Now we may set[13] $\alpha = \cos\varphi - i\sin\varphi$. Then we have

$$\tau(\mathfrak{f}_\nu) + i\,\tau(\mathfrak{g}_\nu) = \mathfrak{f}_\nu\cos\varphi + \mathfrak{g}_\nu\sin\varphi + i(\mathfrak{g}_\nu\cos\varphi - \mathfrak{f}_\nu\sin\varphi).$$

---

[12] Since the matrix of τ can be transformed into diagonal form over the complex number field, it follows from the proof of Theorem 1 of this section that a basis of V_n can be obtained by choosing a basis for each of the spaces $L_{+1}, L_{-1}, L_\alpha, L_{\bar{\alpha}}, L_{\alpha'}, L_{\bar{\alpha}'}, \ldots$ and combining these basis elements. Thus the sum of the dimensions of these subspaces equals the sum of the dimensions of $L_{+1}, L_{-1}, L_{\alpha,\bar{\alpha}}, L_{\alpha',\bar{\alpha}'}, \ldots$, equals n.

[13] First, α has a representation of the form $\alpha = r(\cos\psi + i\sin\psi)$. But $r = 1$ since $|\alpha| = 1$. If we now set $\psi = -\varphi$, we finally obtain $\alpha = \cos\varphi - i\sin\varphi$.

But this equality between complex vectors holds if and only if the real and imaginary parts of both sides are equal. Thus:

$$(43)\qquad \begin{aligned} \tau(\mathfrak{f}_\nu) &= \mathfrak{f}_\nu \cos\varphi + \mathfrak{g}_\nu \sin\varphi, \\ \tau(\mathfrak{g}_\nu) &= -\mathfrak{f}_\nu \sin\varphi + \mathfrak{g}_\nu \cos\varphi. \end{aligned}$$

Analogous equations hold for $\mathfrak{f}'_\nu$, $\mathfrak{g}'_\nu$, with a new argument φ' etc. From (41) and (43) it follows that the matrix of τ with respect to the basis (40) is of the form

$$(44)\qquad \begin{pmatrix} +1 & & & & & & & & 0 \\ & \ddots & & & & & & & \\ & & +1 & & & & & & \\ & & & -1 & & & & & \\ & & & & \ddots & & & & \\ & & & & & -1 & & & \\ & & & & & & \begin{array}{:cc:} \hdashline \cos\varphi & -\sin\varphi \\ \sin\varphi & \cos\varphi \\ \hdashline \end{array} & & \\ & & & & & & & \ddots & \\ & & & & & & & & \begin{array}{:cc:} \hdashline \cos\varphi' & -\sin\varphi' \\ \sin\varphi' & \cos\varphi' \\ \hdashline \end{array} \\ 0 & & & & & & & & \ddots \end{pmatrix}.$$

The principal diagonal of (44) begins with $+1$ appearing p times; then -1 appears q times. Then follow two-by-two square boxes of the form

$$\begin{array}{:cc:} \cos\varphi & -\sin\varphi \\ \sin\varphi & \cos\varphi \end{array}\,, \quad \begin{array}{:cc:} \cos\varphi' & -\sin\varphi' \\ \sin\varphi' & \cos\varphi' \end{array}\,, \quad \ldots,$$

with exactly r boxes involving φ, and r' boxes involving φ', etc.

We have thus obtained a real normal form for the orthogonal transformation τ. (44) is an orthogonal matrix since it is a matrix of an orthogonal transformation with respect to a real normal orthogonal basis.

From the fact that the basis (40) is a normal orthogonal system, we deduce, as in the case of unitary transformations, the following

THEOREM 9. *For any real orthogonal matrix B, there is a second real orthogonal matrix T such that $T \cdot B \cdot T^{-1}$ is in the normal form* **(44)**.

For in the coordinate system $[\mathfrak{e}_1, \mathfrak{e}_2, \cdots, \mathfrak{e}_n]$, there corresponds to a real orthogonal matrix B an orthogonal transformation τ. Corresponding to τ, we can find a real normal orthogonal basis (40) with respect to which the matrix of τ takes on the normal form (44). This normal form is then $T \cdot B \cdot T^{-1}$ where the columns of T^{-1} are the components of the basis vectors (40). Thus T^{-1} (and hence also T) is an orthogonal matrix.

We can easily gain insight into the geometric structure of rigid motions in euclidean R_n by using the real normal forms for orthogonal transformations. For this purpose consider a system of equations

$$(45) \qquad y_i = \sum_{k=1}^{n} b_{ik} x_k, \qquad i = 1, 2, \cdots, n,$$

with a real orthogonal matrix (b_{ik}). This system represents, by § 12, a rigid motion[14] with respect to some cartesian coordinate system of euclidean R_n, say with respect to $[O; \mathfrak{e}_1, \mathfrak{e}_2, \ldots, \mathfrak{e}_n]$ (cf. the bottom of page 117). If we determine the basis (40) corresponding to the orthogonal matrix (b_{ik}) and go over to the coordinate system with the same origin O, but with the vectors (40) as basis vectors, then the rigid motion (45) is represented in this coordinate system by a system of equations whose matrix is of the form (44). Referring to the form of the matrix (44) we see that in this coordinate system, the first p equations are of the form $y_i = x_i$. This means that our rigid motion leaves fixed every point of the linear space spanned by the first p coordinate axes. We see that in the q-dimensional linear space through the next q axes, our rigid motion reflects each point through the origin; for all the coordinates of a point in this space change their sign under our rigid motion. Finally, we note that a mapping is induced in each (two-dimensional) coordinate plane corresponding to one of the square boxes of the matrix (44); this mapping is given by equations of the form

$$\begin{aligned} y_1 &= x_1 \cos\varphi - x_2 \sin\varphi, \\ y_2 &= x_1 \sin\varphi + x_2 \cos\varphi, \end{aligned}$$

so that it is a rotation about the origin (cf. p. 167).

As an example we consider affine R_3 and apply the above considera-

[14] This is not the most general rigid motion, since the right-hand side of (45) is free of constant terms. But we know that any motion is of this type followed by the most simple of all rigid motions, namely a translation.

tions to it. The only possibilities for the normal form (44) in R_3 are

$$\begin{pmatrix}1&0&0\\0&1&0\\0&0&1\end{pmatrix},\quad \begin{pmatrix}1&0&0\\0&1&0\\0&0&-1\end{pmatrix},\quad \begin{pmatrix}1&0&0\\0&-1&0\\0&0&-1\end{pmatrix},$$

$$\begin{pmatrix}-1&0&0\\0&-1&0\\0&0&-1\end{pmatrix},\quad \begin{pmatrix}1&0&0\\0&\cos\varphi&-\sin\varphi\\0&\sin\varphi&\cos\varphi\end{pmatrix},\quad \begin{pmatrix}-1&0&0\\0&\cos\varphi&-\sin\varphi\\0&\sin\varphi&\cos\varphi\end{pmatrix}.$$

The system of equations of the corresponding rigid motions are

$$\text{(46)}\qquad \begin{array}{llll} y_1 = x_1, & y_1 = x_1, & y_1 = x_1, & y_1 = -x_1, \\ \text{I. } y_2 = x_2, & \text{II. } y_2 = x_2, & \text{III. } y_2 = -x_2, & \text{IV. } y_2 = -x_2, \\ y_3 = x_3; & y_3 = -x_3; & y_3 = -x_3; & y_3 = -x_3; \end{array}$$

$$\begin{array}{ll} y_1 = x_1, & y_1 = -x_1, \\ \text{V. } y_2 = x_2\cos\varphi - x_3\sin\varphi, & \text{VI. } y_2 = x_2\cos\varphi - x_3\sin\varphi, \\ y_3 = x_2\sin\varphi + x_3\cos\varphi; & y_3 = x_2\sin\varphi + x_3\cos\varphi. \end{array}$$

These systems of equations represent the following:

I. The identity;
II. a reflection through a plane;
III. a reflection through a line;
IV. a reflection through a point;
V. a rotation about an axis;
VI. a rotation about an axis and a reflection through a plane perpendicular to this axis.

The first four cases may be considered as special cases of the last two. For, the system of equations V of (46) is the system I if $\varphi = 0$, and is the system III if $\varphi = \pi$. And if we substitute $\varphi = 0$ and $\varphi = \pi$ in VI, we obtain the system II (the first and third coordinates interchanged) and IV, respectively.

Except for translations we have thus obtained once more all of the cases of § 12.

Hermitian and Symmetric Matrices

(Principal Axis Transformation)

A matrix $A = (a_{ik})$ whose elements are complex numbers is called *hermitian* if $A' = \overline{A}$, or in other words if $a_{ik} = \overline{a}_{ki}$ for every i and k. For such matrices we first prove

THEOREM 10. *The characteristic polynomial and the minimal polynomial of a hermitian matrix have real roots only.*

Proof: By Theorem 6 of this section the characteristic polynomial and the minimal polynomial have the same roots. Let a be one such, so that $|A - aE| = 0$. Then there is a matrix[15] (x) whose first column does not vanish, and for which $(A - aE)(x) = O$. This may be written

$$A \cdot (x) = a(x). \tag{47}$$

By transposing both sides of this equation, and then taking conjugates, we have, since $\overline{A'} = A$, that

$$(\bar{x})' \cdot A = \bar{a}(\bar{x})'. \tag{48}$$

If we multiply (47) on the left by $(\bar{x})'$ and (48) on the right by (x), then the left-hand sides of both equations are equal. Comparing the right-hand sides we have

$$(a - \bar{a})(\bar{x})'(x) = O.$$

But the matrix $(\bar{x})'(x)$ is not O since the element in the first row and first column is $\sum_{i=1}^{n} \bar{x}_i x_i$, which is certainly not 0 since by hypothesis the x_i do not all vanish. Thus $a - \bar{a} = 0$, i.e. a is real.

We next prove

THEOREM 11. *Every hermitian matrix A can be transformed into diagonal form.*

Proof: We shall show that the criterion of Theorem 7 is satisfied. That is, in matrix notation: For every root a of the characteristic polynomial of A, it follows from $(A - aE)^2(x) = O$ that

$$(A - aE)(x) = O.$$

For suppose $(A - aE)^2(x) = O$. Then by multiplication on the left by $(\bar{x})'$ we obtain

$$((\bar{A} - aE)(\bar{x}))' \cdot (A - aE)(x) = O. \tag{49}$$

The matrix $(A - aE)(x)$ has nothing but zeros in the second through the n-th columns, so that the left-hand side of (49) is a product of the form $(\bar{y})'(y)$, and hence vanishes only when $(y) = O$. Thus, from (49) we obtain $(A - aE)(x) = O$, as was to be proved.

[15] Of course (x) is the matrix defined on p. 293 in equation (31).

Having proved that for a hermitian matrix the diagonal form is attainable, we shall obtain a more precise result as in Theorem 8 for unitary matrices and Theorem 9 for orthogonal matrices. In fact, we have

THEOREM 12. *For every hermitian matrix A, there is a unitary matrix T such that $T \cdot A \cdot T^{-1}$ is in diagonal form.*

Proof: As in the proof of Theorems 8 and 9 we first consider the linear transformation σ on complex V_n corresponding to the hermitian matrix A in the coordinate system $[\mathfrak{e}_1, \mathfrak{e}_2, \ldots, \mathfrak{e}_n]$. As in the proof of Theorem 8, we must show that there is an orthonormal basis of complex V_n with respect to which the matrix of σ is in diagonal form. We first decompose V_n into the invariant vector spaces corresponding to the linear factors of the minimal polynomial of σ. If α is a zero of the characteristic polynomial, and thus of the minimal polynomial, then the corresponding invariant subspace consists of all vectors $\{x_1, x_2, \ldots, x_n\}$ which satisfy the matrix equation

$$(A - \alpha E)(x) = O. \tag{50}$$

Now for each characteristic root α, determine an orthonormal basis for the corresponding invariant subspace as given by (50). The totality of these basis elements is a basis of V_n with respect to which the matrix of σ is in diagonal form. To show that this basis is orthonormal we need only prove that the spaces represented by (50) are orthonormal to each other. The proof of this is similar to the proof of Theorem 10. For let

$$A(x) = \alpha(x), \quad A(y) = \beta(y), \qquad \alpha \neq \beta, \tag{51}$$

be two equations of the form (50). Multiply the first of them by $(\overline{y})'$ on the left. Now take transposes in the second equation and then take conjugates of both sides. Then multiply the new equation by (x) on the right. Using $\overline{A}' = A$, we see that the left-hand sides of the two equations are now identical. Thus

$$(\overline{\beta} - \alpha)(\overline{y})'(x) = O.$$

But $(\overline{\beta} - \alpha) \neq 0$, since $\overline{\beta} = \beta$ by Theorem 10 and since we had taken $\beta \neq \alpha$. Thus $(\overline{y})' \cdot (x) = O$, as was to be proved, since this shows that any two solutions of two different equations (51) are orthogonal to each other.

We may specialize our result to the case where the hermitian matrix A has real entries only. We assert that in this case, the matrix T of the last theorem may be taken to be real orthogonal. To prove this, it suffices to show that the orthonormal basis we have used in the proof of Theorem 12 may in the present case be chosen in such a way that all its vectors are real. But in this case, the system of equations (50) has real coefficients only (Theorem 10). Thus the required orthonormal basis of the vector space represented by (50) can be chosen as a real orthogonal system. This proves the result.

If the hermitian matrix A is real, then its defining property reduces to $A' = A$, or $a_{ik} = a_{ki}$. Such a matrix is called **symmetric.**

A real orthogonal matrix T satisfies $T \cdot T' = E$, i.e. $T' = T^{-1}$ as a special case of equation (36) on p. 333. The last result may thus be stated in the following form:

THEOREM 13. *For every real symmetric matrix A, there is a real orthogonal matrix T such that $T' \cdot A \cdot T$ is in diagonal form.*[16]

We further note that T may even be assumed to be a *proper* orthogonal matrix, i.e. such that $|T| = +1$. For in any case $|T| = \pm 1$.[17] For if $|T| = -1$ we need only change the sign of one of the basis vectors. Then all of the elements of some definite column of T change their sign, so that for the new T, we have $|T| = +1$.

The transformation of a real symmetric matrix into diagonal form by an orthogonal matrix is called a "*principal axis transformation.*" The reader will later learn the geometric meaning of this transformation, which will explain its name.

Exercises

1. A matrix A is said to be of *finite order*, if there is an integer $k > 0$ such that $A^k = E = (\delta_{ik})$. Show that a complex matrix of finite order can always be transformed into diagonal form in the field of complex numbers.

2. A matrix A is called *nilpotent* if there is an integer $k > 0$ such that $A^k = O$. Show that a nilpotent matrix $A \neq O$ can *never* be transformed into diagonal form (in any field).

3. Determine whether the following matrices can be transformed into diagonal form in 1. the field of rational numbers, 2. the field of real numbers, 3. the field of complex numbers:

---

[16] Here we have interchanged the role of T and T^{-1}, with an eye to further applications. This merely represents a change in notation.

[17] Cf. p. 130.

$$\begin{pmatrix}1 & 2\\0 & 1\end{pmatrix},\quad \begin{pmatrix}2 & -1\\1 & 3\end{pmatrix},\quad \begin{pmatrix}2 & -6 & 6\\3 & -7 & 6\\3 & -6 & 5\end{pmatrix},\quad \begin{pmatrix}-1 & 0 & -1\\4 & 1 & 2\\4 & 1 & 3\end{pmatrix}!$$

4. Let $a_1, a_2, \cdots, a_n$ be n complex numbers. When can the n-by-n square matrix

$$\begin{pmatrix}0 & & & a_1\\ & & a_2 & \\ & \cdot^{\cdot^{\cdot}} & & \\ a_n & & & 0\end{pmatrix}$$

be transformed into diagonal form?

§ 25. The Elementary Divisors of a Polynomial Matrix

In the preceding section, we investigated the question of how to find coordinate systems in which the matrices of a certain class of linear transformations are as simple as possible. It is the goal of this and the next section to solve this problem in the general case, so that the matrix of *every* linear transformation may be put into a particularly simple and characteristic form, the so-called normal form. The usefulness of this normal form will be demonstrated (in the second half of the next section) by a few applications. For example, we shall be able to describe the class of all matrices which belong to a given linear transformation in all possible coordinate systems.

In this section we first obtain some tools which are necessary and useful in carrying out the solution of the general problem. These tools in addition are of interest in themselves and are also of importance for a number of applications to other branches of mathematics.

What we shall do is analogous to what was done in § 20 in the proof of the Basis Theorem for abelian groups. The reason for this analogy will first be made clear in the next section.

Consider an n-by-n square matrix

$$(1)\qquad \begin{pmatrix}f_{11}(u) & f_{12}(u) & \cdots & f_{1n}(u)\\ f_{21}(u) & f_{22}(u) & \cdots & f_{2n}(u)\\ \cdot & \cdot & \cdot & \cdot\\ f_{n1}(u) & f_{n2}(u) & \cdots & f_{nn}(u)\end{pmatrix}$$

whose elements $f_{ik}(u)$ are polynomials in one variable u with coefficients in a fixed field F. We denote the *polynomial matrix* (1) by $(f_{ik}(u))$ or by $F(u)$. We shall subject such matrices to certain simple transformations similar to those given in § 20 for matrices with integer entries. We make the following definition:

An **elementary operation** on a polynomial matrix of the form (1) is any of the following four operations:

I. *Multiplication of a row by a non-zero element of* F.

II. *Multiplication of a row by an arbitrary polynomial* $f(u)$ *and addition of the resulting row to another row.*

I*. *Multiplication of a column by a non-zero element of* F.

II*. *Multiplication of a column by an arbitrary polynomial* $f(u)$ *and addition of the resulting column to another column.*

If a polynomial matrix $G(u)$ can be obtained from $F(u)$ by a finite succession of elementary operations, we say that $G(u)$ *is equivalent to* $F(u)$. We easily verify the following:

Every polynomial matrix is equivalent to itself (*reflexivity* of equivalence).

If $G(u)$ is equivalent to $F(u)$, then $F(u)$ is equivalent to $G(u)$ (*symmetry*).

If $F(u)$ is equivalent to $G(u)$ and $G(u)$ is equivalent to $H(u)$, then $F(u)$ is equivalent to $H(u)$ (*transitivity*).

We shall express the fact that $F(u)$ and $G(u)$ are equivalent by writing $F(u) \sim G(u)$.

In contrast to § 20, we have not taken the *interchange of two rows or columns* as an elementary operation. This is not necessary, for it can be obtained by a finite succession of elementary operations of the types just defined.[1] For example, we shall show how to accomplish in this way the interchange of the first two rows of the matrix (1). The required elementary operations, arranged in proper order, are the following: 1. Addition of the first row to the second. 2. Subtraction of the (new) second row from the first. 3. Addition of the first row to the second. 4. Multiplication of the first row by — 1. The scheme

$$\begin{pmatrix} f_{1i} \\ f_{2i} \end{pmatrix} \to \begin{pmatrix} f_{1i} \\ f_{2i}+f_{1i} \end{pmatrix} \to \begin{pmatrix} -f_{2i} \\ f_{2i}+f_{1i} \end{pmatrix} \to \begin{pmatrix} -f_{2i} \\ f_{1i} \end{pmatrix} \to \begin{pmatrix} f_{2i} \\ f_{1i} \end{pmatrix}$$

indicates the effect of these transformations.

We shall now show, as in § 20, that every polynomial matrix can be brought into diagonal form by elementary operations, and moreover into a diagonal form of a very special kind.

---

[1] In § 20, the interchange of rows or columns was one of the elementary operations. Thus there was no need to show that this operation can be derived from the others.

We thus consider an arbitrary n-by-n polynomial matrix $F(u) = (f_{ik}(u))$. Assume that not all $f_{ik}(u)$ are 0. Now consider all matrices which are equivalent to $F(u)$. We then find the least possible degree of all polynomials $\neq 0$ appearing in any of these matrices. Let $G(u) = (g_{ik}(u))$ be one such matrix. We may assume that $g_{11}(u)$ is the polynomial of least degree since otherwise this may be achieved by suitable interchanges of rows or of columns.

We prove, as in § 20, that *all of the polynomials in the first row and first column of* $G(u)$ *are divisible by* $g_{11}(u)$. For let $g_{ik}(u)$ be an element of the first row. Then we may divide by $g_{11}(u)$ to obtain an equation of the form

$$g_{1k}(u) = g_{11}(u) \cdot q(u) + r(u). \tag{2}$$

The remainder $r(u)$ is either 0 or its degree is less than that of $g_{11}(u)$. If it were not 0, we could add $-q(u)$ times the first column to the k-th column and obtain the polynomial $r(u)$ in the first row and k-th column. But the degree of $r(u)$ is less than that of $g_{11}(u)$, which would contradict the choice of $g_{11}(u)$ as a polynomial of least degree appearing in any of the matrices equivalent to $F(u)$. Thus we must have $r(u) = 0$ in (2). Analogously we may prove this result for the first column.

From the above result we see that by addition of suitable multiples of the first row (column) to the other rows (columns) all of the first column (row) except $g_{11}(u)$ may be made equal to 0. We thus obtain a matrix of the form

$$\begin{pmatrix} g_{11}(u) & 0 & 0 & \cdots & 0 \\ 0 & h_{22}(u) & h_{23}(u) & \cdots & h_{2n}(u) \\ \cdot & \cdot & \cdot & \cdot & \cdot \\ 0 & h_{n2}(u) & h_{n3}(u) & \cdots & h_{nn}(u) \end{pmatrix} \tag{3}$$

where $h_{ik}(u)$ are certain polynomials.

We now easily see that $g_{11}(u)$ is a divisor of each of the polynomials of the matrix (3), and that this is so for any matrix equivalent to $F(u)$ whose first row and column agree with those of (3). The proof of this is similar to the corresponding proof in § 20 and depends again on the choice of minimal degree for $g_{11}(u)$.

If not all of the polynomials $h_{ik}(u)$ are 0, we proceed in the same way. By elementary operations on the $(n-1)$-by-$(n-1)$ matrix of the $h_{ik}(u)$ (considered as in § 20 as elementary operations on the matrix (3)) we may transform (3) into the matrix

$$
(4) \qquad \begin{pmatrix} g_{11}(u) & 0 & 0 & \cdots & 0 \\ 0 & h_{22}(u) & 0 & \cdots & 0 \\ 0 & 0 & l_{33}(u) & \cdots & l_{3n}(u) \\ \cdot & \cdot & \cdot & \cdot & \cdot \\ 0 & 0 & l_{n3}(u) & \cdots & l_{nn}(u) \end{pmatrix},
$$

where $h_{22}(u)$ divides all of the polynomials $l_{ik}(u)$:

By repeating this process sufficiently often, we can finally transform our matrix into

$$
(5) \qquad \begin{pmatrix} e_1(u) & & & & & & 0 \\ & e_2(u) & & & & & \\ & & \ddots & & & & \\ & & & e_r(u) & & & \\ & & & & 0 & & \\ & & & & & \ddots & \\ 0 & & & & & & 0 \end{pmatrix}
$$

where no $e_i(u)$ is 0. By construction of this matrix, $e_1(u)$ divides $e_2(u)$, $e_2(u)$ divides $e_3(u)$, and more generally, $e_i(u)$ divides $e_{i+1}(u)$ for $i = 1, 2, \ldots, r-1$ (cf. § 20).

Observe that our algorithm can actually be carried out, say as follows: If the polynomial of least degree in the given matrix $(f_{ik}(u))$ does not divide the remaining $f_{ik}(u)$, we can obtain by elementary operations, as above, an equivalent matrix containing a polynomial of smaller degree. We continue this until we obtain a polynomial dividing the remaining polynomials of the matrix. We bring this polynomial into the upper left-hand corner, and reduce the matrix to the form (3). We then apply the same process to the remaining $(n-1)$-by-$(n-1)$ matrix, and continue until the diagonalization is complete.

Since the rows of our matrix may be multiplied by any constants $\neq 0$, we may assume that the polynomials $e_1(u), e_2(u), \ldots, e_r(u)$ of the matrix (5) all have leading coefficient 1. Once this is done, the matrix is in a form which is characterized uniquely by its properties. The following arguments will prove the uniqueness of this form.

We consider, for a fixed $k \leqq n$, all the k-rowed subdeterminants of the polynomial matrix $F(u)$. All of these subdeterminants are polynomials in u. Let $d_k(u)$ be their greatest common divisor. If all of these determinants are 0, then $d_k(u)$ would be $= 0$. We also assume that the leading coefficient of $d_k(u)$ is 1, provided that $d_k(u) \neq 0$. Then we assert that $d_k(u)$ *is invariant under elementary operations.* This means that if $G(u)$ is equivalent to $F(u)$, and if $d_k'(u)$ is the greatest common divisor of all k-rowed subdeterminants of $G(u)$, then $d_k'(u) = d_k(u)$. It suffices, of course, to prove this for the case where $G(u)$ can be obtained from $F(u)$ by a single elementary operation.

To prove this, let $G(u)$ first be a polynomial matrix obtained from $F(u)$ by an elementary operation of type I. Thus a row of $F(u)$, say the i-th, has been multiplied by a constant $c \neq 0$. Now any k-rowed subdeterminant of $G(u)$ is either a k-rowed subdeterminant of $F(u)$, or else is obtained from one by multiplying one of its rows by c. This depends on whether or not elements of the i-th row of $F(u)$ appear in the given subdeterminant. Thus the k-rowed subdeterminants of $G(u)$ are precisely the k-rowed subdeterminants of $F(u)$ up to a constant factor (c or 1). But the determination of the greatest common divisor is independent of these constant factors, so that $d_k(u) = d_k'(u)$.

Next let $F(u)$ be carried into $G(u)$ by an elementary operation of type II. Let the h-th row be multiplied by $f(u)$ and then added to the i-th. Those k-rowed subdeterminants of $F(u)$ which contain no elements in the i-th row of $F(u)$ remain unchanged under the application of II to $F(u)$. Similarly the k-rowed subdeterminants which contain elements of both the i-th and the h-th rows of $F(u)$, do not change their value, since all that is happening to one such is that a multiple of one of its rows is added to another row.

On the other hand, consider a k-rowed subdeterminant D which contains elements of the i-th row but none of the h-th row of our matrix. Let, say,

$$D = \begin{vmatrix} \cdot & \cdot & \cdot & \cdot & \cdot & \cdot & \cdot & \cdot & \cdot & \cdot \\ f_{i\nu_1}(u) & & f_{i\nu_2}(u) & & \cdots & & f_{i\nu_k}(u) \\ \cdot & \cdot & \cdot & \cdot & \cdot & \cdot & \cdot & \cdot & \cdot & \cdot \\ \cdot & \cdot & \cdot & \cdot & \cdot & \cdot & \cdot & \cdot & \cdot & \cdot \end{vmatrix}.$$

Applying the elementary operation under consideration to $F(u)$, the value of D does change, but in a very simple way. Let D be that k-rowed determinant obtained from D by replacing the elements

$$f_{i\nu_1}(u), f_{i\nu_2}(u), \cdots, f_{i\nu_k}(u)$$

by the elements

$$f_{h\nu_1}(u), f_{h\nu_2}(u), \cdots, f_{h\nu_k}(u)$$

so that

$$\bar{D} = \begin{vmatrix} \cdot & \cdot & \cdot & \cdot & \cdot & \cdot & \cdot \\ f_{h\nu_1}(u) & f_{h\nu_2}(u) & \cdots & f_{h\nu_k}(u) \\ \cdot & \cdot & \cdot & \cdot & \cdot & \cdot & \cdot \\ \cdot & \cdot & \cdot & \cdot & \cdot & \cdot & \cdot \end{vmatrix}.$$

Except for a possible change in sign, $\bar{D}$ is a k-rowed subdeterminant of $F(u)$. By application of the operation of type II to $F(u)$, D is changed into

$$\begin{vmatrix} \cdot & \cdot & \cdot & \cdot & \cdot & \cdot & \cdot \\ f_{i\nu_1}(u) + f(u) \cdot f_{h\nu_1}(u) & \cdots & f_{i\nu_k}(u) + f(u) \cdot f_{h\nu_k}(u) \\ \cdot & \cdot & \cdot & \cdot & \cdot & \cdot & \cdot \\ \cdot & \cdot & \cdot & \cdot & \cdot & \cdot & \cdot \end{vmatrix},$$

where all of the elements denoted by dots remain unchanged. The value of this new determinant is $D + f(u) \cdot \bar{D}$.

In all cases we see that the polynomial $d_k(u)$ is a divisor of the k-rowed subdeterminants of the transformed matrix $G(u)$ obtained from $F(u)$ by elementary operation II. Thus $d_k(u)$ divides $d_k'(u)$.

But $F(u)$ can conversely be obtained from $G(u)$ by an elementary operation of type II, namely by adding $-f(u)$ times the h-th row of $G(u)$ to its i-th row. Thus, by the above result, $d_k'(u)$ divides $d_k(u)$. Hence the two polynomials $d_k(u)$ and $d_k'(u)$ divide one another, and thus differ at most by a constant, non-zero factor. Since both have leading coefficient 1 (or both vanish), they are equal.

The equality of $d_k(u)$ and $d_k'(u)$ under elementary operations of type I* and II* can be proved either as above, or by consideration of the transposed matrix.[2]

We combine these results in the following theorem:

THEOREM 1. *Let $F(u)$ and $G(u)$ be two equivalent polynomial matrices. Then the greatest common divisor of the k-rowed subdeterminants of $F(u)$ is equal to the greatest common divisor of the k-rowed subdeterminants of $G(u)$.*

Now let us take for $G(u)$ the particular matrix (5), obtained from $F(u)$ by elementary operations. We wish to determine the greatest

[2] Let $F'(u)$ and $G'(u)$ be the transposes of $F(u)$ and $G(u)$ respectively. Let $F(u)$ be transformed into $G(u)$ by an elementary operation I*, II*. Then $F'(u)$ is transformed into $G'(u)$ by the corresponding operation I or II. Now $d_k(u)$ is invariant under the change from $F(u)$ to $F'(u)$ and, by the above proof, it does not change as $F'(u)$ changes to $G'(u)$ and is finally unchanged by the transition from $G'(u)$ to $G(u)$. Consequently $d_k(u)$ is invariant with respect to the elementary operations I*, II*.

common divisor $d_k(u)$ of all of the k-rowed subdeterminants of (5). If $k > r$, then all of these determinants are 0. If $k \leqq r$, we easily see that the only non-zero k-rowed subdeterminants are those which are of the form

$$(6) \qquad \begin{vmatrix} e_{\nu_1}(u) & & & 0 \\ & e_{\nu_2}(u) & & \\ & & \ddots & \\ 0 & & & e_{\nu_k}(u) \end{vmatrix}$$

where $1 \leqq \nu_1 < \nu_2 < \ldots < \nu_k \leqq r$. The determinant (6) is equal to the product

$$(7) \qquad e_{\nu_1}(u) \cdot e_{\nu_2}(u) \cdot \ \ldots \ \cdot e_{\nu_k}(u).$$

One of the products (7) is

$$(8) \qquad e_1(u) \cdot e_2(u) \cdot \ \ldots \ \cdot e_k(u).$$

Since $e_i(u)$ is a divisor of $e_{i+1}(u)$, and since in (6) we have $1 \leqq \nu_1$, $2 \leqq \nu_2$, $\ldots$, $k \leqq \nu_k$, we see that in (7), $e_i(u)$ is a divisor of $e_{\nu_i}(u)$ for $i = 1, 2, \ldots, k$. Thus the product (8) is a common divisor of all products (7), i.e. of all k-rowed subdeterminants of (5). But (8) itself is such a determinant, so that it *itself* is their greatest common divisor. Finally, all of the $e_i(u)$ have leading coefficient 1, so that this is true of the product (8). Hence (8) is the desired polynomial $d_k(u)$, so that for $k = 1, 2, \ldots, r$ we have

$$(9) \qquad d_k(u) = e_1(u) e_2(u) \ldots e_k(u)$$

and for $k = r + 1, r + 2, \ldots, n$ we have

$$(10) \qquad d_k(u) = 0.$$

By (9) we also have

$$(11) \qquad d_{k-1}(u) = e_1(u)\ e_2(u) \ldots e_{k-1}(u).$$

Comparing (9) and (11) for $k = 2, 3, \ldots, r$ gives

$$(12) \qquad e_k(u) = \frac{d_k(u)}{d_{k-1}(u)}.$$

Formula (12) also holds for $k = 1$ if we set $d_0(u) = 1$.

By Theorem 1, $d_k(u)$ is also the greatest common divisor of all of the k-rowed subdeterminants of the original matrix $F(u)$. Thus the polynomials $d_k(u)$ are uniquely determined by $F(u)$; and considering (12), so are the polynomials $e_k(u)$. Thus the matrix (5) is uniquely determined. We have proved

THEOREM 2. *For any given polynomial matrix* $F(u)$, *there is one and only one polynomial matrix* $G(u)$ *with the following properties:*

1. $G(u) \sim F(u)$;
2. $G(u)$ *is of the form* (5);
3. $e_i(u)$ *divides* $e_{i+1}(u)$ *for* $i = 1, 2, \ldots, r-1$;
4. *the polynomials* $e_i(u)$ *all have leading coefficient* 1.

If $r < n$ in (5) we set[3]

$$e_{r+1}(u) = e_{r+2}(u) = \ldots = e_n(u) = 0.$$

By (10), equation (9) also holds for $k = r+1, r+2, \ldots, n$. We call the polynomials $e_1(u), e_2(u), \ldots, e_n(u)$ which are uniquely determined by $F(u)$ *the* ***elementary divisors*** *of the matrix* $F(u)$.

From Theorem 1 and formulas (12) we see that equivalent polynomial matrices have the same elementary divisors. Conversely, suppose that the matrices $F(u)$ and $G(u)$ have the same sequence of elementary divisors.[4] Then $F(u)$ and $G(u)$ can both be brought into the same form (5) by a finite number of elementary operations, i.e. they are both equivalent to the same matrix (5). Thus $F(u) \sim G(u)$. We thus have

THEOREM 3. *Two polynomial matrices are equivalent if and only if they have the same sequence of elementary divisors.*

By equation (9) and Theorem 3, it is clear that a necessary and sufficient condition that two polynomial matrices be equivalent is that their corresponding $d_k(u)$ be equal.

We will need a further criterion for equivalence of polynomial matrices. To obtain this, we shall first show that each elementary operation on a matrix may be performed by multiplying the matrix by certain other matrices. We first consider the matrix A which is obtained from the n-by-n identity matrix by multiplying its i-th row by a constant $c \neq 0$. A has the form

---

[3] Observe that the polynomials $e_1(u), e_2(u), \cdots, e_r(u)$ are $\neq 0$ by definition.

[4] The order of the elementary divisors is prescribed by the condition 3. of Theorem 2.

i-th column

(13)
$$A = \begin{pmatrix} 1 & & & & \vdots & & & 0 \\ & \ddots & & & \vdots & & & \\ & & 1 & 0 & & & & \\ \cdots & \cdots & 0 & c & 0 & \cdots & \cdots & \\ & & 0 & 1 & & & & \\ & & & & \vdots & \ddots & & \\ 0 & & & & \vdots & & 1 & \end{pmatrix} \quad i\text{-th row}$$

Let us multiply this matrix on the left or on the right by a given n-by-n polynomial matrix $F(u)$. We then see that the matrix $A \cdot F(u)$ is obtained from $F(u)$ by multiplying the i-th row of $F(u)$ by c, and the matrix $F(u) \cdot A$ is obtained from $F(u)$ by multiplying the i-th column of $F(u)$ by c. *Therefore elementary operation I can be performed by left multiplication of the given polynomial matrix by A; operation I*, by right multiplication by A.*

Let B be the matrix which is obtained from the identity matrix by replacing the 0 in the i-th row and k-th column $(i \neq k)$ by an arbitrary polynomial $f(u)$. Thus

i-th column k-th column

(14)
$$B = \begin{pmatrix} 1 & & \vdots & & \vdots & & 0 \\ & \ddots & \vdots & & \vdots & & \\ \cdots & \cdots & 1 & \cdots & f(u) & \cdots & \cdots \\ & & \vdots & \ddots & \vdots & & \\ \cdots & \cdots & 0 & \cdots & 1 & \cdots & \cdots \\ & & \vdots & & \vdots & \ddots & \\ 0 & & \vdots & & \vdots & & 1 \end{pmatrix} \begin{matrix} \\ \\ i\text{-th row} \\ \\ k\text{-th row} \\ \\ \\ \end{matrix}$$

Now consider the matrices $B \cdot F(u)$ and $F(u) \cdot B$. We easily see that the matrix $B \cdot F(u)$ is obtained from $F(u)$ by multiplying the k-th row of $F(u)$ by $f(u)$ and adding the result to the i-th row, i.e. *by an elementary operation II*; similarly, *the matrix $F(u) \cdot B$ is obtained from $F(u)$ by an elementary operation II**.

It now follows that if a polynomial matrix $G(u)$ is obtained from $F(u)$ by a finite succession of elementary operations, then $G(u)$ can be obtained from $F(u)$ by successive multiplications of $F(u)$ by suitable matrices of the forms (13) and (14). Thus we must have an equation of the form

$$G(u) = M_1 M_2 \ldots M_r F(u) \cdot N_1 N_2 \ldots N_s, \tag{15}$$

where the M_i and N_i are polynomial matrices[5] of the forms (13) and (14).

Now set

$$M(u) = M_1 M_2 \ldots M_r, \quad N(u) = N_1 N_2 \ldots N_s. \tag{16}$$

By calculating the determinants of (13) and (14) we obtain

$$|A| = c, \quad |B| = 1 \tag{17}$$

i.e. $|A|$ and $|B|$ are polynomials of degree zero. By (16), this is also true of $|M(u)|$ and $|N(u)|$. *Thus if $F(u)$ and $G(u)$ are equivalent, there is a relation of the form*

$$G(u) = M(u) \cdot F(u) \cdot N(u), \tag{18}$$

where $M(u)$ and $N(u)$ are polynomial matrices whose determinants are non-zero constants.

The converse of this result is also true.

To prove this, suppose we have an equation of the form (18). We want to prove that $F(u) \sim G(u)$. For this purpose, we shall show that every polynomial matrix with a constant, non-zero determinant is a product of matrices of the form (13) and (14), which would prove that a relation of the type (15) exists between $F(u)$ and $G(u)$, and thus that $F(u) \sim G(u)$.

In order to prove this factorization of $M(u)$, we calculate the elementary divisors of this matrix. We employ formula (9) of p. 350. First $d_n(u) = 1$, since $|M(u)|$ is a constant $\neq 0$. It then follows from equation (9) that all the elementary divisors $e_1(u), e_2(u), \ldots, e_n(u)$ are different from 0 and that they all have degree 0. Thus

$$e_1(u) = e_2(u) = \ldots = e_n(u) = 1. \tag{19}$$

Hence the matrix of the form (5) to which $M(u)$ is equivalent is in this case, by (19),

[5] Of course the matrices of the form (13) can also be considered to be polynomial matrices. They contain only polynomials of degree 0 as their elements.

$$\begin{pmatrix} 1 & & & 0 \\ & 1 & & \\ & & \ddots & \\ 0 & & & 1 \end{pmatrix} = E.$$

Hence, as has just been proved, there is an equation relating $M(u)$ and E of the form

$$M(u) = M_1 \cdot M_2 \cdot \ldots \cdot M_r \cdot E \cdot N_1 \cdot N_2 \cdot \ldots \cdot N_s \tag{20}$$

where the M_i and N_i are polynomial matrices of the forms (13) and (14). But equation (20) is the desired factorization and our proof is complete.

We combine these results in

THEOREM 4. *Two polynomial matrices $F(u)$ and $G(u)$ are equivalent if and only if an equation of the form* (18) *holds, where $M(u)$ and $N(u)$ are polynomial matrices having constant, non-zero determinants.*

Exercises

1. Which of the following matrices are equivalent?

$$A = \begin{pmatrix} 1 & -u & 0 & 2 \\ 0 & 2 & -1-u & -2 \\ u & -1-u^2 & 1 & 2+u \\ 1 & -u^2 & 0 & 1+u \end{pmatrix}, \quad B = \begin{pmatrix} 1-u^2 & 1-u & -1 & 2u-2 \\ -u & -1 & 1 & 2 \\ -2 & -1-u & 2+u & 4 \\ -1-u & -2 & 3 & 5-u \end{pmatrix}$$

$$C = \begin{pmatrix} 1 & -u & u-1 & 0 \\ 0 & u & -1 & 1-u \\ u-1 & 0 & 1 & -u \\ -1 & 1-u & 0 & u \end{pmatrix}.$$

For the pairs of equivalent ones among them, determine the factors $M(u)$ and $N(u)$ of Theorem 4.

2. All of the theorems of this section carry over to matrices whose elements are integers, where the elementary operations on such matrices have been defined in § 20. Carry this through. Which matrices take the place of the polynomial matrices with constant determinants in Theorem 4?

As an application use the theory of elementary divisors to determine the greatest common divisor of all the two-by-two and of all the three-by-three subdeterminants of the matrix

$$\begin{pmatrix} 11 & 12 & -7 & 1 \\ -2 & -4 & 4 & 2 \\ 6 & 8 & 0 & -2 \\ 3 & 4 & -1 & -1 \end{pmatrix}.$$

§ 26. The Normal Form

We now approach the problem outlined at the beginning of § 25, and return to our discussion of a vector space L (over a field F). We begin by further generalizations of some concepts of § 20.[1] The first concept to be generalized will be the concept of a "system of generators" ("generating system"). Thus far, this term has been used in two connections, namely for vector spaces and for abelian groups. Let us compare the two uses of this term to see what they have in common. If we consider a vector space L as an abelian group in which vector addition is taken as its group operation, then a generating system in the sense of a vector space is not, in general, a generating system in the sense of abelian groups. But the converse is true. For what is the form of the "power products" considered in § 20, in the case of our present abelian group? They represent linear combinations of a finite number of vectors with integral coefficients (the "exponents" of the power product). A generating system in the sense of abelian groups is a generating system in the sense of vector spaces since its integral linear combinations alone will span the vector space. However a generating system $\mathfrak{a}_1, \mathfrak{a}_2, \ldots, \mathfrak{a}_k$ in the sense of vector space theory has the property that any vector of L can be expressed as some linear combination $\sum_{i=1}^{k} \lambda_i \mathfrak{a}_i$ with arbitrary λ_i from the field F. The second concept is a generalization of the first, because any generating system of the first kind (if such exist) is also one of the second,[2] while the converse is not in general true.

But not even the second concept of "generating system" is general enough for our present purposes. We shall extend it by using some fixed linear transformation σ on L, as follows:

A system of vectors $\mathfrak{a}_1, \mathfrak{a}_2, \ldots, \mathfrak{a}_k$ is called a (finite) *σ-generating system of* L if for every vector $\mathfrak{x}$ of L there exist polynomials $f_1(u)$, $f_2(u), \ldots, f_k(u)$ such that the relation

---

[1] We deal here with a special case of an "abelian group with operators," which W. Krull has introduced and applied to matrix theory. (Cf. W. Krull, *Theorie und Anwendung der verallgemeinerten Abelschen Gruppen*, Sitzungsber. der Heidelberger Akad. d. Wiss., 1926, p. 3.)

[2] For, a product $n \cdot \mathfrak{a}$, in which a vector $\mathfrak{a}$ is multiplied by an integer n, can also be considered as a product of $\mathfrak{a}$ with an element of F, namely the element obtained by adding the unity to itself n times (cf. p. 200). An analogous statement holds for integral linear combinations of vectors.

(1) $$\mathfrak{x} = \sum_{i=1}^{k} f_i(\sigma)(\mathfrak{a}_i)$$

holds.

The linear transformation σ is an essential part of this definition, and we have therefore included a reference to it in the name of this new concept.

In a corresponding manner, we generalize the concept of a "basis" of an abelian group, as follows:

A *σ-basis of* L is a σ-generating system $\mathfrak{a}_1, \mathfrak{a}_2, \ldots, \mathfrak{a}_k$ such that any two representations of a vector $\mathfrak{x}$ in the form (1) are equivalent. This means that if

$$\mathfrak{x} = \sum_{i=1}^{k} f_i(\sigma)(\mathfrak{a}_i) = \sum_{i=1}^{k} g_i(\sigma)(\mathfrak{a}_i)$$

then $f_i(\sigma)(\mathfrak{a}_i) = g_i(\sigma)(\mathfrak{a}_i)$ for all i. Exactly as on p. 261 ff. we see that it suffices to say that any two representations of the null vector are equivalent, i.e. that if $\sum_{i=1}^{n} f_i(\sigma)(\mathfrak{a}_i) = 0$ then $f_i(\sigma)(\mathfrak{a}_i) = 0$ for all i.

In strict analogy with the method of proof in § 20 we shall construct a σ-basis of L for any given linear transformation σ. The existence of a finite generating system was one of the hypotheses in the statement of the Basis Theorem. This hypothesis is satisfied trivially in the present case. For example, any vector basis of L in the usual sense is a σ-generating system of L.

Thus let a definite basis $\mathfrak{a}_1, \mathfrak{a}_2, \ldots, \mathfrak{a}_n$ of the vector space L be given. To carry out a construction as in § 20, we shall need as our starting point a matrix which will correspond to the fundamental matrix of § 20. A fundamental matrix is obtained from the exponent vectors of relations among the generators. We shall now construct a corresponding matrix for our σ-generating system and σ-basis. Such relations will be equations of the form (1) in which $\mathfrak{x} = 0$.

We can obtain such relations from the matrix $A = (a_{ik})$ of σ with respect to the basis $\mathfrak{a}_1, \mathfrak{a}_2, \ldots, \mathfrak{a}_n$. For by the law of construction of this matrix we have $\sigma(\mathfrak{a}_k) = \sum_{i=1}^{n} a_{ik}\mathfrak{a}_i$, that is

(2) $$\sum_{i=1}^{n} (a_{ik}\sigma^0 - \delta_{ik}\sigma)(\mathfrak{a}_i) = 0.$$

Now we write the coefficients of these relations as the rows of a matrix, where we formally replace σ by the variable[3] u, obtaining the matrix

$$(3) \qquad \begin{pmatrix} a_{11}-u & a_{21} & \cdots & a_{n1} \\ a_{12} & a_{22}-u & \cdots & a_{n2} \\ \cdot & \cdot & \cdot & \cdot \\ a_{1n} & a_{2n} & \cdots & a_{nn}-u \end{pmatrix} = A' - uE.$$

The matrix (3), and its transpose[4] as well, is called the **characteristic matrix** *of* σ *in the coordinate system* $[\mathfrak{a}_1, \mathfrak{a}_2, \ldots, \mathfrak{a}_n]$.

It is not hard to prove that the second defining property of a fundamental matrix is satisfied for (3), namely that every "relation" among the σ-generators $\mathfrak{a}_i$ is a consequence of equations (2) (cf. exercise 8). But we shall not have to make use of this. Instead, we note that the determinant of (3) is a polynomial of the n-th degree (the characteristic polynomial of σ), which will serve the same purpose.

In the proof of the Basis Theorem in § 20, we used the fact that a fundamental matrix goes into another fundamental matrix under elementary operations, perhaps with respect to a different generating system. We shall now prove a similar statement about polynomial matrices equivalent (in the sense of § 25) to the characteristic matrix of σ. Since the determinants of two equivalent polynomial matrices have the same degree (for they differ at most by a constant factor), we need only prove

THEOREM 1. *If the polynomial matrix* $F(u) = (f_{ik}(u))$ *is equivalent to the characteristic matrix of* σ, *then there is a* σ*-generating system* $\mathfrak{b}_1, \mathfrak{b}_2, \ldots, \mathfrak{b}_n$ *in* L *such that the equation*

$$(4) \qquad \sum_{k=1}^{n} f_{ik}(\sigma)(\mathfrak{b}_k) = 0$$

holds for every i.

Proof: It suffices to show that if Theorem 1 is true for a polynomial matrix $F(u)$, then it is true for every polynomial matrix $F'(u)$ which is obtained from $F(u)$ by a single elementary operation. For by repeated application of this result, the validity of Theorem 1 will follow for any polynomial matrix arising from the characteristic matrix by a finite sequence of elementary operations.

---

[3] We use this substitution since we wish to apply the results of the preceding section to (3). The definition of equality differs for polynomials in one variable from that for polynomials in a matrix.

[4] The matrix (3) is equivalent in the sense of § 8 to its transpose, since every polynomial matrix is equivalent to its transpose. Why is this so?

Thus let $F(u) = (f_{ik}(u))$ be a polynomial matrix for which Theorem 1 holds, and let $\mathfrak{b}_1, \mathfrak{b}_2, \ldots, \mathfrak{b}_n$ be a fixed σ-generating system for which equations (4) hold.

We shall consider, one after another, all possible elementary operations which can be applied to $F(u)$.

If the elementary operation applied to $F(u)$ is I or II then the old σ-generating system $\mathfrak{b}_1, \mathfrak{b}_2, \ldots, \mathfrak{b}_n$ satisfies the conditions of Theorem 1 with respect to the resulting matrix $F'(u)$. For suppose that $F'(u)$ is obtained from $F(u)$ by, say, multiplying the h-th row of $F(u)$ by a constant $c \neq 0$. Then the same equations (4) hold for $F'(u)$ except that the h-th equation is multiplied by c. If operation II is applied, say by adding $f(u)$ times the j-th row to the h-th row, then the same equations (4) will hold for $F'(u)$, since by multiplying the j-th equation of (4) by $f(\sigma)$ and adding it to the h-th equation, we obtain, as the only new relation for $F'(u)$, the following:

$$\sum_{i=1}^{n} [f_{hi}(\sigma) + f(\sigma)\, f_{ji}(\sigma)]\, (\mathfrak{b}_i) = 0.$$

For the elementary operations I*, II*, the system $\mathfrak{b}_1, \mathfrak{b}_2, \ldots, \mathfrak{b}_n$ must be replaced by a suitable new σ-generating system. First consider I*. Suppose the h-th column of $F(u)$ is multiplied by a constant $c \neq 0$. Replace $\mathfrak{b}_h$ by $\frac{\mathfrak{b}_h}{c}$, in the sequence $\mathfrak{b}_1, \mathfrak{b}_2, \ldots, \mathfrak{b}_n$. The resulting system is the desired system of vectors. To begin with, it is evidently itself a σ-generating system of L.

The equations corresponding to (4), formed with the rows of the new matrix, are

$$f_{i1}(\sigma)(\mathfrak{b}_1) + \cdots + f_{i,h-1}(\sigma)(\mathfrak{b}_{h-1}) + c \cdot f_{ih}(\sigma)\left(\frac{\mathfrak{b}_h}{c}\right) + f_{i,h+1}(\sigma)(\mathfrak{b}_{h+1}) + \cdots$$
$$\cdots + f_{in}(\sigma)(\mathfrak{b}_n) = 0.$$

But these equations are true by virtue of (4).

Finally assume that $F'(u)$ is obtained from $F(u)$ by adding $f(u)$ times the j-th column to the h-th column. Then a σ-generating system which satisfies the conditions of Theorem 1, is obtained by replacing $\mathfrak{b}_j$ by $\mathfrak{b}_j - f(\sigma)(\mathfrak{b}_h)$ in the system $\mathfrak{b}_1, \mathfrak{b}_2, \ldots, \mathfrak{b}_n$. It is certainly a σ-generating system, since an equation of the form

$$\mathfrak{x} = \sum_{i=1}^{n} p_i(\sigma)(\mathfrak{b}_i)$$

implies

$$\mathfrak{x} = \sum_{\substack{i=1 \\ i \neq h,j}}^{n} p_i(\sigma)(\mathfrak{b}_i) + [p_h(\sigma) + f(\sigma) p_j(\sigma)](\mathfrak{b}_h) + p_j(\sigma)(\mathfrak{b}_j - f(\sigma)(\mathfrak{b}_h)).$$

Moreover the equations corresponding to (4) for $F'(u)$ follow from (4), since

$$\sum_{\substack{k=1 \\ k \neq h,j}}^{n} f_{ik}(\sigma)(\mathfrak{b}_k) + [f_{ih}(\sigma) + f(\sigma) f_{ij}(\sigma)](\mathfrak{b}_h) + f_{ij}(\sigma)(\mathfrak{b}_j - f(\sigma)(\mathfrak{b}_h)) = 0.$$

The construction of a σ-basis now proceeds along the lines of § 20. First, transform the characteristic matrix (3) into diagonal form by means of elementary operations, obtaining, say,

$$(5) \qquad \begin{pmatrix} e_1(u) & & & 0 \\ & e_2(u) & & \\ & & \ddots & \\ 0 & & & e_n(u) \end{pmatrix},$$

where the $e_i(u)$ are the elementary divisors. Let $\mathfrak{b}_1, \mathfrak{b}_2, \ldots, \mathfrak{b}_n$ be a σ-generating system which corresponds to (5) in the sense of Theorem 1. Then the following equations, analogous to (4), will hold:

$$(6) \qquad e_i(\sigma)(\mathfrak{b}_i) = 0.$$

We shall prove that the $\mathfrak{b}_i$ *form a σ-basis of* L. To prove this, let

$$(7) \qquad \mathfrak{x} = \sum_{i=1}^{n} f_i(\sigma)(\mathfrak{b}_i)$$

be a representation of an arbitrary vector $\mathfrak{x}$ of L. Divide $f_i(u)$ by $e_i(u)$ and determine the remainder, say $r_i(u) = f_i(u) - h_i(u)\, e_i(u)$. Either $r_i(u)$ vanishes or its degree is less than that of $e_i(u)$. By (6) we have $h_i(\sigma)\, e_i(\sigma)(\mathfrak{b}_i) = 0$. Subtracting this from (7) for all i, we obtain

$$(8) \qquad \mathfrak{x} = \sum_{i=1}^{n} r_i(\sigma)(\mathfrak{b}_i).$$

Let ν_i be the degree of $e_i(u)$. Then each of the summands $r_i(\sigma)(\mathfrak{b}_i)$ in (8) is a linear combination of the vectors

$$(9) \qquad \mathfrak{b}_i,\ \sigma(\mathfrak{b}_i),\ \cdots,\ \sigma^{\nu_i - 1}(\mathfrak{b}_i)$$

with coefficients in F. For since the degree of $r_i(u)$ is less than ν_i, we may write $r_i(u) = c_{i0} + c_{i1} u + \cdots + c_{i,\nu_i-1} u^{\nu_i - 1}$ so that

$$r_i(\sigma)(\mathfrak{b}_i) = c_{i0}\, \mathfrak{b}_i + c_{i1} \sigma(\mathfrak{b}_i) + \cdots + c_{i,\nu_i-1} \sigma^{\nu_i-1}(\mathfrak{b}_i).$$

is the desired linear combination. Thus, the right-hand side of (8) may also be considered as a linear combination of the vectors

$$\mathfrak{b}_1, \sigma(\mathfrak{b}_1), \cdots, \sigma^{\nu_1-1}(\mathfrak{b}_1); \mathfrak{b}_2, \sigma(\mathfrak{b}_2), \cdots, \sigma^{\nu_2-1}(\mathfrak{b}_2); \cdots; \mathfrak{b}_n, \sigma(\mathfrak{b}_n), \cdots, \sigma^{\nu_n-1}(\mathfrak{b}_n)$$

with coefficients in F.

But we know that the determinant of (5), i.e. the product of the $e_i(u)$ has degree n. Thus

$$\nu_1 + \nu_2 + \ldots + \nu_n = n. \tag{10}$$

It may of course happen that some of the ν_i vanish. But in this case the corresponding $e_i(\sigma)$ would be the identity transformation so that we would have $\mathfrak{b}_i = 0$ by (6). But those $e_i(u)$ which are of degree 0 must be the first ones in the sequence of the $e_i(u)$ since $e_{i+1}(u)$ is always a multiple of $e_i(u)$. Suppose that $\nu_1 = \nu_2 = \ldots = \nu_{h-1} = 0$, $\nu_h > 0$. Since L is spanned by the vectors

$$\begin{aligned} \mathfrak{b}_h, \ \sigma(\mathfrak{b}_h), \ \cdots, \ \sigma^{\nu_h-1}(\mathfrak{b}_h); \ \mathfrak{b}_{h+1}, \ \sigma(\mathfrak{b}_{h+1}), \ \cdots, \ \sigma^{\nu_{h+1}-1}(\mathfrak{b}_{h+1}); \ \cdots \\ \cdots; \ \mathfrak{b}_n, \ \sigma(\mathfrak{b}_n), \ \cdots, \ \sigma^{\nu_n-1}(\mathfrak{b}_n), \end{aligned} \tag{11}$$

and because of (10), we see that (11) consists of n linearly independent vectors (for, n was the dimension of L). They thus form a basis of L in the usual sense.

We can now prove that the σ-generating system $\mathfrak{b}_1, \mathfrak{b}_2, \ldots, \mathfrak{b}_n$ belonging to the matrix (5) is a σ-basis. This means that if $\mathfrak{x} = 0$ in (7), then $f_i(\sigma)(\mathfrak{b}_i) = 0$ for all i. This is trivial for $i < h$ since, in this case $\mathfrak{b}_i = 0$. But from (8) (for $\mathfrak{x} = 0$) it follows that all of the coefficients of $r_i(u)$ vanish for $i \geqq h$, since the vectors (11) are linearly independent. Thus $f_i(u)$ is a multiple of $e_i(u)$ and so by (6), $f_i(\sigma)(\mathfrak{b}_i) = 0$ holds also for $i \geqq h$. Thus our assertion is proved.

What have we accomplished towards finding a normal form for the matrix of σ? This normal form is obtained by finding the matrix of σ with respect to the basis (11) of L. As we know, the first column of this matrix consists of the components of $\sigma(\mathfrak{b}_h)$. But this vector is precisely the second basis vector of (11). Thus $\sigma(\mathfrak{b}_h)$ has the components $\{0, 1, 0, \ldots, 0\}$ with respect to (11). Analogous results hold for all columns through the $(\nu_h - 1)$-st. The ν_h-th column consists of the components of the vector $\sigma(\sigma^{\nu_h-1}(\mathfrak{b}_h)) = \sigma^{\nu_h}(\mathfrak{b}_h)$. Since $\sigma^{\nu_h}(\mathfrak{b}_h)$

is not one of the basis vectors (11), we must seek a representation of it in terms of the basis (11). But this is easy, using (6). Let, say,

$$e_i(u) = a_{i1} + a_{i2}u + \cdots + a_{i\nu_i}u^{\nu_i - 1} + u^{\nu_i}$$

(Recall that the elementary divisors of a polynomial matrix have leading coefficient 1.) Applying (6) for $i = h$, we obtain

$$\sigma^{\nu_h}(\mathfrak{b}_h) = -a_{h1}\,\mathfrak{b}_h - a_{h2}\,\sigma(\mathfrak{b}_h) - \cdots - a_{h\nu_h}\,\sigma^{\nu_h - 1}(\mathfrak{b}_h),$$

showing that the ν_h-th column of our matrix will have the elements $-a_{h1}, -a_{h2}, \cdots, -a_{h\nu_h}$, followed by zeros. The remaining columns of the matrix are found in the very same way.[5] The $(\nu_h + \nu_{h+1})$-st, $(\nu_h + \nu_{h+1} + \nu_{h+2})$-nd etc. columns contain the negatives of the coefficients of $e_{h+1}(u)$, $e_{h+2}(u)$, etc. in their proper order. We finally obtain the matrix

$$\left(\begin{array}{cccc|cccc|c|cccc}
0 & \cdots & 0 & -a_{h,1} & & & & & & & & & \\
1 & \ddots & \vdots & \vdots & & & & & & & & 0 & \\
\vdots & \ddots & 0 & -a_{h,\nu_h-1} & & & & & & & & & \\
0 & \cdots & 1 & -a_{h,\nu_h} & & & & & & & & & \\
\hline
 & & & & 0 & \cdots & 0 & -a_{h+1,1} & & & & & \\
 & & & & 1 & \ddots & \vdots & \vdots & & & & & \\
 & & & & \vdots & \ddots & 0 & -a_{h+1,\nu_{h+1}-1} & & & & & \\
 & & & & 0 & \cdots & 1 & -a_{h+1,\nu_{h+1}} & & & & & \\
\hline
 & & & & & & & & \ddots & & & & \\
\hline
 & & & & & & & & & 0 & \cdots & 0 & -a_{n,1} \\
 & & & & & & & & & 1 & \ddots & \vdots & \vdots \\
 & & & & & & & & & \vdots & \ddots & 0 & -a_{n,\nu_n-1} \\
0 & & & & & & & & & 0 & \cdots & 1 & -a_{n,\nu_n}
\end{array}\right)$$

Along the principal diagonal we have square boxes of the form

[5] Observe the position of the individual components. The components of the image of $\mathfrak{b}_{h+1}$, i.e. the components of $\sigma(\mathfrak{b}_{h+1})$, are

$$\underbrace{0, 0, \cdots, 0}_{(\nu_h+1)\text{ times}}, 1, 0, \cdots, 0.$$

For, the vector $\sigma(\mathfrak{b}_{h+1})$ is the $(\nu_h + 2)$-nd vector in the sequence (11).

$$(13)\qquad \begin{vmatrix} 0 & \cdots\cdots & 0 & -a_{i,1} \\ 1 & 0 & \vdots & \vdots \\ \vdots & 1 \;\ddots & \vdots & \vdots \\ \vdots & \ddots & 0 & -a_{i,\nu_i-1} \\ 0 & \cdots\cdots & 1 & -a_{i,\nu_i} \end{vmatrix}$$

one right after the other. All entries outside these boxes are zeros. The first box has ν_h rows, the second, ν_{h+1} rows, etc. The individual boxes have the negatives of the coefficients of one of the elementary divisors $e_i(u)$ up to but not including the leading coefficient, in its last column, and a sequence of ones just below the main diagonal. The remaining entries of the box are zeros.[6]

The boxes have a simple significance. As an incidental result of our above discussion, we found that for any definite $i \geqq h$ the images of the vectors (9) are linear combinations of these vectors. Thus the vector space L_i spanned by them is invariant with respect to σ. The box corresponding to (9) is therefore simply the matrix of the linear transformation induced by σ on L_i.

The matrix (12) is completely determined by the coefficients of the elementary divisors of the characteristic matrix of σ. Hence it is known once these elementary divisors are given. The elementary divisors are in turn uniquely determined by the characteristic matrix (§ 25, Theorem 2). Now offhand it might still seem possible that the different characteristic matrices of σ in various coordinate systems have different elementary divisors. However, this can not be the case, as will be shown by a simple consideration based on Theorem 4 of § 25. In fact, let A, B be matrices of σ in two different coordinate systems. Then an equation of the form $TAT^{-1} = B$ holds. Thus we must also have

$$T(A - uE)T^{-1} = B - uE$$

for the characteristic matrices $A - uE$ and $B - uE$. But this equation implies, by § 25, Theorem 4, that the matrices $A - uE$ and $B - uE$ are equivalent, and thus have the same elementary divisors.

Thus among all the matrices belonging to a given linear transformation σ in all possible coordinate systems, we have singled out a unique one which is in a simple form and which is easily calculated by means of the elementary divisors of the characteristic matrix of σ.

---

[6] If $\nu_h = 1$, then the first box takes on the form $\begin{vmatrix} -a_{h1} \end{vmatrix}$.

We therefore call the matrix (12) the ***normal form***[7] *of the matrix of* σ.

In order to actually produce the normal form of a transformation σ we need only know the elementary divisors of the characteristic matrix of σ; knowledge of the basis (11) is not necessary. We required this basis only for the proof that there exists a coordinate system in which the matrix (12) corresponds to σ.

The fact that the matrix of a linear transformation σ may be brought into normal form by passing to a suitable coordinate system, may be expressed entirely in terms of matrix terminology. Our result then reads as follows:

Every matrix A can be be transformed[8] *by a non-singular matrix into the normal form* (12) *which is formed from the coefficients of the elementary divisors of its characteristic matrix* $A - uE$.

Consequences

Using the normal form, we may now give a criterion for two matrices A and B to be transformable into one another, i.e. for A and B to be matrices of the *same* linear transformation in two different coordinate systems. This criterion is

THEOREM 2. *Two matrices A and B can be transformed into one another by a non-singular matrix if and only if their characteristic matrices* $A - uE$ *and* $B - uE$ *have the same elementary divisors.*

Proof: We already know that this condition is necessary (p. 362). Now assume that $A - uE$ and $B - uE$ have the same elementary divisors. Then A and B both have the same normal form N, since the normal form is completely determined by the elementary divisors of a matrix. Thus, there are two non-singular matrices T_1 and T_2 such that

(14) $$N = T_1 \cdot A \cdot T_1^{-1} = T_2 \cdot B \cdot T_2^{-1}.$$

It then follows that

(15) $$B = T_2^{-1} \cdot T_1 \cdot A \cdot (T_2^{-1} \cdot T_1)^{-1},$$

where $T_2^{-1} \cdot T_1$ is also a non-singular matrix.

---

[7] G. Kowalewski, who introduced this normal form (Leipziger Berichte, 1917, p. 325 ff.) called it the *"natural" normal form*. The transpose of (12) is also found in the literature as a normal form. Theorem 2 below shows that the transpose of (12) also represents σ. Cf. p. 370 for the *"Jordan normal form."*

[8] Do not confuse this "transformation" with the elementary operations. They are two different things. Compare the definition of "transformation" in § 22, Theorem 4 with the characterization of elementary transformations given by Theorem 4 of § 25.

The above derivation of the normal form yields several interesting conclusions concerning the minimal polynomial and the characteristic polynomial. As on p. 362, let L_i be the invariant vector space spanned by the vectors (9). The vectors (9), as part of the basis (11), are linearly independent and therefore forms a basis of L_i. Let σ_i be the linear transformation induced by σ on L_i. We shall prove that *the minimal polynomial of σ_i is $e_i(u)$.*

In fact, using (6) and Theorem 3 of § 23, we have

$$(16) \qquad e_i(\sigma_i)(\sigma_i^k(\mathfrak{b}_i)) = e_i(\sigma)(\sigma^k(\mathfrak{b}_i)) = \sigma^k(e_i(\sigma)(\mathfrak{b}_i)) = 0.$$

Thus the linear transformation $e_i(\sigma_i)$ maps each of the basis vectors (9) on the null vector. It follows that $e_i(\sigma_i)$ is the null transformation on L_i. Theorem 1 of § 23, applied to σ_i, now implies that the minimal polynomial of σ_i is a divisor of $e_i(u)$.

But if the degree t of the minimal polynomial of σ_i were less than the degree of $e_i(u)$, it would follow that the vectors $\mathfrak{b}_i, \sigma(\mathfrak{b}_i), \ldots, \sigma^t(\mathfrak{b}_i)$ would be linearly dependent, contradicting the linear independence of the vectors (9). Thus the minimal polynomial is not a proper divisor of $e_i(u)$ and is therefore $e_i(u)$ itself.

We may now easily prove

THEOREM 3. *The last elementary divisor $e_n(u)$ of the characteristic matrix of σ is the minimal polynomial of σ.*

Proof: First we see that $e_n(u)$ is a multiple of this minimal polynomial, since $e_n(\sigma)$ is the null transformation on L. For, $e_n(u)$ is a multiple of $e_i(u)$, and thus by what has just been proved, $e_n(\sigma)$ maps the vectors (9), for every i ($i = h, h+1, \ldots, n$), on the null vector. On the other hand, $e_n(u)$ is a divisor of the minimal polynomial of σ, since this minimal polynomial certainly has the induced linear transformation σ_n as a zero and hence must be a multiple of the minimal polynomial of σ_n; therefore the minimal polynomial of σ must itself be $e_n(u)$.

The characteristic polynomial of σ and the product of the elementary divisors $e_i(u)$, being the determinants of equivalent polynomial matrices, are the same except for a possible constant factor (which is ± 1 by comparing the leading coefficients). Thus the characteristic polynomial is a multiple of the minimal polynomial $e_n(u)$. This proves

THEOREM 4. *Every linear transformation is a zero of its characteristic polynomial.*

This of course implies

THEOREM 4a. *(The Hamilton-Cayley Theorem). Every (square) matrix is a zero of its characteristic polynomial.*

Since the degree of the characteristic polynomial is n we also have

THEOREM 5. *The degree of the minimal polynomial of σ is $\leqq n$. The characteristic polynomial is a multiple of the minimal polynomial.*

Linear Transformations with Prescribed Elementary Divisors

Up to now we started with a given linear transformation whose characteristic matrix determined n polynomials $e_i(u)$ as its elementary divisors. We now propose the converse problem. Given n polynomials $e_1(u), e_2(u), \ldots, e_n(u)$, none of which vanish, whose leading coefficients are 1, and which are such that $e_i(u)$ divides $e_{i+1}(u)$ for $i = 1, 2, \ldots, n-1$, does there exist an n-by-n matrix (or a linear transformation) whose characteristic matrix has these as elementary divisors?

If there does exist such a matrix, then the sum of the degrees of the $e_i(u)$ is necessarily n (since the product of the elementary divisors must be a polynomial of degree n). If this is so, the answer is in the affirmative. Some of the $e_i(u)$ may be equal to 1. Let $e_1(u) = e_2(u) = \ldots = e_{h-1}(u) = 1$ and let $e_h(u)$ be the first of the given polynomials whose degree is > 0. Then all of the polynomials $e_{h+1}(u)$, $e_{h+2}(u)$, $\ldots$, $e_n(u)$, being multiples of $e_h(u)$, have positive degrees. For $h \leqq i \leqq n$, let $e_i(u)$ have degree ν_i and be of the form

$$e_i(u) = a_{i1} + a_{i2}u + \cdots + a_{i\nu_i}u^{\nu_i-1} + u^{\nu_i}.$$

We now construct the matrix (12) from the coefficients of these polynomials. *This matrix is of the desired form, i.e. its characteristic matrix has the polynomials $e_i(u)$ as elementary divisors.*

The characteristic matrix of (12) is obtained by adding $-u$ everywhere along the main diagonal. The individual boxes take on the form

$$(17) \qquad \begin{vmatrix} -u & \cdots & 0 & -a_{i,1} \\ 1 & -u & \vdots & \vdots \\ \vdots & 1 \ddots & \ddots \vdots & \vdots \\ \vdots & \ddots & -u & -a_{i,\nu_i-1} \\ 0 & \cdots & 1 & -a_{i,\nu_i}-u \end{vmatrix}.$$

An elementary operation on such a box can be considered as an elementary operation on (12) keeping the rest of the matrix (12) fixed. This is clear when we realize that the characteristic matrix of (12) has zeros everywhere outside the boxes.

Now bring every such box into diagonal form using elementary operations. This is easily accomplished. If (17) has only one row,[9] it is already in diagonal form, namely

$$\left\| -a_{i1} - u \right\| = \left\| -e_i(u) \right\| .$$

Otherwise multiply the last row by u and add it to the preceding row, then multiply the next to the last row by u and add it to the preceding row, and continue in this way. We then obtain

$$(18) \qquad \left\| \begin{matrix} 0 & \cdots\cdots & 0 & -a_{i,1} - a_{i,2}u - \cdots - u^{\nu_i} \\ 1 & 0 & \vdots & \vdots \\ \vdots & 1 \ddots & \vdots & \vdots \\ \vdots & \ddots & 0 & -a_{i,\nu_i-1} - a_{i,\nu_i}u - u^2 \\ 0 & \cdots\cdots & 1 & -a_{i,\nu_i} - u \end{matrix} \right\| .$$

The first element of the last column is $-e_i(u)$. Now add proper multiples of the first $\nu_i - 1$ columns to the last column to make all of the last column vanish except the element in the first row. Next, multiply the last column by -1 and, by suitable interchanges of rows, bring the box into the form

$$(19) \qquad \left\| \begin{matrix} 1 & & & & 0 \\ & 1 & & & \\ & & \ddots & & \\ & & & 1 & \\ 0 & & & & e_i(u) \end{matrix} \right\| .$$

Perform this operation on each of the boxes along the principal diagonal of the characteristic matrix of (12). The latter then takes on the form

---

[9] This is so if $\nu_i = 1$, so that $e_i(u) = a_{i1} + u$. (Cf. footnote 6 on p. 362.)

$$
(20) \qquad \begin{pmatrix}
\begin{array}{ccc:ccc:c:ccc}
1 & & 0 & & & & & & & 0 \\
 & \ddots & & & & & & & & \\
 & & 1 & & & & & & & \\
0 & & e_h(u) & & & & & & & \\
\hdashline
 & & & 1 & & 0 & & & & \\
 & & & & \ddots & & & & & \\
 & & & & & 1 & & & & \\
 & & & 0 & & e_{h+1}(u) & & & & \\
\hdashline
 & & & & & & \ddots & & & \\
\hdashline
 & & & & & & & 1 & & 0 \\
 & & & & & & & & \ddots & \\
 & & & & & & & & & 1 \\
0 & & & & & & & 0 & & e_n(u)
\end{array}
\end{pmatrix}.
$$

Finally, we may obtain

$$
(21) \qquad \begin{pmatrix}
\underbrace{1 \; \cdots \; 1}_{h-1 \text{ times}} & & & 0 \\
 & e_h(u) & & \\
 & & \ddots & \\
0 & & & e_n(u)
\end{pmatrix}
$$

from (20) by suitable row and column interchanges. The matrix (21) satisfies the conditions of Theorem 2, § 25 and therefore contains in its principal diagonal the elementary divisors of the characteristic matrix of (12). This proves our assertion.

In particular we have solved the problem of finding a linear transformation with a given characteristic polynomial. Of course, the normal form (12) is not in general uniquely determined by the characteristic polynomial.

The Jordan Normal Form

For some applications, the normal form (12) is not the most suitable one. As a rule, Theorem 2 is a useful tool for deciding whether or not a given matrix can be transformed into other canonical forms that may be needed. We shall illustrate this point by considering the question of when a matrix can be transformed into one which has only zeros on one side of the main diagonal.

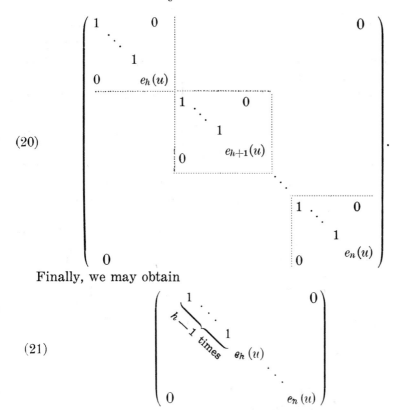

A necessary condition for this may easily be given. For consider the characteristic polynomial of such a matrix. It is a product of n linear factors, namely of the n polynomial of the form $\alpha - u$ which are found in the main diagonal of the characteristic matrix.

But this condition is also sufficient. To prove this, let us assume that the characteristic polynomial of the linear transformation σ can be factored into linear factors in $F[u]$. This is then true of each of the elementary divisors $e_i(u)$ of σ.

We shall obtain, for our given matrix, a transformed matrix of the required type and in a special form which is often used. Let a fixed elementary divisor $e_i(u) \neq 1$ be factored[10] into the irreducible factors

$$(22)\quad e_i(u) = (u-\alpha_1)^{s_1}\cdot(u-\alpha_2)^{s_2}\cdot \ldots \cdot(u-\alpha_r)^{s_r}, \quad s_k \geqq 1, \quad \alpha_j \neq \alpha_k \text{ for } j \neq k.$$

As before, denote its degree by ν_i, so that

$$(23)\qquad \nu_i = s_1 + s_2 + \ldots + s_r.$$

Employing the zeros $\alpha_1, \alpha_2, \ldots, \alpha_r$ of (22), we form the ν_i-by-ν_i matrix

$$(24)\qquad A_i = \begin{pmatrix} \underbrace{\begin{matrix} \alpha_1 & 1 & & 0 \\ & \ddots & \ddots & \\ & & \ddots & 1 \\ 0 & & & \alpha_1 \end{matrix}}_{s_1\text{-rowed}} & & & 0 \\ & \underbrace{\begin{matrix} \alpha_2 & 1 & & 0 \\ & \ddots & \ddots & \\ & & \ddots & 1 \\ 0 & & & \alpha_2 \end{matrix}}_{s_2\text{-rowed}} & & \\ & & \ddots & \\ 0 & & & \overbrace{\begin{matrix} \alpha_r & 1 & & 0 \\ & \ddots & \ddots & \\ & & \ddots & 1 \\ 0 & & & \alpha_r \end{matrix}}^{s_r\text{-rowed}} \end{pmatrix}.$$

There are r square boxes along the main diagonal of this matrix, one for each root $\alpha_1, \alpha_2, \ldots, \alpha_r$ of $e_i(u)$, and only zeros outside these boxes. The box corresponding to the zero α_k has s_k rows and columns and

[10] The zeros $\alpha_1, \alpha_2, \cdots, \alpha_r$ and their multiplicities $s_1, s_2, \cdots, s_r$ should be indicated by another index i, since they correspond to the i-th elementary divisor. But since this index i is held fixed in the discussion, we may ignore this difficulty.

contains a_k along its main diagonal s_k times, ones just above the main diagonal, and zeros everywhere else.[11]

What are the elementary divisors of the characteristic matrix[12] $A_i - uE$ of (24)? We use equation (12) on p. 350, i.e. we shall first calculate the $d_k(u)$ for $A_i - uE$. Now d_{ν_i} (i.e. the greatest common divisor of "all" the ν_i-by-ν_i subdeterminants of $A_i - uE$) is given by

$$d_{\nu_i} = e_i(u).$$

We next calculate the greatest common divisor of all the $(\nu_i - 1)$-by-$(\nu_i - 1)$ subdeterminants of $A_i - uE$. One such determinant is obtained by striking out the first column and the s_1-st row, and calculating the determinant of this new matrix. Its value is

$$(\alpha_2 - u)^{s_2} \cdot (\alpha_3 - u)^{s_3} \cdot \dots \cdot (\alpha_r - u)^{s_r}$$

as can be seen by using the general Laplace expansion theorem. By striking out the $(s_1 + s_2 + \dots + s_{k-1} + 1)$-st column and the $(s_1 + s_2 + \dots + s_k)$-th row we similarly obtain another $(\nu_i - 1)$-by-$(\nu_i - 1)$ subdeterminant whose value is

$$(\alpha_1 - u)^{s_1} \cdot \dots \cdot (\alpha_{k-1} - u)^{s_{k-1}} \cdot (\alpha_{k+1} - u)^{s_{k+1}} \cdot \dots \cdot (\alpha_r - u)^{s_r}$$

by the same methods. The greatest common divisor of the r determinants obtained for $k = 1, 2, \dots, r$ is 1. Thus the greatest common divisor $d_{\nu_i - 1}$ of all $(\nu_i - 1)$-by-$(\nu_i - 1)$ subdeterminants is 1.

By formula (12) on p. 350, the last elementary divisor of the characteristic matrix $A_i - uE$ is

$$\frac{d_{\nu_i}}{d_{\nu_i - 1}} = e_i(u).$$

But, by (9) on p. 350, the polynomial $d_{\nu_i - 1}$ is the product of the first $\nu_i - 1$ elementary divisors of $A_i - uE$, so that these elementary divisors are all 1. This shows that the characteristic matrix $A_i - uE$ can, by means of elementary operations, be brought into the form

$$(25) \qquad \begin{pmatrix} 1 & & & & 0 \\ & 1 & & & \\ & & \ddots & & \\ & & & 1 & \\ 0 & & & & e_i(u) \end{pmatrix}.$$

[11] This condition means, for the case $s_k = 1$ that the s_k-by-s_k (i.e. one-by-one) box is of the form $\vdots \alpha_k \vdots$.

[12] E here represents the ν_i-by-ν_i identity matrix.

We now construct a matrix of σ which has only zeros below the main diagonal. We form this matrix from the matrices A_i corresponding to the elementary divisors $e_i(u) \neq 1$ of its characteristic matrix. Let $e_1(u) = e_2(u) = \ldots = e_{h-1}(u) = 1$ and let $e_i(u)$ have positive degree for $i \geqq h$. Now place the matrices $A_k, A_{k+1}, \ldots, A_n$ along the main diagonal of an n-by-n square matrix, putting zeros everywhere outside these matrices. We thus obtain a matrix which is represented by the scheme

$$\begin{pmatrix} A_h & & & 0 \\ & A_{h+1} & & \\ & & \ddots & \\ 0 & & & A_n \end{pmatrix}. \tag{26}$$

We shall now show that (26) represents the linear transformation σ, by finding the elementary divisors of its characteristic matrix and applying Theorem 2. We shall, by elementary operations, bring this characteristic matrix into diagonal form. The characteristic matrix of (26) is obtained by replacing each box A_i by $A_i - uE$. An elementary operation on $A_i - uE$ can be effected by an elementary operation on the entire characteristic matrix of (26), which alters only $A_i - uE$. Thus, by elementary operations on this characteristic matrix, we may bring each box $A_i - uE$ into the form (25). From this point on, the characteristic matrix of (26) may be brought into the form

$$\begin{pmatrix} \underbrace{1 \; \cdots \; 1}_{h-1 \text{ times}} & & & & 0 \\ & e_h(u) & & & \\ & & e_{h+1}(u) & & \\ & & & \ddots & \\ 0 & & & & e_n(u) \end{pmatrix}$$

by simple row and column interchanges. *Hence* (26) *is indeed the matrix of* σ *in a suitable coordinate system.*

The matrix (26) is called the **Jordan normal form** of the matrix of σ. We express our result in

THEOREM 6. *A matrix can be transformed into the Jordan normal form by a non-singular matrix T (whose elements are in* F) *if and* *only if its characteristic polynomial may be decomposed into linear factors in* F$[u]$.

We may replace the characteristic polynomial by the minimal polynomial in this criterion. For if the minimal polynomial factors into linear factors, then so do all of the elementary divisors, being also divisors of the minimal polynomial, and hence so does their product, i.e. the characteristic polynomial. The converse is trivial.

If the field F has the property that any polynomial in F$[u]$ can be factored into linear factors, then the matrix of every linear transformation may be brought into Jordan normal form. In this case we may use the Jordan normal form as a general normal form. The field of complex numbers is an example of such a field. Therefore the following holds:

If F *is the field of complex numbers, then for every matrix A with elements in* F*, there exists a non-singular matrix T such that the matrix $T \cdot A \cdot T^{-1}$ is in Jordan Normal form.*

We finally remark that any matrix which can be transformed into (26) can also be transformed into the transpose of (26). For we could have carried out our reasoning with the transposes of the matrices.

Exercises

1. What are the elementary divisors of the characteristic matrix $A - uE$ of the matrix

$$A = \begin{pmatrix} -5 & -3 & -2 & 4 \\ 2 & 0 & 1 & -1 \\ 10 & 7 & 4 & -9 \\ 2 & 0 & 1 & 0 \end{pmatrix}?$$

What are the zeros of its characteristic polynomial? Transform A into the normal form.

2. Let A be an n-by-n square matrix with complex entries. Let

$$|f(A) - uE| = (f(\alpha_1) - u) \cdot (f(\alpha_2) - u) \cdot \ldots \cdot (f(\alpha_n) - u).$$

Let $f(u)$ be any polynomial with complex coefficients. Prove that we have, for the characteristic polynomial of the matrix $f(A)$ that

$$|A - uE| = (\alpha_1 - u) \cdot (\alpha_2 - u) \cdot \ldots \cdot (\alpha_n - u).$$

3. Let V_n be the n-dimensional vector space over the field of complex numbers. Discuss all possible cases which arise in connection with the general normal form and the Jordan normal form of a linear transformation for $n = 2$, 3, and 4.

4. Let σ be a linear transformation on a vector space L over any field F. Let $q(u)^a$ be the highest power of an irreducible polynomial $q(u)$ which divides the minimal polynomial of σ, and let $q(u)^s$ be the highest power of $q(u)$ which divides

the characteristic polynomial of σ. Then the dimension of the null space of the linear transformation $q(\sigma)^a$ is equal to the degree of $q(u)^s$.

5. Let σ be a linear transformation on a k-dimensional vector space L whose minimal polynomial is $m(u) = (u-\alpha)^k$. There is a vector $\mathfrak{a}$ in L such that $(\sigma-\alpha\sigma^0)^{k-1}(\mathfrak{a}) \neq 0$. Then $\mathfrak{a}, (\sigma-\alpha\sigma^0)(\mathfrak{a}), \cdots, (\sigma-\alpha\sigma^0)^{k-1}(\mathfrak{a})$ form a basis of L. What is the matrix of σ with respect to this basis?

6. Let σ be a linear transformation on an n-dimensional vector space L such that its minimal polynomial $m(u)$ has degree n and is the product of n linear factors in F$[u]$. Find a basis of L with respect to which the matrix of σ is in Jordan normal form.

Hint: Use Theorem 13 of § 23, and exercise 5.

7. Let σ be a linear transformation whose minimal polynomial can be factored into linear factors in F$[u]$. As on p. 360, let

$$e_1(u) = e_2(u) = \cdots = e_{h-1}(u) = 1, \quad e_h(u) \neq 1, \quad e_{h+1}(u), \quad \cdots, \quad e_n(u)$$

be the elementary divisors of the characteristic matrix of σ. Let L_i $(i \geqq h)$ be the vector space, defined as on p. 362, corresponding to the elementary divisor $e(u)$, and let σ_i be the linear transformation induced by σ on L. Apply exercise 6 to each σ_i on L to obtain a basis of L with respect to which the matrix of σ is in Jordan normal form.

8. Adjoin an equation of the form (4) on p. 356 to the system (2) on p. 357. Show that an equation (4) is always a consequence of (2), in the sense that there are polynomials $h_k(u)$ such that

$$f_i(u) = \sum_{k=1}^{n} h_k(u)\ (a_{ik} - \delta_{ik} u)$$

holds for every i.

Hint: Subtract suitable multiples of the equations (2) from (4) to successively lower the degree of the polynomials $f_i(u)$ to zero.

9. The analogy between the developments of the present section and those of § 20 may be extended. For example, we may generalize the concept of the "order" of a group element, as follows: Define the *order of a vector* $\mathfrak{a}$ *with respect to a linear transformation* σ to be the polynomial $f(u) \neq 0$ of least degree for which $f(\sigma)(\mathfrak{a}) = 0$. (This polynomial is uniquely determined, up to a constant factor.) Prove that if $\mathfrak{a}_1, \mathfrak{a}_2, \cdots, \mathfrak{a}_r$ is a σ-Basis of the vector space L, then the sum of the degrees of the orders of $\mathfrak{a}_i$ is equal to the dimension of L.

In analogy with exercise 5 of § 20, let $L^{(\varphi)}$ ($\varphi(u)$ a polynomial) be the vector space consisting of all vectors of the form $\varphi(\sigma)(\mathfrak{x})$ for an arbitrary $\mathfrak{x}$ of L. The theorem of § 20, exercise 5, then immediately carries over. Furthermore, in analogy with § 20, exercise 6, let $e_i(u)$ be the order of $\mathfrak{a}_i$, and let $e_i(u)$ divide $e_{i+1}(u)$. Let ν_i be the degree of $e_i(u)$. Then if i is fixed and if $k(u)$ is a divisor of $e_{i+1}(u)$ of degree u, the dimension of $L^{(k)}$ is

$$\geqq (\nu_{i+1}-\mu)+(\nu_{i+2}-\mu)+ \cdots +(\nu_r - u);$$

equality holding if and only if $k(u)$ is a multiple of $e_i(u)$. The content of § 20, exercise 7, now also carries over easily.

INDEX

ABELIAN GROUP, 246, 255, 260 ff.
abscissa, 1 ff.
addition, in a field, 188 ff.
  of complex numbers, 219
  of fractions, 199
  of linear transformations, 275
  of matrices, 287
  of polynomials, 205
  of vectors, 10, 12, 118, 201
addition theorem for determinants, 72
additive group of residue classes modulo n, 255
affine group of R_n, 257
affine space of n dimensions, 30
affine transformation, 180 ff., 315
  non-singular, 184
  singular, 184
algebraic complement, 98
algebraic equation in one unknown, 230
amplitude of a complex number, 221
angle between two vectors, 58, 59
application of a vector, 7
argument of a complex number, 221
associated polynomials, 212
axioms, 188
  field, 202
  group, 245, 246

BASIS, 260, 273, 356
  of a vector space, basis vectors, 23
basis theorem for abelian groups, 260 ff., 262, 270
basis vectors, 23
binomial theorem, 236
Bolzano-Weierstrass, theorem of, 227
bounded sequences of complex numbers, 225, 227

CANCELLATION LAW, 249
cancellation of a common non-zero factor in a fraction, 198
Cartesian coordinate system, 51, 128
Cartesian space, p-dimensional, 178
Cauchy-Schwarz inequality, 55
Cayley, *see* Hamilton
centroid, 186
change of coordinate system, 293 ff.
characteristic matrix of a linear transformation, 357
characteristic polynomials, of a linear transformation, 327
  of a matrix, 326
characteristic properties of determinants, 69
characteristic roots of a linear transformation, 327
circuit, 138
closure, axiom of, 245
coefficient matrix, 36, 285
coefficients, 204
  real, 240
column vector, of a determinant, 89 ff.
  of a matrix, 34
columns, interchange of, of a matrix, 41
common divisor, 208
    greatest, of all k-rowed sub-determinants of a polynomial matrix, 348
  of a polynomial, 208
common multiples, of two polynomials, 216
  least, 216, 310
common perpendicular of two linear spaces, 147
commutative group, 246
commutative law, of addition, 188
  of addition of linear transformations, 277
  of addition of matrices, 290
  of multiplication, 194
  of vector addition, 12
complete permutation group of a set, 256
complex conjugate numbers, 222
complex conjugate polynomials, 241
complex numbers, 218 ff.
complex vector space, 324, 327
complex vectors, 328
complex of a group, 251
components of vectors, 12, 117, 201, 284
convergent sequences of complex numbers, 223
cofactor, 98
complement, algebraic, 98
complementary sub-determinants, 110
constants, 204
continuity of a polynomial, 231
continuous deformation of a linear coordinate system, 131 ff.
coordinate, 1 ff., 5, 30, 117
coordinate axes, 3 f.
coordinate plane, 3
coordinate system, 2 ff.
  change of, 293 f.
  in a vector space, 284
  linear, 30
  polar, 221
coordinate transformation, 293
coset, left, 252
  right, 252
Cramer's rule, 101
cube, n-dimensional, 66
cyclic group, finite, 269
  infinite, 269

DECOMPOSITION OF POLYNOMIAL INTO IRREDUCIBLE FACTORS, 212
decomposition of polynomial with real coefficients into irreducible real factors, 243
decomposition of vector space into invariant sub-spaces, 310 ff.

deformation, continuous, of a linear coordinate system, 131 ff.
degree of a polynomial, 204
dependence, linear, of matrices, 298
  of vectors, 16, 201
derivative of a polynomial, 243
derived relation, 263
determinant, 69, 296
  development of, 87
    by rows or columns, 98 ff.
  as function of its column vectors, 89
  of a linear transformation, 297
  under rigid motions, 162
determinant theorem, Vandermonde's, 115
determinants, computation of, by rows or columns, 82
development of a determinant, 87
diagonal, main, 94
  principal, 94
diagonal form, of a matrix, 320, 321
  of hermitian matrices, 341
  of a symmetric matrix, 343
  for unitary matrices, 330 ff., 334
  transformation of a matrix into, 323, 327
dimension, 1
  of a linear space, 28
  of a vector space, 23
direct product of cyclic groups, 270
direct sum of a vector space, 312
directed segment, 6 f., 11
distance between two points, 53 ff.
distributive law, in a field, 196
  of vector addition, 14 f.
distributive laws, for linear transformations, 277
  for matrices, 290
divergent sequences of complex numbers, 223
division algorithm for polynomials, 206
division, 194, 246
  of two fractions, 199
divisor, elementary, 351, 364
  normal, 254
divisor of a polynomial, 206
  improper, 210
dodecahedron group, 259
double sum, 61

EDGE VECTOR OF n-DIMENSIONAL PARALLELOTOPE, 65
elementary divisors of a polynomial matrix, 351, 364
elementary operations on matrix whose elements are integers, 354
elementary operation on polynomial matrix, 345, 352
elementary transformations, 263, 264 ff.
equality of linear transformations, 274
equality of matrices, 285 f.
equality of polynomials, 204
equality of vectors, 6, 201
equations, linear, 33
  of transformation, 121
  system of, of affine transformation, 315
  of a linear transformation, 284 f.
equivalence of polynomial matrices, 345, 351, 353, 354
euclidean length, 50 ff., 53
euclidean space, 53
expansion theorem of Laplace, 105 ff.

FACTORS, decomposition into irreducible, 212
field, 202
  axioms of, 202
  finite, 203
  of complex numbers, 218 ff.
  of rational functions in one indeterminate, 300
finite cyclic group, 269
finite fields, 203
finite order, matrix of, 343
finite system of generators of an abelian group, 259
foot of perpendicular, 144, 149
fundamental properties of determinant, 69
fundamental system of relations of abelian group, 263
fundamental theorem for abelian groups, 262
fundamental theorem of algebra, 238

GENERATING SYSTEM, 355
generators, system of, 260
  finite system of, of abelian group, 260
greatest common divisor of polynomials, 210
group, abelian, 246, 255, 260 ff.
group, additive, of residue classes modulo n, 255
  affine, of R_n, 257
  commutative, 246
  complete permution, of a set, 256
  cyclic, 269
  definition of, 245 f.
  icosahedral, 259
  infinite, 269 f.
  of linear transformation with respect to addition, 279
  of non-singular linear transformations with respect to multiplication, 281
  of rigid motions of euclidean R_n, 258
  order of, 253
  symmetric, 256
group axioms, 245

HAMILTON-CAYLEY THEOREM, 365
hermitian matrix, 340
Hesse normal form, 147
homogeneity property of determinants, 69

homogeneous linear equations, system of, 36, 105
hyperplane, 29, 47, 114

ICOSAHEDRAL GROUP, 259
ideal, 207
 null, 207
 principal, 207
identity, identity mapping, 164, 175
 general Lagrange's, 116
identity element of a group, 248
identity transformation, 278
image of a linear space, 156
imaginary unit, 220
imaginary component of a complex number, 220
imaginary part of a complex number, 220
improper divisor of a polynomial, 210
improper rigid motion, 160
improper subspace of a vector space, 25
independence, linear, of vectors, 17
 of matrices, 298
 of two vectors, 202
indeterminate, 204
index of a subgroup, 254
induced linear transformation, 305
induction, mathematical, 21 ff.
infinite sequences of complex numbers, 223
infinite cyclic group, 269
infinite groups, 269, 270
interchange of rows and columns of matrix, 41
intersection, of two vector spaces, 25
 of two linear spaces, 32, 156
invariance, of determinants, 69
 of linear transformations under change of coordinate system, 325
invariant subspace, 303, 310
invariant vector, 163
invariant subgroup, 254
invariants of polynomial matrices with respect to elementary operations, 347
inverse, of a group element, 249
 of a matrix, 291
 of a non-singular linear transformation, 281
 of a product of group elements, 249
inverse mapping, 161
inversion, 88
irreducible polynomials, 211, 239
isomorphisms, 289

JORDAN NORMAL FORM, 267
 possibility of transforming matrix into, 370

KRONECKER DELTA, 100

LAGRANGE'S IDENTITY, general, 116
Laplace's expansion theorem, 105 ff.
law, associative, of addition, 188
 of addition and multiplication of linear transformations, 277
 of addition and multiplication of matrices, 290
 for groups, 245
 of multiplication, 194
 of vector addition, 13
laws of signs in a field, 197
least common multiple, of two polynomials, 216
 of r polynomials, 310
left coset, 252
left-handed system of vectors, 139
left identity, 247
left inverse, 250
length, of common perpendicular of two linear spaces, 147
 of perpendicular, 144 ff.
 of a vector, 54, 327
  in a normal orthogonal system, 142
limit of a sequence of complex numbers, 223
limit point of a sequence of complex numbers, 228
line, 9
 in parametric representation, 11
linear combination, 18, 209
 of matrices, 298
linear coordinate system, 3 f., 117 ff.
linear coordinates, general, 117 ff.
linear dependence and independence, of matrices, 298
 of vectors, 17, 201
linear equations, 33, 100 ff., 125
 homogeneous, 36
 non-homogeneous, 40
linear independence of vectors, 17, 202
linear polynomial, 239
linear space, 27 ff., 123 ff.
 p-dimensional, 202
linear transformation, 181, 273 ff., 284
 determinant of, 297
linear vector space, 125

MAIN DIAGONAL OF A DETERMINANT, 94
mapping, identity, 164, 175
 inverse, 161
 one-one, 155
 one-to-one, 155
 single-valued, 153
mathematical induction, 21 ff.
matric polynomials, 298
matrix, 34, 283 ff.
 augmented, 36
 characteristic polynomial of a, 326
 hermitian, 340
 minimal polynomial of, 304, 364
 nilpotent, 343
 of finite order, 343
 of fundamental system, 263
 of linear transformation, 285
 nilpotent, 343

matrix (*continued*)
  non-singular, 291
  orthogonal, 128, 334
  residual, 266
  symmetric, 343
  unitary, 333
matrix coefficient, 36, 285
midpoint of a segment, 60
minimal polynomial, 303
  of linear transformation and of a matrix, 304, 364
modulus of a complex number, 220
motions, rigid, 153
    in R_2, 162 ff., 168
    group of, 258
    in R_3, 168 ff., 178
    normal form for, 339
    proper and improper, 159, 160
multiple, common, of two polynomials, 216
  least common, 216, 310
  of a polynomial, 206
multiplication, as field operation, 194
  in a group, 245
  of complex numbers, 219, 222
  of complexes in a group, 252
  of linear transformations, 278
  of matrices, 288
  of polynomials, 205
  of sums, 62
  of vector by elementary of the field, 201
  rule of, of fractions, 199
multiplication theorem for determinants, 96
multiplicity of a root, 240

NEGATIVE SENSE OF ROTATION, 138
nilpotent matrix, 343
non-homogeneous linear equation, 40 ff.
non-singular matrix, 291
non-singular linear transformation, 281
normal divisor, 254
normal form, Hesse, 147
  Jordan, of a matrix, 370
  of a matrix of a linear transformation, 363 f.
  real, for orthogonal transformations, 338
normal orthogonal system, 127, 140 ff., 328
normal subgroup, 254
normalization of determinants, 69
null ideal, 207
null space of a linear transformation, 306
null transformation, 278
null vector, 9, 12

OCTAHEDRON GROUP, 259
one-one map, 155
one-to-one mapping, 155
operations, elementary, 345, 352 f., 354

order, of a group, 253
  of a group element, 270
  matrix of finite, 343
ordinate, 2
origin, 1, 3, 4
  of the coordinate system, 1, 30
orthogonal matrix, 128, 334
orthogonal system, normal, 127, 140 ff., 328
orthogonal transformation, 334
  real normal form for, 338
orthogonal vectors, 15, 44, 60, 328
  with respect to a linear space, 142
orthonormal system, 328

PARALLELEPIPED, volume of, 64, 85
parallel linear spaces, 32
parallel projection, 317
parallelogram, volume of, 63, 85
parallelotope, 64, 153, 178
  volume of n-dimensional, 85 ff., 125, 179
    under rigid motions, 162
parametric representation of the straight line, 11
permutation, 88
permutation group, complete, of a set, 256
perpendicular, 144
  foot of, 144
perpendicular projection of a set of points on a linear space, 152
perpendicular vectors, 59
plane, 2, 29
point solution of a linear system of equations, 45 ff.
polar coordinates, 221
polynomial, 204
  characteristic, of a matrix and of a linear transformation, 326, 365
  in a linear transformation, 282
  irreducible, 211
  linear, 239
  matric, 298
  of a matrix, 292
  reducible, 211, 239
  relatively prime, 210
polynomial domain, 205, 217
polynomial matrix, 344 ff.
positive sense of rotation, 138
power-product of group elements, 260
powers, in a field, 200
  in one variable, 205
  of group element, 249
  of linear transformation, 281
  of matrix, 292
principal diagonal of a matrix, 267
principal ideal, 207
product, direct, of cyclic groups, 270
  of one-to-one mappings, 255 f.
  of two complex numbers, 219, 222
  of two determinants, 97
  of two elements of a field, 194

product (*continued*)
of two polynomials, 205
scalar, 14 ff., 58 ff., 126, 154, 161, 201, 219
product rule for sums, 62
projection, orthogonal, of a set of points on a linear space, 152
proper basis of an abelian group, 268
proper divisor of a polynomial, 210
proper rigid motions, 159
proper subspace of a vector space, 25

QUOTIENT GROUP, 255

RADIUS VECTOR, 221
rank of a matrix, 36, 41, 101
rational functions in one indeterminate, field of, 300
real coefficients, 240
real normal form for orthogonal transformations, 338
real part (*or component*) of a complex number, 220
reciprocal group element, 249
recursion formula for determinants, 82, 98 ff.
reducible polynomial, 211
reflection, in a line of the plane, 166
in a plane, 176, 177
through a point, in space, 177
reflection of a determinant, 94
around the principal diagonal, 94
reflexive, 299
relation, derived, 263
relatively prime polynomials, 210
remainder of two polynomials, 206
replacement theorem of Steinitz, 20
representation, parametric, of straight line, 11
representative of a coset, 252
residual matrix, 266
residue classes mod n, 203, 255
reversibility, of addition, 188, 192
of group operation, 246
of multiplication, 194, 246
of linear transformations, 279
rigid motions, *see* motions
right coset, 252
right identity, 247
right inverse, 250
right-handed system of vectors, 139
root, characteristic, of a linear transformation, 327
of a polynomial, 230
multiplicity of, 240
roots of unity, group of the n-th, 262
rotation, of a plane about a fixed point, 168
of space about a line, 174, 177
sense of, positive and negative, 138
rows of a matrix, 34
interchange of, 41
row vector, of a determinant, 69
of a matrix, 41

SCALAR PRODUCT, 14 ff., 58 ff., 126, 154, 161, 201, 219
Schwarz, Cauchy-Schwarz inequality, 55
segment, 9, 11
directed, 6, 11
sequence of complex numbers, infinite, 223
similar matrix, 296
similarity transformation, 179
singular linear transformation, 280
singular matrix, 291
solvabality of an algebraic equation in one unknown in the field of complex numbers, 230
solution, of a system of linear equations, 33 ff., 45 ff., 100 ff., 101
of vector equations, 14
space, linear, 27
p-dimensional, 202
n-dimensional vector, 273
one-, two-, three-, n-dimensional, 1-5
space, vector, n-dimensional, 273
spanned, vector space spanned by vectors, 20
Steinitz, replacement theorem of, 20
straight line, 1, 11, 29
in parametric representation, 11
sub-determinant, 102
subgroups, 251 ff.
index of, 254
invariant, 254
normal, 254
of the group of rigid motions of euclidean R_n, 258 ff.
subsequence of a sequence of complex numbers, 227
subspace, invariant, 303, 310
of a vector space, proper and improper, 25
subtraction, 188, 192
of fractions, 199
sum, of two vector spaces, 25, 148
of vector spaces, 310
direct, 312
of vectors, 10, 12, 118, 201
summation sign, calculating with, 60 ff.
symmetric group of degree n, 256
symmetric matrix, 343
system of linear equation, 33
of rigid motions, 340

TETRAHEDRON GROUP, 259
transformability of a matrix into diagonal form, 327
transformations, affine, 180 ff., 315
coordinate, 293
elementary, 263, 264 ff.
equations of, 293, 294
linear, 181, 273 ff., 284
characteristic roots of, 327
induced, 305
non-singular, 281

transformations, linear (*continued*)
system of equations of, 284
of a matrix by means of a non-singular matrix, 296
of coordinates, 121
of matrix into normal form, 363
of principal axis, 343
orthogonal, 334
possibility of, of one matrix into another, 363
similarity, 179
unitary, 329
transforming, possibility of, of matrix, into Jordan normal form, 370
into diagonal form, 323
transitivity, 299
translation, 164
along a line, 175
in a plane, 164
in space, 175
parallel to a plane, 176
translations, group of, 260
transpose of a matrix, 43, 301
triangle inequality, 56

UNIQUE DECOMPOSITION OF POLYNOMIALS INTO IRREDUCIBLE FACTORS 213 ff.
unit matrix, 290, 333
unit point, 1, 3, 4
unit vectors, 17
unit volume, 66
unitary transformation, 329
zeros of characteristic polynomial of, 330
unity element of a field, 195 f.

VALUE, ABSOLUTE, OF COMPLEX NUMBERS, 220
of complex vector, 327
of a matrix, 54
Vandermonde's determinant, 114
vanishing polynomial, 205
variable, 204
vector, 6 ff., 11
complex conjugate, 328
edge, 65
n-dimensional, over a field, 273
over a field, 201
vector addition, 10, 12, 201
vector components, 7, 12, 201
with respect to a basis, 284
vector solutions of a linear system of equations, 37
vector space, 273
complex, 324, 328
linear, 19
n-dimensional, over a field, 273
p-dimensional, 202
in R, 19 ff.
volume, of a parallelepiped, 64, 85
of a parallelogram, 63, 85
of a parallelotope, 65, 83 ff., 125
under rigid motion, 162

WEIERSTRASS, THEOREM OF BOLZANO AND, 228

ZERO ELEMENT IN A FIELD, 193
zero matrix, 290

CHELSEA

SCIENTIFIC

BOOKS

KREIS UND KUGEL

By W. BLASCHKE

Isoperimetric properties of the circle and sphere, the (Brunn-Minkowski) theory of convex bodies, and differential-geometric properties (in the large) of convex bodies. A standard work.

—x + 169 pp. 5½x8½. [59] Cloth **$3.50**
[115] Paper **$1.50**

VORLESUNGEN ÜBER INTEGRAL-GEOMETRIE. Vols. I and II

By W. BLASCHKE

EINFÜHRUNG IN DIE THEORIE DER SYSTEME VON DIFFERENTIAL-GLEICHUNGEN

By E. KÄHLER

—222 pp. 5½x8½. [64] Three Vols. in One **$4.50**

VORLESUNGEN ÜBER FOURIERSCHE INTEGRALE

By S. BOCHNER

"A readable account of those parts of the subject useful for applications to problems of mathematical physics or pure analysis."

—*Bulletin of the A. M. S.*

—1932. 237 pp. 5½x8½. Orig. pub. at $6.40. [42] **$3.50**

ALMOST PERIODIC FUNCTIONS

By H. BOHR

Translated by H. COHN. From the famous series *Ergebnisse der Mathematik und ihrer Grenzgebiete,* a beautiful exposition of the theory of Almost Periodic Functions written by the creator of that theory.

—1951. 120 pp. 6x9. Lithotyped. German edition was $4.50.
[27] **$2.50**

LECTURES ON THE CALCULUS OF VARIATIONS

By O. BOLZA

A standard text by a major contributor to the theory.

—Ready June or July, 1961. Corr. repr of first ed. xi + 267 pp. 5⅜x8. [145] Cloth **$3.25**
[152] Paper **$1.19**

THEORIE DER KONVEXEN KÖRPER

By T. BONNESEN and W. FENCHEL

"Remarkable monograph."

—*J. D. Tamarkin, Bulletin of the A. M. S.*

—1934. 171 pp. 5½x8½. Orig. publ. at $7.50 [54] **$3.95**

THE CALCULUS OF FINITE DIFFERENCES

By G. BOOLE

A standard work on the subject of finite differences and difference equations by one of the seminal minds in the field of finite mathematics.

Some of the topics covered are: *Interpolation, Finite Integration, Summation of Series, General Theory of Difference and Differential Equations of First Order, Linear DEqns with Variable Coefficients, Linear DEqns, Geometrical Applications.* Numerous exercises with answers.

—Fourth edition. 1958. xii + 336 pp. 5x8. [121] Cloth **$3.95**
[148] Paper **$1.39**

A TREATISE ON DIFFERENTIAL EQUATIONS

By G. BOOLE

Including the Supplementary Volume.

—Fifth edition. 1959. xxiv + 735 pp. 5¼x8. [128] **$6.00**

THEORY OF FUNCTIONS

By C. CARATHÉODORY

Translated by F. STEINHARDT. The recent, and already famous textbook, *Funktionentheorie.*

Partial Contents: **Part One.** Chap. I. Algebra of Complex Numbers. II. Geometry of Complex Numbers. III. Euclidean, Spherical, and Non-Euclidean Geometry. **Part Two.** Theorems from Point Set Theory and Topology. Chap. I. Sequences and Continuous Complex Functions. II. Curves and Regions. III. Line Integrals. **Part Three.** Analytic Functions. Chap. I. Foundations. II. The Maximum-modulus principle. III. Poisson Integral and Harmonic Functions. IV. Meromorphic Functions. **Part Four.** Generation of Analytic Functions by Limiting Processes. Chap. I. Uniform Convergence. II. Normal Families of Meromorphic Functions. III. Power Series. IV. Partial Fraction Decomposition and the Calculus of Residues. **Part Five.** Special Functions. Chap. I. The Exponential Function and the Trigonometric Functions. II. Logarithmic Function. III. Bernoulli Numbers and the Gamma Function.

Vol. II.: **Part Six.** Foundations of Geometric Function Theory. Chap. I. Bounded Functions. II. Conformal Mapping. III. The Mapping of the Boundary. **Part Seven.** The Triangle Function and Picard's Theorem. Chap. I. Functions of Several Complex Variables. II. Conformal Mapping of Circular-Arc Triangles. III. The Schwarz Triangle Functions and the Modular Function. IV. Essential Singularities and Picard's Theorems.

"A book by a master . . . Carathéodory himself regarded [it] as his finest achievement . . . written from a catholic point of view."—*Bulletin of A.M.S.*

—Vol. I. Second edition. 1958. 310 pp. 6x9. [97] **$4.95**
—Vol. II. Second edition. 1960. 220 pp. 6x9. [106] **$4.95**

ALGEBREN

By M. DEURING

—(Ergeb. der Math.) 1935. v + 143 pp. 5½x8½. Orig. pub. at $6.60. [50] **$3.95**

HISTORY OF THE THEORY OF NUMBERS

By L. E. DICKSON

"**A monumental work** . . . Dickson always has in mind the needs of the investigator . . . The author has [often] expressed in a nut-shell the main results of a long and involved paper *in a much clearer way than the writer of the article did himself.* The ability to reduce complicated mathematical arguments to simple and elementary terms is highly developed in Dickson."—*Bulletin of A. M. S.*

—Vol. I (Divisibility and Primality) xii + 486 pp. Vol. II (Diophantine Analysis) xxv + 803 pp. Vol. III (Quadratic and Higher Forms) v + 313 pp. [86] Three vol. set **$19.95**

STUDIES IN THE THEORY OF NUMBERS

By L. E. DICKSON

A systematic exposition, starting from first principles, of the arithmetic of quadratic forms, chiefly (but not entirely) ternary forms, including numerous original investigations and correct proofs of a number of classical results that have been stated or proved erroneously in the literature.

—1930. viii + 230 pp. 5⅜x8. [151] **In prep.**

THE INTEGRAL CALCULUS

By J. W. EDWARDS

A leisurely, immensely detailed, textbook of over 1,900 pages, rich in illustrative examples and manipulative techniques and containing much interesting material that must of necessity be omitted from less comprehensive works.

There are forty large chapters in all. The earlier cover a leisurely and a more-than-usually-detailed treatment of all the elementary standard topics. Later chapters include: Jacobian Elliptic Functions, Weierstrassian Elliptic Functions, Evaluation of Definite Integrals, Harmonic Analysis, Calculus of Variations, etc. Every chapter contains many exercises (with solutions).

—2 vols. 1,922 pp. 5x8. Originally published at $31.50 the set. [102], [105] Each volume **$7.50**

AUTOMORPHIC FUNCTIONS

By L. R. FORD

"Comprehensive . . . remarkably clear and explicit."—*Bulletin of the A. M. S.*

—2nd ed. (Cor. repr.) x + 333 pp. 5⅜x8. [85] **$4.95**

THE THEORY OF MATRICES

By F. R. GANTMACHER

Translated from the Russian, with further revisions by the Author.

This treatise by one of Russia's leading mathematicians gives, in easily accessible form, a coherent account of matrix theory with a view to applications in mathematics, theoretical physics, statistics, electrical engineering, etc. The individual chapters have been kept as far as possible independent of each other, so that the reader acquainted with the contents of Chapter I can proceed immediately to the chapters that especially interest him. Much of the material has been available until now only in the periodical literature.

Partial Contents. .VOL. ONE. I. Matrices and Matrix Operations. II. The Algorithm of Gauss and Applications. III. Linear Operators in an n-Dimensional Vector Space. IV. Characteristic Polynomial and Minimal Polynomial of a Matrix (Generalized Bézout Theorem, Method of Faddeev for Simultaneous Computation of Coefficients of Characteristic Polynomial and Adjoint Matrix, . . .). V. Functions of Matrices (Various Forms of the Definition, Components, Application to Integration of System of Linear Differential Eqns, Stability of Motion, . . .). VI. Equivalent Transformations of Polynomial Matrices; Analytic Theory of Elementary Divisors. VII. The Structure of a Linear Operator in an n-Dimensional Space (Minimal Polynomial, Congruence, Factor Space, Jordan Form, Krylov's Method of Transforming Secular Eqn, . . .). VIII. Matrix Equations (Matrix Polynomial Eqns, Roots and Logarithm of Matrices, . . .). IX. Linear Operators in a Unitary Space. X. Quadratic and Hermitian Forms.

VOLUME TWO. XI. Complex Symmetric, Skew-symmetric, and Orthogonal Matrices. XII. Singular Pencils of Matrices. XIII. Matrices with Non-Negative Elements (General Properties, Spectral Properties, Reducible Matrices, Primitive and Imprimitive Matrices, Stochastic Matrices, Limiting Probabilities for Homogeneous Markov Chain, Totally Non-Negative Matrices, Oscillatory Matrices . . .). XIV. Applications of the Theory of Matrices to the Investigation of Systems of Linear Differential Equations (Systems with Variable Coefficients, Lyapunov Transformations, Reducible Systems, Erugin's Theorem, Multiplicative Integral, Volterra's Calculus, Differential Systems in Complex Domain, Analytic Functions of Several Matrices, The Research of Lappo-Danilevskii, . . .). XV. The Problem of Routh-Hurwitz and Related Questions (Routh's Algorithm, Lyapunov's Theorem, Method of Quadratic Forms, Infinite Hankel Matrices of Finite Rank, Stability, Markov Parameters, Problem of Moments. Theorems of Markov and Chebyshev. Generalized Routh-Hurwitz Problem, . . .). Bibliography.

—Vol. I. 1960. x + 374 pp. 6x9. [131] **$6.00**
—Vol. II. 1960. x + 277 pp. 6x9. [133] **$6.00**

Grundzüge Einer Allgemeinen Theorie der LINEAREN INTEGRALGLEICHUNGEN

By D. HILBERT

—306 pp. 5½x8¼. [91] **$4.50**

PRINCIPLES OF MATHEMATICAL LOGIC

By D. HILBERT and W. ACKERMANN

The famous *Grundüge der Theoretischen Logik* translated into English, with added notes and revisions by PROF. R. E. LUCE.

"The best textbook in a Western European language for a student wishing a fairly thorough treatment."—*Bulletin of the A. M. S.*

—1950-59. xii + 172 pp. 6x9. [69] **$3.75**

GEOMETRY AND THE IMAGINATION

By D. HILBERT and S. COHN-VOSSEN

The theme of this book is *insight.* Not merely proofs, but proofs that offer *insight*—intuitive understanding—into *why they are true.* Not merely properties of the hyperboloid or of Pascal's hexagon, but insight into *why they have these properties.* In this wide-ranging survey, one of the world's greatest and most original mathematicians uses insight as both his technique and his aim. Both the beginner and the mature mathematician will learn much from this fascinating treatise.

Translated from the German by P. NEMENYI.

CHAPTER HEADINGS: I. The Simplest Curves and surfaces. II. Regular Systems of Points. III. Projective Configurations. IV. Differential Geometry. V. Kinematics. VI. Topology.

"A mathematical classic . . . The purpose is to make the reader *see* and *feel* the proofs."—*Science.*

"A fascinating tour of the 20th-century mathematical zoo."—*Scientific American.*

"Students . . . will experience the sensation of being taken into the friendly confidence of a great mathematician and being shown the *real significance* of things."—*Science Progress.*

"A glance down the index (*twenty-five columns of it*) reveal the breadth of range:—

"Annulus; Atomic structure; Automorphic functions; Bubble, soap; Caustic Curve; Color problem; Density of packing, of circles; Four-dimensional space; Gears, hyperboloidal; Graphite; Lattices; Mapping; "Monkey Saddle"; Table salt; Zinc.

"*These are but a few of the topics* . . . The title evokes the imagination and the text must surely capture it."—*Math. Gazette.*

—1952. 358 pp. 6x9. [87] **$6.00**

IDEALTHEORIE

By W. KRULL

—(Ergeb. der Math.) 1935. 159 pp. 5½x8½. Orig. publ. (paper bound) at $7.00. [48] Cloth, **$3.95**

GROUP THEORY

By A. KUROSH

Translated from the second Russian edition and with added notes by PROF. K. A. HIRSCH.

A complete rewriting of the first, and already famous, Russian edition.

Partial Contents: PART ONE: The Elements of Group Theory. Chap. I. Definition. II. Subgroups (Systems, Cyclic Groups, Ascending Sequences of Groups). III. Normal Subgroups. IV. Endomorphisms and Automorphisms. Groups with Operators. V. Series of Subgroups. Direct Products. Defining Relations, etc. PART TWO: Abelian Groups. VI. Foundations of the Theory of Abelian Groups (Finite Abelian Groups, Rings of Endomorphisms, Abelian Groups with Operators). VII. Primary and Mixed Abelian Groups. VIII. Torsion-Free Abelian Groups. Editor's Notes. Bibliography.

Vol. II. PART THREE: Group-Theoretical Constructions. IX. Free Products and Free Groups (Free Products with Amalgamated Subgroup, Fully Invariant Subgroups). X. Finitely Generated Groups. XI. Direct Products. Lattices (Modular, Complete Modular, etc.). XII. Extensions of Groups (of Abelian Groups, of Non-commutative Groups, Cohomology Groups). PART FOUR: Solvable and Nilpotent Groups. XIII. Finiteness Conditions, Sylow Subgroups, etc. XIV. Solvable Groups (Solvable and Generalized Solvable Groups, Local Theorems). XV. Nilpotent Groups (Generalized, Complete, Locally Nilpotent Torsion-Free, etc.). Editor's Notes. Bibliography.

—Vol. I. 2nd ed. 1959. 271 pp. 6x9. [107] **$4.95**
—Vol. II. 2nd ed. 1960. 308 pp. 6x9. [109] **$4.95**

DIFFERENTIAL AND INTEGRAL CALCULUS

By E. LANDAU

Landau's sparkling *Einführung* in English translation. Completely rigorous, completely self-contained, borrowing not even the fundamental theorem of algebra (of which it gives a rigorous elementary proof), it develops the entire calculus including Fourier series, starting only with the properties of the number system. A masterpiece of rigor and clarity.

—2nd ed. 1960. 372 pp. 6x9. [78] **$6.00**

ELEMENTARE ZAHLENTHEORIE

By E. LANDAU

"Interest is enlisted at once and sustained by the accuracy, skill, and enthusiasm with which Landau marshals . . . facts and simplifies . . . details."

—*G. D. Birkhoff, Bulletin of the A. M. S.*

—1927. vii + 180 + iv pp. 5½x8¼. [26] **$3.50**

VORLESUNGEN ÜBER ZAHLENTHEORIE

By E. LANDAU

The various sections of this important work (Additive, Analytic, Geometric, and Algebraic Number Theory) can be read independently of one another.

—Vol. I, Pt. 2. * (Additive Number Theory) xii + 180 pp. Vol. II. (Analytical Number Theory and Geometrical Number Theory) viii + 308 pp. Vol. III. (Algebraic Number Theory and Fermat's Last Theorem) viii + 341 pp. 5¼x8¼. * (Vol. I, Pt. 1 is issued as **Elementary Number Theory.**) Originally publ. at $26.40
[32] Three vols. in one **$14.00**

ELEMENTARY NUMBER THEORY

By E. LANDAU

The present work is a translation of Prof. Landau's famous *Elementare Zahlentheorie*, with added exercises by Prof. Paul T. Bateman.

PART ONE. Foundations of Number Theory. I. Divisors. II. Prime Numbers, Prime Factorization. III. G.C.D. IV. Number-theoretic Functions. V. Congruences. VI. Quadratic Residues. VII. Pell's Equation. PART TWO. Brun's Theorem and Dirichlet's Theorem. PART THREE. Decomposition into Two, Three, and Four Squares. I. Farey Fractions. II. Dec. into 2 Squares. III. Dec. into 4 Squares. IV. Dec. into 3 Squares. PART FOUR. Class Numbers of Binary Quadratic Forms. II. Classes of Forms. III. Finiteness of Class Number. IV. Primary Representation . . . VI. Gaussian Sums . . . IX. Final Formulas for Class Number.

EXERCISES for Parts One, Two, and Three.

—1958. 256 pp. 6x9. [125] **$4.95**

EINFÜHRUNG IN DIE ELEMENTARE UND ANALYTISCHE THEORIE DER ALGEBRAISCHE ZAHLEN UND DER IDEALE

By E. LANDAU

—2nd ed. vii + 147 pp. 5½x8. [62] **$2.95**

GRUNDLAGEN DER ANALYSIS

By E. LANDAU

The student who wishes to study mathematical German will find Landau's famous *Grundlagen der Analysis* ideally suited to his needs.

Only a few score of German words will enable him to read the entire book with only an occasional glance at the Vocabulary! [A COMPLETE German-English vocabulary, prepared with the novice especially in mind, has been appended to the book.]

—3rd ed. 1960. 173 pp. 5⅜x8. [24] Cloth **$3.50**
[141] Paper **$1.95**

ELEMENTS OF ALGEBRA

By HOWARD LEVI

"This book is addressed to beginning students of mathematics. . . . The level of the book, however, is so unusually high, mathematically as well as pedagogically, that it merits the attention of professional mathematicians (as well as of professional pedagogues) interested in the wider dissemination of their subject among cultured people . . . **a closer approximation to the right way to teach mathematics to beginners than anything else now in existence."**—*Bulletin of the A. M. S.*

—Third ed. 1960. xi + 161 pp. 5⅜x8. [103] **$3.25**

LE CALCUL DES RÉSIDUS

By E. LINDELÖF

Important applications in a striking diversity of mathematical fields: statistics, number theory, the theory of Fourier series, the calculus of finite differences, mathematical physics and advanced calculus, as well as function theory itself.

—151 pp. 5½x8½. [34] **$3.25**

THE THEORY OF MATRICES

By C. C. MacDUFFEE

"No mathematical library can afford to be without this book."—*Bulletin of the A. M. S.*

—(Ergeb. der Math.) 2nd edition. 116 pp. 6x9. Orig. publ. at $5.20. [28] **$2.95**

MACMAHON, "Introduction . . ." see Klein

COMBINATORY ANALYSIS, Vols. I and II

By P. A. MACMAHON

TWO VOLUMES IN ONE.

A broad and extensive treatise on an important branch of mathematics.

—xx + 300 + xx + 340 pp. 5⅜x8. [137] Two vols. in one. **$7.50**

FORMULAS AND THEOREMS FOR THE FUNCTIONS OF MATHEMATICAL PHYSICS

By W. MAGNUS and F. OBERHETTINGER

Gathered into a compact, handy and well-arranged reference work are thousands of results on the many important functions needed by the physicist, engineer and applied mathematician.

Translated by J. WERMER.

—1954. 182 pp. 6x9. German edition was $7.00. [51] **$3.90**

FUNCTIONS OF REAL VARIABLES
FUNCTIONS OF A COMPLEX VARIABLE

By W. F. OSGOOD

TWO VOLUMES IN ONE.

"*Well-organized courses, systematic, lucid, fundamental,* with many brief sets of appropriate exercises, and occasional suggestions for more extensive reading. The technical terms have been kept to a minimum, and have been clearly explained. The aim has been to develop the student's power and to furnish him with a substantial body of classic theorems, whose proofs illustrate the methods and whose results provide equipment for further progress."—*Bulletin of A. M. S*

—676 pp. 5x8. 2 vols. in 1. [124] **$4.95**

DIE LEHRE VON DEN KETTENBRUECHEN

By O. PERRON

Both the Arithmetic Theory and the Analytic Theory are treated fully.

"An indispensable work . . . Perron remains the best guide for the novice. The style is simple and precise and presents no difficulties."

—*Mathematical Gazette.*

—2nd ed. 536 pp. 5¼x8. [73] **$5.95**

IRRATIONALZAHLEN

By O. PERRON

Methods of introducing irrational numbers (Cauchy, Bolzano, Weierstrass, Dedekind, Cantor, Méray, Bachman, etc.) *Systematic fractions, continued fractions, Cantor's series and algorithm, Lüroth's and Engel's series, Cantor's products.* Approximations, *Kronecker theorem, Algebraic and transcendental numbers (including transcendency proofs for e and π; Liouville numbers, etc.)*

—2nd ed. 1939. 207 pp. 5¼x8¼. [47] Cloth **$3.25**
[113] Paper **$1.50**

EIGHT-PLACE TABLES OF TRIGONOMETRIC FUNCTIONS

By J. PETERS

With an appendix on the computation to twenty decimal places.

—Approx. 950 pp. 8x11. [154] **In prep.**

SUBHARMONIC FUNCTIONS

By T. RADO

—(Ergeb. der Math.) 1937. iv + 56 pp. 5½x8½. [60] **$2.00**